2009
OCR
Biology AS

Student Workbook

OCR *Biology AS* 2009

Student Workbook

First edition 2008

ISBN 978-1-877462-16-0

Copyright © **2008** Richard Allan
Published by **BIOZONE International Ltd**

Printed by REPLIKA PRESS PVT LTD using paper
produced from renewable and waste materials

About the Writing Team

Tracey Greenwood joined the staff of Biozone at the beginning of
1993. She has a Ph.D in biology, specialising in lake ecology, and
taught undergraduate and graduate biology at the University of
Waikato for four years.

Lissa Bainbridge-Smith worked in industry in a research and
development capacity for eight years before joining Biozone as an
author in 2007. Lissa has an M.Sc from Waikato University.

Richard Allan has had 11 years experience teaching senior biology
at Hillcrest High School in Hamilton, New Zealand. He attained a
Masters degree in biology at Waikato University, New Zealand.

Purchases of this workbook may be made direct from the publisher:

BIOZONE

www.biozone.co.uk

UNITED KINGDOM:

BIOZONE Learning Media (UK) Ltd.
P.O. Box 23698, Edinburgh EH5 2WX, **Scotland**
Telephone: 131-557-5060
FAX: 131-557-5030
E-mail: sales@biozone.co.uk

AUSTRALIA:

BIOZONE Learning Media Australia
P.O. Box 7523, GCMC 4217 QLD, **Australia**
Telephone: +61 7-5575-4615
FAX: +61 7-5572-0161
E-mail: info@biozone.com.au

NEW ZEALAND:

BIOZONE International Ltd.
P.O. Box 13-034, Hamilton 3251, **New Zealand**
Telephone: +64 7-856-8104
FAX: +64 7-856-9243
E-mail: sales@biozone.co.nz

Preface to the 2009 Edition

This is the first year Biozone has offered a workbook specifically designed to meet the needs of students enrolled in biology courses for the **OCR** and Cambridge International Examinations (**CIE**). The specific nature of this workbook allows fast and easy location of material for both students and educators. The chapters are organised into blocks of related information which align to the OCR units, and the introduction of each chapter outlines the relevant learning objectives for each course, clearly directing students to the required activities. Tabs identifying "**Related activities**" and "**Web links**" will help students to locate related material within the workbook and indicates web links and activities (including animations) that will enhance their understanding of the topic. See page 8 to find out more about these. Supplementary material and extension activities are available with a limited photocopy licence on Biozone's **Teacher Resource CD-ROM**. A guide to using the Teacher Resource CD-ROM to best effect has been included in the introductory section of the workbook and can be used in conjunction with the revised course guides. The TRC also contains glossary lists and crosswords to test vocabulary in a student friendly manner. This workbook will be regularly updated to keep abreast of new developments in biology and to reflect changes to the OCR and CIE curricula. Biozone continues to be committed to providing up-to-date, relevant, interesting, and accurate information.

A Note to the Teacher

This workbook has been produced as a student-centred resource, and benefits students by facilitating independent learning and critical thinking. Biozone's workbooks motivate and challenge a wide range of students by providing a highly visual format, a clear map through the course, and a synopsis of supplementary resources. In modern biology, a single textbook may no longer provide all the information a student needs to grasp a topic. This workbook is a generic resource and **not a textbook**, and we make a point of referencing texts from other publishers. Above all, we are committed to continually revising and improving this resource. The price remains below £11 for students, as a reflection of our commitment to providing high-quality, cost effective resources for biology. Please **do not photocopy** from this workbook. We cannot afford to supply single copies to schools and still provide annual updates as we intend. If you think it is worth using, then we recommend that the students themselves own this resource and keep it for their own use. A free model answer book is supplied with your **first order** of 5 or more workbooks.

How Teachers May Use This Workbook

This workbook may be used in the classroom to guide students through each topic. Some activities may be used to introduce topics while others may be used to consolidate and test concepts already covered by other means. The workbook may be used as the primary tool in teaching some topics, but it should not be at the expense of good, 'hands-on' biology. Students may attempt the activities on their own or in groups. The latter provides opportunities for healthy discussion and peer-to-peer learning. Many of the activities may be set as homework exercises. Each page is perforated, allowing for easy removal of pages to be submitted for marking. This has been facilitated this year by the back-to-back format of two page activities. Teachers may prescribe the activities to be attempted by the students (using the check boxes next to the objectives for each topic), or they may allow students a degree of freedom with respect to the activities they attempt. The objectives for each topic will allow students to keep up to date even if they miss lessons and teachers who are away from class may set work easily in their absence. I thank you for your support.

Richard Allan

Acknowledgements

We would like to thank those who have contributed towards this edition:
• Sue Fitzgerald, Mary McDougall, and Gwen Gilbert for their efficient handling of the office, • Adam Luckenbach and the North Carolina State University for use of the poster image on sex determination in flounder. • Joseph E. Armstrong, Professor of Botany, Head Curator at ISU Herbarium, USA for his permission to use the photo showing a child with kwashiorkor • PASCO for their images of probeware • Alan Sheldon, Sheldon's Nature Photography, Wisconsin for the photo of the lizard without its tail • Stephen Moore for his photos of freshwater insects • Dan Butler for his photograph of a wounded finger • Dr Roger Wagner, • Dept of Biological Sciences, University of Delaware, for the LS of a capillary • www.coastalplanning.net for the image of a marine quadrat • The three-spined stickleback image was originally prepared by Ellen Edmonson as part of the 1927-1940 New York Biological Survey. Permission for use granted by the New York State Department of Environmental Conservation • PIER digital library for the image of the coronary artery • Marc King for photographs of comb types in chickens • TechPool Studios, for their clipart collection of human anatomy: Copyright ©1994, TechPool Studios Corp. USA (some of these images were modified by Richard Allan and Tracey Greenwood) • Totem Graphics, for their clipart collection of plants and animals • John Mahn PLU, for the cross section of a dicot leaf • Corel Corporation, for use of their eps clipart of plants and animals from the Corel MEGAGALLERY collection

Cover Photographs

Main photograph: The peregrine falcon (*Falco peregrinus*), is a large bird of prey which mainly hunts other birds, and occasionally small mammals. The peregrine falcon hunts by soaring to locate its prey and then diving steeply at speeds of over 322 km/h (200 mph) to capture its prey. PHOTO: Geoff Kuchera, iStock Photos www.istockphoto.com
Background photograph: Autumn leaves, Image ©2005 JupiterImages Corporation www.clipart.com

Contents

Activity is marked: ◦ to be done   ✓ when completed

CONTENTS *(continued)*

Activity is marked:　　　　　■ to be done　　　　✓ when completed

CONTENTS *(continued)*

Activity is marked: ☐ to be done   ✓ when completed

How to Use this Workbook

This workbook is designed to provide you with a resource that will make the subject of biology more enjoyable and fun to study. It is suitable for students in their AS year of **OCR** and Cambridge International Examinations (**CIE**). The course guides on pages 11-12 (or on the Teacher Resource CD-ROM) indicate where the material required by your syllabus is covered. This workbook will reinforce and extend the ideas developed by your teacher. It is **not a textbook**; its aim is to complement and reinforce the textbookss written for your course. The workbook provides the following useful resources for each topic:

Guidance Provided for Each Topic

Learning objectives:

These provide a map of the topic content. Completing the relevant learning objectives will help you to satisfy the knowledge requirements of your course. Your teacher may add to or omit points from this list.

Topic outcomes:

This panel provides a summary of the content of the OCR or CIE unit of work to which this topic applies. See pages 11-12 for a synopsis of the syllabus requirements for your course.

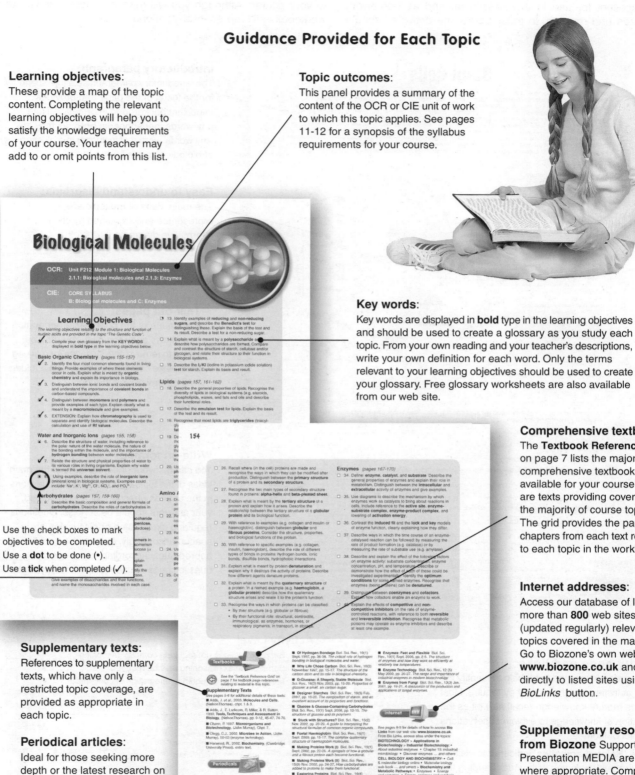

Key words:

Key words are displayed in **bold** type in the learning objectives and should be used to create a glossary as you study each topic. From your own reading and your teacher's descriptions, write your own definition for each word. Only the terms relevant to your learning objectives should be used to create your glossary. Free glossary worksheets are also available from our web site.

Comprehensive textbooks

The **Textbook Reference Grid** on page 7 lists the major comprehensive textbooks available for your course (these are texts providing coverage of the majority of course topics). The grid provides the pages or chapters from each text relevant to each topic in the workbook.

Internet addresses:

Access our database of links to more than **800** web sites (updated regularly) relevant to topics covered in the manual. Go to Biozone's own web site: **www.biozone.co.uk** and link directly to listed sites using the *BioLinks* button.

Supplementary texts:

References to supplementary texts, which have only a restricted topic coverage, are provided as appropriate in each topic.

Periodical articles:

Ideal for those seeking more depth or the latest research on a specific topic. Articles are sorted according to their suitability for student or teacher reference. Visit your school, public, or university library for these articles.

Supplementary resources from Biozone Supporting Presentation MEDIA are noted where appropriate. Computer software and videos relevant to every topic in the workbook are provided on the **Teacher Resource CD-ROM** (which may be purchased separately). See page 10 for details.

Activity Pages

The activities and exercises make up most of the content of this book. They are designed to reinforce the concepts you have learned about in the topic. Your teacher may use the activity pages to introduce a topic for the first time, or you may use them to revise ideas already covered. They are excellent for use in the classroom, and as homework exercises and revision. In most cases, the activities should not be attempted until you have carried out the necessary background reading from your textbook. Your teacher should have a model answers book with the answers to each activity. Because this workbook caters for more than one exam board, you will find some activities that may not be relevant to your course. Although you will miss out these pages, our workbooks still represent exceptional value.

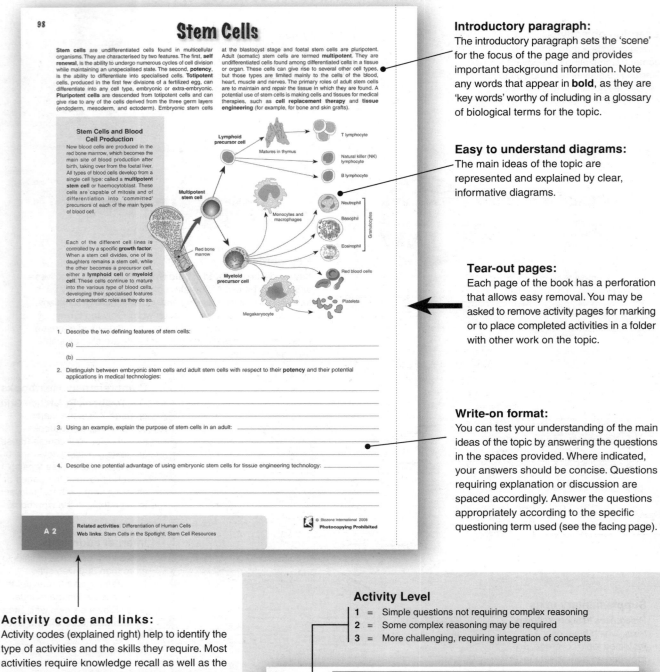

Introductory paragraph:
The introductory paragraph sets the 'scene' for the focus of the page and provides important background information. Note any words that appear in **bold**, as they are 'key words' worthy of including in a glossary of biological terms for the topic.

Easy to understand diagrams:
The main ideas of the topic are represented and explained by clear, informative diagrams.

Tear-out pages:
Each page of the book has a perforation that allows easy removal. You may be asked to remove activity pages for marking or to place completed activities in a folder with other work on the topic.

Write-on format:
You can test your understanding of the main ideas of the topic by answering the questions in the spaces provided. Where indicated, your answers should be concise. Questions requiring explanation or discussion are spaced accordingly. Answer the questions appropriately according to the specific questioning term used (see the facing page).

Activity code and links:
Activity codes (explained right) help to identify the type of activities and the skills they require. Most activities require knowledge recall as well as the application of knowledge to explain observations or predict outcomes.

Use the **'Related activities'** indicated to visit pages that may help you with understanding the material or answering the questions.

Web links indicate additional material of assistance or interest (either web pages or pdf activities). You can access these from: www.biozone.co.uk/weblink/OCR-AS-2160.html

Activity Level
1 = Simple questions not requiring complex reasoning
2 = Some complex reasoning may be required
3 = More challenging, requiring integration of concepts

A 2	**Related activities**: Differentiation of Human Cells **Web links**: Stem Cells in the Spotlight, Stem Cell Resources

Type of Activity
D = Includes some data handling and/or interpretation
P = includes a paper practical
R = May require research outside the page
A = Includes application of knowledge to solve a problem
E = Extension material

Explanation of Terms

Questions come in a variety of forms. Whether you are studying for an exam or writing an essay, it is important to understand exactly what the question is asking. A question has two parts to it: one part of the question will provide you with information, the second part of the question will provide you with instructions as to how to answer the question. Following these instructions is most important. Often students in examinations know the material but fail to follow instructions and do not answer the question appropriately. Examiners often use certain key words to introduce questions. Look out for them and be clear as to what they mean. Below is a description of terms commonly used when asking questions in biology.

Commonly used Terms in Biology

The following terms are frequently used when asking questions in examinations and assessments. Students should have a clear understanding of each of the following terms and use this understanding to answer questions appropriately.

Account for: Provide a satisfactory explanation or reason for an observation.

Analyse: Interpret data to reach stated conclusions.

Annotate: Add **brief** notes to a diagram, drawing or graph.

Apply: Use an idea, equation, principle, theory, or law in a new situation.

Appreciate: To understand the meaning or relevance of a particular situation.

Calculate: Find an answer using mathematical methods. Show the working unless instructed not to.

Compare: Give an account of similarities and differences between two or more items, referring to both (or all) of them throughout. Comparisons can be given using a table. Comparisons generally ask for similarities more than differences (see contrast).

Construct: Represent or develop in graphical form.

Contrast: Show differences. Set in opposition.

Deduce: Reach a conclusion from information given.

Define: Give the precise meaning of a word or phrase as concisely as possible.

Derive: Manipulate a mathematical equation to give a new equation or result.

Describe: Give a detailed account, including all the relevant information.

Design: Produce a plan, object, simulation or model.

Determine: Find the only possible answer.

Discuss: Give an account including, where possible, a range of arguments, assessments of the relative importance of various factors, or comparison of alternative hypotheses.

Distinguish: Give the difference(s) between two or more different items.

Draw: Represent by means of pencil lines. Add labels unless told not to do so.

Estimate: Find an approximate value for an unknown quantity, based on the information provided and application of scientific knowledge.

Evaluate: Assess the implications and limitations.

Explain: Give a clear account including causes, reasons, or mechanisms.

Identify: Find an answer from a number of possibilities.

Illustrate: Give concrete examples. Explain clearly by using comparisons or examples.

Interpret: Comment upon, give examples, describe relationships. Describe, then evaluate.

List: Give a sequence of names or other brief answers with no elaboration. Each one should be clearly distinguishable from the others.

Measure: Find a value for a quantity.

Outline: Give a brief account or summary. Include essential information only.

Predict: Give an expected result.

Solve: Obtain an answer using algebraic and/or numerical methods.

State: Give a specific name, value, or other answer. No supporting argument or calculation is necessary.

Suggest: Propose a hypothesis or other possible explanation.

Summarise: Give a brief, condensed account. Include conclusions and avoid unnecessary details.

In Conclusion

Students should familiarise themselves with this list of terms and, where necessary throughout the course, they should refer back to them when answering questions. The list of terms mentioned above is not exhaustive and students should compare this list with past examination papers / essays etc. and add any new terms (and their meaning) to the list above. The aim is to become familiar with interpreting the question and answering it appropriately.

Resources Information

Your set textbook should always be a starting point for information. There are also many other resources available, including scientific journals, magazine and newspaper articles, supplementary texts covering restricted topic areas, dictionaries, computer software and videos, and the internet.

A synopsis of currently available resources is provided below. Access to the publishers of these resources can be made directly from Biozone's web site through our resources hub: www.biozone.co.uk/resource-hub.html, or by typing in the relevant addresses provided below. Most titles are also available through amazon.co.uk. Please note that our listing any product in this workbook does not, in any way, denote Biozone's endorsement of that product.

Comprehensive Biology Texts Referenced

Appropriate texts for this course are referenced in this workbook. Page or chapter references for each text are provided in the text reference grid on page 7. These will enable you to identify the relevant reading as you progress through the activities in this workbook. For further details of text content, or to make purchases, link to the publisher via Biozone's resources hub or by typing: www.biozone.co.uk > Resources > Textbooks > UK

OCR and CIE Specific

Jones, M., 2007
Biology 1 for OCR
Publisher: Cambridge University Press
Pages: 278
ISBN: 978-0521717632
Comments: *A new resource written for the 2008 OCR specification. Provides how science works themes and summaries. Interactive CD-ROM provides further resources.*

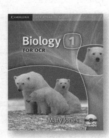

Jones, M., R. Fosbery, D. Taylor, and J. Gregory, 2007
CIE Biology AS and A Level, 2 ed.
Publisher: Cambridge University Press
Pages: 424
ISBN: 0-521-53674-X
Comments: *This text meets the new CIE requirements and covers the complete AS level syllabus, the core A level syllabus, and the new Applications of Biology section.*

Sochaki, F., and Kennedy, P. 2008
OCR Biology
Publisher: Heinemann
Pages: 288
ISBN: 978-0435691806
Comments: *A new book tailored for the new OCR specification. Includes an exam cafe CD-ROM with exam type questions and worked examples. This text is endorsed as an Official Publishing Partner for OCR Biology.*

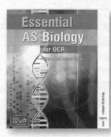

Toole G. and S. Toole, 2004
Essential AS Biology for OCR
Publisher: NelsonThornes
Pages: 280
ISBN: 0-7487-8511-6
Comments: *A text written to meet the AS specifications for the earlier OCR course. The 2-page-spread format is appealing and student-friendly. Includes glossary.*

Exam Board Independent

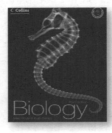

Boyle, M., D, Boyle and K. Senior, 2008
Collins Advanced Science: Biology, 3 ed.
Publisher: HarperCollins Publishers Ltd.
Pages: approx. 624
ISBN: 978-0007267453
Comments: *Revised edition for the new OCR course. Includes how science works features, stretch and challenge boxes, and putting science into context.*

Clegg, C.J. and D.G. MacKean, 2000
Advanced Biology: Principles and Applications 2 ed.
Publisher: John Murray
Pages: 712
ISBN: 0-7195-7670-9
Comments: *Student study guide also available. A general text with specific references for use by biology students of the AS and A2 curricula in the UK.*

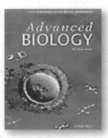

Kent, N. A. 2000
Advanced Biology
Publisher: Oxford University Press
Pages: 624
ISBN: 0-19-914195-9
Comments: *Each book comes with a free CD-ROM to help with specification planning. Book is formatted as a series of two page concept spreads.*

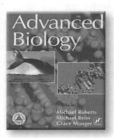

Roberts, M., G. Monger, M. Reiss, 2000
Advanced Biology
Publisher: NelsonThornes
Pages: approx. 781
ISBN: 0-17-438732-6
Comments: *Provides thorough coverage of the Advanced Level specifications within one volume.*

Williams, G., 2000
Advanced Biology for You
Publisher: NelsonThornes
Pages: 464
ISBN: 0-7487-5298-6
Comments: *Covers most current AS-level specifications and the core topics of all A2 specifications.*

Supplementary Texts

For further details of text content, or to make purchases, link to the relevant publisher via Biozone's resources hub or by typing:
www.biozone.co.uk > resources > supplementary

Barnard, C., F. Gilbert, F., and P. McGregor, 2007
Asking Questions in Biology: Key Skills for Practical Assessments & Project Work, 256 pp.
Publisher: Benjamin Cummings
ISBN: 978-0132224352
Comments: *Covers many aspects of design, analysis and presentation of practical work.*

Cadogan, A. and Ingram, M., 2002
Maths for Advanced Biology
Publisher: NelsonThornes
ISBN: 0-7487-6506-9
Comments: *Covers the maths requirements of AS/A2 biology. Includes worked examples.*

Freeland, P., 1999
Hodder Advanced Science: Microbes, Medicine, and Commerce, 160 pp.
Publisher: Hodder and Stoughton
ISBN: 0-340-73103-6
Comments: *Combines biotechnology, pathology, microbiology, and immunity in a thorough text.*

Fullick, A., 1998
Human Health and Disease, 162 pp.
Publisher: Heinemann Educational Publishers
ISBN: 0435570919
Comments: *An excellent supplement for courses with modules in human health and disease. Includes infectious and non-infectious disease.*

Hudson, T. and K. Mannion, 2001.
Microbes and Disease, 104 pp.
ISBN: 0-00-327742-9
Coverage of selected aspects of microbiology including the culture and applications of bacteria, and the role of bacteria and viruses in disease. Immunity, vaccination, and antimicrobial drug use are covered in the concluding chapter.

Indge, B., 2003
Data and Data Handling for AS and A Level Biology, 128 pp.
Publisher: Hodder Arnold H&S
ISBN: 1340856475
Comments: *Examples and practice exercises to improve skills in data interpretation and analysis.*

Jones, N., A. Karp., & G. Giddings, 2001.
Essentials of Genetics, 224 pp.
Publisher: John Murray
ISBN: 0-7195-8611-9
One of several titles in the Advanced Biology Reader series providing comprehensive coverage of genetics and evolution (including cell division, molecular genetics, and genetic engineering).

Jones, A., R. Reed, and J. Weyers, 4th ed. 2007
Practical Skills in Biology, approx. 300 pp.
Publisher: Pearson
ISBN: 978-0-131775-09-3
Comments: *Provides information on all aspects of experimental and field design, implementation, and data analysis. Contact www.amazon.co.uk*

Morgan, S., 2002
Advanced Level Practical Work for Biology, 128 pp.
Publisher: Hodder and Stoughton
ISBN: 0-340-84712-3
Comments: *Caters for the investigative requirements of A level studies: experimental planning, techniques, observation and measurement, and interpretation and analysis.*

Cambridge Advanced Sciences (Cambridge UP)
Modular-style texts covering material for the A2 options for OCR, but suitable as student extension for core topics in other courses.

Harwood, R. 2002.
Biochemistry, 96 pp.
ISBN: 0521797519
Methodical coverage of the structure and role of the main groups of biological molecules. Questions and exercises are provided and each chapter includes an introduction and summary.

Jones, M. and G. Jones, 2002.
Mammalian Physiology and Behaviour, 104 pp.
ISBN: 0521797497
Covers mammalian nutrition, the structure and function of the liver, support and locomotion, the nervous system, and senses and behaviour. Each chapter includes an introduction and summary.

Lowrie, P. & S. Wells, 2000.
Microbiology and Biotechnology, 112 pp.
ISBN: 0521787238
This text covers the microbial groups important in biotechnology, basic microbiological techniques, and the various applications of microbes, including the industrial-scale production and use of microbial enzymes.

Reiss, M. & J. Chapman, 2000.
Environmental Biology, 104 pp.
ISBN: 0521787270
An introduction to environmental biology covering agriculture, pollution, resource conservation and conservation issues, and practical work in ecology. Questions and exercises are provided, and each chapter includes an introduction and summary.

Illustrated Advanced Biology (John Murray Publishers)
Modular-style supplements for AS and A2 level biology courses.

Clegg, C.J., 2002.
Microbes in Action, 92 pp.
ISBN: 0-71957-554-0
Microbes and their roles in disease and biotechnology. It includes material on the diversity of the microbial world, microbiological techniques, and a short, but useful, account of enzyme technology.

Clegg, C.J., 1999.
Genetics and Evolution, 96 pp.
ISBN: 0-7195-7552-4
Concise but thorough coverage of molecular genetics, genetic engineering, inheritance, and evolution. An historical perspective is included by way of introduction, and a glossary and a list of abbreviations used are included.

Clegg, C.J., 1998.
Mammals: Structure & Function, 96 pp.
ISBN: 0-7195-7551-6
An excellent, clearly written supplementary text covering most aspects of basic mammalian anatomy and physiology. Note: This text is now out of print from the publishers, but many schools will still have copies in their collections and it is still available from amazon: www.amazon.co.uk

Clegg, C.J., 2003
Green Plants: The Inside Story, approx. 96 pp.
ISBN: 0-7195-7553-2
The emphasis in this text is on flowering plants. Topics include leaf, stem, and root structure in relation to function, reproduction, economic botany, sensitivity and adaptation.

Nelson Advanced Sciences (NelsonThornes)
Modular-style texts covering material for the A2 specifications for Edexcel, but are suitable as teacher reference and student extension reading for core topics in other AS/A2 biology courses.

Adds, J., E. Larkcom & R. Miller, 2004.
Exchange and Transport, Energy and Ecosystems, revised edition 240 pp.
ISBN: 0-7487-7487-4
Includes exchange processes (gas exchanges, digestion, absorption), transport systems, adaptation, sexual reproduction, energy and the environment, and human impact. Practical activities are included in several of the chapters.

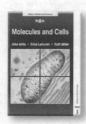

Adds, J., E. Larkcom & R. Miller, 2003.
Molecules and Cells, revised edition 112 pp.
ISBN: 0-7487-7484-X
Includes coverage of the basic types of biological molecules, with extra detail on the structure and function of nucleic acids and enzymes, cellular organisation, and cell division. Practical activities are provided for most chapters.

Biology Dictionaries

Access to a good biology dictionary is valuable when dealing with biological terms. Some selected titles are listed below. All are available from www.amazon.co.uk. For further details, link to the relevant publisher via Biozone's resources hub or by typing:
www.biozone.co.uk > resources > dictionaries

Clamp, A.
AS/A-Level Biology. Essential Word Dictionary, 2000, 161 pp. Philip Allan Updates.
ISBN: 0-86003-372-4.
Carefully selected essential words for AS and A2. Concise definitions are supported by further explanation and illustrations where required.

Collin, P.H.
A Dictionary of Ecology and Environment 5 ed., 2001, 560 pp. Peter Collin Publishers Ltd
ISBN: 0747572011
A revised edition, with over 9000 definitions from all areas of ecology and environmental science, including climate and energy conservation.

Hale, W.G. **Collins: Dictionary of Biology** 4 ed., 2005, 528 pp. Collins.
ISBN: 0-00-720734-4.
Updated to take in the latest developments in biology and now internet-linked. This dictionary is specifically designed for advanced school students, and undergraduates in the life sciences.

King, R.C. & W.D. Stansfield **A Dictionary of Genetics**, 6 ed., 2002, 544 pp. Oxford Uni. Press.
ISBN: 0-19-514325-6
A dictionary specifically addressing the needs of students and teachers for an up to date reference source for genetics and related fields. More than 7000 definitions and 395 illustrations.

McGraw-Hill (ed). **McGraw-Hill Dictionary of Bioscience**, 2 ed., 2002, 662 pp. McGraw-Hill.
ISBN: 0-07-141043-0
22 000 entries encompassing more than 20 areas of the life sciences. It includes synonyms, acronyms, abbreviations, and pronunciations for all terms. Accessible, yet comprehensive.

Thain, M. **Penguin Dictionary of Biology**, 2004, 750 pp. Penguin.
ISBN: 0-14-101396-6
Concise reference with definitions to more than 6000 terms. It covers fundamental concepts, core vocabulary, and new advances in the subject.

Periodicals, Magazines and Journals

Articles in *Biological Sciences Review (Biol. Sci. Rev.)*, *New Scientist*, and *Scientific American* can be of great value in providing current information on specific topics. Periodicals may be accessed in your school, local, public, and university libraries. Listed below are the periodicals referenced in this workbook. For general enquiries and further details regarding subscriptions, link to the relevant publisher via Biozone's resources hub or by typing:
www.biozone.co.uk > resources > journals

Biological Sciences Review: *An informative and very readable quarterly publication for teachers and students of biology.* Enquiries: Philip Allan Publishers, Market Place, Deddington, Oxfordshire OX 15 OSE.
Tel: 01869 338652
Fax: 01869 338803
E-mail: sales@philipallan.co.uk
or subscribe from their web site.

New Scientist: *Widely available weekly magazine. Provides summaries of research in articles ranging from news releases to 3-5 page features on recent research.*
Subscription enquiries:
Reed Business Information Ltd
151 Wardour St. London WIV 4BN
Tel: (UK and intl):+44 (0) 1444 475636
E-mail: ns.subs@qss-uk.com
or subscribe from their web site.

Scientific American: *A monthly magazine containing mostly specialist feature articles. Articles range in level of reading difficulty and assumed knowledge.*
Subscription enquiries:
415 Madison Ave. New York. NY10017-1111
Tel: (outside North America): 515-247-7631
or subscribe from their web site.

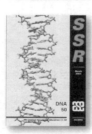

School Science Review: *A quarterly journal published by the ASE for science teachers in 11-19 education. SSR includes articles, reviews, and news on current research and curriculum development. Free to Ordinary Members of the ASE or available on subscription.* Subscription enquiries:
Tel: 01707 28300
Email: info@ase.org.uk *or visit their web site.*

Biologist: *Published five times a year, this journal from the IOB includes articles relevant to teachers of biology in the UK. Articles referenced in the workbook can be identified by title and volume number. The IOB also publish the Journal of Biological Education, which provides articles and reviews relevant to those in the teaching profession. Archived articles from both journals are available online at no cost to IOB members and subscribers. Visit their web site for more information.*

Textbook Reference Grid

Guide to use:
Page numbers or chapters in the grid refer to the material in each text that is relevant to the stated topic in the workbook.

TOPIC IN WORKBOOK	Boyle et al 2008	Clegg & MacKean 2000	Jones 2007	Jones et al. 2007	Kent 2000	Roberts et al. 2000	Sochacki & Kennedy 2008	Toole & Toole 2004	Williams 2000
Skills in Biology		N/A	N/A	App. 3	N/A	Appendix	Pg 194-199	Chpt. 17	Extra section
Cell Structure		Chpt. 7	Chpt. 1	Chpt. 1	Chpt. 4	Chpt. 3	Pg 4-15	Chpt. 1	Chpt. 2
Cell Membranes and Transport		Chpt. 7 & 11	Chpt. 2	Chpt. 4	Chpt. 4	Chpt. 3 & 7	Pg 16-27	Chpt. 4	Chpt. 3
Cell Division		Chpt. 9	Chpt. 3	Chpt. 5 & 6	Chpt. 4	Chpt. 4 & 26	Pg 28-37	Chpt. 6	Chpt. 7
Gas Exchange in Animals		Chpt. 15	Chpt. 4	Chpt. 11	Chpt. 7	Chpt. 10	Pg 44-51	Chpt. 4 & 13	Chpt. 10
Animal Transport Systems		Chpt. 17	Chpt. 5	Chpt. 8 & 9	Chpt. 7	Chpt. 13 & 14	Pg 52-67	Chpt. 8 & 9	Chpt. 11
Plant Transport Systems		Chpt. 16	Chpt. 6	Chpt. 10	Chpt. 13	Chpt. 15	Pg 68-81	Chpt. 10	Chpt. 12
Biological Molecules		Chpt. 6 & 8	Chpt. 7 & 9	Chpt. 2 & 3 Appendix 1	Chpt. 2 & 3	Chpt. 2 & 8	Pg 86-110, 122-145	Chpt. 2 & 3	Chpt. 1 & 4
The Genetic Code		Chpt. 9	Chpt. 8	Chpt. 5 Appendix 2	Chpt. 2 & 18	Chpt. 34	Pg 116-122	Chpt. 5	Chpt. 6
Food and Health		Chpt. 5, 13 & 30	Chpt. 10	Chpt. 22 & 23	Chpt. 16 & 17	Chpt. 9, 19 & 35	Pg 150-159, 182-183	Chpt. 5 & 12	Chpt. 13
Defence and the Immune System		Chpt. 17 & 24	Chpt. 11	Chpt. 14	Chpt. 15 & 16	Chpt. 19	Pg 166-177	Chpt. 16	Chpt. 15
Human Disease		Chpt. 24	Chpt. 11	Chpt. 12 & 13	Chpt. 15 & 16	Chpt. 19	Pg 160-165, 178-185	Chpt 11, 14 & 15	Chpt. 14 & 15
Classification		Chpt. 2	Chpt. 13	N/A	N/A	Chpt. 5 & 6	Pg 200-209	N/A	Chpt. 21
Biodiversity and Conservation		Chpt. 4	Chpt. 12 & 15	Chpt. 20	Chpt. 21 & 22	Chpt. 6 & 39	Pg 190-199, 220-229	N/A	Chpt. 24
Evolution		Chpt. 5 & 30	Chpt. 14	Chpt. 18	Chpt. 20	Chpt. 42 & 43	Pg 210-219	N/A	Chpt. 21
Ecological Principles		Chpt. 3	N/A	Chpt. 7	N/A	Chpt. 37 & 38	N/A	Chpt. 7	Chpt. 22

Contents not available at time of printing (Boyle et al 2008)

Using the Internet

The internet is a powerful resource for locating information. There are several key areas of Biozone's web site that may be of interest to you. Go to the **BioLinks** area to browse through the hundreds of web sites hosted by other organisations. These sites provide a supplement to the activities provided in our workbooks and have been selected on the basis of their accurate, current, and relevant content. We have also provided links to biology-related **podcasts** and **RSS newsfeeds**. These provide regularly updated information about new discoveries in biology; perfect for those wanting to keep abreast of changes in this dynamic field.

The BIOZONE website: www.biozone.co.uk

The current internet address (URL) for the web site is displayed here. You can type a new address directly into this space.

Use Google to search for web sites of interest. The more precise your search words are, the better the list of results. EXAMPLE: If you type in "biotechnology", your search will return an overwhelmingly large number of sites, many of which will not be useful to you. Be more specific, e.g. "biotechnology medicine DNA uses".

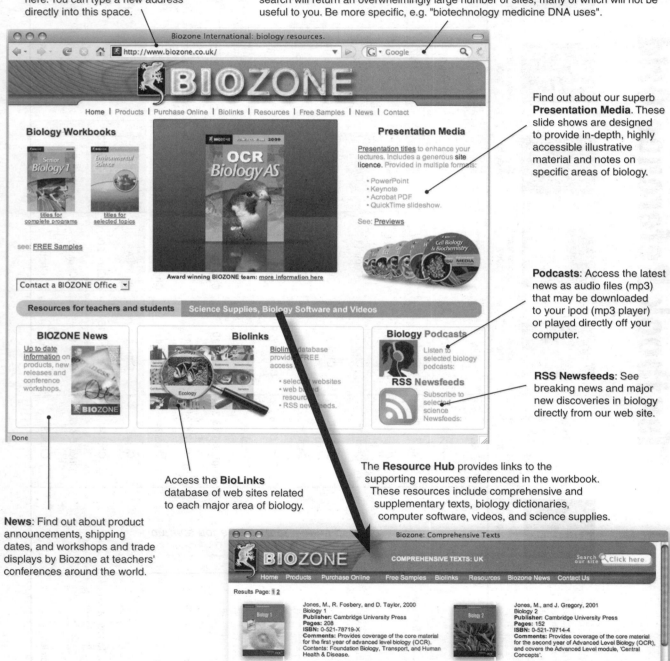

Find out about our superb **Presentation Media**. These slide shows are designed to provide in-depth, highly accessible illustrative material and notes on specific areas of biology.

Podcasts: Access the latest news as audio files (mp3) that may be downloaded to your ipod (mp3 player) or played directly off your computer.

RSS Newsfeeds: See breaking news and major new discoveries in biology directly from our web site.

News: Find out about product announcements, shipping dates, and workshops and trade displays by Biozone at teachers' conferences around the world.

Access the **BioLinks** database of web sites related to each major area of biology.

The **Resource Hub** provides links to the supporting resources referenced in the workbook. These resources include comprehensive and supplementary texts, biology dictionaries, computer software, videos, and science supplies.

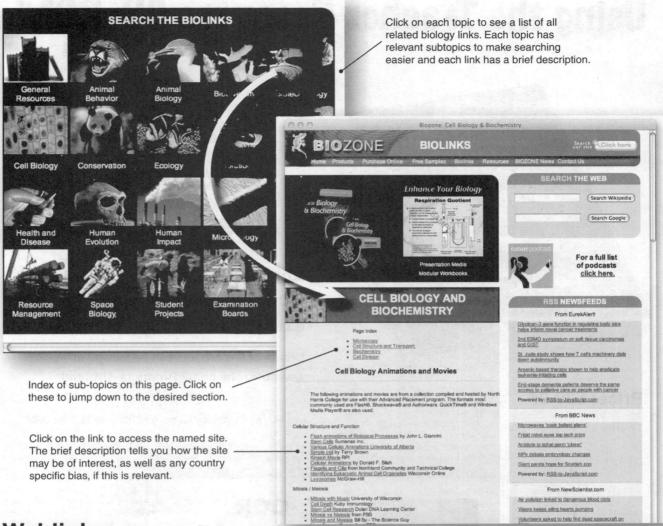

Click on each topic to see a list of all related biology links. Each topic has relevant subtopics to make searching easier and each link has a brief description.

Index of sub-topics on this page. Click on these to jump down to the desired section.

Click on the link to access the named site. The brief description tells you how the site may be of interest, as well as any country specific bias, if this is relevant.

Weblinks:

Go to: **www.biozone.co.uk/weblink/OCR-AS-2160.html**

Throughout this workbook, some pages make reference to additional or alternative activities, as well as web sites that have particular relevance to the activity. See example of page reference below:

| Related activities: Plant Cells, Animal Cells | RA 2 |
| Web links: Eukaryotic Cells Interactive Animation | |

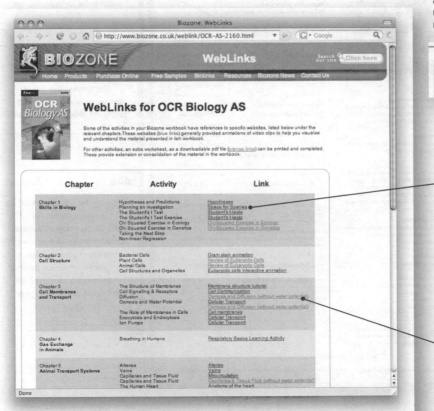

Web Link: provides a link to an **external web site** with supporting information for the activity

Web Link: provides a link to a downloadable **Acrobat (PDF) file** which may provide an additional activity or a different activity with an alternative set of features.

Using the Teacher Resource CD-ROM

Price: £29.95

Supporting resources for this workbook

Acrobat PDF files supplied on CD-ROM provide hyperlinks to an extensive collection of resources.

Details of this product can be viewed at:
www.biozone.co.uk/Products_UK.html

NOTE: Photocopy licence EXPIRES on **30 June 2009**

Click on the **chapter title** to see a digital (**PDF**) version of each page of your workbook suitable for data projection.

Click on this link next to each chapter title to see a comprehensive list of **software** and commercially produced **videos** for that topic.

Click on the links provided to access dozens of **supplementary activities**. Activities are available for each of the exam boards listed and complement the core material in the workbook. They are provided with a **one year** photocopy licence.

Link to **crossword puzzles**.

Link to **glossary** worksheets.

Link to a **digital copy** of the model answers.

Link to a collection of *Excel* ® **spreadsheets** which showcase various graphing techniques and statistical tests.

OCR

Candidates taking the new OCR AS biology course (to be first taught in 2008) are required to complete the units F211, F212 and F213. Candidates taking the OCR A2 course in 2008 will need to complete the requirements for the AS course, as well as 2804, 2805 (one of the five offered options), and 2806 (either components 01 and 02, or components 01 and 03). It should be noted that the new OCR A2 course will be first available for teaching in 2009, at which time the A2 course requirements will be altered.

AS Module	Topics in OCR AS workbook (unless indicated)
Unit F211: Cells, Exchange and Transport	
Module 1: Cells	
1.1.1 Microscopy techniques & stains, organelle structure and function, protein secretion, eukaryote & prokaryote cells characteristics.	Cell Structure
1.1.2 Membrane structure and function. Membrane transport systems. Cell signaling & receptors. Osmosis & water potential.	Cell Membranes & Transport
1.1.3 Mitosis, homologous chromosomes. Stem cells, cell differentiation, and tissue organisation.	Cell Division
Module 2: Exchange and Transport	
1.2.1 Surface area to volume ratio, diffusion. Mammalian lung & gas exchange system. Breathing in humans, measuring breathing.	Gas Exchange in Animals
1.2.2 Animal transport systems, mammalian heart & the cardiac cycle. Structure and function of arteries, veins and capillaries, tissue fluid and lymph. Haemoglobin and oxygen binding.	Animal Transport Systems
1.2.3 Plant transport systems. Structure and function of transport tissues. Transpiration, translocation. Water potential, water movement.	Plant Transport Systems
Unit F212: Molecules, Biodiversity, Food and Health	
Module 1: Biological Molecules	
2.1.1 Water. Amino acids, peptide bonds. Structure and function of proteins, carbohydrates & lipids. Hydrolysis and condensation. Food testing methods.	Biological Molecules
2.1.2 Nucleic acids, structure of DNA, DNA replication, protein synthesis.	The Genetic Code
2.1.3 Enzyme structure and function, mode of action, enzyme activity, inhibitors, cofactors.	Biological Molecules
Module 2: Food and Health	
2.2.1 Diet & nutrition, nutritional diseases, CHD. Importance of plants. Selective breeding, uses of microorganisms, increasing food production, food preservation.	Food and Health
2.2.2 Health and disease, pathogens. Malaria, HIV, TB. Health effects of smoking. Immune system and the body's defences. Immunity and vaccination. New medicines.	Human Disease / Defence and the Immune System
Module 3: Biodiversity and Evolution	
2.3.1 Species, habitat and biodiversity. Sampling and measuring biodiversity.	Biodiversity & Conservation
2.3.2 Classification systems. Features of the five kingdoms, identification keys.	Classification
2.3.3 Darwin's theory of natural selection, speciation, variation. Mechanisms and evidence for evolution. Presticide resistance. Antibiotic and other drug resistance.	Evolution / Human Disease
2.3.4 Conservation. Maintaining Biodiversity, global climate change and Biodiversity.	Biodiversity & Conservation
Unit F213: Practical Skills in Biology 1	
1. Qualitative Task Use of appropriate qualitative skills to perform a practical task. Safe techniques, accurate observation and recording.	Skills in Biology / Cell Structure
2. Quantitative Task Use of appropriate quantitative skills to perform a practical task safely. Accurate measurements and use of the correct degree of precision.	Skills in Biology
3. Evaluation Task Processing & recording results, evaluating trends & drawing conclusions. Identifying limitations. Reliability and validity of data.	Skills in Biology

A2 Module	Topics in A2 workbook (unless indicated)
5.4 Module 2804: Central Concepts	
5.4.1 Structure and role of ATP. Biochemistry of respiration. Respiratory quotients.	Cellular Metabolism
5.4.2 Dicot leaf structure. Chloroplasts. Biochemistry of photosynthesis. Limiting factors.	
5.4.3 Population dynamics and species interactions. Ecological succession.	Populations & Interactions
Sampling distribution and abundance. Conservation v production. Sustainable management of forest ecosystems.	Practical Ecology / Populations & Interactions
5.4.4 Meiosis. Genetic crosses, sex linkage, codominance, multiple alleles. Chi-squared.	Inheritance
Mutation. Genes and environment	Sources of Variation
Gene regulation in bacteria (Lac operon).	Cellular metabolism
Implications of the HGP.	Sources of Variation
5.4.5 Five kingdom classification system.	Biodiversity & Classification
Species & phylogeny. Natural selection. Factors affecting gene pools. Speciation. Adaptation to environment.	Popn Genetics & Speciation
5.4.6 Homeostasis. Kidney structure and function.	Homeostasis
Nervous system structure and function.	Responses & Coordination
Endocrine regulation (blood glucose).	Homeostasis
Role of hormones in flowering plants.	Responses & Coordination
5.5 Module 2805: Options in Biology	
01: Growth, Development & Reproduction Growth and development, asexual reproduction, sexual reproduction in humans and angiosperms. Role of hormones in growth and rreproduction.	TRC: Option 01 *Growth, Development, and Reproduction*
02: Applications of genetics Genetic variation, selective breeding, GE techniques, genetic screening and gene therapy, genetic fingerprinting, transplant compatibility. Ethical issues.	TRC: Option 02 *Applications of Genetics*
03: Environmental Biology Practical ecology, pollution, agricultural ecosystems, resource conservation (fisheries, land reclamation, recycling), nation and international conservation.	TRC: Option 03 *Environmental Biology*
04: Microbiology and Biotechnology Nature of microorganisms, culturing techniques, applications of biotechnology.	TRC: Option 04 *Microbiology and Biotechnology*
05: Mammalian Physiology & Behaviour Mammalian nutrition, the liver, locomotion, nervous system and sensory reception, principles of behaviour (innate and learned).	TRC: Option 05 *Mammalian Physiology and Behaviour*
5.10 Module 2806: Unifying Concepts in Biology Experimental Skills 2	
Component 01: Unifying concepts in Biology (compulsory) Exam questions based on concepts covered in the AS scheme, and module 2804 of A2.	
Experimental Skills 2: *Option (candidates take either 02 or 03)*	
Component 02: Coursework 2 Internal assessment of experimental and investigative work. Skills include planning and implementing a study, recording, analysing, and evaluating data, drawing conclusions.	OCR AS Skills in Biology / Practical Ecology
Component 03: Coursework 3 External assessment of experimental and investigative skills including planning and implementing a study, recording, analysing, and evaluating data, drawing conclusions. Components consist of planning a task, experimentation, and microscopy.	OCR AS Skills in Biology / OCR AS Cell Structure / Practical Ecology

CIE

The subject content of the **Cambridge International Examinations** (CIE) programme is divided into AS and A2. The A2 includes a core and an Applications of Biology section, which is studied in its entirety, by all A2 candidates. Candidates taking the CIE AS will be assessed on the Learning Outcomes A-K. A level candidates will be assessed on the Learning Outcomes L-U. The *Applications of Biology* section accounts for about 12% of the A level course. The acquisition of practical skills (and their assessment) underpins the course.

AS Module	Topics in OCR/CIE AS workbook
Core Syllabus *(sections L-U are in Advanced biology A2)*	
A Light microscopy, electron microscopy, and cell structure. Eukaryote and prokaryote cells. Functions of organelles.	Cell Structure
B Structure and role of carbohydrates, lipids, and proteins. Water and inorganic ions. Hydrolysis and condensation reactions. Biochemical food testing.	Biological Molecules
C Enzyme action, enzyme activity and enzyme inhibitors.	Biological Molecules
D Fluid mosaic model of membrane structure. Transport across the membrane. Water potential	Cell Membranes and Transport
E Replication and division of nuclei and cells. Role of meiosis in sexual reproduction. Chromosome behaviour during mitosis. Uncontrolled cell division (cancer).	Cell Division
F DNA structure and replication. The role of DNA in protein synthesis. Nucleotide base pairing.	The Genetic Code
G Transport in multicellular plants: structure and distribution of xylem and phloem in dicots. Transpiration. Translocation. Xerophytes.	Plant Transport Systems
Structure and function of mammalian transport systems. The heart and the cardiac cycle. Haemoglobin and gas transport, gas exchange and altitude.	Animal Transport Systems
H The structure and function of the human respiratory system. Gas exchange.	Gas Exchange in Animals
The effects of smoking on gas exchange. Smoking related diseases.	Human Disease
I Causes and transmission of infectious diseases, their control and prevention. HIV/AIDS, TB, cholera and malaria. The use of antibiotics.	Human Disease
J Structure and function of the immune system. Types of immunity. Vaccinations.	Defence and the Immune System
K The ecosystem concept (habitat, niche, populations, communities). Energy transfer, ecological efficiency, the nitrogen cycle.	Ecological Principles
Meeting Assessment Objectives	
A Knowledge with understanding, including the use of scientific vocabulary, understanding scientific ideas and concepts, using instruments and scientific measurements, applying of scientific and technological techniques.	Skills in Biology
B Handling information and solving problems: organising and extracting information. Manipulating and presenting data, and drawing conclusions. Applying knowledge to solve problems.	
C Experimental skills and investigations. Following detailed instructions, using techniques and apparatus correctly, making accurate observations, and interpreting the data to form predictions. Designing, planning and carrying out a scientific experiment or investigation.	

A2 Module	Topics in A2 workbook *(unless indicated)*
Core Syllabus *(sections A-K are in Advanced biology AS)*	
L Energy requirements in living organisms. The structure and function of ATP. Cellular respiration, and energy transfer. Aerobic and anaerobic respiration. Respiratory quotient and the energy value of substrates. Respirometers.	Cellular Metabolism
M Photosynthesis and energy transfer. The biochemistry of photosynthesis. Limiting factors in photosynthesis. The structure of a dicot leaf.	Cellular Metabolism
N Homeostasis principles. Kidney function and structure. Nervous system: sensory receptors, neurones, action potential, and synapses. Endocrine glands (pancreas). Control of blood glucose (diabetes treatment). Role of hormones in flowering plants.	Homeostasis Responses & Coordination
O Genetic transfer. Meiosis. Genes and alleles. Monohybrid and dihybrid crosses, sex linkage, codominance, multiple alleles. Chi-squared. Mutations and environmental effects on phenotype.	Sources of Variation Inheritance
P Natural and artificial selection. The role of natural selection in evolution. The role of environmental factors and isolating mechanisms. The role of artificial selection on livestock improvement. Factors affecting allele frequencies (malaria and sickle cell anaemia).	Population Genetics and Speciation
Q The five kingdom classification system. The importance of biodiversity. Conservation issues: endangered species and strategies to protect them.	Biodiversity & Classification ● TRC: Conservation Issues
R Gene technology, techniques in gene technology. Uses of gene technology (insulin production, DNA sequencing, genetic fingerprinting, and genetic screening). Benefits and hazards of gene technology. Ethical issues.	AS Gene Technology
S Biotechnology. Industrial use of microorganisms. Large scale production of microorganisms. Enzyme technology. The use of monoclonal antibodies.	● TRC: Biotechnology
T Crop plant reproduction and adaptations. Methods of improving crop production.	● TRC: Crop Plants
U Human reproduction. Gametogenesis (mitosis, growth, meiosis and maturation). The role of hormones in the menstrual cycle. Contraception. In-vitro fertilisation.	● TRC: Aspects of Human Reproduction
Meeting Assessment Objectives	
A Knowledge with understanding. Including the use of scientific vocabulary, understanding scientific ideas and concepts, using instruments and scientific measurements, the application of scientific and technological techniques.	Skills in Biology Practical Ecology
B Handling information and solving problems. Understand how to organise and extract information. Know how to manipulate and present data, and draw conclusions. Apply knowledge to problem solve.	
C Experimental skills and investigations. Following detailed instructions, using techniques and apparatus correctly, making accurate observations, and interpreting the data to form predictions. Designing, planning and carrying out a scientific experiment or investigation.	

Skills in Biology

OCR: AS Unit F213: Practical Skills in Biology 1

A2 Unit F216: Practical Skills in Biology 2

CIE: Paper 3: Practical experimental skills

Paper 5: Skills: planning , analysis, and evaluation

Learning Objectives

☐ 1. Compile your own glossary from the **KEY WORDS** displayed in **bold type** in the learning objectives below.

☐ 2. Demonstrate an understanding of the meaning of the following terms: **compare**, **contrast**, **define**, **describe**, **discuss**, **explain** (or account for), **evaluate**, **identify**, **illustrate**, **list**, **outline**, **state**, **suggest**, **summarise**. A correct understanding of these terms will enable you to answer questions appropriately (see page 3 for help).

Planning an Investigation (pages 15-25)

☐ 3. Recall the role of **observation** as a prelude to forming a **hypothesis**. In your research, you will make observations, and use these to formulate a hypothesis, from which you can generate testable predictions.

☐ 4. Appreciate that your study design will be determined by the nature of the investigation, i.e. a controlled experiment vs a population study in the field. Some of the following objectives apply specifically to controlled experiments. They will also apply, with modification if necessary, to field studies.

☐ 5. Formulate a **hypothesis** from which you can generate **predictions** about the outcome of your investigation. Consider a **pilot study**, to test the experimental procedure you have in mind.

☐ 6. Define and explain the purpose of each of the following variables in a controlled experiment:
- **Independent variable** (manipulated variable)
- **Dependent variable** (response variable)
- **Controlled variables** (to control nuisance factors)

☐ 7. For your own investigation distinguish clearly between:
- A **data value** for a particular **variable**, e.g. height.
- The individual sampling unit, e.g. a test-tube with an enzyme at a particular pH.
- The sample size, e.g. the number of test-tubes in each treatment.

☐ 8. Determine the amount of data that you need to collect in order to reasonably test your hypothesis.
- For lab based investigations, determine the **sample size** (e.g. the number of samples within each treatment) and the number of **treatments** (the range of the independent variable).
- For field based investigations, determine the size of the sampling unit (it may be an individual organism or a quadrat size) and the sample size (e.g. the number of organisms or quadrats).

☐ 9. Determine the type of data that you will collect (e.g. counts, measurements) and how you will collect it. Have a clear idea about how you are going to analyse your data before you start and appreciate why this is important. Understand why it is desirable to collect **quantitative** rather than **qualitative** data.

☐ 10. Describe any **controls** in your investigation and identify any assumptions made in the investigation.

☐ 11. Identify different methods for systematically recording data: tables, spreadsheets, and software linked to **dataloggers**. Decide on the method by which you will **systematically record** the data as they are collected.

☐ 12. Identify **sources of error** in your experimental design and explain how you will minimise these.

☐ 13. Recognise that all biological investigations should be carried out with appropriate regard for safety and the well-being of living organisms and their environment.

Dealing with Data (pages 26-35, 47-48)

☐ 14. Collect and record data systematically according to your plan (#11). Critically evaluate the **accuracy** of your methods for data collection, any **measurement errors**, and the repeatability (**precision**) of any measurements.

☐ 15. Demonstrate an ability to perform simple and appropriate **data transformations**, e.g. totals, percentages, increments, reciprocals, rates, and log.

☐ 16. Demonstrate an ability to use **SI units** and an appropriate number of **significant figures**. Understand the relationship between the appropriate number of significant figures and the accuracy of a measurement.

☐ 17. Describe the benefits of graphing data. Recognise the **x axis** and **y axis** of graphs and identify which variable (dependent or independent) is plotted on each.

☐ 18. Demonstrate an ability to plot data in an appropriate way using different methods of graphical presentation: **scatter plots**, **line graphs**, **pie graphs**, **bar graphs** (and column graphs), **kite graphs**, and **histograms**.

☐ 19. Explain what is meant by a '**line of best fit**' and when it is appropriate to use it. Draw 'lines of best fit' to graphs with plotted points. Use error bars to place your line or try a computer generated fit (see #26).

☐ 20. Make good **biological drawings** as a way of recording information where appropriate to your investigation.

Descriptive Statistics (pages 36-41)

☐ 21. Distinguish between a **statistic** and a **parameter**. Demonstrate an understanding of the calculation and use of the following **descriptive statistics**:
- (a) Sample **mean** and **standard deviation**. Identify when the use of these statistics is appropriate.
- (b) **Median** and **mode** (calculated from your own, or second hand, data). Explain what each statistic summarises and when its use is appropriate.

☐ 22. Calculate measures of dispersion for your data, related to the true population parameters. Consider:
- (a) The **standard error** of the mean.
- (b) The **95% confidence intervals** and the **95% confidence limits**.

□ 23. Identify **trends** in your data for further analysis and discussion. Evaluate unexpected results and outlying data points and be prepared to discuss them.

Statistical Tests *(pages 36-37, 42-46 and the TRC)*

□ 24. Use the flow chart provided in this topic to help you decide on the appropriate analysis for your data. Some further guidelines are provided below.

Tests for a trend
Recognise tests for trends (relationships) in data.

□ 25. **Correlation:** Data are **correlated** when there is a relationship between the two variables in question, but neither is assumed to be dependent on the other. A test for correlation can demonstrate that two measures are associated; it cannot establish cause and effect.

□ 26. **Regression:** A regression is appropriate when the magnitude of one variable (the dependent variable) is determined by the magnitude of the second variable (the independent variable). Recognise:

Linear regression: This is the simplest functional relationship of one variable to another and is indicated by a straight line relationship on a scatter plot. Generate a **line of best fit** for plotted data and comment on the fit of the data to the line. Discuss the **predictive** nature of linear regression analyses.

Non-linear regression: Many relationships between an independent variable and its corresponding biological response are not linear (e.g. change in respiration rate with changes in salinity). If your data plot in a non-linear scatter, consider a non-linear regression to test the relationship.

Tests for difference
Recognise tests for difference between groups.

□ 27. **Chi-squared** is a test for difference between two groups where the observed result is compared to an expected outcome. It is often used in ecology and for testing the outcome of simple genetic crosses.

□ 28. **Student's *t* test** is a test for difference between two means, and can be used even when sample sizes are small. It is often used to test differences between densities of organisms in different habitats.

□ 29. **ANOVA** (analysis of variance) is a test for difference between more than two means. ANOVA is a good test for investigations involving a biological response to specific treatments, such as different fertilisers or soils.

Writing a Report *(pages 49-55)*

□ 30. Write up your report. Give it a concise, descriptive title, and organise it into the following sections:

(a) **Introduction:** State your aim and hypothesis, and summarise the state of knowledge in the topic area.

(b) **Materials and methods:** Describe how you carried out your investigation in a way that allows the method to be reproduced by others.

(c) **Results:** Use text, graphs, and tables to describe your results; do not discuss them at this stage.

(d) **Discussion:** Discuss your results, including a critical evaluation of any discrepancies in your results. Include reference to published work.

(e) **Conclusion:** Summarise your findings with respect to your original hypothesis. Draw conclusions only about the variable that you planned to investigate.

(f) **Reference list:** List all sources of information, including personal communications.

 See the 'Textbook Reference Grid' on page 7 for textbook page references relating to material in this topic.

Supplementary Texts
See pages 5-6 for additional details of these texts:
■ Barnard, C., *et al.*, 2007. **Asking Questions in Biology**, 3 edn (Prentice Hall).
■ Cadogan, A. and Ingram, M., 2002. **Maths for Advanced Biology** (NelsonThornes).
■ Indge, B., 2003. **Data and Data Handling for AS and A Level Biology** (Hodder Arnold H&S).
■ Jones, A., *et al.*, 2007. **Practical Skills in Biology** (Pearson).
■ Morgan, S., 2002. **Advanced Level Practical Work for Biology** (Hodder and Stoughton).

See pages 8-9 for details of how to access **Bio Links** from our web site: **www.biozone.co.uk**. From Bio Links, access sites under the topics:

STUDENT PROJECTS > General: • AP Biology training • Mr Knight's AP lab activities • StudyZones.com > **Skills in Biology:** • A scientific report • Scientific investigation • Study skills - biology • The scientific method • Tree lupins • Woodlice online > **Statistics:** • Chi-square lesson • What is a P value? ... *and others*

See page 6 for details of publishers of periodicals:

STUDENT'S REFERENCE
■ **Drawing Graphs** Biol. Sci. Rev., 19(3) Feb. 2007, pp. 10-13. *A guide to creating graphs.*
■ **AS: A Word at the Start?** Biol. Sci. Rev., 13(1) Sept. 2000, pp. 6-8. *A useful summary of the importance of understanding the facts, reading carefully, and accurately communicating your knowledge when answering examination questions.*
■ **Size Does Matter** Biol. Sci. Rev., 17 (3) February 2005, pp. 10-13. *Measuring the size of organisms and calculating magnification and scale.*
■ **Percentages** Biol. Sci. Rev., 17(2) Nov. 2004, pp. 28-29. *The calculation of percentage and the appropriate uses of this important transformation.*
■ **The Variability of Samples** Biol. Sci. Rev., 13(4) March 2001, pp. 34-35. *The variability of sample data and the use of sample statistics as estimators for population parameters.*
■ **Experiments** Biol. Sci. Rev., 14(3) February 2002, pp. 11-13. *The basics of experimental design and execution: determining variables, measuring them, and establishing a control.*
■ **Descriptive Statistics** Biol. Sci. Rev., 13 (5) May 2001, pp. 36-37. *A synopsis of descriptive statistics. The appropriate use of standard error and standard deviation is discussed.*
■ **Dealing with Data** Biol. Sci. Rev., 12 (4) March 2000, pp. 6-8. *A short account of the best ways in which to deal with the interpretation of graphically presented data in examinations.*
■ **Describing the Normal Distribution** Biol. Sci. Rev., 13(2) Nov. 2000, pp. 40-41. *The normal distribution, with an introduction to data spread, mean, median, variance, and standard deviation.*

■ **Statistical Modelling** New Scientist, 17 Sept. 1994 (Inside Science). *Useful presentation of data; distributions, normal curves, and histograms.*
■ **The Truth is Out There** New Scientist, 26 Feb. 2000 (Inside Science). *The philosophy of scientific method explained clearly and with examples.*
■ **Statistical Sampling** New Scientist, 10 June 1995 (Inside Science). *Hypotheses, sampling methodology, significance, & central limit theorem.*
■ **Estimating the Mean and Standard Deviation** Biol. Sci. Rev., 13(3) January 2001, pp. 40-41. *Simple statistical analysis. Includes formulae for calculating sample mean and standard deviation.*
■ **Correlation** Biol. Sci. Rev., 14(3) February 2002, pp. 38-41. *An examination of the relationship between variables. An excellent synopsis.*
■ **Ecological Projects** Biol. Sci. Rev., 8(5) May 1996, pp. 24-26. *Planning and carrying out a field-based project (includes analysis and reporting).*
■ **Fieldwork - Sampling Animals** Biol. Sci. Rev., 10(4) March 1998, pp. 23-25. *The appropriate methodology for collecting animals in the field.*
■ **Fieldwork Sampling - Plants** Biol. Sci. Rev., 10(5) May 1998, pp. 6-8. *Methods for sampling plant communities (transects and quadrats).*

TEACHER'S REFERENCE
■ **Biology Statistics made Simple using Excel** SSR 83(303), Dec. 2001, pp. 29-34. *An instructional account on the use of spreadsheets for statistics in A level science (excellent).*

Working spreadsheets support this topic:

Teacher Resource CD-ROM
• **Statistics spreadsheets**

Hypotheses and Predictions

Scientific knowledge grows through a process called the **scientific method**. This process involves observation and measurement, hypothesising and predicting, and planning and executing investigations designed to test formulated **hypotheses**. A scientific hypothesis is a tentative explanation for an observation, which is capable of being tested by experimentation. Hypotheses lead to **predictions** about the system involved and they are accepted or rejected on the basis of findings arising from the investigation. Rejection of the hypothesis may lead to new, alternative explanations (hypotheses) for the observations. Acceptance of the hypothesis as a valid explanation is not necessarily permanent: explanations may be rejected at a later date in light of new findings. This process eventually leads to new knowledge (theory, laws, or models).

Skills in Biology

Making Observations

These may involve the observation of certain behaviours in wild populations, physiological measurements made during previous experiments, or 'accidental' results obtained when seeking answers to completely unrelated questions.

Testing predictions may lead to new observations

Asking Questions

The observations lead to the formation of questions about the system being studied.

Testing the Predictions

The predictions are tested out in the practical part of an investigation.

Accept or reject the hypothesis

Forming a Hypothesis

Features of a sound hypothesis:

- It is based on observations and prior knowledge of the system.
- It offers an explanation for an observation.
- It refers to only one independent variable.
- It is written as a definite statement and not as a question.
- It is testable by experimentation.
- It leads to predictions about the system.

Designing an Investigation

Investigations are planned so that the predictions about the system made in the hypothesis can be tested. Investigations may be laboratory or field based.

Generating a Null Hypothesis

A hypothesis based on observations is used to generate the **null hypothesis** (H_0); the hypothesis of no difference or no effect. Hypotheses are expressed in the null form for the purposes of statistical testing. H_0 may be rejected in favour of accepting the alternative hypothesis, H_A.

Making Predictions

Based on a hypothesis, **predictions** (expected, repeatable outcomes) can be generated about the behaviour of the system. Predictions may be made on any aspect of the material of interest, e.g. how different variables (factors) relate to each other.

Related activities: Experimental Method
Web links: Hypotheses

A 2

Useful Types of Hypotheses

A hypothesis offers a tentative explanation to questions generated by observations. Some examples are described below. Hypotheses are often constructed in a form that allows them to be tested statistically. For every hypothesis, there is a corresponding **null hypothesis**; a hypothesis against the prediction. Predictions are tested with laboratory and field experiments and carefully focused observations. For a hypothesis to be accepted it should be possible for anyone to test the predictions with the same methods and get a similar result each time.

Hypothesis involving manipulation
Used when the effect of manipulating a variable on a biological entity is being investigated. **Example**: The composition of applied fertiliser influences the rate of growth of plant A.

Hypothesis of choice
Used when species preference, e.g. for a particular habitat type or microclimate, is being investigated. **Example**: Woodpeckers (species A) show a preference for tree type when nesting.

Hypothesis involving observation
Used when organisms are being studied in their natural environment and conditions cannot be changed. **Example**: Fern abundance is influenced by the degree to which the canopy is established.

1. Generate a prediction for the hypothesis: *"Moisture level of the microhabitat influences woodlouse distribution"*:

   _____

2. During the course of any investigation, new information may arise as a result of observations unrelated to the original hypothesis. This can lead to the generation of further hypotheses about the system. For each of the incidental observations described below, formulate a prediction, and an outline of an investigation to test it. *The observation described in each case was not related to the hypothesis the experiment was designed to test:*

   (a) **Bacterial cultures**

   Prediction: _____

   _____

   Outline of the investigation: _____

   _____

   _____

   _____

   _____

   _____

Bacterial Cultures

Observation: During an experiment on bacterial growth, the girls noticed that the cultures grew at different rates when the dishes were left overnight in different parts of the laboratory.

   (b) **Plant cloning**

   Prediction: _____

   _____

   _____

   Outline of the investigation: _____

   _____

   _____

   _____

   _____

   _____

   _____

Plant Cloning

Observation: During an experiment on plant cloning, a scientist noticed that the root length of plant clones varied depending on the concentration of a hormone added to the agar.

Planning an Investigation

Investigations involve written stages (planning and reporting), at the start and end. The middle stage is the practical work when the data are collected. Practical work may be laboratory or field based. Typical lab based studies involve investigating how a biological response is affected by manipulating a particular **variable**, e.g. temperature. Field work often involves investigating features of a population or community. These may be interrelationships, such as competition, or patterns, such as zonation. Where quantitative information must be gathered from the population or community, particular techniques (such as quadrat sampling) and protocols (e.g. random placement of sampling units) apply. These aspects of practical work are covered in *Advanced Biology A2*. Investigations in the field are usually more complex than those in the laboratory because natural systems have many more variables that cannot easily be controlled or accounted for.

Planning	Execution	Analysis and Reporting

Planning

- Formulate your hypothesis from an observation.
- Use a checklist (see the next activity) or a template (above) to construct a plan.

Execution

- Spend time (as appropriate to your study) collecting the data.
- Record the data in a systematic format (e.g. a table or spreadsheet).

Analysis and Reporting

- Analyse the data using graphs, tables, or statistics to look for trends or patterns.
- Write up your report including all the necessary sections.

Identifying Variables

A variable is any characteristic or property able to take any one of a range of values. Investigations often look at the effect of changing one variable on another. It is important to identify all variables in an investigation: independent, dependent, and controlled, although there may be nuisance factors of which you are unaware. In all fair tests, only one variable is changed by the investigator.

Dependent variable

- Measured during the investigation.
- Recorded on the y axis of the graph.

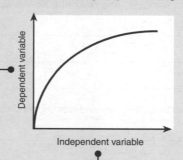

Controlled variables

- Factors that are kept the same or controlled.
- List these in the method, as appropriate to your own investigation.

Independent variable

- Set by the person carrying out the investigation.
- Recorded on the x axis of the graph.

Assumptions

In any experimental work, you will make certain assumptions about the biological system you are working with.

Assumptions are features of the system (and your experiment) that you assume to be true but do not (or cannot) test.

Examples of Investigations

Aim		Variables	
Investigate the effect of varying …	on the following …	Independent variable	Dependent variable
Temperature	Leaf width	Temperature	Leaf width
Light intensity	Activity of woodlice	Light intensity	Woodlice activity
Soil pH	Plant height at age 6 months	pH	Plant height

Related activities: Variables and Data, Experimental Method
Web links: Space for Species

A 2

In order to write a sound method for your investigation, you need to determine how the independent, dependent, and controlled variables will be set and measured (or monitored). A good understanding of your methodology is crucial to a successful investigation. You need to be clear about how much data, and what type of data, you will collect. You should also have a good idea about how you will analyse the data. Use the example below to practise your skills in identifying this type of information.

Case Study: Catalase Activity

Catalase is an enzyme that converts hydrogen peroxide (H_2O_2) to oxygen and water. An experiment investigated the effect of temperature on the rate of the catalase reaction. Small (10 cm^3) test tubes were used for the reactions, each containing 0.5 cm^3 of enzyme and 4 cm^3 of hydrogen peroxide. Reaction rates were assessed at four temperatures (10°C, 20°C, 30°C, and 60°C). For each temperature, there were two reaction tubes (e.g. tubes 1 and 2 were both kept at 10°C). The height of oxygen bubbles present after one minute of reaction was used as a measure of the reaction rate; a faster reaction rate produced more bubbles. The entire experiment, involving eight tubes, was repeated on two separate days.

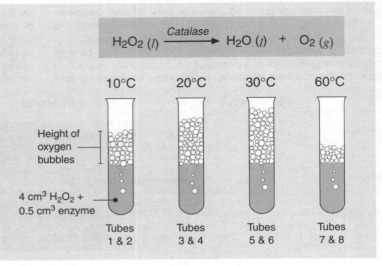

1. Write a suitable aim for this experiment: _____

_____

2. Write a suitable hypothesis for this experiment: _____

_____

3. (a) Identify the **independent variable**: _____

   (b) State the range of values for the independent variable: _____

   (c) Name the unit for the independent variable: _____

   (d) List the equipment needed to set the independent variable, and describe how it was used: _____

   _____

4. (a) Identify the **dependent variable**: _____

   (b) Name the unit for the dependent variable: _____

   (c) List the equipment needed to measure the dependent variable, and describe how it was used: _____

   _____

5. (a) Each temperature represents a treatment/sample/trial (circle one):

   (b) State the number of tubes at each temperature: _____

   (c) State the sample size for each treatment: _____

   (d) State how many times the whole investigation was repeated: _____

6. Explain why it would have been desirable to have included an extra tube containing no enzyme: _____

   _____

7. Identify three variables that might have been controlled in this experiment, and how they could have been monitored:

   (a) _____

   (b) _____

   (c) _____

8. Explain why controlled variables should be monitored carefully: _____

   _____

Experimental Method

An aim, hypothesis, and method for an experiment are described below. Explanations of the types of variables for which data are collected, and methods of recording these, are provided in the next two activities. The method described below includes numbered steps and incorporates other features identified in the previous activity. The method can be thought of as a 'statement of intent' for the practical work, and it may need slight changes during execution. The investigation described below was based on the observation that plant species 'A' was found growing in soil with a low pH (pH 4-5). The investigators wondered whether plant species 'A' was adapted to grow more vigorously under acid conditions than under alkaline or neutral conditions.

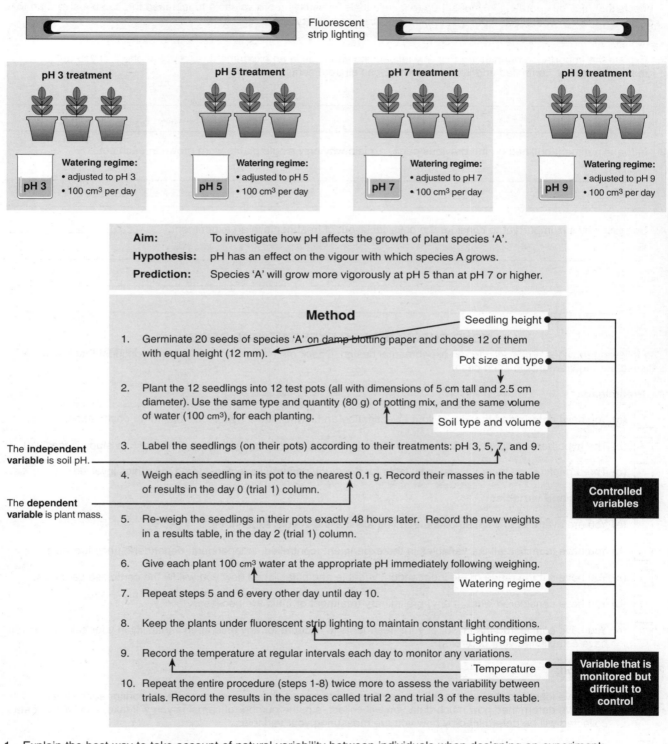

Fluorescent strip lighting

pH 3 treatment — Watering regime: • adjusted to pH 3 • 100 cm³ per day

pH 5 treatment — Watering regime: • adjusted to pH 5 • 100 cm³ per day

pH 7 treatment — Watering regime: • adjusted to pH 7 • 100 cm³ per day

pH 9 treatment — Watering regime: • adjusted to pH 9 • 100 cm³ per day

Skills in Biology

Aim: To investigate how pH affects the growth of plant species 'A'.

Hypothesis: pH has an effect on the vigour with which species A grows.

Prediction: Species 'A' will grow more vigorously at pH 5 than at pH 7 or higher.

Method

Seedling height • Pot size and type • Soil type and volume •

1. Germinate 20 seeds of species 'A' on damp blotting paper and choose 12 of them with equal height (12 mm).

2. Plant the 12 seedlings into 12 test pots (all with dimensions of 5 cm tall and 2.5 cm diameter). Use the same type and quantity (80 g) of potting mix, and the same volume of water (100 cm³), for each planting.

3. Label the seedlings (on their pots) according to their treatments: pH 3, 5, 7, and 9.

The **independent variable** is soil pH.

4. Weigh each seedling in its pot to the nearest 0.1 g. Record their masses in the table of results in the day 0 (trial 1) column.

The **dependent variable** is plant mass.

5. Re-weigh the seedlings in their pots exactly 48 hours later. Record the new weights in a results table, in the day 2 (trial 1) column.

6. Give each plant 100 cm³ water at the appropriate pH immediately following weighing.

7. Repeat steps 5 and 6 every other day until day 10.

8. Keep the plants under fluorescent strip lighting to maintain constant light conditions.

9. Record the temperature at regular intervals each day to monitor any variations.

10. Repeat the entire procedure (steps 1-8) twice more to assess the variability between trials. Record the results in the spaces called trial 2 and trial 3 of the results table.

Controlled variables

Watering regime • Lighting regime • Temperature •

Variable that is monitored but difficult to control

1. Explain the best way to take account of natural variability between individuals when designing an experiment:

_____
_____
_____
_____

Related activities: Variables and Data

Replication in experiments

Replication refers to the number of times you repeat your entire experimental design (including controls). True replication is not the same as increasing the sample size (*n*) although it is often used to mean the same thing. Replication accounts for any unusual and unforseen effects that may be operating in your set-up (e.g. field trials of plant varieties where soil type is variable). Replication is necessary when you expect that the response of treatments will vary because of factors outside your control. It is a feature of higher level experimental designs, and complex statistics are needed to separate differences between replicate treatments. For simple experiments, it is usually more valuable to increase the sample size than to worry about replicates.

2. Explain the importance of ensuring that any influencing variables in an experiment (except the one that you are manipulating) are controlled and kept constant across all treatments:

_____

_____

3. In the experiment outlined on the previous page, explain why only single plants were grown in each pot:

_____

_____

4. Suggest why it is important to consider the physical layout of treatments in an experiment: _____

_____

_____

_____

YOUR CHECKLIST FOR EXPERIMENTAL DESIGN

The following provides a checklist for an experimental design. Check off the points when you are confident that you have satisfied the requirements in each case:

1. **Preliminary:**

☐ (a) You have determined the aim of your investigation and formulated a hypothesis based on observation(s).

☐ (b) The hypothesis (and its predictions) are testable using the resources you have available (the study is feasible).

☐ (c) The organism you have chosen is suitable for the study and you have considered the ethics involved.

2. **Assumptions and variables:**

☐ (a) You are aware of any assumptions that you are making in your experiment.

☐ (b) You have identified all the variables in the experiment (controlled, independent, dependent, uncontrollable).

☐ (c) You have set the range of the independent variable and established how you will fix the controlled variables.

☐ (d) You have considered what (if any) preliminary treatment or trials are necessary.

☐ (e) You have considered the layout of your treatments to account for any unforseen variability in your set-up and you have established your control(s).

3. **Data collection:**

☐ (a) You have identified the units for all variables and determined how you will measure or monitor each variable. You have determined how much data you will collect, e.g. the number of samples you will take. The type of data collected will be determined by how you are measuring your variables.

☐ (b) You have considered how you will analyse the data you collect and made sure that your experimental design allows you to answer the questions you have asked.

☐ (c) You have designed a method for systematically recording your results and had this checked with a teacher. The format of your results table or spreadsheet accommodates all your raw results, any transformations you intend to make, and all trials and treatments.

☐ (d) You have recorded data from any preliminary trials and any necessary changes to your methodology.

Recording Results

Designing a table to record your results is part of planning your investigation. Once you have collected all your data, you will need to analyse and present it. To do this, it may be necessary to transform your data first, by calculating a mean or a rate. An example of a table for recording results is presented below. This example relates to the investigation described in the previous activity, but it represents a relatively standardised layout. The labels on the columns and rows are chosen to represent the design features of the investigation. The first column contains the entire range chosen for the independent variable. There are spaces for multiple sampling units, repeats (trials), and averages. A version of this table should be presented in your final report.

Dependent variable and its units

Space for repeats of the experimental design (in this case, three trials).

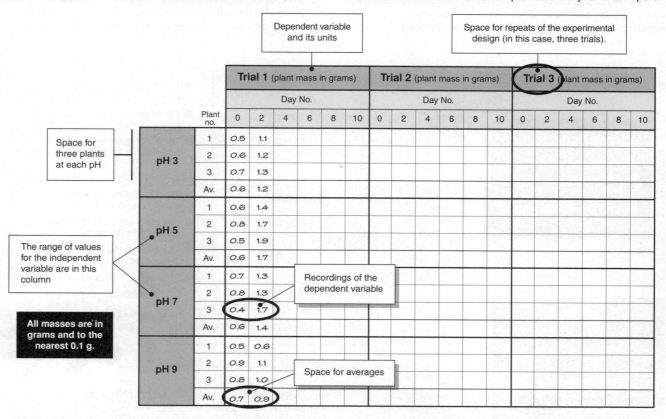

Space for three plants at each pH

The range of values for the independent variable are in this column

All masses are in grams and to the nearest 0.1 g.

Recordings of the dependent variable

Space for averages

	Plant no.	Trial 1 (plant mass in grams)						Trial 2 (plant mass in grams)						Trial 3 (plant mass in grams)					
		Day No.						Day No.						Day No.					
		0	2	4	6	8	10	0	2	4	6	8	10	0	2	4	6	8	10
pH 3	1	0.5	1.1																
	2	0.6	1.2																
	3	0.7	1.3																
	Av.	0.6	1.2																
pH 5	1	0.6	1.4																
	2	0.8	1.7																
	3	0.5	1.9																
	Av.	0.6	1.7																
pH 7	1	0.7	1.3																
	2	0.8	1.3																
	3	0.4	1.7																
	Av.	0.6	1.4																
pH 9	1	0.5	0.6																
	2	0.9	1.1																
	3	0.8	1.0																
	Av.	0.7	0.9																

1. In the space (below) design a table to collect data from the case study below. Include space for individual results and averages from the three set ups (use the table above as a guide).

Case Study
Carbon dioxide levels in a respiration chamber

A datalogger was used to monitor the concentrations of carbon dioxide (CO_2) in respiration chambers containing five green leaves from one plant species. The entire study was performed in conditions of full light (quantified) and involved three identical set-ups. The CO_2 concentrations were measured every minute, over a period of ten minutes, using a CO_2 sensor. A mean CO_2 concentration (for the three set-ups) was calculated. The study was carried out two more times, two days apart.

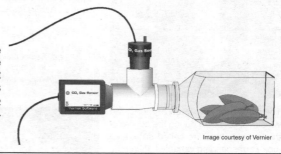

Image courtesy of Vernier

2. Next, the effect of various light intensities (low light, half-light, and full light) on CO_2 concentration was investigated. Describe how the results table for this investigation would differ from the one you have drawn above (for full light only):

_____

_____

Skills in Biology

Related activities: Transforming Raw Data, Data Presentation

DA 2

Variables and Data

When planning a biological investigation, it is important to consider the type of data that will be collected. It is best, whenever possible, to collect quantitative data, as these data lend themselves well to analysis and statistical testing. Recording data in a systematic way as you collect it, e.g. using a table or spreadsheet, is important, especially if data manipulation and transformation are required. It is important to calculate summary, **descriptive statistics** (e.g. mean) as you proceed. These will help you to recognise important trends or features in your data as they become apparent. The biggest hurdle in undertaking an experimental study will be in choosing a topic that lends itself to the aims of the investigation and is designed in such a way that analysis is straightforward and biologically meaningful. Guidelines are given below, together with a synopsis of types of variables. You should be familiar with the qualities of data before you start, as this will help you to develop a well designed investigation.

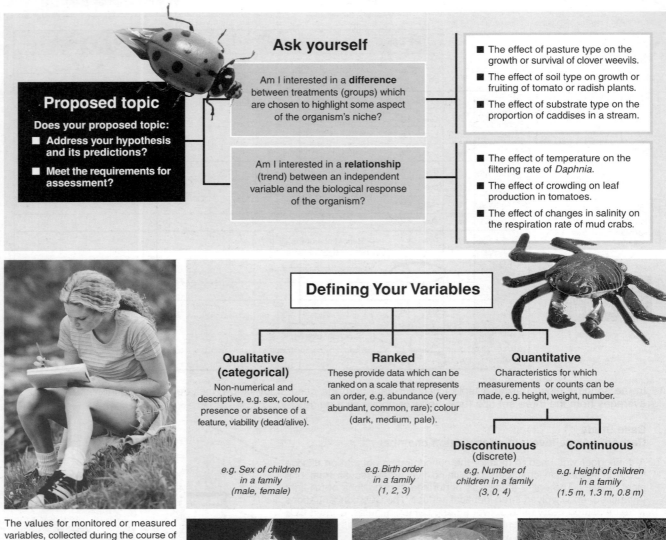

Ask yourself

Proposed topic

Does your proposed topic:
- Address your hypothesis and its predictions?
- Meet the requirements for assessment?

Am I interested in a **difference** between treatments (groups) which are chosen to highlight some aspect of the organism's niche?

- The effect of pasture type on the growth or survival of clover weevils.
- The effect of soil type on growth or fruiting of tomato or radish plants.
- The effect of substrate type on the proportion of caddises in a stream.

Am I interested in a **relationship** (trend) between an independent variable and the biological response of the organism?

- The effect of temperature on the filtering rate of *Daphnia*.
- The effect of crowding on leaf production in tomatoes.
- The effect of changes in salinity on the respiration rate of mud crabs.

Defining Your Variables

Qualitative (categorical)

Non-numerical and descriptive, e.g. sex, colour, presence or absence of a feature, viability (dead/alive).

e.g. Sex of children in a family (male, female)

Ranked

These provide data which can be ranked on a scale that represents an order, e.g. abundance (very abundant, common, rare); colour (dark, medium, pale).

e.g. Birth order in a family (1, 2, 3)

Quantitative

Characteristics for which measurements or counts can be made, e.g. height, weight, number.

Discontinuous (discrete)

e.g. Number of children in a family (3, 0, 4)

Continuous

e.g. Height of children in a family (1.5 m, 1.3 m, 0.8 m)

The values for monitored or measured variables, collected during the course of the investigation, are called **data**. Like their corresponding variables, data may be quantitative, qualitative, or ranked.

Leaf shape: qualitative

Number per litter: quantitative, discontinuous

Fish length: quantitative, continuous

1. Suggest how you might measure the colour of light (red, blue, green) quantitatively: _____

_____

_____

2. Sometimes, ranked data are given numerical values, e.g. rare = 1, occasional = 2, frequent = 3, common = 4, abundant = 5. Suggest why these data are sometimes called semi-quantitative:

_____

_____

Related activities: Descriptive Statistics

Transforming Raw Data

Data often have to be transformed as a first step in the initial analysis of results. Transforming data can make them more useful by helping to highlight trends and making important features more obvious. Data transformations may be quite simple (e.g. percentages, totals, and rates) or they may be more complex transformations used before statistical procedures (e.g. log transformations). Some of the simple transformations are outlined below.

Transformation	Rationale for transformation
Frequency table	A tally chart of the number of times a value occurs in a data set. It is a useful first step in data analysis as a neatly constructed tally chart can double as a simple histogram.
Total	The sum of all data values for a variable. Useful as an initial stage in data handling, especially in comparing replicates. Used in making other data transformations.
Percentages	Provide a clear expression of what proportion of data fall into any particular category. This relationship may not be obvious from the raw data values.
Rates	Expressed as a measure per unit time. Rates show how a variable changes over a standard time period (e.g. one second, one minute or one hour). Rates allow meaningful comparison of data that may have been recorded over different time periods.
Reciprocals	Reciprocals of time (1/data value) can provide a crude measure of rate in situations where the variable measured is the total time taken to complete a task, e.g. time taken for a colour change to occur in an enzyme reaction.
Relative values	These involve expression of data values relative to a standard value e.g. number of road deaths per 1000 cars or calorie consumption per gram of body weight. They allow data from different sample sizes or different organisms to be meaningfully compared. Sometimes they are expressed as a percentage (e.g. 35%) or as a proportion (e.g. 0.35).

Skills in Biology

1. (a) Explain what it means to **transform data**: _____

    _____

    (b) Briefly explain the general purpose of transforming data: _____

    _____

    _____

2. For each of the following examples, state a suitable transformation, together with a reason for your choice:

    (a) Determining relative abundance from counts of four plant species in two different habitat areas:

    Suitable transformation: _____

    Reason: _____

    (b) Making a meaningful comparison between animals of different size in the volume of oxygen each consumed:

    Suitable transformation: _____

    Reason: _____

    (c) Making a meaningful comparison of the time taken for chemical precipitation to occur in a flask at different pH values:

    Suitable transformation: _____

    Reason: _____

    (d) Determining the effect of temperature on the production of carbon dioxide by respiring seeds:

    Suitable transformation: _____

    Reason: _____

3. Complete the transformations for each of the tables on the right. The first value is provided in each case.

(a) TABLE: *Incidence of cyanogenic clover in different areas*

Working: 124 ÷ 159 = 0.78 = 78%

This is the number of cyanogenic clover out of the total.

Incidence of cyanogenic clover in different areas

Clover plant type	Frost free area		Frost prone area		Totals
	Number	%	Number	%	
Cyanogenic	124	78	26		
Acyanogenic	35		115		
Total	159				

(b) TABLE: *Plant transpiration loss using a bubble potometer*

Working: (9.0 – 8.0) ÷ 5 min = 0.2

This is the distance the bubble moved over the first 5 minutes. Note that there is no data entry possible for the first reading (0 min) because no difference can be calculated.

Plant transpiration loss using a bubble potometer

Time /min	Pipette arm reading /cm^3	Plant water loss /cm^3 min^{-1}
0	9.0	–
5	8.0	0.2
10	7.2	
15	6.2	
20	4.9	

(c) TABLE: *Photosynthetic rate at different light intensities*

Working: 1 ÷ 15 = 0.067

This is time taken for the leaf to float. A reciprocal gives a per minute rate (the variable measured is the time taken for an event to occur).

NOTE: In this experiment, the flotation time is used as a crude measure of photosynthetic rate. As oxygen bubbles are produced as a product of photosynthesis, they stick to the leaf disc and increase its buoyancy. The faster the rate, the sooner they come to the surface. The rates of photosynthesis should be measured over similar time intervals, so the rate is transformed to a 'per minute' basis (the reciprocal of time).

Photosynthetic rate at different light intensities

Light intensity /%	Average time for leaf disc to float / min	Reciprocal of time / min^{-1}
100	15	0.067
50	25	
25	50	
11	93	
6	187	

(d) TABLE: *Frequency of size classes in a sample of eels*

Working: (7 ÷ 270) x 100 = 2.6 %

This is the number of individuals out of the total that appear in the size class 0-50 mm. The relative frequency is rounded to one decimal place.

Frequency of size classes in a sample of eels

Size class /mm	Frequency	Relative frequency/ %
0-50	7	2.6
50-99	23	
100-149	59	
150-199	98	
200-249	50	
250-299	30	
300-349	3	
Total	270	

Terms and Notation

The definitions for some commonly encountered terms related to making biological investigations are provided below. Use these as you would use a biology dictionary when planning your investigation and writing up your report. It is important to be consistent with the use of terms i.e. use the same term for the same procedure or unit throughout your study. Be sure, when using a term with a specific statistical meaning, such as sample, that you are using the term correctly.

Skills in Biology

General Terms

Data: Facts collected for analysis.

Qualitative: Not quantitative. Described in words or terms rather than by numbers. Includes subjective descriptions in terms of variables such as colour or shape.

Quantitative: Able to be expressed in numbers. Numerical values derived from counts or measurements.

The Design of Investigations

Hypothesis: A tentative explanation of an observation, capable of being tested by experimentation. Hypotheses are written as clear statements, not as questions.

Control treatment (control): A standard (reference) treatment that helps to ensure that responses to other treatments can be reliably interpreted. There may be more than one control in an investigation.

Dependent variable: A variable whose values are determined by another variable (the independent variable). In practice, the dependent variable is the variable representing the biological response.

Independent variable: A variable whose values are set, or systematically altered, by the investigator.

Controlled variables: Variables that may take on different values in different situations, but are controlled (fixed) as part of the design of the investigation.

Experiment: A contrived situation designed to test (one or more) hypotheses and their predictions. It is good practice to use sample sizes that are as large as possible for experiments.

Investigation: A very broad term applied to scientific studies; investigations may be controlled experiments or field based studies involving population sampling.

Parameter: A numerical value that describes a characteristic of a population (e.g. the mean height of all 17 year-old males).

Prediction: The prediction of the response (Y) variable on the basis of changes in the independent (X) variable.

Random sample: A method of choosing a sample from a population that avoids any subjective element. It is the equivalent to drawing numbers out of a hat, but using random number tables. For field based studies involving quadrats or transects, random numbers can be used to determine the positioning of the sampling unit.

Repeat / Trial: The entire investigation is carried out again at a different time. This ensures that the results are reproducible. Note that repeats or trials are not **replicates** in the true sense unless they are run at the same time.

Replicate: A duplication of the entire experimental design run at the same time.

Sample: A sub-set of a whole used to estimate the values that might have been obtained if every individual or response was measured. A sample is made up of **sampling units**, In lab based investigations, the sampling unit might be a test-tube, while in field based studies, the sampling unit might be an individual organism or a quadrat.

Sample size (n): The number of samples taken. In a field study, a typical sample size may involve 20-50 individuals or 20 quadrats. In a lab based investigation, a typical sample size may be two to three sampling units, e.g. two test-tubes held at 10°C.

Sampling unit: Sampling units make up the sample size. Examples of sampling units in different investigations are an individual organism, a test tube undergoing a particular treatment, an area (e.g. quadrat size), or a volume. The size of the sampling unit is an important consideration in studies where the area or volume of a habitat is being sampled.

Statistic: An estimate of a parameter obtained from a sample (e.g. the mean height of all 17 year-old males in your class). A precise (reliable) statistic will be close to the value of the parameter being estimated.

Treatments: Well defined conditions applied to the sample units. The response of sample units to a treatment is intended to shed light on the hypothesis under investigation. What is often of most interest is the comparison of the responses to different treatments.

Variable: A factor in an experiment that is subject to change. Variables may be controlled (fixed), manipulated (systematically altered), or represent a biological response.

Precision and Significance

Accuracy: The correctness of the measurement (the closeness of the measured value to the true value). Accuracy is often a function of the calibration of the instrument used for measuring.

Measurement errors: When measuring or setting the value of a variable, there may be some difference between your answer and the 'right' answer. These errors are often as a result of poor technique or poorly set up equipment.

Objective measurement: Measurement not significantly involving subjective (or personal) judgment. If a second person repeats the measurement they should get the same answer.

Precision (of a measurement): The repeatability of the measurement. As there is usually no reason to suspect that a piece of equipment is giving inaccurate measures, making precise measurements is usually the most important consideration. You can assess or quantify the precision of any measurement system by taking repeated measurements from individual samples.

Precision (of a statistic): How close the statistic is to the value of the parameter being estimated. Also called **reliability**.

The Expression of Units

The value of a variable must be written with its units where possible. Common ways of recording measurements in biology are: volume in litres, mass in grams, length in metres, time in seconds. The following example shows different ways to express the same term. Note that ml and cm^3 are equivalent.

Oxygen consumption (millilitres per gram per hour)

Oxygen consumption ($ml\,g^{-1}h^{-1}$) or ($mL\,g^{-1}h^{-1}$)

Oxygen consumption ($ml/g/h$) or ($mL/g/h$)

Oxygen consumption/$cm^3g^{-1}h^{-1}$

Statistical significance: An assigned value that is used to establish the probability that an observed trend or difference represents a true difference that is not due to chance alone. If a level of significance is less than the chosen value (usually 1-10%), the difference is regarded as statistically significant. Remember that in rigorous science, it is the hypothesis of no difference or no effect (the null hypothesis, H_0) that is tested. The alternative hypothesis (your tentative explanation for an observation) can only be accepted through statistical rejection of H_0.

Validity: Whether or not you are truly measuring the right thing.

Data Presentation

Data can be presented in a number of ways. **Tables** provide an accurate record of numerical values and allow you to organise your data in a way that helps to identify trends and facilitate analysis. **Graphs** provide a visual representation of trends in the data that may not be evident from a table. It is useful to plot your data as soon as possible, even during your experiment, as this will help you to evaluate your results as you proceed and make adjustments as necessary (e.g. to the sampling interval). The choice between graphing or tabulation in the final report depends on the type and complexity of the data and the information that you are wanting to convey. Usually, both are appropriate. Some of the basic rules for constructing tables and graphs are outlined below. Note that values for standard deviation and 95% confidence intervals are provided in these examples. Calculating these will help you to understand your data better and critically evaluate your results. Always allow enough space for a graph, e.g. one third to one half of an A4 page. The examples in this workbook are usually reduced for reasons of space.

Presenting Data in Tables

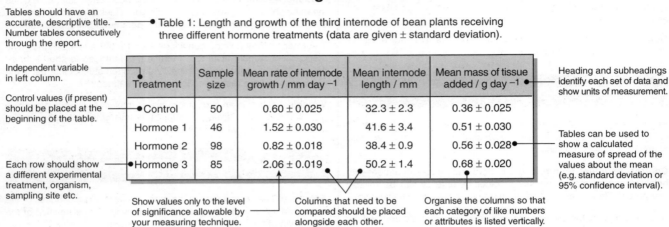

Tables should have an accurate, descriptive title. Number tables consecutively through the report.

Table 1: Length and growth of the third internode of bean plants receiving three different hormone treatments (data are given ± standard deviation).

Independent variable in left column.

Control values (if present) should be placed at the beginning of the table.

Each row should show a different experimental treatment, organism, sampling site etc.

Treatment	Sample size	Mean rate of internode growth / mm day^{-1}	Mean internode length / mm	Mean mass of tissue added / g day^{-1}
Control	50	0.60 ± 0.025	32.3 ± 2.3	0.36 ± 0.025
Hormone 1	46	1.52 ± 0.030	41.6 ± 3.4	0.51 ± 0.030
Hormone 2	98	0.82 ± 0.018	38.4 ± 0.9	0.56 ± 0.028
Hormone 3	85	2.06 ± 0.019	50.2 ± 1.4	0.68 ± 0.020

Heading and subheadings identify each set of data and show units of measurement.

Tables can be used to show a calculated measure of spread of the values about the mean (e.g. standard deviation or 95% confidence interval).

Show values only to the level of significance allowable by your measuring technique.

Columns that need to be compared should be placed alongside each other.

Organise the columns so that each category of like numbers or attributes is listed vertically.

Presenting Data in Graph Format

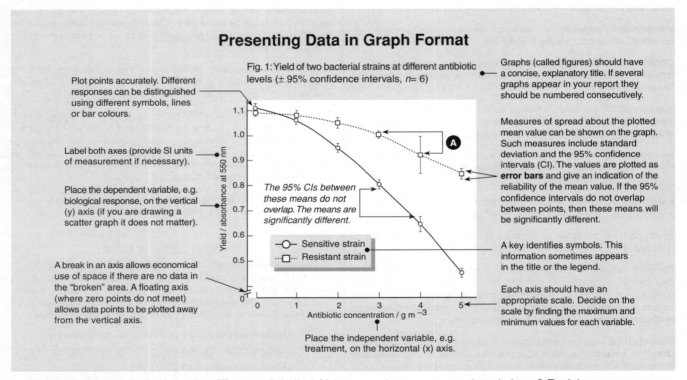

Fig. 1: Yield of two bacterial strains at different antibiotic levels (± 95% confidence intervals, $n = 6$)

Plot points accurately. Different responses can be distinguished using different symbols, lines or bar colours.

Label both axes (provide SI units of measurement if necessary).

Place the dependent variable, e.g. biological response, on the vertical (y) axis (if you are drawing a scatter graph it does not matter).

A break in an axis allows economical use of space if there are no data in the "broken" area. A floating axis (where zero points do not meet) allows data points to be plotted away from the vertical axis.

The 95% CIs between these means do not overlap. The means are significantly different.

—○— Sensitive strain
····□···· Resistant strain

Place the independent variable, e.g. treatment, on the horizontal (x) axis.

Graphs (called figures) should have a concise, explanatory title. If several graphs appear in your report they should be numbered consecutively.

Measures of spread about the plotted mean value can be shown on the graph. Such measures include standard deviation and the 95% confidence intervals (CI). The values are plotted as **error bars** and give an indication of the reliability of the mean value. If the 95% confidence intervals do not overlap between points, then these means will be significantly different.

A key identifies symbols. This information sometimes appears in the title or the legend.

Each axis should have an appropriate scale. Decide on the scale by finding the maximum and minimum values for each variable.

1. What can you conclude about the difference (labelled **A**) between the two means plotted above? Explain your answer:

   _____

2. Discuss the reasons for including both graphs and tables in a final report: _____

   _____

   _____

   _____

   _____

Drawing Bar Graphs

Guidelines for Bar Graphs

Bar graphs are appropriate for data that are non-numerical and **discrete** for at least one variable, i.e. they are grouped into separate categories. There are no dependent or independent variables. Important features of this type of graph include:

- Data are collected for discontinuous, non-numerical categories (e.g. place, colour, and species), so the bars do not touch.

- Data values may be entered on or above the bars if you wish.

- Multiple sets of data can be displayed side by side for direct comparison (e.g. males and females in the same age group).

- Axes may be reversed so that the categories are on the x axis, i.e. the bars can be vertical or horizontal. When they are vertical, these graphs are sometimes called column graphs.

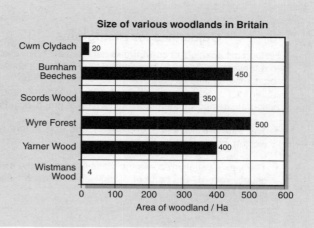

Size of various woodlands in Britain

1. Counts of eight mollusc species were made from a series of quadrat samples at two sites on a rocky shore. The summary data are presented here.

   (a) Tabulate the mean (**average**) numbers per square metre at each site in Table 1 (below left).

   (b) Plot a **bar graph** of the tabulated data on the grid below. For each species, plot the data from both sites side by side using different colours to distinguish the sites.

Average abundance of 8 mollusc species from two sites along a rocky shore.

Species	Average/ no m^{-2}	
	Site 1	Site 2

Field data notebook

Total counts at site 1 (11 quadrats) and site 2 (10 quadrats). Quadrats 1 sq. m.

Species	Site 1 Total	Site 1 Mean No m^{-2}	Site 2 Total	Site 2 Mean No m^{-2}
Ornate limpet	232	21	299	30
Radiate limpet	68	6	344	34
Limpet sp. A	420	38	0	0
Cats-eye	68	6	16	2
Top shell	16	2	43	4
Limpet sp. B	628	57	389	39
Limpet sp. C	0	0	22	2
Chiton	12	1	30	3

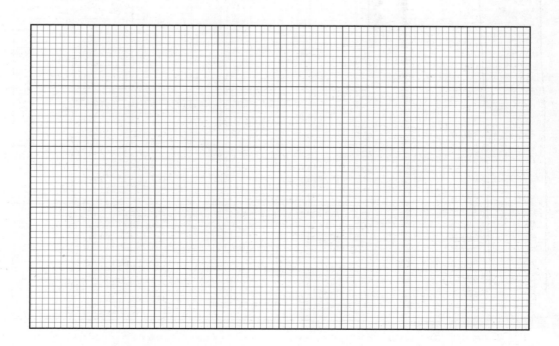

Related activities: Transforming Raw Data

DA 2

Skills in Biology

Drawing Histograms

Guidelines for Histograms

Histograms are plots of **continuous** data and are often used to represent frequency distributions, where the y-axis shows the number of times a particular measurement or value was obtained. For this reason, they are often called frequency histograms. Important features of this type of graph include:

- The data are numerical and continuous (e.g. height or weight), so the bars touch.

- The x-axis usually records the class interval. The y-axis usually records the number of individuals in each class interval (frequency).

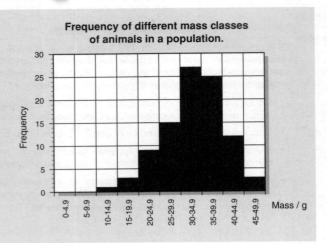

Frequency of different mass classes of animals in a population.

1. The weight data provided below were recorded from 95 individuals (male and female), older than 17 years.

   (a) Create a tally chart (frequency table) in the frame provided, organising the weight data into a form suitable for plotting. An example of the tally for the weight grouping 55-59.9 kg has been completed for you as an example. Note that the raw data values, once they are recorded as counts on the tally chart, are crossed off the data set in the notebook. It is important to do this in order to prevent data entry errors.

   (b) Plot a **frequency histogram** of the tallied data on the grid provided below.

Weight /kg	Tally	Total
45-49.9		
50-54.9		
55-59.9	LHT //	7
60-64.9		
65-69.9		
70-74.9		
75-79.9		
80-84.9		
85-89.9		
90-94.9		
95-99.9		
100-104.9		
105-109.9		

Lab notebook

Weight (in kg) of 95 individuals

63.4	81.2	65
56.5	83.3	75.6
84	95	76.8
81.5	105.5	67.8
73.4	82	68.3
56	73.5	63.5
60.4	75.2	58
83.5	63	58.5
82	70.4	50
61	82.2	92
55.2	87.8	91.5
48	86.5	88.3
53.5	85.5	81
63.8	87	72
69	98	66.5
82.8	71	61.5
68.5	76	66
67.2	72.5	65.5
82.5	61	67.4
83	60.5	73
78.4	67	67
76.5	86	71
83.4	85	70.5
77.5	93.5	65.5
77	62	68
87	62.5	90
89	63	83.5
93.4	60	73
83	71.5	66
80	73.8	57.5
76	77.5	76
56	74	

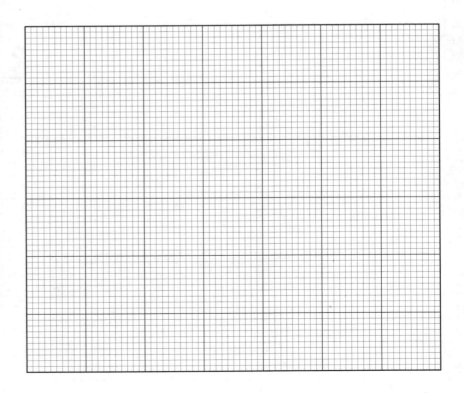

Drawing Pie Graphs

Guidelines for Pie Graphs

Pie graphs can be used instead of bar graphs, generally in cases where there are six or fewer categories involved. A pie graph provides strong visual impact of the relative proportions in each category, particularly where one of the categories is very dominant. Features of pie graphs include:

- The data for one variable are discontinuous (non-numerical or categories).

- The data for the dependent variable are usually in the form of counts, proportions, or percentages.

- Pie graphs are good for visual impact and showing relative proportions.

- They are not suitable for data sets with a large number of categories.

Average residential water use

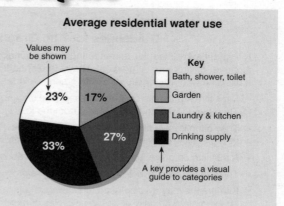

Values may be shown → 23% | 17%

33% | 27%

Key
- Bath, shower, toilet
- Garden
- Laundry & kitchen
- Drinking supply

A key provides a visual guide to categories

1. The data provided below are from a study of the diets of three vertebrates.

   (a) Tabulate the data from the notebook in the frame provided. Calculate the angle for each percentage, given that each percentage point is equal to 3.6° (the first example is provided: 23.6 x 3.6 = 85).

   (b) Plot a pie graph for each animal in the circles provided. The circles have been marked at 5° intervals to enable you to do this exercise without a protractor. For the purposes of this exercise, begin your pie graphs at the 0° (= 360°) mark and work in a clockwise direction from the largest to the smallest percentage. Use one key for all three pie graphs.

Field data notebook

% of different food items in the diet

Food item	Stoats	Rats	Cats
Birds	23.6	1.4	6.9
Crickets	15.3	23.6	0
Other insects (not crickets)	15.3	20.8	1.9
Voles	9.2	0	19.4
Rabbits	8.3	0	18.1
Rats	6.1	0	43.1
Mice	13.9	0	10.6
Fruits and seeds	0	40.3	0
Green leaves	0	13.9	0
Unidentified	8.3	0	0

Percentage occurrence of different foods in the diet of stoats, rats, and cats. Graph angle representing the % is shown to assist plotting.

Food item in diet	Stoats		Rats		Cats	
	% in diet	Angle / °	% in diet	Angle / °	% in diet	Angle / °
Birds	23.6	85				

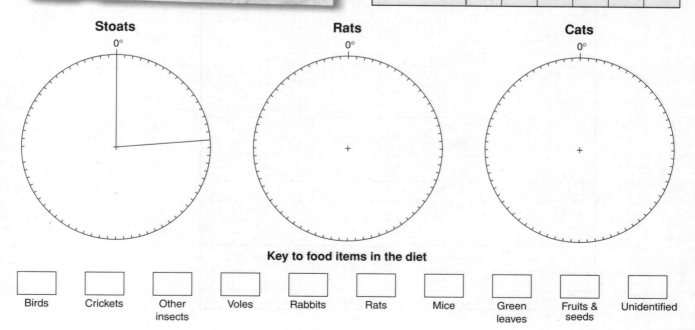

Stoats   0°

Rats   0°

Cats   0°

Key to food items in the diet

| Birds | Crickets | Other insects | Voles | Rabbits | Rats | Mice | Green leaves | Fruits & seeds | Unidentified |

Related activities: Transforming Raw Data

Drawing Kite Graphs

Guidelines for Kite Graphs

Kite graphs are ideal for representing distributional data, e.g. abundance along an environmental gradient. They are elongated figures drawn along a baseline. Important features of kite graphs include:

- Each kite represents changes in species abundance across a landscape. The abundance can be calculated from the kite width.
- They often involve plots for more than one species; this makes them good for highlighting probable differences in habitat preferences between species.
- A thin line on a kite graph represents species absence.
- The axes can be reversed depending on preference.
- Kite graphs may also be used to show changes in distribution with time, for example, with daily or seasonal cycles of movement.

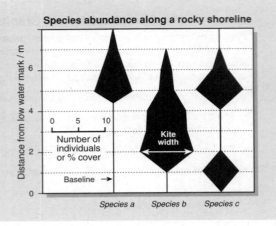

Species abundance along a rocky shoreline

1. The following data were collected from three streams of different lengths and flow rates. Invertebrates were collected at 0.5 km intervals from the headwaters (0 km) to the stream mouth. Their wet weight was measured and recorded (per m^2).

   (a) Tabulate the data below for plotting.

   (b) Plot a **kite graph** of the data from all three streams on the grid provided below. Do not forget to include a scale so that the weight at each point on the kite can be calculated.

Field data notebook
Mass per m^2 of invertebrates from 3 streams.

Stream A: Slow flowing

Km from mouth	g m^{-2}
5.0	0.3
4.5	2.5
4.0	0.2
3.5	0.7
3.0	0.1
2.5	0.6
2.0	0.3
1.5	0.3
1.0	0.4
0.5	0.5
0	0.4

Stream B: Fast, steep

Km from mouth	g m^{-2}
2.5	0.3
2.0	0.4
1.5	0.5
1.0	0.1
0.5	0.6
0	0.4

Stream C: Steep torrent

Km from mouth	g m^{-2}
1.5	0.2
1.0	0
0.5	0.5
0	0

Wet mass of invertebrates along three different streams

Distance from mouth/ km	Wet weight/ g m^{-2}		
	Stream A	Stream B	Stream C

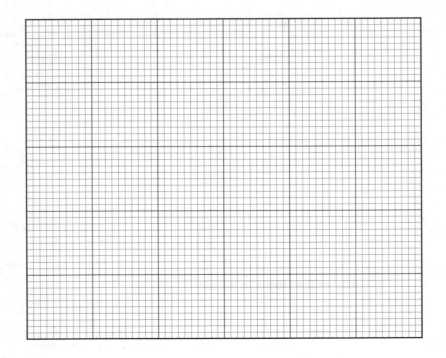

DA 2   **Related activities:** Transforming Raw Data

Drawing Line Graphs

Guidelines for Line Graphs

Line graphs are used when one variable (the independent variable) affects another, the dependent variable. Line graphs can be drawn without a measure of spread (top figure, right) or with some calculated measure of data variability (bottom figure, right). Important features of line graphs include:

- The data must be continuous for both variables.

- The dependent variable is usually the biological response.

- The independent variable is often time or the experimental treatment.

- In cases where there is an implied trend (e.g. one variable increases with the other), a line of best fit is usually plotted through the data points to show the relationship.

- If fluctuations in the data are likely to be important (e.g. with climate and other environmental data) the data points are usually connected directly (point to point).

- Line graphs may be drawn with measure of error. The data are presented as points (the calculated means), with bars above and below, indicating a measure of variability or spread in the data (e.g. standard error, standard deviation, or 95% confidence intervals).

- Where no error value has been calculated, the scatter can be shown by plotting the individual data points vertically above and below the mean. By convention, bars are not used to indicate the range of raw values in a data set.

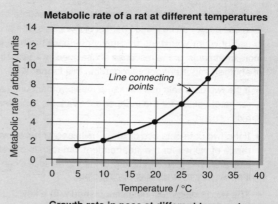

Metabolic rate of a rat at different temperatures

Line connecting points

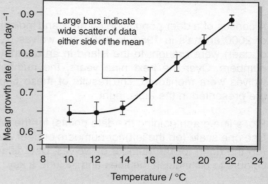

Growth rate in peas at different temperatures

Large bars indicate wide scatter of data either side of the mean

Skills in Biology

1. The results (shown right) were collected in a study investigating the effect of temperature on the activity of an enzyme.

   (a) Using the results provided in the table (right), plot a line graph on the grid below:

   (b) Estimate the rate of reaction at 15°C: _____

Lab Notebook

An enzyme's activity at different temperatures

Temperature /°C	Rate of reaction /mg of product formed per minute
10	1.0
20	2.1
30	3.2
35	3.7
40	4.1
45	3.7
50	2.7
60	0

Related activities: Transforming Raw Data, The Reliability of the Mean, Interpreting Line graphs

DA 2

Plotting Multiple Data Sets

A single figure can be used to show two or more data sets, i.e. more than one curve can be plotted per set of axes. This type of presentation is useful when you want to visually compare the trends for two or more treatments, or the response of one species against the response of another. Important points regarding this format are:

- If the two data sets use the same measurement units and a similar range of values for the independent variable, one scale on the y axis is used.

- If the two data sets use different units and/or have a very different range of values for the independent variable, two scales for the y axis are used (see example provided). The scales can be adjusted if necessary to avoid overlapping plots

- The two curves must be distinguished with a key.

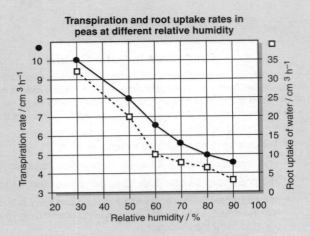

Transpiration and root uptake rates in peas at different relative humidity

2. A census of a deer population on an island indicated a population of 2000 animals in 1960. In 1961, ten wolves (natural predators of deer) were brought to the island in an attempt to control deer numbers. Over the next nine years, the numbers of deer and wolves were monitored. The results of these population surveys are presented in the table, right.

Plot a line graph (joining the data points) for the tabulated results. Use one scale (on the left) for numbers of deer and another scale (on the right) for the number of wolves. Use different symbols or colours to distinguish the lines and include a key.

Field data notebook
Results of a population survey on an island

Time /yr	Wolf numbers	Deer numbers
1961	10	2000
1962	12	2300
1963	16	2500
1964	22	2360
1965	28	2244
1966	24	2094
1967	21	1968
1968	18	1916
1969	19	1952

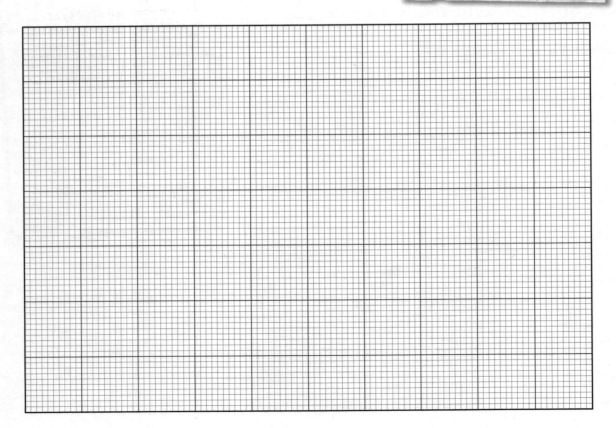

(b) Study the line graph that you plotted for the wolf and deer census on the previous page. Provide a plausible explanation for the pattern in the data, stating the evidence available to support your reasoning:

_____

_____

_____

_____

3. In a sampling programme, the number of perch and trout in a hydro-electric reservoir were monitored over a period of time. A colony of black shag was also present. Shags take large numbers of perch and (to a lesser extent) trout. In 1960-61, 424 shags were removed from the lake during the nesting season and nest counts were made every spring in subsequent years. In 1971, 60 shags were removed from the lake, and all existing nests dismantled. The results of the population survey are tabulated below (for reasons of space, the entire table format has been repeated to the right for 1970-1978).

(a) Plot a line graph (joining the data points) for the survey results. Use one scale (on the left) for numbers of perch and trout and another scale for the number of shag nests. Use different symbols to distinguish the lines and include a key.

(b) Use a vertical arrow to indicate the point at which shags and their nests were removed.

Results of population survey at reservoir

Time/ year	Fish number (average per haul)		Shag nest numbers	Time/ year continued	Fish number (average per haul)		Shag nest numbers
	Trout	Perch			Trout	Perch	
1960	–	–	16	1970	1.5	6	35
1961	–	–	4	1971	0.5	0.7	42
1962	1.5	11	5	1972	1	0.8	0
1963	0.8	9	10	1973	0.2	4	0
1964	0	5	22	1974	0.5	6.5	0
1965	1	1	25	1975	0.6	7.6	2
1966	1	2.9	35	1976	1	1.2	10
1967	2	5	40	1977	1.2	1.5	32
1968	1.5	4.6	26	1978	0.7	2	28
1969	1.5	6	32				

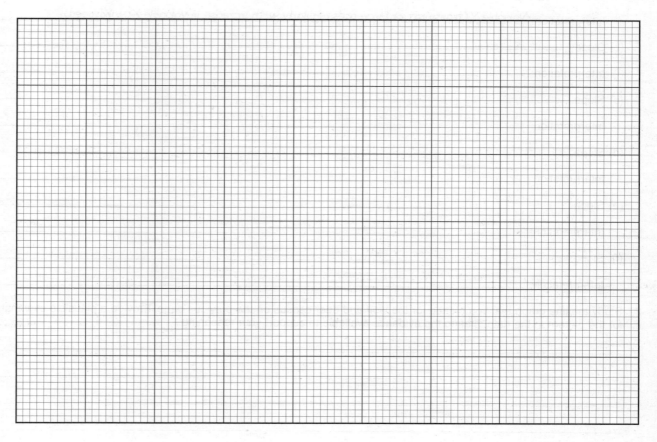

Skills in Biology

Interpreting Line & Scatter Graphs

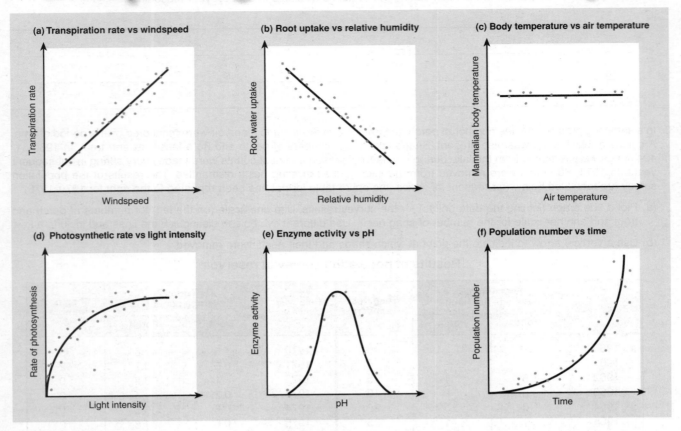

1. For each of the graphs (b-f) above, give a description of the slope and an interpretation of how one variable changes with respect to the other. For the purposes of your description, call the independent variable (horizontal or x-axis) in each example "variable X" and the dependent variable (vertical or y-axis) "variable Y". Be aware that the existence of a relationship between two variables does not necessarily mean that the relationship is causative (although it may be).

(a) Slope: _Positive linear relationship, with constantly rising slope_ _____

   Interpretation: _Variable Y (transpiration) increases regularly with increase in variable X (windspeed)_ ____

(b) Slope: _____

   Interpretation: _____

(c) Slope: _____

   Interpretation: _____

(d) Slope: _____

   Interpretation: _____

(e) Slope: _____

   Interpretation: _____

(f) Slope: _____

   Interpretation: _____

2. Study the line graph that you plotted for the wolf and deer census on the previous page. Provide a plausible explanation for the pattern in the data, stating the evidence available to support your reasoning:

_____

_____

_____

_____

Related activities: Drawing Line Graphs

Drawing Scatter Plots

Guidelines for Scatter Graphs

A scatter graph is a common way to display continuous data where there is a relationship between two interdependent variables.

- The data for this graph must be continuous for both variables.
- There is no independent (manipulated) variable, but the variables are often correlated, i.e. they vary together in some predictable way.
- Scatter graphs are useful for determining the relationship between two variables.
- The points on the graph need not be connected, but a line of best fit is often drawn through the points to show the relationship between the variables (this may be drawn be eye or computer generated).

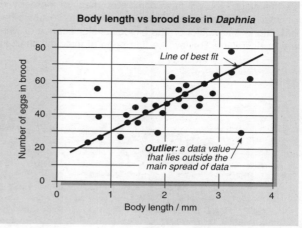

Body length vs brood size in *Daphnia*

1. In the example below, metabolic measurements were taken from seven Antarctic fish *Pagothenia borchgrevinski*. The fish are affected by a gill disease, which increases the thickness of the gas exchange surfaces and affects oxygen uptake. The results of oxygen consumption of fish with varying amounts of affected gill (at rest and swimming) are tabulated below.

(a) Using **one** scale only for oxygen consumption, plot the data on the grid below to show the relationship between oxygen consumption and the amount of gill affected by disease. Use different symbols or colours for each set of data (at rest and swimming).

(b) Draw a line of best fit through each set of points.

2. Describe the relationship between the amount of gill affected and oxygen consumption in the fish:

(a) For the **at rest** data set:

_____

_____

_____

_____

_____

_____

_____

(b) For the **swimming** data set:

_____

_____

_____

_____

_____

_____

_____

_____

Oxygen consumption of fish with affected gills

Fish number	Percentage of gill affected	Oxygen consumption/ cm3 g-1 h-1	
		At rest	**Swimming**
1	0	0.05	0.29
2	95	0.04	0.11
3	60	0.04	0.14
4	30	0.05	0.22
5	90	0.05	0.08
6	65	0.04	0.18
7	45	0.04	0.20

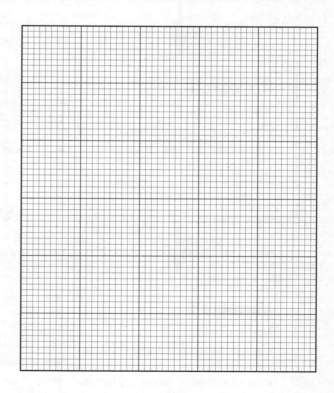

3. Describe how the gill disease affects oxygen uptake in resting fish: _____

_____

Related activities: Interpreting Line Graphs

DA 2

Taking the Next Step

By this stage, you will have completed many of the early stages of your investigation. Now is a good time to review what you have done and reflect on the biological significance of what you are investigating. Review the first page of this flow chart in light of your findings so far. You are now ready to begin a more in-depth analysis of your results. Never under-estimate the value of plotting your data, even at a very early stage. This will help you decide on the best type of data analysis (see the next page).

Photos courtesy of Pasco

Observation

Something ...

- Changes or affects something else.
- Is more abundant, etc. along a transect, at one site, temperature, concentration, etc. than others.
- Is bigger, taller, or grows more quickly.

Pilot study

Lets you check ...

- Equipment, sampling sites, sampling interval.
- How long it takes to collect data.
- Problems with identification or other unforeseen issues.

Research

To find out ...

- Basic biology and properties.
- What other biotic or abiotic factors may have an effect.
- Its place within the broader biological context.

Analysis

Are you looking for a ...

- **Difference**.
- **Trend** or relationship.
- **Goodness of fit** (to a theoretical outcome).

GO TO NEXT PAGE

Be prepared to revise your study design in the light of the results from your pilot study

Variables

Next you need to ...

- Identify the key variables likely to cause the effect.
- Identify variables to be controlled in order to give the best chance of showing the effect that you want to study.

Hypothesis

Must be ...

- Testable
- Able to generate predictions

so that in the end you can say whether your data supports or allows you to reject your hypothesis.

© Biozone International 2008

Related activities: The Reliability of the Mean, The Student's t Test, Using Chi-squared in Ecology, Using Chi-squared Genetics

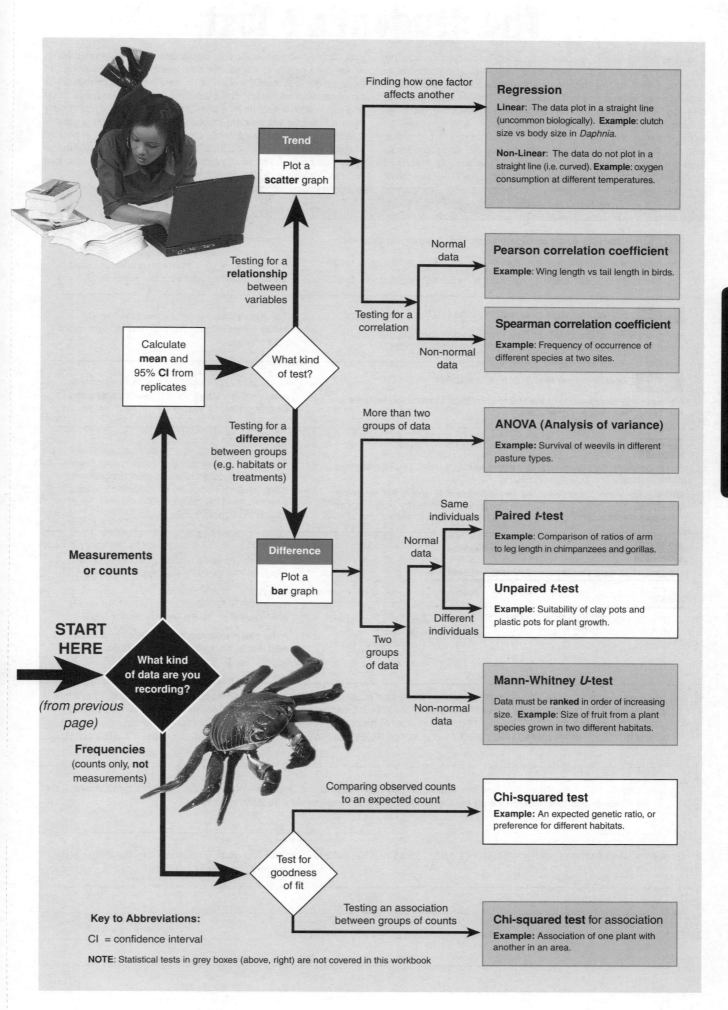

The Student's t Test

The Student's t test is a commonly used test when comparing two sample means e.g. means for a treatment and a control in an experiment, or the means of some measured characteristic between two animal or plant populations. The test is a powerful one, i.e. it is a good test for distinguishing real but marginal differences between samples. The t test is a simple test to apply, but it is only valid for certain situations. It is a two-group test and is not appropriate for multiple use i.e. sample 1 vs 2, then sample 1 vs 3. *You must have only two sample means to compare*. You are also assuming that the data have a normal (not skewed) distribution, and the scatter (standard deviations) of the data points is similar for both samples. You may wish to exclude obvious outliers from your data set for this reason. A simple outline of the general steps involved in a Student's t test is given below. It describes a simple example using a set of data from a fictitious experiment involving a treatment and a control (the units are not relevant in this case, only the values). A portion of the Student's t table of critical values is provided, sufficient to carry out the test. Follow the example through, making sure that you understand what is being done at each step.

Steps in performing a Student's *t* test	Explanatory notes
Step 1 *Calculate basic summary statistics for your two data sets* Control (A): 6.6, 5.5, 6.8, 5.8, 6.1, 5.9 $n_A = 6$, $\bar{X}_A = 6.12$, $s_A = 0.496$ Treatment (B): 6.3, 7.2, 6.5, 7.1, 7.5, 7.3 $n_B = 6$, $\bar{X}_B = 6.98$, $s_B = 0.475$	n_A and n_B are the number of values in the first and second data sets respectively (these need not be the same). $\bar{x}$ is the mean. s is the standard deviation (a measure of scatter in the data).
Step 2 *Set up and state your null hypothesis (H_0)* H_0: there is no treatment effect. The differences in the data sets are the result of chance variation only and they are not really different.	The alternative hypothesis is that there is a treatment effect and the two sets of data are truly different.
Step 3 *Decide if your test is one or two tailed* This tells you what section of the t table to consult. Most biological tests are two-tailed. Very few are one-tailed.	A one-tailed test looks for a difference only in one particular direction. A two-tailed test looks for any difference (+ or –).
Step 4 *Calculate the t statistic* For our sample data above the calculated value of t is –3.09. The degrees of freedom (df) are $n_1 + n_2 - 2 = 10$. Calculation of the t value uses the variance which is simply the square of the standard deviation (s^2). You may compute the t value by entering your data onto a computer and using a simple statistical programme.	It does not matter if your calculated t value is a positive or negative (the sign is irrelevant). If you do not have access to a statistical programme, computation of t is not difficult. Step 4 (calculating t) is detailed in the t test exercise following (both manual and spreadsheet versions).
Step 5 *Consult the t table of critical values* Selected critical values for Student's t statistic (two-tailed test) | Degrees of freedom	$P = 0.05$	$P = 0.01$	$P = 0.001$ | |---|---|---|---| | 5 | 2.57 | 4.03 | 6.87 | | 10 | 2.23 | 3.17 | 4.59 | | 15 | 2.13 | 2.95 | 4.07 | | 20 | 2.09 | 2.85 | 3.85 | Critical value of t for 10 degrees of freedom. The calculated t value must exceed this to show a difference.	The absolute value of the t statistic (3.09) well exceeds the critical value for $P = 0.05$ at 10 degrees of freedom. *We can reject H_0 and conclude that the means are different at the 5% level of significance.* If the calculated absolute value of t had been less than 2.23, we could not have rejected H_0.

1. (a) In an experiment, data values were obtained from four plants in experimental conditions and three plants in control conditions. The mean values for each data set (control and experimental conditions) were calculated. The t value was calculated to be 2.16. The null hypothesis was: "The plants in the control and experimental conditions are not different". State whether the calculated t value supports the null hypothesis or its alternative (consult t table above):

   _____

   (b) The experiment was repeated, but this time using six control and six "experimental" plants. The new t value was 2.54. State whether the calculated t value supports the null hypothesis or its alternative now:

   _____

2. Explain why, in terms of applying Student's t test, extreme data values (outliers) are often excluded from the data set(s):

   _____

   _____

3. Explain what you understand by statistical significance (for any statistical test): _____

   _____

   _____

DA 3

Related activities: Descriptive Statistics, The Reliability of the Mean
Web links: Student's t-Tests

Student's t Test Exercise

Provided below are data from two flour beetle populations. Ten samples were taken from each population and the number of beetles in each sample were counted. The experimenter wanted to test if the densities of the two populations were significantly different. The exercise below involves workbook computation to determine a t value. Follow the steps to complete the test. If you do not have access to a statistical programme, you will be able to use the steps outlined here to analyse your results (if the t test is appropriate). The calculations are very simply done using a spreadsheet if you wish (see the following page).

1. (a) Complete the calculations to perform the t test for these two populations. Some calculations are provided for you.

x (counts)		x − x̄ (deviation from the mean)		(x − x̄)² (deviation from mean)²	
Popn A	Popn B	Popn A	Popn B	Popn A	Popn B
465	310	9.3	−10.6	86.5	112.4
475	310	19.3	−10.6	372.5	112.4
415	290				
480	355				
436	350				
435	335				
445	295				
460	315				
471	316				
475	330				

$n_A = 10$ $\quad$ $n_B = 10$

The number of samples in each data set

The sum of each column is called the sum of squares

$\Sigma(x − \bar{x})^2$ $\quad$ $\Sigma(x − \bar{x})^2$

(b) The variance for population A: $\quad s^2_A =$

$\quad$ The variance for population B: $\quad s^2_B =$

(c) The difference between the population means

$\quad (\bar{X}_A − \bar{X}_B) =$

(d) t (calculated) =

(e) Determine degrees of freedom (d.f.)

$\quad$ d.f. $(n_A + n_B − 2) =$

(f) $P =$

$\quad t$ (critical value) =

(g) Your decision is:

Step 1: Summary statistics

Tabulate the data as shown in the first 2 columns of the table (left). Calculate the mean and give the n value for each data set. Compute the standard deviation if you wish.

Popn A $\quad \bar{X}_A = 455.7 \quad$ Popn B $\quad \bar{X}_B = 320.6$
$\quad\quad\quad n_A = 10 \quad\quad\quad\quad\quad\quad n_B = 10$
$\quad\quad\quad s_A = 21.76 \quad\quad\quad\quad\quad\quad s_B = 21.64$

Step 2: State your null hypothesis

Step 3: Decide if your test is one or two-tailed

Calculating the t value

Step 4a: Calculate sums of squares

Complete the computations outlined in the table left. The sum of each of the final two columns (left) is called the sum of squares.

Step 4b: Calculate the variances

Calculate the variance (s^2) for each set of data. This is the sum of squares divided by $n−1$ (number of samples in each data set − 1). In this case the n values are the same, but they need not be.

$$s^2_A = \frac{\Sigma(x − \bar{x})^2}{n_A − 1} {}_{(A)} \quad\quad s^2_B = \frac{\Sigma(x − \bar{x})^2}{n_B − 1} {}_{(B)}$$

Step 4c: Difference between means

Calculate the *actual* difference between the means

$$(\bar{X}_A − \bar{X}_B)$$

Step 4d: Calculate t

Calculate the t value. Ask for assistance if you find interpreting the lower part of the equation difficult

$$t = \frac{(\bar{X}_A − \bar{X}_B)}{\sqrt{\dfrac{s^2_A}{n_A} + \dfrac{s^2_B}{n_B}}}$$

Step 4e: Determine degrees of freedom

Degrees of freedom (d.f.) are defined by the number of samples (e.g. counts) taken: d.f. = $n_A + n_B − 2$ where n_A and n_B are the number of counts in each of populations A and B.

Step 5: Consult the t table

Consult the t-tables (opposite page) for the critical t value at the appropriate degrees of freedom and the acceptable probability level (e.g. $P = 0.05$).

Step 5a: Make your decision

Make your decision whether or not to reject H_0. If your t value is large enough you may be able to reject H_0 at a lower P value (e.g. 0.001), increasing your confidence in the alternative hypothesis.

Skills in Biology

Related activities: The Student's t Test
Web links: Student's t-Tests

EDA 3

2. The previous example (workbook calculation for two beetle populations) is outlined below in a spreadsheet (created in *Microsoft Excel*). The spreadsheet has been shown in a special mode with the formulae displayed. Normally, when using a spreadsheet, the calculated values will appear as the calculation is completed (entered) and a formula is visible only when you click into an individual cell. When setting up a spreadsheet, you can arrange your calculating cells wherever you wish. What is important is that you accurately identify the cells being used for each calculation. Also provided below is a summary of the spreadsheet notations used and a table of critical values of *t* at different levels of *P*. Note that, for brevity, only some probability values have been shown. To be significant at the appropriate level of probability, calculated values must be greater than those in the table for the appropriate degrees of freedom.

(a) Using the data in question 1, set up a spreadsheet as indicated below to calculate *t*. Save your spreadsheet. Print it out and staple the print-out into your workbook.

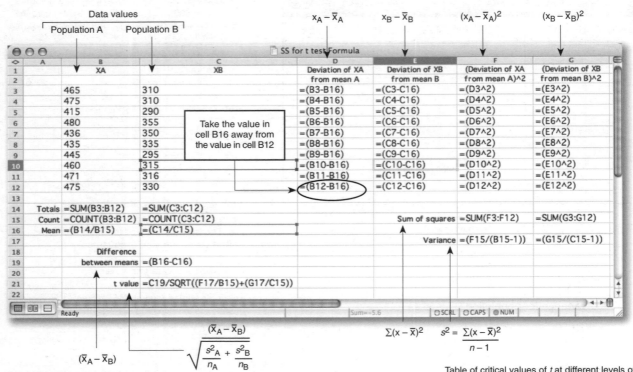

Table of critical values of *t* at different levels of *P*.

Notation	Meaning
Columns and rows	Columns are denoted A, B, C ... at the top of the spreadsheet, rows are 1, 2, 3, ... on the left. Using this notation a cell can be located e.g. C3
=	An "equals" sign *before* other entries in a cell denotes a formula.
( )	Parentheses are used to group together terms for a single calculation. This is important for larger calculations (see cell C21 above)
C3:C12	Cell locations are separated by a colon. C3:C12 means "every cell between and including C3 and C12"
SUM	Denotes that what follows is added up. =SUM(C3:C12) means "add up the values in cells C3 down to C12"
COUNT	Denotes that the number of values is counted =COUNT(C3:C12) means "count up the number of values in cells C3 down to C12"
SQRT	Denotes "take the square root of what follows"
^2	Denotes an exponent e.g. x^2 means that value x is squared.

Above is a table explaining some of the spreadsheet notations used for the calculation of the *t* value for the exercise on the previous page. It is not meant to be an exhaustive list for all spreadsheet work, but it should help you to become familiar with some of the terms and how they are used. This list applies to *Microsoft Excel*. Different spreadsheets may use different notations. These will be described in the spreadsheet manual.

Degrees of freedom	Level of Probability		
	0.05	0.01	0.001
1	12.71	63.66	636.6
2	4.303	9.925	31.60
3	3.182	5.841	12.92
4	2.776	4.604	8.610
5	2.571	4.032	6.869
6	2.447	3.707	5.959
7	2.365	3.499	5.408
8	2.306	3.355	5.041
9	2.262	3.250	4.781
10	2.228	3.169	4.587
11	2.201	3.106	4.437
12	2.179	3.055	4.318
13	2.160	3.012	4.221
14	2.145	2.977	4.140
15	2.131	2.947	4.073
16	2.120	2.921	4.015
17	2.110	2.898	3.965
18	2.101	2.878	3.922
19	2.093	2.861	3.883
20	2.086	2.845	3.850

(b) Save your spreadsheet under a different name and enter the following new data values for population B: **425, 478, 428, 465, 439, 475, 469, 445, 421, 438**. Notice that, as you enter the new values, the calculations are updated over the entire spreadsheet. Re-run the t-test using the new *t* value. State your decision for the two populations now:

New *t* value: _____ Decision on null hypothesis (delete one): Reject / Do not reject

Using Chi-Squared in Ecology

The **chi-squared test** (χ^2), like the student's *t* test, is a test for difference between data sets, but it is used when you are working with frequencies (counts) rather than measurements. It is a simple test to perform but the data must meet the requirements of the test. These are as follows:

■ It can only be used for data that are raw counts (not measurements or derived data such as percentages).

■ It is used to compare an experimental result with an expected theoretical outcome (e.g. an expected Mendelian ratio or a theoretical value indicating "no preference" or "no difference"

between groups in some sort of response such as habitat or microclimate preference).

■ It is not a valid test when sample sizes are small (<20).

Like all statistical tests, it aims to test the null hypothesis; the hypothesis of no difference between groups of data. The following exercise is a worked example using chi-squared for testing an ecological study of habitat preference. As with most of these simple statistical tests, chi-squared is easily calculated using a spreadsheet. Guidelines for this are available on the Teacher Resource CD-ROM.

Using χ^2 in Ecology

In an investigation of the ecological niche of the mangrove, *Avicennia marina var. resinifera*, the density of pneumatophores was measured in regions with different substrate. The mangrove trees were selected from four different areas: mostly sand, some sand, mostly mud, and some mud. Note that the variable, substrate type, is categorical in this case. Quadrats (1 m by 1 m) were placed around a large number of trees in each of these four areas and the numbers of pneumatophores were counted. Chi-squared was used to compare the observed results for pneumatophore density (as follows) to an expected outcome of no difference in density between substrates.

Pneumatophores

Mangrove pneumatophore density in different substrate areas

Mostly sand	85	Mostly mud	130
Some sand	102	Some mud	123

Using χ^2, the probability of this result being consistent with the expected result could be tested. Worked example as follows:

Step 1: Calculate the expected value (E)

In this case, this is the sum of the observed values divided by the number of categories.

$$\frac{440}{4} = 110$$

Step 2: Calculate O – E

The difference between the observed and expected values is calculated as a measure of the deviation from a predicted result. Since some deviations are negative, they are all squared to give positive values. This step is usually performed as part of a tabulation (right, darker grey column).

Category	O	E	O – E	$(O - E)^2$	$\dfrac{(O - E)^2}{E}$
Mostly sand	85	110	−25	625	5.68
Some sand	102	110	−8	64	0.58
Mostly mud	130	110	20	400	3.64
Some mud	123	110	13	169	1.54

Total = 440 χ^2 $\Sigma = 11.44$

Step 3: Calculate the value of χ^2

$$\chi^2 = \sum \frac{(O - E)^2}{E}$$

Where: O = the observed result
E = the expected result
Σ = sum of

The calculated χ^2 value is given at the bottom right of the last column in the tabulation.

Step 5a: Using the χ^2 table

On the χ^2 table (part reproduced in Table 1 below) with 3 degrees of freedom, the calculated value for χ^2 of 11.44 corresponds to a probability of between 0.01 and 0.001 (see arrow). *This means that by chance alone a χ^2 value of 11.44 could be expected between 1% and 0.1% of the time.*

Step 4: Calculating degrees of freedom

The probability that any particular χ^2 value could be exceeded by chance depends on the number of degrees of freedom. This is simply **one less than the total number of categories** (this is the number that could vary independently without affecting the last value). **In this case: 4–1 = 3.**

Step 5b: Using the χ^2 table

The probability of between 0.1 and 0.01 is lower than the 0.05 value which is generally regarded as significant. The null hypothesis can be rejected and we have reason to believe that the observed results differ significantly from the expected (at $P = 0.05$).

Table 1: Critical values of χ^2 at different levels of probability. By convention, the critical probability for rejecting the null hypothesis (H_0) is 5%. If the test statistic is less than the tabulated critical value for $P = 0.05$ we cannot reject H_0 and the result is not significant. If the test statistic is greater than the tabulated value for $P = 0.05$ we reject H_0 in favour of the alternative hypothesis.

Degrees of freedom	Level of probability (*P*)									
	0.98	0.95	0.80	0.50	0.20	0.10	0.05	0.02	0.01	0.001
1	0.001	0.004	0.064	0.455	1.64	2.71	3.84	5.41	6.64	10.83
2	0.040	0.103	0.466	1.386	3.22	4.61	5.99	7.82	9.21	13.82
3	0.185	0.352	1.005	2.366	4.64	6.25	7.82	9.84	11.35	16.27
4	0.429	0.711	1.649	3.357	5.99	7.78	9.49	11.67	13.28	18.47
5	0.752	0.145	2.343	4.351	7.29	9.24	11.07	13.39	15.09	20.52

← *Do not reject H_0*   *Reject H_0* →

Related activities: Using Chi-squared in Genetics
Web links: Chi-squared Exercise in Ecology

Using Chi-Squared in Genetics

The **chi-squared test**, χ^2, is frequently used for testing the outcome of dihybrid crosses against an expected (predicted) Mendelian ratio, and it is appropriate for use in this way. When using the chi-squared test for this purpose, the null hypothesis predicts the ratio of offspring of different phenotypes according to the expected Mendelian ratio for the cross, assuming independent assortment of alleles (no linkage). Significant departures from the predicted Mendelian ratio indicate linkage of the alleles in question. Raw counts should be used and a large sample size is required for the test to be valid.

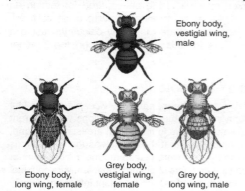

Ebony body, vestigial wing, male

Ebony body, long wing, female

Grey body, vestigial wing, female

Grey body, long wing, male

Images of *Drosophila* courtesy of **Newbyte Educational Software**: *Drosophila* Genetics Lab (www.newbyte.com)

Using χ^2 in Mendelian Genetics

In a *Drosophila* genetics experiment, two individuals were crossed (the details of the cross are not relevant here). The predicted Mendelian ratios for the offspring of this cross were 1:1:1:1 for each of the four following phenotypes: grey body-long wing, grey body-vestigial wing, ebony body-long wing, ebony body-vestigial wing. The observed results of the cross were not exactly as predicted. The following numbers for each phenotype were observed in the offspring of the cross:

Observed results of the example *Drosophila* cross

Grey body, long wing	98	Ebony body, long wing	102
Grey body, vestigial wing	88	Ebony body, vestigial wing	112

Using χ^2, the probability of this result being consistent with a 1:1:1:1 ratio could be tested. Worked example as follows:

Step 1: Calculate the expected value (E)

In this case, this is the sum of the observed values divided by the number of categories (see note below)

$$\frac{400}{4} = 100$$

Step 2: Calculate O – E

The difference between the observed and expected values is calculated as a measure of the deviation from a predicted result. Since some deviations are negative, they are all squared to give positive values. This step is usually performed as part of a tabulation (right, darker grey column).

Category	O	E	O – E	$(O-E)^2$	$\frac{(O-E)^2}{E}$
Grey, long wing	98	100	–2	4	0.04
Grey, vestigial wing	88	100	–12	144	1.44
Ebony, long wing	102	100	2	4	0.04
Ebony, vestigial wing	112	100	12	144	1.44

Total = 400 χ^2 $\Sigma = 2.96$

Step 3: Calculate the value of χ^2

$$\chi^2 = \sum \frac{(O-E)^2}{E}$$

Where: O = the observed result
E = the expected result
Σ = sum of

The calculated χ^2 value is given at the bottom right of the last column in the tabulation.

Step 5a: Using the χ^2 table

On the χ^2 table (part reproduced in Table 1 below) with 3 degrees of freedom, the calculated value for χ^2 of 2.96 corresponds to a probability of between 0.2 and 0.5 (see arrow). *This means that by chance alone a χ^2 value of 2.96 could be expected between 20% and 50% of the time.*

Step 4: Calculating degrees of freedom

The probability that any particular χ^2 value could be exceeded by chance depends on the number of degrees of freedom. This is simply **one less than the total number of categories** (this is the number that could vary independently without affecting the last value). **In this case: 4–1 = 3.**

Step 5b: Using the χ^2 table

The probability of between 0.2 and 0.5 is higher than the 0.05 value which is generally regarded as significant. The null hypothesis cannot be rejected and we have no reason to believe that the observed results differ significantly from the expected (at $P = 0.05$).

Footnote: Many Mendelian crosses involve ratios other than 1:1. For these, calculation of the expected values is not simply a division of the total by the number of categories. Instead, the total must be apportioned according to the ratio. For example, for a total of 400 as above, in a predicted 9:3:3:1 ratio, the total count must be divided by 16 (9+3+3+1) and the expected values will be 225: 75: 75: 25 in each category.

Table 1: Critical values of χ^2 at different levels of probability. By convention, the critical probability for rejecting the null hypothesis (H_0) is 5%. If the test statistic is less than the tabulated critical value for $P = 0.05$ we cannot reject H_0 and the result is not significant. If the test statistic is greater than the tabulated value for $P = 0.05$ we reject H_0 in favor of the alternative hypothesis.

Degrees of freedom	Level of probability (*P*)									
	0.98	0.95	0.80	0.50	0.20	0.10	0.05	0.02	0.01	0.001
1	0.001	0.004	0.064	0.455 χ^2 1.64		2.71	3.84	5.41	6.64	10.83
2	0.040	0.103	0.466	1.386	3.22	4.61	5.99	7.82	9.21	13.82
3	0.185	0.352	1.005	2.366	4.64	6.25	7.82	9.84	11.35	16.27
4	0.429	0.711	1.649	3.357	5.99	7.78	9.49	11.67	13.28	18.47
5	0.752	0.145	2.343	4.351	7.29	9.24	11.07	13.39	15.09	20.52

← Do not reject H_0 Reject H_0 →

Related activities: Using Chi-squared in Ecology
Web links: Chi-squared Exercise in Genetics

Descriptive Statistics

For most investigations, measures of the biological response are made from more than one sampling unit. The sample size (the number of sampling units) will vary depending on the resources available. In lab based investigations, the sample size may be as small as two or three (e.g. two test-tubes in each treatment). In field studies, each individual may be a sampling unit, and the sample size can be very large (e.g. 100 individuals). It is useful to summarise the data collected using **descriptive statistics**.

Descriptive statistics, such as mean, median, and mode, can help to highlight trends or patterns in the data. Each of these statistics is appropriate to certain types of data or distributions, e.g. a mean is not appropriate for data with a skewed distribution (see below). Frequency graphs are useful for indicating the distribution of data. Standard deviation and standard error are statistics used to quantify the amount of spread in the data and evaluate the reliability of estimates of the true (population) mean.

Variation in Data

Whether they are obtained from observation or experiments, most biological data show variability. In a set of data values, it is useful to know the value about which most of the data are grouped; the centre value. This value can be the mean, median, or mode depending on the type of variable involved (see schematic below). The main purpose of these statistics is to summarise important trends in your data and to provide the basis for statistical analyses.

Variability in continuous data is often displayed as a **frequency distribution**. A frequency plot will indicate whether the data have a normal distribution (A), with a symmetrical spread of data about the mean, or whether the distribution is skewed (B), or bimodal (C). The shape of the distribution will determine which statistic (mean, median, or mode) best describes the central tendency of the sample data.

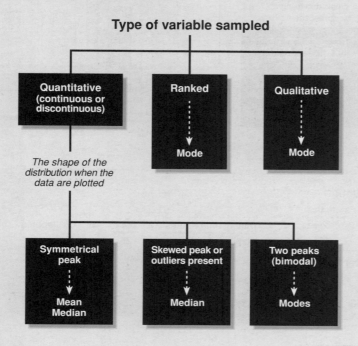

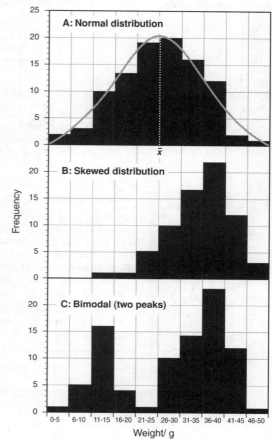

Statistic	Definition and use	Method of calculation
Mean	• The average of all data entries. • Measure of central tendency for normally distributed data.	• Add up all the data entries. • Divide by the total number of data entries.
Median	• The middle value when data entries are placed in rank order. • A good measure of central tendency for skewed distributions.	• Arrange the data in increasing rank order. • Identify the middle value. • For an even number of entries, find the mid point of the two middle values.
Mode	• The most common data value. • Suitable for bimodal distributions and qualitative data.	• Identify the category with the highest number of data entries using a tally chart or a bar graph.
Range	• The difference between the smallest and largest data values. • Provides a crude indication of data spread.	• Identify the smallest and largest values and find the difference between them.

When NOT to calculate a mean:

In certain situations, calculation of a simple arithmetic mean is inappropriate.

Remember:

• *DO NOT* calculate a mean from values that are already means (averages) themselves.

• *DO NOT* calculate a mean of ratios (e.g. percentages) for several groups of different sizes; go back to the raw values and recalculate.

• *DO NOT* calculate a mean when the measurement scale is not linear, e.g. pH units are not measured on a linear scale.

Related activities: The Reliability of the Mean

DA 2

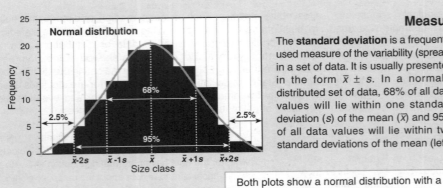

Normal distribution

Measuring Spread

The **standard deviation** is a frequently used measure of the variability (spread) in a set of data. It is usually presented in the form $\bar{x} \pm s$. In a normally distributed set of data, 68% of all data values will lie within one standard deviation (s) of the mean ($\bar{x}$) and 95% of all data values will lie within two standard deviations of the mean (left).

Two different sets of data can have the same mean and range, yet the distribution of data within the range can be quite different. In both the data sets pictured in the histograms below, 68% of the values lie within the range $\bar{x} \pm 1s$ and 95% of the values lie within $\bar{x} \pm 2s$. However, in B, the data values are more tightly clustered around the mean.

Both plots show a normal distribution with a symmetrical spread of values about the mean.

Histogram B has a smaller standard deviation; the values are clustered more tightly around the mean.

Histogram A has a larger standard deviation; the values are spread widely around the mean.

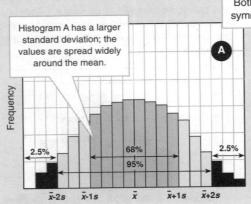

A

Calculating s

Standard deviation is easily calculated using a spreadsheet.

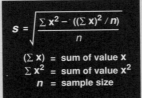

$$s = \sqrt{\frac{\sum x^2 - ((\sum x)^2 / n)}{n}}$$

$(\sum x)$ = sum of value x
$\sum x^2$ = sum of value x^2
n = sample size

B

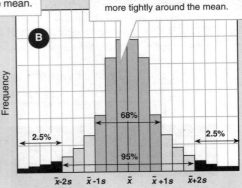

Case Study: Fern Reproduction

Fern spores

Raw data (below) and descriptive statistics (right) from a survey of the number of spores found on the fronds of a fern plant.

Raw data: Number of spores per frond

64	60	64	62	68	66	63
69	70	63	70	70	63	62
71	69	59	70	66	61	70
67	64	63	64			

$$\frac{\text{Total of data entries}}{\text{Number of entries}} = \frac{1641}{25} = 66 \text{ spores}$$

Mean

Number of spores per frond (in rank order)	
59	66
60	66
61	67
62	68
62	69
63	69
63	70
63	70
63	70
64	70
64	70
64	71
64	

Median

Spores per frond	Tally	Total
59	✔	1
60	✔	1
61	✔	1
62	✔✔	2
63	✔✔✔✔	4
64	✔✔✔✔	4
65		0
66	✔✔	2
67	✔	1
68	✔	1
69	✔✔	2
70	✔✔✔✔✔	5
71	✔	1

Mode

1. Give a reason for the difference between the mean, median, and mode for the fern spore data:

_____

_____

_____

_____

2. Calculate the mean, median, and mode for the data on beetle masses below. Draw up a tally chart and show all calculations:

Beetle masses / g		
2.2	2.1	2.6
2.5	2.4	2.8
2.5	2.7	2.5
2.6	2.6	2.5
2.2	2.8	2.4

_____

_____

_____

_____

_____

The Reliability of the Mean

You have already seen how to use the **standard deviation** (*s*) to quantify the spread or **dispersion** in your data. The **variance** (*s²*) is another such measure of dispersion, but the standard deviation is usually the preferred of these two measures because it is expressed in the original units. Usually, you will also want to know how good your sample mean ($\bar{x}$) is as an estimate of the true population mean (μ). This can be indicated by the standard error of the mean (or just **standard error** or SE). **SE** is often used as an error measurement simply because it is small, rather than for any good statistical reason. However, it is does allow you to calculate the **95% confidence interval (95% CI)**. The calculation and use of 95% CIs is outlined below and on the next page. By the end of this activity you should be able to:

- Enter data and calculate descriptive statistics using a spreadsheet programme such as *Microsoft Excel*. You can follow this procedure for any set of data.
- Calculate standard error and 95% confidence intervals for sample data and plot these data appropriately with error bars.
- Interpret the graphically presented data and reach tentative conclusions about the findings of the experiment.

Reliability of the Sample Mean

When we take measurements from samples of a larger population, we are using those samples as indicators of the trends in the whole population. Therefore, when we calculate a sample mean, it is useful to know how close that value is to the true population mean (μ). This is not merely an academic exercise; it will enable you to make **inferences** about the aspect of the population in which you are interested. For this reason, statistics based on samples and used to estimate population parameters are called **inferential statistics.**

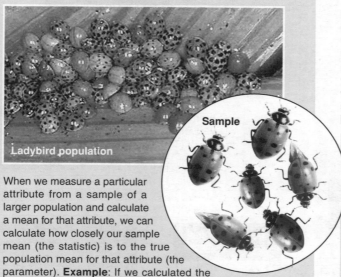

Ladybird population

Sample

When we measure a particular attribute from a sample of a larger population and calculate a mean for that attribute, we can calculate how closely our sample mean (the statistic) is to the true population mean for that attribute (the parameter). **Example**: If we calculated the mean number of carapace spots from a sample of six ladybird beetles, how reliable is this statistic as an indicator of the mean number of carapace spots in the whole population? We can find out by calculating the **95% confidence interval**.

The Standard Error (SE)

The standard error (SE) is simple to calculate and is usually a small value. Standard error is given by:

$$SE = \frac{s}{\sqrt{n}}$$

where *s* = the standard deviation, and *n* = sample size.

Standard errors are sometimes plotted as error bars on graphs, but it is more meaningful to plot the **95% confidence intervals** (see box below). All calculations are easily made using a spreadsheet (see opposite).

The 95% Confidence Interval

SE is required to calculate the 95% confidence interval (CI) of the mean. This is given by:

$$95\% \ CI = SE \times t_{P(n-1)}$$

Do not be alarmed by this calculation; once you have calculated the value of the SE, it is a simple matter to multiply this value by the value of *t* at *P* = 0.05 (from the *t* table) for the appropriate degrees of freedom (df) for your sample (*n* – 1).

For example: where the SE = 0.6 and the sample size is 10, the calculation of the 95% CI is:

$$95\% \ CI = 0.6 \times 2.262 = \boxed{1.36}$$

Part of the *t* table is given to the right for *P* = 0.05. Note that, as the sample becomes very large, the value of *t* becomes smaller. For very large samples, *t* is fixed at 1.96, so the 95% CI is slightly less than twice the SE.

All these statistics, including a plot of the data with Y error bars, can be calculated using a programme such as *Microsoft Excel* (opposite).

Critical values of Student's *t* distribution at *P* = 0.05.

df	*P*
	0.05
1	12.71
2	4.303
3	3.182
4	2.776
5	2.571
6	2.447
7	2.365
8	2.306
9	2.262
10	2.228
20	2.086
30	2.042
40	2.021
60	2.000
120	1.980
>120	1.960

Value of *t* at *n*–1 = 9

Maximum value of *t* at this level of *P*

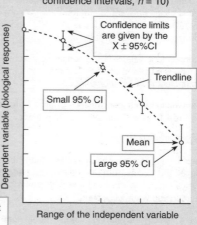

Relationship of Y against X (± 95% confidence intervals, *n* = 10)

Confidence limits are given by the X ± 95%CI

Trendline

Small 95% CI

Mean

Large 95% CI

Dependent variable (biological response)

Range of the independent variable

Plotting your confidence intervals

Once you have calculated the 95% CI for the means in your data set, you can plot them as error bars on your graph. Note that the **95% confidence limits** are given by the value of the **mean ± 95%CI**. A 95% confidence limit (i.e. *P* = 0.05) tells you that, on average, 95 times out of 100, the limits will contain the true population mean.

Related activities: Descriptive Statistics, Taking the Next Step

DA 3

Comparing Treatments Using Descriptive Statistics

In an experiment, the growth of newborn rats on four different feeds was compared by weighing young rats after 28 days on each of four feeding regimes. The suitability of each food type for maximising growth in the first month of life was evaluated by comparing the means of the four experimental groups. Each group comprised 10 individual rats. All 40 newborns were born to sibling mothers with the same feeding history. For this activity, follow the steps outlined below and reproduce them yourself.

Calculating Descriptive Statistics

Entering your data and calculating descriptive statistics.

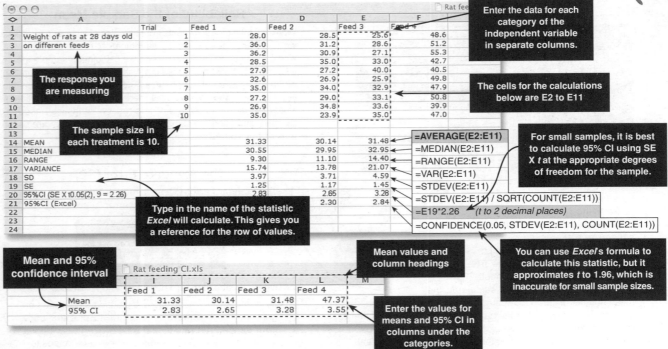

Enter the data for each category of the independent variable in separate columns.

The response you are measuring

The cells for the calculations below are E2 to E11

The sample size in each treatment is 10.

	A	B Trial	C Feed 1	D Feed 2	E Feed 3	F Feed 4
1		Trial	Feed 1	Feed 2	Feed 3	Feed 4
2	Weight of rats at 28 days old	1	28.0	28.5	25.6	48.6
3	on different feeds	2	36.0	31.2	28.6	51.2
4		3	36.2	30.9	27.1	55.3
5		4	28.5	35.0	33.0	42.7
6		5	27.9	27.2	40.0	40.5
7		6	32.6	26.9	25.9	49.8
8		7	35.0	34.0	32.9	47.9
9		8	27.2	29.0	33.1	50.8
10		9	26.9	34.8	33.6	39.9
11		10	35.0	23.9	35.0	47.0
12						
13						
14	MEAN		31.33	30.14	31.48	
15	MEDIAN		30.55	29.95	32.95	
16	RANGE		9.30	11.10	14.40	
17	VARIANCE		15.74	13.78	21.07	
18	SD		3.97	3.71	4.59	
19	SE		1.25	1.17	1.45	
20	95%CI (SE X t0.05(2), 9 = 2.26)		2.83	2.65	3.28	
21	95%CI (Excel)			2.30	2.84	

=AVERAGE(E2:E11)
=MEDIAN(E2:E11)
=RANGE(E2:E11)
=VAR(E2:E11)
=STDEV(E2:E11)
=STDEV(E2:E11) / SQRT(COUNT(E2:E11))
=E19*2.26 *(t to 2 decimal places)*
=CONFIDENCE(0.05, STDEV(E2:E11), COUNT(E2:E11))

For small samples, it is best to calculate 95% CI using SE X *t* at the appropriate degrees of freedom for the sample.

Type in the name of the statistic *Excel* will calculate. This gives you a reference for the row of values.

You can use *Excel*'s formula to calculate this statistic, but it approximates *t* to 1.96, which is inaccurate for small sample sizes.

Mean and 95% confidence interval

Mean values and column headings

Rat feeding CI.xls

	I	J	K	L	M
	Feed 1	Feed 2	Feed 3	Feed 4	
Mean	31.33	30.14	31.48	47.37	
95% CI	2.83	2.65	3.28	3.55	

Enter the values for means and 95% CI in columns under the categories.

Drawing the Graph

To plot the graph, you will need to enter the data values you want to plot in a format that *Excel* can use (above). To do this, enter the values in columns under each category.

■ Each column will have two entries: mean and 95% CI. In this case, we want to plot the mean weight of 28 day rats fed on different foods and add the 95% confidence intervals as error bars.

■ The independent variable is categorical, so the correct graph type is a column chart. Select the row of mean values (including column headings)

1 From the menu bar choose: **Insert > Chart > Column**. This is **Step 1** in the Chart Wizard. Click **Next**.

2 At **Step 2**, click **Next**.

3 At **Step 3**, you have the option to add a title, labels for your X and Y axes, turn off gridlines, and add (or remove) a legend. When you have added all the information you want, click **Next**.

4 At **Step 4**, specify the chart location. It should appear "as object in" Sheet 1 by default. Click on the chart and move it to reveal the data.

5 A chart will appear on the screen. **Right click** (Ctrl-click on Mac) on any part of any column and choose **Format data series**. To add error bars, select the **Y error bars** tab, and click on the symbol that shows Display both. Click on Custom, and use the data selection window to select the row of 95% CI data for "+" and "−" fields.

6 Click on OK and your chart will plot with error bars.

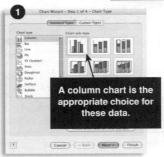

A column chart is the appropriate choice for these data.

Add information for your graph in here ...

... and here

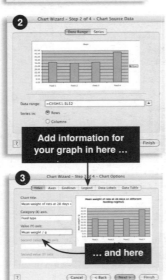

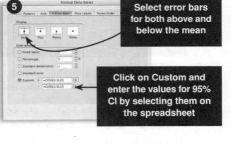

Select error bars for both above and below the mean

Click on Custom and enter the values for 95% CI by selecting them on the spreadsheet

Your column chart will appear with the confidence intervals marked.

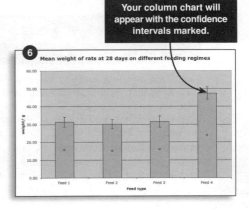

Mean weight of rats at 28 days on different feeding regimes

Biological Drawings

Microscopes are a powerful tool for examining cells and cell structures. In order to make a permanent record of what is seen when examining a specimen, it is useful to make a drawing. It is important to draw **what is actually seen**. This will depend on the **resolution** of the microscope being used. Resolution refers to the ability of a microscope to separate small objects that are very close together. Making drawings from mounted specimens is a skill. Drawing forces you to observe closely and accurately. While photographs are limited to representing appearance at a single moment in time, drawings can be composites of the observer's cumulative experience, with many different specimens of the same material. The total picture of an object thus represented can often communicate information much more effectively than a photograph. Your attention to the outline of suggestions below will help you to make more effective drawings. If you are careful to follow the suggestions at the beginning, the techniques will soon become habitual.

1. **Drawing materials**: All drawings should be done with a clear pencil line on good quality paper. A sharp HB pencil is recommended. A soft rubber of good quality is essential. Diagrams in ballpoint or fountain pen are unacceptable because they cannot be corrected.

2. **Positioning**: Centre your diagram on the page. Do not draw it in a corner. This will leave plenty of room for the addition of labels once the diagram is completed.

3. **Size**: A drawing should be large enough to easily represent all the details you see without crowding. Rarely, if ever, are drawings too large, but they are often too small. Show only as much as is necessary for an understanding of the structure; a small section shown in detail will often suffice. It is time consuming and unnecessary, for example, to reproduce accurately the entire contents of a microscope field.

4. **Accuracy**: Your drawing should be a complete, accurate representation of the material you have observed, and should communicate your understanding of the material to anyone who looks at it. Avoid making "idealised" drawings; your drawing should be a picture of what you actually see, not what you imagine should be there. Proportions should be accurate. If necessary, measure the lengths of various

parts with a ruler. If viewing through a microscope, estimate them as a proportion of the field of view, then translate these proportions onto the page. When drawing shapes that indicate an outline, make sure the line is complete. Where two ends of a line do not meet (as in drawing a cell outline) then this would indicate that the structure has a hole in it.

5. **Technique**: Use only simple, narrow lines. Represent depth by stippling (dots close together). Indicate depth only when it is essential to your drawing (usually it is not). Do not use shading. Look at the specimen while you are drawing it.

6. **Labels**: Leave a good margin for labels. All parts of your diagram must be labelled accurately. Labelling lines should be drawn with a ruler and should not cross. Where possible, keep label lines vertical or horizontal. Label the drawing with:
   - A title, which should identify the material (organism, tissues or cells).
   - Magnification under which it was observed, or a scale to indicate the size of the object.
   - Names of structures.
   - In living materials, any movements you have seen.

Remember that drawings are intended as records for you, and as a means of encouraging close observation; artistic ability is not necessary. Before you turn in a drawing, ask yourself if you know what every line represents. If you do not, look more closely at the material. *Take into account the rules for biological drawings and draw what you see, not what you think you see!*

Examples of acceptable biological drawings: The diagrams below show two examples of biological drawings that are acceptable. The example on the left is of a whole organism and its size is indicated by a scale. The example on the right is of plant tissue: a group of cells that are essentially identical in the structure. It is not necessary to show many cells even though your view through the microscope may show them. As few as 2-4 will suffice to show their structure and how they are arranged. Scale is indicated by stating how many times larger it has been drawn. Do not confuse this with what magnification it was viewed at under the microscope. The abbreviation **T.S.** indicates that the specimen was a *cross* or *transverse section*.

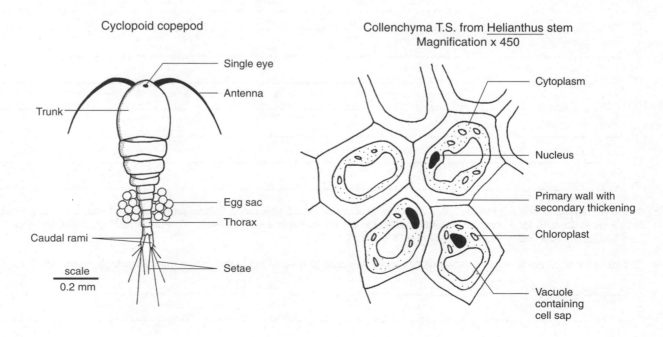

Cyclopoid copepod

Single eye
Antenna
Trunk
Egg sac
Thorax
Caudal rami
scale
0.2 mm
Setae

Collenchyma T.S. from <u>Helianthus</u> stem
Magnification x 450

Cytoplasm
Nucleus
Primary wall with secondary thickening
Chloroplast
Vacuole containing cell sap

Related activities: Optical Microscopes

A 2

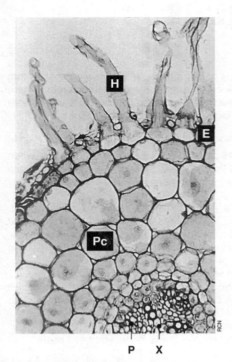

P   X

Specimen used for drawing

The photograph above is a light microscope view of a stained transverse section (cross section) of a root from a *Ranunculus* (buttercup) plant. It shows the arrangement of the different tissues in the root. The vascular bundle is at the centre of the root, with the larger, central xylem vessels (**X**) and smaller phloem vessels (**P**) grouped around them. The root hair cells (**H**) are arranged on the external surface and form part of the epidermal layer (**E**). Parenchyma cells (**Pc**) make up the bulk of the root's mass. The distance from point **X** to point **E** on the photograph (above) is about 0.15 mm (150 µm).

An Unacceptable Biological Drawing

The diagram below is an example of how *not* to produce a biological drawing; it is based on the photograph to the left. There are many aspects of the drawing that are unacceptable. The exercise below asks you to identify the errors in this student's attempt.

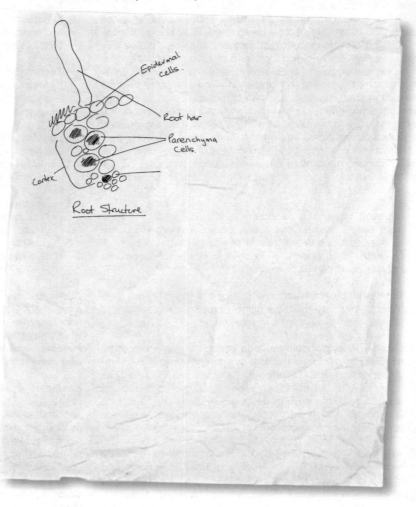

1. Identify and describe eight unacceptable features of the student's biological diagram above:

   (a) _____

   (b) _____

   (c) _____

   (d) _____

   (e) _____

   (f) _____

   (g) _____

   (h) _____

2. In the remaining space next to the 'poor example' (above) or on a blank piece of refill paper, attempt your own version of a biological drawing for the same material, based on the photograph above. Make a point of correcting all of the errors that you have identified in the sample student's attempt.

3. Explain why accurate biological drawings are more valuable to a scientific investigation than an 'artistic' approach:

   _____

   _____

   _____

The Structure of a Report

Once you have collected and analysed your data, you can write your report. You may wish to present your findings as a written report, a poster presentation, or an oral presentation. The structure of a scientific report is described below using a poster presentation (which is necessarily very concise) as an example. When writing your report, it is useful to write the methods or the results first, followed by the discussion and conclusion. Although you should do some reading in preparation, the introduction should be one of the last sections that you write. Writing the other sections first gives you a better understanding of your investigation within the context of other work in the same area.

To view this and other examples of posters, see the excellent NC State University web site listed below

1. Title (and author)
Provides a clear and concise description of the project.

2. Introduction
Includes the aim, hypothesis, and background to the study

Flounder Exhibit Temperature-Dependent Sex Determination
J. Adam Luckenbach*, John Godwin and Russell Borski
Department of Zoology, Box 7617, North Carolina State University, Raleigh, NC 27695

Introduction
Southern flounder (*Paralichthys lethostigma*) support valuable fisheries and show great promise for aquaculture. Female flounder are known to grow faster and reach larger adult... Therefore, information on sex det... might increase the ratio of female... important for aquaculture.

3. Materials and Methods
A description of the materials and procedures used.

Objective
This study was conducted to determine whether southern flounder exhibit temperature-dependent sex determination (TSD), and if growth is affected by rearing temperature.

Methods
- Southern flounder broodstock were strip spawned to collect eggs and sperm for *in vitro* fertilization.
- Hatched larvae were weaned from a natural diet (rotifers/*Artemia*) to high protein pelleted feed and fed until satiation at least twice daily.
- Upon reaching a mean total length of 40 mm, the juvenile flounder were stocked at equal densities into one of three temperatures 18, 23, or 28°C for 245 days.
- Gonads were preserved and later sectioned at 2-6 microns.
- Sex-distinguishing markers were used to distinguish males (spermatogenesis) from females (oogenesis).

Histological Analysis

Male Differentiation   **Female Differen...**

Temperature Affects Sex Determination

4. Results
An account of results including tables and graphs. This section should not discuss the result, just present them.

Growth Does Not Differ by Sex

Temperature (°C)

Results
- Sex was discernible in most fish greater than 120 mm long.
- High (28°C) temperature produced 4% females.
- Low (18°C) temperature produced 22% females.
- Mid-range (23°C) temperature produced 44% females.
- Fish raised at high or low temperatures showed reduced growth compared to those at the mid-range temperature.
- Up to 245 days, no differences in growth existed between sexes.

5. Discussion
An discussion of the findings in light of the biological concepts involved. It should include comments on any limitations of the study.

6. Conclusion
A clear statement of whether tor not the findings support the hypothesis. In abbreviated poster presentations, these sections may be combined.

Conclusions
- These findings indicate that sex determination in southern flounder is temperature-sensitive and temperature has a profound effect on growth.
- A mid-range rearing temperature (23°C) appears to maximize the number of females and promote better growth in young southern flounder.
- Although adult females are known to grow larger than males, no difference in growth between sexes occurred in age-0 (< 1 year) southern flounder.

7. References & acknowledgements
An organised list of all sources of information. Entries should be consistent within your report. Your teacher will advise you as to the preferred format.

Acknowledgements
The authors acknowledge the Saltonstall-Kennedy Program of the National Marine Fisheries Service and the University of North Carolina Sea Grant College Program for funding this research. Special thanks to Lea Ware and Beth Shimps for help with the work.

Skills in Biology

1. Explain the purpose of each of the following sections of a report. The first has one been completed for you:

    (a) Introduction: *Provides the reader with the background to the topic and the rationale for the study*

    (b) Methods:

    (c) Results:

    (d) Discussion:

    (e) References and acknowledgements:

2. Posters are a highly visual method of presenting the findings of a study. Describe the positive features of this format:

Related activities: Hypotheses and Predictions, Report Checklist
Web links: NC State University: Creating Effective Poster Presentations

RA 2

Writing the Methods

The materials and methods section of your report should be brief but informative. All essential details should be included but those not necessary for the repetition of the study should be omitted. The following diagram illustrates some of the important details that should be included in a methods section. Obviously, a complete list of all possible equipment and procedures is not possible because each experiment or study is different. However, the sort of information that is required for both lab and field based studies is provided.

Field Studies	Laboratory Based Studies

Study site & organisms
- Site location and features
- Why that site was chosen
- Species involved

Specialised equipment
- pH and oxygen meters
- Thermometers
- Nets and traps

Data collection
- Number and timing of observations/collections
- Time of day or year
- Sample sizes and size of the sampling unit
- Methods of preservation
- Temperature at time of sampling
- Weather conditions on the day(s) of sampling
- Methods of measurement/sampling
- Methods of recording

Data collection
- Pre-treatment of material before experiments
- Details of treatments and controls
- Duration and timing of experimental observations
- Temperature
- Sample sizes and details of replication
- Methods of measurement or sampling
- Methods of recording

Experimental organisms
- Species or strain
- Age and sex
- Number of individuals used

Specialised equipment
- pH meters
- Water baths & incubators
- Spectrophotometers
- Centrifuges
- Aquaria & choice chambers
- Microscopes and videos

Special preparations
- Techniques for the preparation of material (staining, grinding)
- Indicators, salt solutions, buffers, special dilutions

General guidelines for writing a methods section

- Choose a suitable level of detail. *Too little detail and the study could not be repeated. Too much detail obscures important features.*
- Do NOT include the details of standard procedures (e.g. how to use a balance) or standard equipment (e.g. beakers and flasks).
- Include details of any statistical analyses and data transformations.
- Outline the reasons why procedures were done in a certain way or in a certain order, if this is not self-evident.
- If your methodology involves complicated preparations (e.g. culture media) then it is acceptable to refer just to the original information source (e.g. lab manual) or include the information as an appendix.

1. The following text is part of the methods section from a report. Using the information above and on the checklist on page 63, describe eight errors (there are ten) in the methods. The errors are concerned with a lack of explanation or detail that would be necessary to repeat the experiment (they are not typographical, nor are they associated with the use of the active voice, which is now considered preferable to the passive):

"We collected the worms for this study from a pond outside the school. We carried out the experiment at room temperature on April 16, 1997. First we added full strength seawater to each of three 200 cm³ glass jars; these were the controls. We filled another three jars with diluted seawater. We blotted the worms dry and weighed them to the nearest 0.1 g, then we added one worm to each jar. We reweighed the worms (after blotting) at various intervals over the next two hours."

(a) _____

(b) _____

(c) _____

(d) _____

(e) _____

(f) _____

(g) _____

(h) _____

Writing Your Results

The results section is arguably the most important part of any research report; it is the place where you can bring together and present your findings. When properly constructed, this section will present your results clearly and in a way that shows you have organised your data and carefully considered the appropriate analysis. A portion of the results section from a scientific paper on the habitat preference of New Zealand black mudfish is presented below (Hicks, B. and Barrier, R. (1996), NZJMFR. 30, 135-151). It highlights some important features of the results section and shows you how you can present information concisely, even if your results are relatively lengthy. Use it as a guide for content when you write up this section.

Results

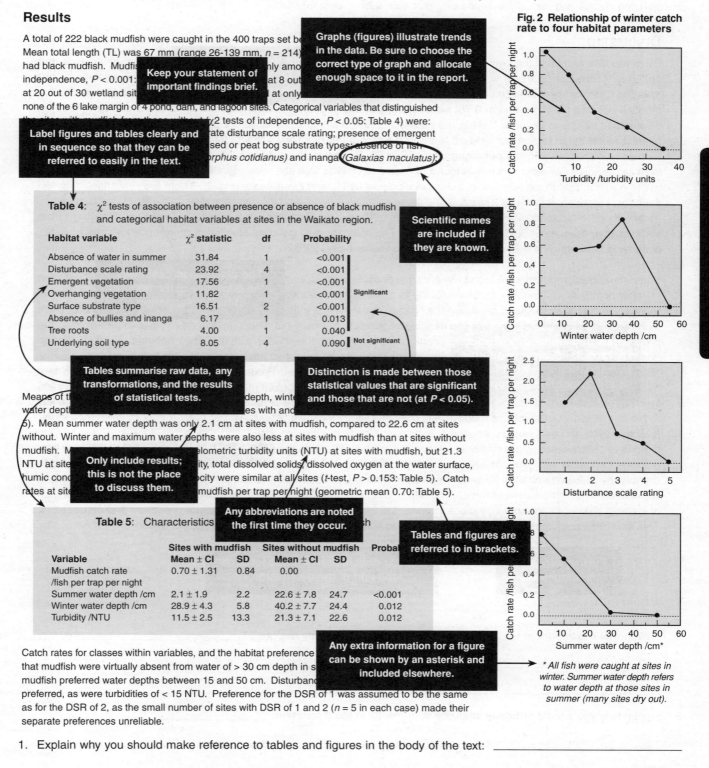

A total of 222 black mudfish were caught in the 400 traps set be[...]. Mean total length (TL) was 67 mm (range 26-139 mm, $n = 214$) [...] had black mudfish. Mudfis[...] [...]ly amo[...] independence, $P < 0.001$: [...] at 8 out[...] at 20 out of 30 wetland sit[...] at only [...] none of the 6 lake margin or 4 pond, dam, and lagoon sites. Categorical variables that distinguished [...] $\chi 2$ tests of independence, $P < 0.05$: Table 4) were: [...]rate disturbance scale rating; presence of emergent [...]sed or peat bog substrate types; absence of fish [...]orphus cotidianus) and inanga (Galaxias maculatus);

Graphs (figures) illustrate trends in the data. Be sure to choose the correct type of graph and allocate enough space to it in the report.

Keep your statement of important findings brief.

Label figures and tables clearly and in sequence so that they can be referred to easily in the text.

Scientific names are included if they are known.

Table 4: χ^2 tests of association between presence or absence of black mudfish and categorical habitat variables at sites in the Waikato region.

Habitat variable	χ^2 statistic	df	Probability	
Absence of water in summer	31.84	1	<0.001	
Disturbance scale rating	23.92	4	<0.001	
Emergent vegetation	17.56	1	<0.001	
Overhanging vegetation	11.82	1	<0.001	Significant
Surface substrate type	16.51	2	<0.001	
Absence of bullies and inanga	6.17	1	0.013	
Tree roots	4.00	1	0.040	
Underlying soil type	8.05	4	0.090	Not significant

Tables summarise raw data, any transformations, and the results of statistical tests.

Distinction is made between those statistical values that are significant and those that are not (at $P < 0.05$).

Means of t[...] [...]depth, wint[...] water depth[...] [...]es with and [...]. Mean summer water depth was only 2.1 cm at sites with mudfish, compared to 22.6 cm at sites without. Winter and maximum water depths were also less at sites with mudfish than at sites without mudfish. M[...] [...]elometric turbidity units (NTU) at sites with mudfish, but 21.3 NTU at site[...] [...]ity, total dissolved solids, dissolved oxygen at the water surface, humic cond[...] [...]ocity were similar at all sites (t-test, $P > 0.153$: Table 5). Catch rates at site[...] [...]mudfish per trap per night (geometric mean 0.70: Table 5).

Only include results; this is not the place to discuss them.

Any abbreviations are noted the first time they occur.

Table 5: Characteristics [...] [...]sh

Variable	Sites with mudfish Mean ± CI	SD	Sites without mudfish Mean ± CI	SD	Proba[...]
Mudfish catch rate /fish per trap per night	0.70 ± 1.31	0.84	0.00		
Summer water depth /cm	2.1 ± 1.9	2.2	22.6 ± 7.8	24.7	<0.001
Winter water depth /cm	28.9 ± 4.3	5.8	40.2 ± 7.7	24.4	0.012
Turbidity /NTU	11.5 ± 2.5	13.3	21.3 ± 7.1	22.6	0.012

Tables and figures are referred to in brackets.

Catch rates for classes within variables, and the habitat preference [...] that mudfish were virtually absent from water of > 30 cm depth in s[...] mudfish preferred water depths between 15 and 50 cm. Disturbanc[...] preferred, as were turbidities of < 15 NTU. Preference for the DSR of 1 was assumed to be the same as for the DSR of 2, as the small number of sites with DSR of 1 and 2 ($n = 5$ in each case) made their separate preferences unreliable.

Any extra information for a figure can be shown by an asterisk and included elsewhere.

Fig. 2 Relationship of winter catch rate to four habitat parameters

* All fish were caught at sites in winter. Summer water depth refers to water depth at those sites in summer (many sites dry out).

1. Explain why you should make reference to tables and figures in the body of the text: _____

_____

2. Explain why you might present the same data in a table and as a figure: _____

_____

_____

Related activities: The Structure of a Report, Report Checklist

A 3

Skills in Biology

Writing Your Discussion

In the discussion section of your report, you must interpret your results in the context of the specific questions you set out to answer in the investigation. You should also place your findings in the context of any broader relevant issues. If your results coincide exactly with what you expected, then your discussion will be relatively brief. However, be prepared to discuss any unexpected or conflicting results and critically evaluate any problems with your study design. The Discussion section may (and should) refer to the findings in the Results section, but it is not the place to introduce new results. Try to work towards a point in your discussion where the reader is lead naturally to the conclusion. The conclusion may be presented within the discussion or it may be included separately after the discussion as a separate section.

Discussion:

Black mudfish habitat in the Waikato region can be a **[Support your statements with reference to Tables and Figures from the Results section.]** ses by four variables that are easy to measure: summer water depth, winter wa _____ cated by vegetation), and turbidity. Catch rates of black mudfish can be extreme _____ es ranged from 0.2 to 8.4 mudfish per trap per night (mean 0.70) between May and October 1992, and were similar to those of Dean (1995) in September 1993 and October 1994 in the Whangamarino Wetland complex (0.0-2.0 mudfish per trap per night). The highest mean catch rate in our study, 8.4 mudfish per trap per night, was at Site 24 (Table 1, Figure 1). The second highest (6.4 mudfish per trap per night) was at Site 32, in a drain about 4 km east of Hamilton. Black mudfish in the Waikato region were most commonly found at sites in wetlands with absence of water in summer, moderate depth of water in winter, limited modification of the vegetation (low DSR), and low turbidity (Fig. 2). There are similarities between the habitat requirements of black mudfish and those of brown mudfish and the common river galaxias *(Galaxias vulgaris)*. Brown mudfish inhabited shallow water, sometimes at the edges of deeper water bodies, but were usually absent from water deeper than about 30-50 cm (Eldon 1978). The common river galaxias also has a preference for shallow water, occupying river margins < 20 cm deep (Jowett and Richardson 1995).

[The discussion describes the relevance of the results of the investigation.]

Sites where black mudfish were found were not just shallow or dry in sum _____ al variation in water depth. A weakness of this study is the fact that sites were trap _____ ere spread relatively widely at each site to maximise the chance of catching any fish _____ nt for black mudfish _____ hanging vegetation, or tree roots. The significance of cover in determining the pres _____ predictable, considering the shallow nature of their habitats. Mudfish, though noc _____ require cover during the to protect them from avian predators, such as bitterns *(Bo* _____ fishers *(Halcyon sancta vagans)*. Predation of black mudfish by a swamp bittern has _____ 1). Cover is also important for brown mudfish (Eldon 1978). Black mudfish were found at sites with the predatory mosquitofish and juvenile eels, and the seasonal drying of their habitats may be a key to the successful coexistence of mudfish with their predators. Mosquitofish are known predators of mudfish fry (Barrier & Hicks 1994), and eels would presumably also prey on black mudfish, as t _____ h (Eldon 1979b). If, however, black mudfish are relatively uncompetitive and vulnerable to p _____ s as to how they manage to coexist with juvenile eels and mosquitofish. The habitat varia _____ can be used to classify the suitability of sites for black mudfish in future. The adaptability of black mudfish allows them to survive in some altered habitats, such as farm or roadside drains. From this study, we can conclude that the continued existence of suitable habitats appears to be more important to black mudfish than the presence of predators and competitors. This study has also improved methods of identifying suitable mudfish habitats in the Waikato region.

[State any limitations of your approach in carrying out the investigation and what further studies might be appropriate.]

[Reference is made to the work of others.]

[Further research is suggested]

[A clear conclusion is made towards the end of the discussion.]

1. Explain why it is important to discuss any weaknesses in your study design: _____
   _____
   _____

2. Explain why you should **critically evaluate** your results in the discussion: _____
   _____
   _____
   _____

3. Describe the purpose of the conclusion: _____
   _____

Related activities: The Structure of a Report, Report checklist

Citing and Listing References

Proper referencing of sources of information is an important aspect of report writing. It shows that you have explored the topic and recognise and respect the work of others. There are two aspects to consider: **citing sources** within the text (making reference to other work to support a statement or compare results) and **compiling a reference list** at the end of the report. A **bibliography** lists all sources of information, but these may not necessarily appear as citations in the report. In contrast, a reference list should contain only those texts cited in the report.

Citations in the main body of the report should include only the authors' surnames, publication date, and page numbers (or internet site), and the citation should be relevant to the statement it claims to support. Accepted methods for referencing vary, but your reference list should provide all the information necessary to locate the source material, it should be consistently presented, and it should contain only the references that you have yourself read (not those cited by others). A suggested format is described below.

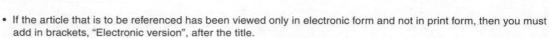

Preparing a Reference List

When teachers ask students to write in "APA style", they are referring to the editorial style established by the **American Psychological Association** (APA). These guidelines for citing **electronic (online) resources** differ only slightly from the **print sources**.

For the Internet

Where you use information from the internet, you must provide the following:
- The website address (URL), the person or organisation who is in charge of the web site and the date you accessed the web page.

This is written in the form: URL (person or organisation's name, day, month, and year retrieved)
This goes together as follows:

> http://www.scientificamerican.com (Scientific American, 17.12.03)

For Periodicals (or Journals)

This is written in the form: author(s), date of publication, article title, periodical title, and publication information.
Example: Author's family name, A. A. (author's initials only), Author, B. B., & Author, C. C. (xxxx = year of publication in brackets). Title of article. Title of Periodical, volume number, page numbers (Note, only use "pp." before the page numbers in newspapers and magazines).
This goes together as follows:

> Bamshad M. J., & Olson S. E. (2003). Does Race Exist? Scientific American, 289(6), 50-57.

For Online Periodicals based on a Print Source

At present, the majority of periodicals retrieved from online publications are exact duplicates of those in their print versions and although they are unlikely to have additional analyses and data attached to them, this is likely to change in the future.

- If the article that is to be referenced has been viewed only in electronic form and not in print form, then you must add in brackets, "Electronic version", after the title.
  This goes together as follows:

  > Bamshad M. J., & Olson S. E. (2003). Does Race Exist? (Electronic version). Scientific American, 289(6), 50-57.

- If you have reason to believe the article has changed in its electronic form, then you will need to add the date you retrieved the document and the URL.
  This goes together as follows:

  > Bamshad M. J., & Olson S. E. (2003). Does Race Exist? (Electronic version). Scientific American, 289(6), 50-57. Retrieved December 17, 2003, from http://www.scientificamerican.com

For Books

This is written in the form: author(s), date of publication, title, and publication information.
Example: Author, A. A., Author, B. B., & Author, C. C. (xxxx). Title (any additional information to enable identification is given in brackets). City of publication: publishers name.
This goes together as follows:

> Martin, R.A. (2004). Missing Links Evolutionary Concepts & Transitions Through Time. Sudbury, MA: Jones and Bartlett

For Citation in the Text of References

This is written in the form: authors' surname(s), date of publication, page number(s) (abbreviated p.), chapter (abbreviated chap.), figure, table, equation, or internet site, in brackets at the appropriate point in text.
This goes together as follows:

> (Bamshad & Olson, 2003, p. 51) or (Bamshad & Olson, 2003, http://www.scientificamerican.com)

This can also be done in the form of footnotes. This involves the use of a superscripted number in the text next to your quoted material and the relevant information listed at the bottom of the page.
This goes together as follows:

> .... Bamshad & Olson reported that ....[1]

---
[1] Bamshad & Olson, 2003, p. 51

Related activities: The Structure of a Report, Report Checklist

A 3

Skills in Biology

54

Example of a Reference List

Lab notes can be listed according to title if the author is unknown.

→ Advanced biology laboratory manual (2000). Cell membranes. pp 16-18. Sunhigh College.

References are listed alphabetically according to the author's surname.

Cooper, G.M. (1997). *The cell: A molecular approach* (2nd ed.). Washington D.C.: ASM Press

Book title in italics (or underlined)   Place of publication: Publisher

Davis, P. (1996) Cellular factories. *New Scientist* 2057: Inside science supplement.

Publication date   Journal title in italics   A supplement may not need page references

If a single author appears more than once, then list the publications from oldest to most recent.

Indge, B. (2001). Diarrhoea, digestion and dehydration. *Biological Sciences Review,* 14(1), 7-9.

Indge, B. (2002). Experiments. *Biological Sciences Review,* 14(3), 11-13.

Article title follows date

Kingsland, J. (2000). Border control. *New Scientist* 2247: Inside science supplement.

Spell out only the last name of authors. Use initials for first and middle names.

Laver, H. (1995). Osmosis and water retention in plants. *Biological Sciences Review* 7(3), 14-18

Volume (Issue number), Pages

Internet sites change often so the date accessed is included. The person or organisation in charge of the site is also included.

→ http://www.cbc.umn.edu/~mwd/cell_intro.html (Dalton, M. "Introduction to cell biology" 12.02.03)

1. Distinguish between a **reference list** and a **bibliography**: _____

_____

_____

_____

2. Explain why internet articles based on a print source are likely to have additional analyses and data attached in the future, and why this point should be noted in a reference list:

_____

_____

_____

3. Following are the details of references and source material used by a student in preparing a report on enzymes and their uses in biotechnology. He provided his reference list in prose. From it, compile a correctly formatted reference list:

Pages 18-23 in the sixth edition of the textbook "Biology" by Neil Campbell. Published by Benjamin/Cummings in California (2002). New Scientist article by Peter Moore called "Fuelled for life" (January 1996, volume 2012, supplement). "Food biotechnology" published in the journal Biological Sciences Review, page 25, volume 8 (number 3) 1996, by Liam and Katherine O'Hare. An article called "Living factories" by Philip Ball in New Scientist, volume 2015 1996, pages 28-31. Pages 75-85 in the book "The cell: a molecular approach" by Geoffrey Cooper, published in 1997 by ASM Press, Washington D.C. An article called "Development of a procedure for purification of a recombinant therapeutic protein" in the journal "Australasian Biotechnology", by I Roberts and S. Taylor, pages 93-99 in volume 6, number 2, 1996.

REFERENCE LIST

_____

_____

_____

_____

_____

_____

_____

Report Checklist

A report of your findings at the completion of your investigation may take one of the following forms: a written document, seminar, poster, web page, or multimedia presentation. The following checklist identifies points to consider when writing each section of your report. Review the list before you write your report and then, on satisfactory completion of each section of your write-up, use the check boxes to tick off the points:

Title:

☐ (a) Gives a clear indication of what the study is about.

☐ (b) Includes the species name and a common name of all organisms used.

Introduction:

☐ (a) Includes a clear aim.

☐ (b) Includes a well written hypothesis.

☐ (c) Includes a synopsis of the current state of knowledge about the topic.

Materials and methods:

☐ (a) Written clearly. Numbered points are appropriate at this level.

☐ (b) Describes the final methods that were used.

☐ (c) Includes details of the how data for the dependent variable were collected.

☐ (d) Includes details of how all other variables were manipulated, controlled, measured, or monitored.

☐ (e) If appropriate, it includes an explanatory diagram of the design of the experimental set-up.

☐ (f) Written in the past tense, and in the active voice (We investigated …) rather than the passive voice (An investigation was done …).

Results:

☐ (a) Includes the raw data (e.g. in a table).

☐ (b) Where necessary, the raw data have been averaged or transformed.

☐ (c) Includes graphs (where appropriate).

☐ (d) Each figure (table, graph, drawing, or photo) has a title and is numbered in a way that makes it possible to refer to it in the text (Fig. 1 etc.).

☐ (e) Written in the past tense and, where appropriate, in the active voice.

Discussion:

☐ (a) Includes an analysis of the data in which the findings, including trends and patterns, are discussed in relation to the biological concepts involved.

☐ (b) Includes an evaluation of sources of error, assumptions, and possible improvements to design.

Conclusion:

☐ (a) Written as a clear statement, which relates directly to the hypothesis.

Bibliography or References:

☐ (a) Lists all sources of information and assistance.

☐ (b) Does not include references that were not used.

Related activities: The Structure of a Report, Writing the Methods, Writing Your Results and Discussion, Citing and Listing References

A 3

Cell Structure

Learning Objectives

☐ 1. Compile your own glossary from the **KEY WORDS** displayed in **bold type** in the learning objectives below.

Features of Cells *(pages 57-70, 77-78)*

☐ 2. Recognise the contribution of microscopy to the development of **cell theory** and our present knowledge of cell structure. Recognise the **cell** as the basic unit of living things. Explain why cells are considered to be living entities and viruses are often not.

☐ 3. Use different units of measurement (mm, µm, nm) to express cell sizes and to describe a range of cell sizes.

☐ 4. Contrast the generalised structure of **prokaryote** and **eukaryote** cells and provide examples of each type.

☐ 5. Describe the structure of a **bacterial cell**, including the **bacterial cell wall** and the structures associated with it (**flagella**, pili), the **bacterial chromosome** and **plasmids**, and the plasma membrane. Identify which of these are unique to prokaryotes.

☐ 6. Describe and interpret drawings and photographs of typical **plant** and **animal cells** as seen using light and electron microscopy. Describe the role of the following:
- **nucleus, nuclear envelope, nucleolus**
- **mitochondria, chloroplasts** (if present),
- rough/smooth **endoplasmic reticulum, ribosomes**,
- **plasma membrane, cell wall** (if present)
- **Golgi apparatus, lysosomes, vacuoles** (if present),
- **cytoplasm, cytoskeleton** (of **microtubules**), **centrioles, cilia** (if present)

☐ 7. Identify which of the cellular structures in #6 would be visible under light microscopy, transmission electron microscopy, and scanning electron microscopy.

☐ 8. Outline the interrelationship between the organelles involved in the production and secretion of proteins.

☐ 9. Identify the differences between plant and animal cells, noting relative size and shape, and presence or absence of particular structures and organelles.

☐ 10. Describe the role of **cell fractionation** in separating cellular components. Explain how it is achieved through homogenisation of a sample followed by **ultracentrifugation**. Explain the role of speed of centrifugation in separating the cellular fractions.

Microscopy *(pages 73-76)*

☐ 11. Describe the basic structure of **optical** and **electron microscopes**. With respect to these, explain and distinguish between **magnification** and **resolution**.

☐ 12. Distinguish between TEM (**transmission electron microscopy**) and SEM (**scanning electron microscopy**). Recognise EM as an important tool in investigating cell structure and function.

☐ 13. Distinguish between **compound** and **stereo light microscopes**. Identify the situations in which these different microscopes would be used.

☐ 14. Demonstrate an ability to correctly use a light microscope to locate material and focus images. Identify the steps required for preparing a **temporary mount** for viewing with a compound light microscope. Understand why **stains** are useful in the preparation of specimens. If required, use simple **staining techniques** to show specific features of cells.

 See the 'Textbook Reference Grid' on page 7 for textbook page references relating to material in this topic.

Supplementary Texts
See pages 5-6 for additional details of these texts:
■ Adds, J., *et al.*, 2003. **Molecules and Cells**, (NelsonThornes), chpt. 4.

 **Presentation MEDIA** to support this topic: **CELL BIO & BIOCHEM** Cell Structure

See page 6 for details of publishers of periodicals:

STUDENT'S REFERENCE
■ **The Beat Goes On: Cilia and Flagella** Biol. Sci. Rev., 18(4) April 2006, pp. 2-6. *The structure and function of cilia and flagella.*

■ **Border Control** New Scientist, 15 July 2000 (Inside Science). *The role of the plasma membrane in cell function: membrane structure and transport, and the role of membrane receptors.*

■ **Lysosomes: The Cell's Recycling Centres** Biol. Sci. Rev., 17(2) Nov. 2004, pp. 21-23. *The nature and role of lysosomes: small membrane-bound organelles found in all eukaryotic cells.*

■ **Lysosomes and their Versatile and Potentially Fatal Membranes** Biol. Sci. Rev., 17(3) Feb. 2005, pp. 14-16. *The critical importance of the lysosome membrane.*

■ **Light Microscopy** Biol. Sci. Rev., 13(1) Sept. 2000, pp. 36-38. *An excellent account of the basis and various techniques of light microscopy.*

■ **Transmission Electron Microscopy** Biol. Sci. Rev., 13(2) Nov. 2000, pp. 32-35. *The techniques and applications of TEM. Includes a diagram comparing features of TEM and light microscopy.*

■ **Scanning Electron Microscopy** Biol. Sci. Rev., 20(1) Sept. 2007, pp. 38-41. *An excellent account of the techniques and applications of SEM. Includes details of specimen preparation and recent advancements in the technology.*

See pages 8-9 for details of how to access **Bio Links** from our web site: **www.biozone.co.uk**. From Bio Links, access sites under the topics:

CELL BIOLOGY AND BIOCHEMISTRY: • Cell and molecular biology online • Cell structure and function web links > **Microscopy:** • A guide to microscopy and microanalysis • Biological applications of electron and light microscopy • Microscopy UK • Scanning Electron Microscope ... *and others* > **Cell Structure and Transport:** • Animal cells • CELLS alive! • Cell breakage and fractionation • Nanoworld ... *and others*

The Cell Theory

The idea that all living things are composed of cells developed over many years and is strongly linked to the invention and refinement of the microscope. Early microscopes in the 1600s (such as Leeuwenhoek's below) opened up a whole new field of biology; the study of cell biology and microorganisms. The cell theory is a fundamental idea of biology.

Early Microscopes

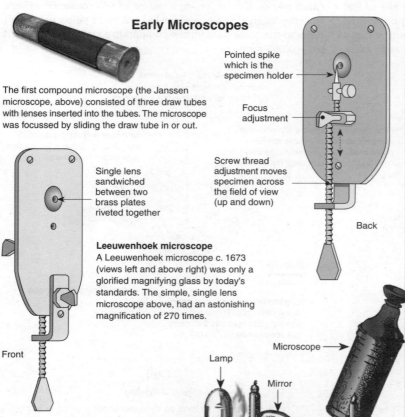

The first compound microscope (the Janssen microscope, above) consisted of three draw tubes with lenses inserted into the tubes. The microscope was focussed by sliding the draw tube in or out.

Single lens sandwiched between two brass plates riveted together

Leeuwenhoek microscope
A Leeuwenhoek microscope c. 1673 (views left and above right) was only a glorified magnifying glass by today's standards. The simple, single lens microscope above, had an astonishing magnification of 270 times.

Front

Pointed spike which is the specimen holder

Focus adjustment

Screw thread adjustment moves specimen across the field of view (up and down)

Back

Robert Hooke c. 1665
Hooke was fascinated by microscopy, and in his book *Micrographia* (1665) he described the use of the compound microscope that he had devised (**right**). He was the first to coin the name cell after he observed the angular spaces that he saw in a thin section of cork.

Microscope

Lamp

Mirror

Milestones in Cell Biology

1500s	Convex lenses with a magnification greater than x5 became available.
1595	Zacharias Janssen of Holland has been credited with the first compound microscope (more than one lens).
Early 1600s	First compound microscopes used in Europe (used two convex lenses to make objects look larger). Suffered badly from colour distortion; an effect called 'spherical aberration'.
1632-1723	**Antoni van Leeuwenhoek** of Holland produced over 500 single lens microscopes, discovering bacteria, human blood cells, spermatozoa, and protozoa. Friend of Robert Hooke.
1661	**Marcello Malpighi** used lenses to study insects. Discovered capillaries and may have described cells in writing of 'globules' and 'saccules'.
1662	**Robert Hooke** of England used the term 'cell' in describing the microscopic structure of cork. He believed that the cell walls were the important part of otherwise empty structures. Published *Micrographia* in 1665.
1672	**Nehemlah Grew** wrote the first of two well-illustrated books on the microscopic anatomy of plants.
1838-1839	Botanist **Matthias Schleiden** and zoologist **Theodor Schwann** proposed the cell theory based on their observations of plant and animal cells.
1855	**Rudolph Virchow** extended the cell theory by stating that "new cells are formed only by the division of previously existing cells".
1880	**August Weismann** added to Virchow's idea by pointing out that "all the cells living today can trace their ancestry back to ancient times", thus making the link between cell theory and evolution.

The Cell Theory

The idea that cells are fundamental units of life is part of the cell theory. The basic principles of the theory (as developed by early biologists) are:

▶ All living things are composed of cells and cell products.

▶ New cells are formed only by the division of preexisting cells.

▶ The cell contains inherited information (genes) that are used as instructions for growth, functioning, and development.

▶ The cell is the functioning unit of life; the chemical reactions of life take place within cells.

Cell Structure

1. Briefly describe the impact the invention of microscopes has had on biology: _____

_____

_____

2. Before the development of the cell theory, it was commonly believed that living organisms could arise by spontaneous generation. Explain what this term means and why it has been discredited as a theory:

_____

_____

_____

Related activities: Optical Microscopes, Electron Microscopes

A 1

Characteristics of Life

With each step in the hierarchy of biological order, new properties emerge that were not present at simpler levels of organisation. Life itself is associated with numerous **emergent properties**, including **metabolism** and growth. The cell is the site of life; it is the functioning unit structure from which living organisms are made. Viruses and cells are profoundly different. Viruses are non-cellular, lack the complex structures found in cells, and show only some of the properties we associate with living things. The traditional view of viruses is as a minimal particle, although the identification in 2004 of a new family of viruses, called mimiviruses, is forcing a rethink of this conservative view. Note the different scale to which the examples below are drawn. Refer to the scale bars for the comparative sizes (1000 nm = 1 µm = 0.001 mm).

Although some viruses may contain an **enzyme**, it is incapable of working until it is inside a host cell's cytoplasm.

Single or double stranded molecule of **RNA** or **DNA**.

A **protein coat** surrounds the viral genetic material and enzyme (if present). There is no cellular membrane.

50 nm
Scale

No metabolism: The absence of cytoplasm means that a virus can not carry out any chemical reactions on its own; it is dependent upon parasitising a cell and using the cell's own machinery.

Metabolism: The total of all the chemical reactions occurring in the cell. Many take place in the cytoplasm.

The genetic material is composed of **chromosomes** of double-stranded DNA molecules. In eukaryotes they are enclosed in a nuclear membrane.

All cell types contain **cytoplasm**; the liquid 'soup' of nutrients, enzymes and the products of metabolism. Eukaryotes contain membrane-bound organelles.

100 000 nm
Scale

Organelles are present in most eukaryotic cells. These are specialised structures that carry out specific roles in the cell.

Plasma membrane

Virus
(e.g. HIV)

Viruses cannot become active outside a living host cell. They simply exist as inert virus particles called **virions**. Only when they invade a cell and take over the cell's metabolic machinery, can the virus carry out its 'living programme'.

Cell
(e.g. Amoeba)

Cells remain alive so long as their metabolic reactions in the cytoplasm are maintained. With a few rare exceptions (that involve freezing certain types of cells) if metabolism is halted, the cell dies.

1. Identify three features that all cells have in common: _____

    _____

2. Describe how cells differ from viruses in the following aspects:

    (a) Size: _____

    _____

    (b) Metabolism: _____

    _____

    (c) Organelles: _____

    _____

    (d) Genetic material: _____

    _____

    (e) Life cycle: _____

    _____

3. Explain why multicellular organisms are said to show emergent properties: _____

    _____

    _____

© Biozone International 2008
Photocopying Prohibited

Related activities: Types of Living Things

Types of Living Things

Living things are called organisms and **cells** are the functioning unit structure from which organisms are made. Under the five kingdom system, cells can be divided into two basic kinds: the **prokaryotes**, which are simple cells without a distinct, membrane-bound nucleus, and the more complex **eukaryotes**. The eukaryotes can be further organised into broad groups according to their basic cell type: the protoctists, fungi, plants, and animals. Viruses are non-cellular and have no cellular machinery of their own. All cells must secure a source of energy if they are to survive and carry out metabolic processes. **Autotrophs** can meet their energy requirements using light or chemical energy from the physical environment. Other types of cell, called **heterotrophs**, obtain their energy from other living organisms or their dead remains.

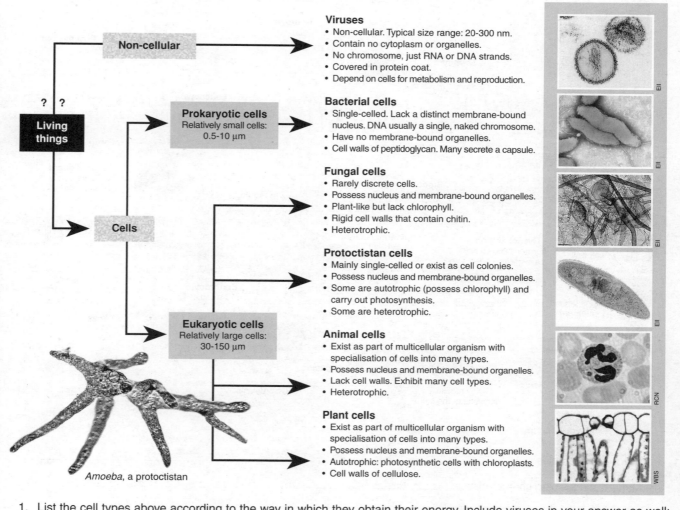

Viruses
• Non-cellular. Typical size range: 20-300 nm.
• Contain no cytoplasm or organelles.
• No chromosome, just RNA or DNA strands.
• Covered in protein coat.
• Depend on cells for metabolism and reproduction.

Bacterial cells
• Single-celled. Lack a distinct membrane-bound nucleus. DNA usually a single, naked chromosome.
• Have no membrane-bound organelles.
• Cell walls of peptidoglycan. Many secrete a capsule.

Fungal cells
• Rarely discrete cells.
• Possess nucleus and membrane-bound organelles.
• Plant-like but lack chlorophyll.
• Rigid cell walls that contain chitin.
• Heterotrophic.

Protoctistan cells
• Mainly single-celled or exist as cell colonies.
• Possess nucleus and membrane-bound organelles.
• Some are autotrophic (possess chlorophyll) and carry out photosynthesis.
• Some are heterotrophic.

Animal cells
• Exist as part of multicellular organism with specialisation of cells into many types.
• Possess nucleus and membrane-bound organelles.
• Lack cell walls. Exhibit many cell types.
• Heterotrophic.

Plant cells
• Exist as part of multicellular organism with specialisation of cells into many types.
• Possess nucleus and membrane-bound organelles.
• Autotrophic: photosynthetic cells with chloroplasts.
• Cell walls of cellulose.

Amoeba, a protoctistan

Cell Structure

1. List the cell types above according to the way in which they obtain their energy. Include viruses in your answer as well:

   (a) Autotrophic: _____

   (b) Heterotrophic: _____

2. Consult the diagram above and determine the two main features distinguishing **eukaryotic** cells from **prokaryotic** cells:

   (a) _____

   (b) _____

3. (a) Suggest why fungi were once classified as belonging to the plant kingdom: _____

   _____

   (b) Explain why, in terms of the distinguishing features of fungi, this classification was erroneous: _____

   _____

   _____

4. Suggest why the Protoctista have traditionally been a difficult group to classify: _____

   _____

Related activities: Plant Cells, Animal Cells, Unicellular Eukaryotes, Cell Sizes, Prokaryotic Cells

A 1

Types of Cells

Cells come in a wide range of types and forms. The diagram below shows a selection of cell types from the five kingdoms. The variety that results from specialisation of undifferentiated cells is enormous. In the following exercise, identify which of the cell types belongs to each of the kingdoms and list the major distinguishing characteristics of their cells.

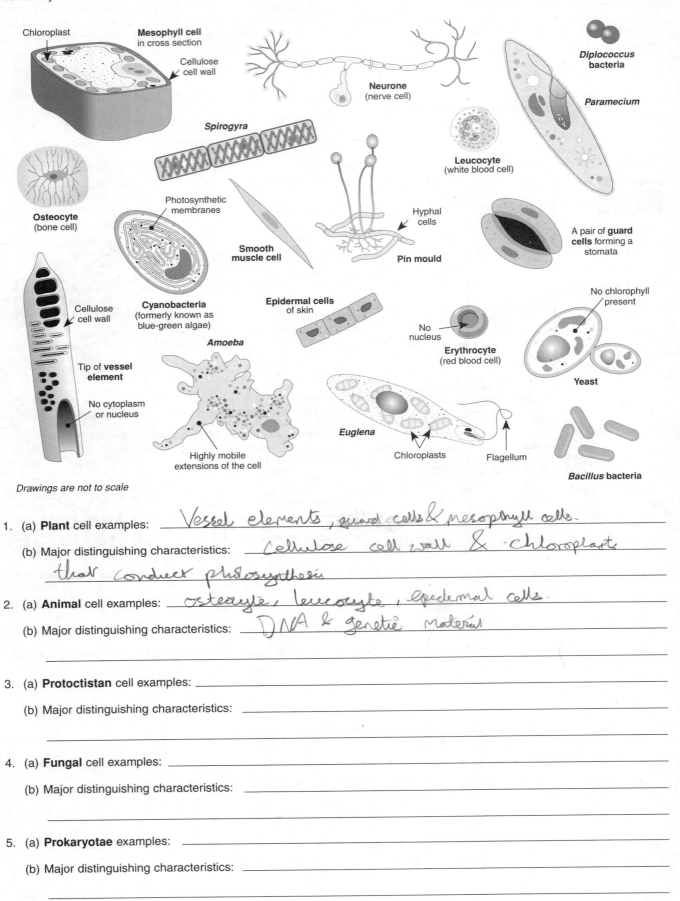

Chloroplast

Mesophyll cell in cross section

Cellulose cell wall

Neurone (nerve cell)

Diplococcus bacteria

Paramecium

Spirogyra

Leucocyte (white blood cell)

Osteocyte (bone cell)

Photosynthetic membranes

Smooth muscle cell

Hyphal cells

Pin mould

A pair of **guard cells** forming a stomata

Cellulose cell wall

Cyanobacteria (formerly known as blue-green algae)

Tip of **vessel element**

No cytoplasm or nucleus

Epidermal cells of skin

Amoeba

Highly mobile extensions of the cell

No nucleus

Erythrocyte (red blood cell)

No chlorophyll present

Yeast

Euglena

Chloroplasts

Flagellum

Bacillus bacteria

Drawings are not to scale

1. (a) **Plant** cell examples: _Vessel elements, guard cells & mesophyll cells._

   (b) Major distinguishing characteristics: _Cellulose cell wall & chloroplast that conduct photosynthesis_

2. (a) **Animal** cell examples: _osteocyte, leucocyte, epidermal cells._

   (b) Major distinguishing characteristics: _DNA & genetic material_

3. (a) **Protoctistan** cell examples: _____

   (b) Major distinguishing characteristics: _____

4. (a) **Fungal** cell examples: _____

   (b) Major distinguishing characteristics: _____

5. (a) **Prokaryotae** examples: _____

   (b) Major distinguishing characteristics: _____

Related activities: Plant Cells, Animal Cells, Unicellular Eukaryotes, Prokaryotic Cells

Cell Sizes

Cells are extremely small and can only be seen properly when viewed through the magnifying lenses of a microscope. The diagrams below show a variety of cell types, together with a virus and a microscopic animal for comparison. For each of these images, note the scale and relate this to the type of microscopy used.

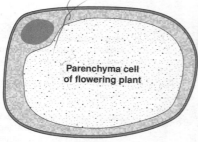

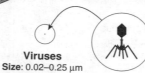

Parenchyma cell of flowering plant

Human white blood cell

Eukaryotic cells
(e.g. plant and animal cells)
Size: 10–100 µm diameter. Cellular organelles may be up to 10 µm.

Prokaryotic cells
Size: Typically 2–10 µm length, 0.2–2 µm diameter. Upper limit, 30 µm long.

Viruses
Size: 0.02–0.25 µm (20–250 nm)

Units of length (International System)

Unit	Metres	Equivalent
1 metre (m)	1 m	= 1000 millimetres
1 millimetre (mm)	10^{-3} m	= 1000 micrometres
1 micrometre (µm)	10^{-6} m	= 1000 nanometres
1 nanometre (nm)	10^{-9} m	= 1000 picometres

Micrometres are sometime referred to as **microns**. Smaller structures are usually measured in nanometres (nm) e.g. molecules (1 nm) and plasma membrane thickness (10 nm).

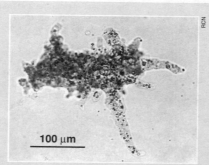

100 µm

An **Amoeba** showing extensions of the cytoplasm called pseudopodia. This protoctist changes its shape, exploring its environment.

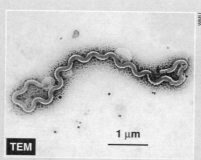

TEM   1 µm

A long thin cell of the spirochete bacterium **Leptospira pomona**, which causes the disease leptospirosis.

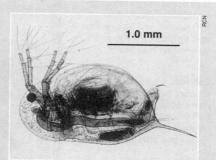

1.0 mm

Daphnia showing its internal organs. These freshwater microcrustaceans are part of the zooplankton found in lakes and ponds.

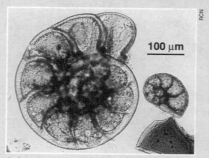

100 µm

A **foraminiferan** showing its chambered, calcified shell. These single-celled protozoans are marine planktonic amoebae.

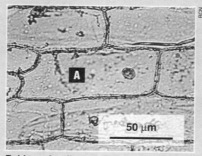

A   50 µm

Epidermal cells (skin) from an onion bulb showing the nucleus, cell walls and cytoplasm. Organelles are not visible at this resolution.

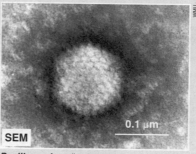

SEM   0.1 µm

Papillomavirus (human wart virus) showing its polyhedral protein coat (20 triangular faces, 12 corners) made of ball-shaped structures.

Cell Structure

1. Using the measurement scales provided on each of the photographs above, determine the longest dimension (length or diameter) of the cell/animal/virus in µm and mm (choose the cell marked **A** for epidermal cells):

   (a) *Amoeba*: _____ µm _____ mm   (d) Epidermis: _____ µm _____ mm

   (b) Foraminiferan: _____ µm _____ mm   (e) *Daphnia*: _____ µm _____ mm

   (c) *Leptospira*: _____ µm _____ mm   (f) *Papillomavirus*: _____ µm _____ mm

2. List these six organisms in order of size, from the smallest to the largest: _____
   _____

3. Study the scale of your ruler and state which of these six organisms you would be able to see with your unaided eye:
   _____

4. Calculate the equivalent length in millimetres (mm) of the following measurements:

   (a) 0.25 µm: _____   (b) 450 µm: _____   (c) 200 nm: _____

Related activities: Optical Microscopes, Electron Microscopes

DA 2

Plant Cells

Plant cells are enclosed in a cellulose cell wall. The cell wall protects the cell, maintains its shape, and prevents excessive water uptake. It does not interfere with the passage of materials into and out of the cell. The diagram below shows the structure and function of a typical plant cell and its organelles.

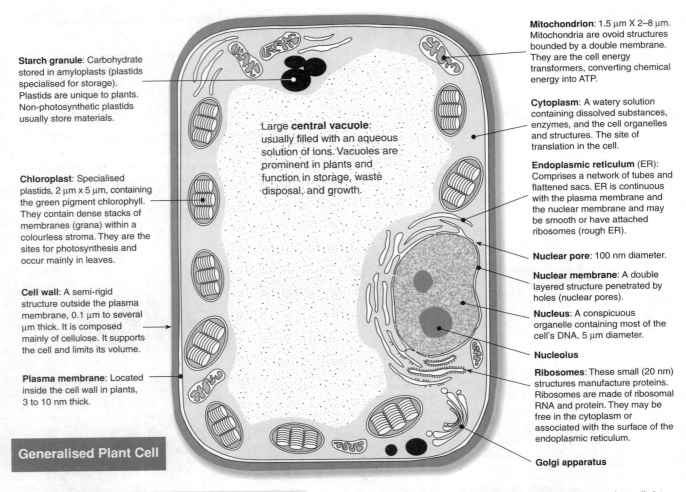

Starch granule: Carbohydrate stored in amyloplasts (plastids specialised for storage). Plastids are unique to plants. Non-photosynthetic plastids usually store materials.

Chloroplast: Specialised plastids, 2 µm x 5 µm, containing the green pigment chlorophyll. They contain dense stacks of membranes (grana) within a colourless stroma. They are the sites for photosynthesis and occur mainly in leaves.

Cell wall: A semi-rigid structure outside the plasma membrane, 0.1 µm to several µm thick. It is composed mainly of cellulose. It supports the cell and limits its volume.

Plasma membrane: Located inside the cell wall in plants, 3 to 10 nm thick.

Large **central vacuole**: usually filled with an aqueous solution of ions. Vacuoles are prominent in plants and function in storage, waste disposal, and growth.

Mitochondrion: 1.5 µm X 2–8 µm. Mitochondria are ovoid structures bounded by a double membrane. They are the cell energy transformers, converting chemical energy into ATP.

Cytoplasm: A watery solution containing dissolved substances, enzymes, and the cell organelles and structures. The site of translation in the cell.

Endoplasmic reticulum (ER): Comprises a network of tubes and flattened sacs. ER is continuous with the plasma membrane and the nuclear membrane and may be smooth or have attached ribosomes (rough ER).

Nuclear pore: 100 nm diameter.

Nuclear membrane: A double layered structure penetrated by holes (nuclear pores).

Nucleus: A conspicuous organelle containing most of the cell's DNA, 5 µm diameter.

Nucleolus

Ribosomes: These small (20 nm) structures manufacture proteins. Ribosomes are made of ribosomal RNA and protein. They may be free in the cytoplasm or associated with the surface of the endoplasmic reticulum.

Golgi apparatus

Generalised Plant Cell

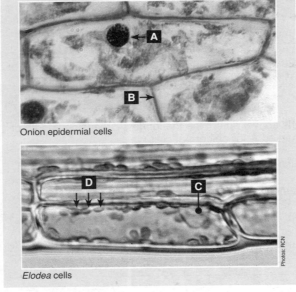

Onion epidermial cells

Elodea cells

Photos: RCN

1. The two photographs (left) show plant cells as seen by a light microscope. Identify the basic features labelled **A-D**:

   A: _Nucleus_

   B: _Cellulose cell wall._

   C: _Cytoplasm._

   D: _Chloroplasts._

2. Cytoplasmic streaming is a feature of eukaryotic cells, often clearly visible with a light microscope in plant (and algal) cells.

   (a) Explain what is meant by cytoplasmic streaming:

   _____

   _____

   (b) For the *Elodea* cell (lower, left), draw arrows to indicate cytoplasmic streaming movements.

3. Describe three structures/organelles present in generalised plant cells but absent from animal cells (also see page 98):

   (a) _____

   (b) _____

   (c) _____

Related activities: Animal Cells, Cell Structure and Organelles, Plant Cells Specialisation   **Web links**: Review of Eukaryotic Cells

Animal Cells

Animal cells, unlike plant cells, do not have a regular shape. In fact, some animal cells (such as phagocytes) are able to alter their shape for various purposes (e.g. engulfment of foreign material). The diagram below shows the structure and function of a typical animal cell and its organelles. Note the differences between this cell and the generalised plant cell.

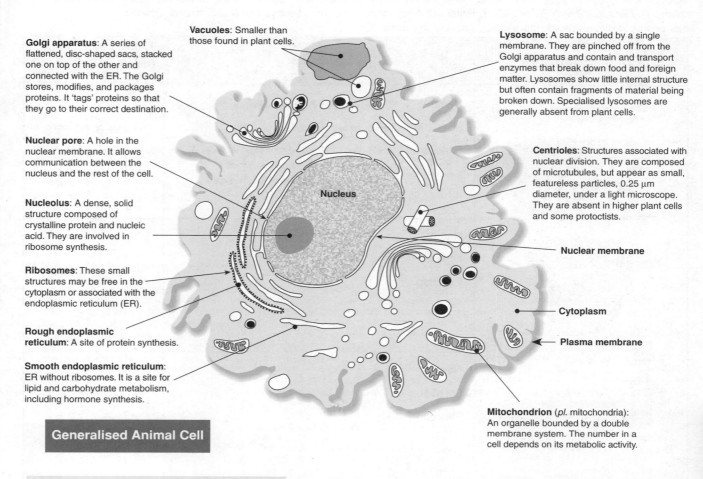

Golgi apparatus: A series of flattened, disc-shaped sacs, stacked one on top of the other and connected with the ER. The Golgi stores, modifies, and packages proteins. It 'tags' proteins so that they go to their correct destination.

Nuclear pore: A hole in the nuclear membrane. It allows communication between the nucleus and the rest of the cell.

Nucleolus: A dense, solid structure composed of crystalline protein and nucleic acid. They are involved in ribosome synthesis.

Ribosomes: These small structures may be free in the cytoplasm or associated with the endoplasmic reticulum (ER).

Rough endoplasmic reticulum: A site of protein synthesis.

Smooth endoplasmic reticulum: ER without ribosomes. It is a site for lipid and carbohydrate metabolism, including hormone synthesis.

Vacuoles: Smaller than those found in plant cells.

Nucleus

Lysosome: A sac bounded by a single membrane. They are pinched off from the Golgi apparatus and contain and transport enzymes that break down food and foreign matter. Lysosomes show little internal structure but often contain fragments of material being broken down. Specialised lysosomes are generally absent from plant cells.

Centrioles: Structures associated with nuclear division. They are composed of microtubules, but appear as small, featureless particles, 0.25 µm diameter, under a light microscope. They are absent in higher plant cells and some protoctists.

Nuclear membrane

Cytoplasm

Plasma membrane

Mitochondrion (*pl.* mitochondria): An organelle bounded by a double membrane system. The number in a cell depends on its metabolic activity.

Generalised Animal Cell

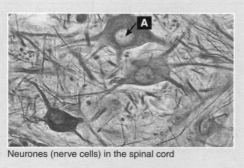

Neurones (nerve cells) in the spinal cord

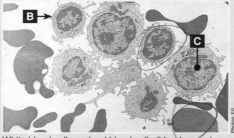

White blood cells and red blood cells (blood smear)

Photos: EII

1. The two photomicrographs (left) show several types of animal cells. Identify the features indicated by the letters **A-C**:

   A: _Nucleus_

   B: _Cytoplasm_

   C: _Plasma membrane._

2. White blood cells are mobile, phagocytic cells, whereas red blood cells are smaller than white blood cells and, in humans, lack a nucleus.

   (a) In the photomicrograph (below, left), circle a white blood cell and a red blood cell:

   (b) With respect to the features that you can see, explain how you made your decision.

   _____

   _____

   _____

   _____

3. Name and describe one structure or organelle present in generalised animal cells but absent from plant cells:

   _____

   _____

Related activities: Plant Cells, Cell Structure and Organelles, Human Cell Specialisation **Web links**: Review of Eukaryotic Cells

RA 2

Cell Structures and Organelles

The table below provides a format to summarise information about structures and organelles of typical eukaryotic cells. Complete the table using the list provided and by referring to a textbook and to other pages in this topic. Fill in the final three columns by writing either 'YES' or 'NO'. The first cell component has been completed for you as a guide and the log scale of measurements (top of next page) illustrates the relative sizes of some cellular structures. **List of structures and organelles**: cell wall, mitochondrion, chloroplast, cell junctions, centrioles, ribosome, flagella, endoplasmic reticulum, Golgi apparatus, nucleus, flagella, cytoskeleton and vacuoles.

Cell Component	Details	Present in Plant cells	Present in Animal cells	Visible under light microscope
(a) Double layer of phospholipids (called the lipid bilayer), Proteins	Name: Plasma (cell surface) membrane Location: Surrounding the cell Function: Gives the cell shape and protection. It also regulates the movement of substances into and out of the cell.	YES	YES	YES (but not at the level of detail shown in the diagram)
(b)	Name: Enzyme? Location: Function:			
(c) Outer membrane, Inner membrane, Matrix, Cristae	Name: Mitochondrion Location: In cytoplasm Function: Cell energy converts Chemical energy → ATP.	Y	Y	Y
(d) Secretory vesicles budding off, Cisternae, Transfer vesicles from the smooth endoplasmic reticulum	Name: Golgi Apparatus Location: Cytoplasm Function: Stores, modifies & packages proteins. Tags them so they go correctly.	Y	Y	Y
(e) Ribosomes, Transport pathway, Rough, Smooth, Vesicles budding off, Flattened membrane sacs	Name: Endoplasmic reticulum. Location: Attached to nucleus. Function: Synthesises proteins.	Y	Y	Y
(f) Grana comprise stacks of thylakoids, Stroma, Lamellae	Name: Chloroplast Location: Cytoplasm Function: Site of photosynthesis	Y	N	Y no detail

64

RA 2

Related Activities: Plant Cells, Animal Cells, Unicellular Eukaryotes
Web links: Eukaryotic Cells Interactive Animation

© Biozone International 2008
Photocopying Prohibited

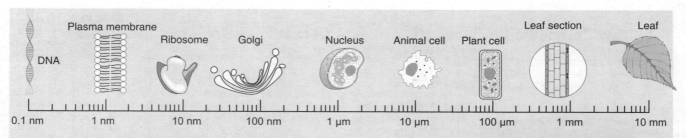

Cell Component	Details	Present in		Visible under light microscope
		Plant cells	Animal cells	
(g)	Name: Lysosome and food vacuole Location: Function:			
(h)	Name: Location: Function:			
(i)	Name: Location: Function:			
(j)	Name: Cilia and flagella (some eukaryotic cells) Location: Function:			

Cell Structure

Cell Component	Details	Present in		Visible under light microscope
		Plant cells	Animal cells	
(k)	Name: Location: Function:			
(l)	Name: Cellulose cell wall Location: Function:			
(m)	Name: Cell junctions Location: Function:			

Differential Centrifugation

Differential centrifugation (also called cell fractionation) is a technique used to extract organelles from cells so that they can be studied. The aim is to extract undamaged intact organelles. Samples must be kept very cool so that metabolism is slowed and self digestion of the organelles is prevented. The samples must also be kept in a buffered, isotonic solution so that the organelles do not change volume and the enzymes are not denatured by changes in pH.

Differential Centrifugation

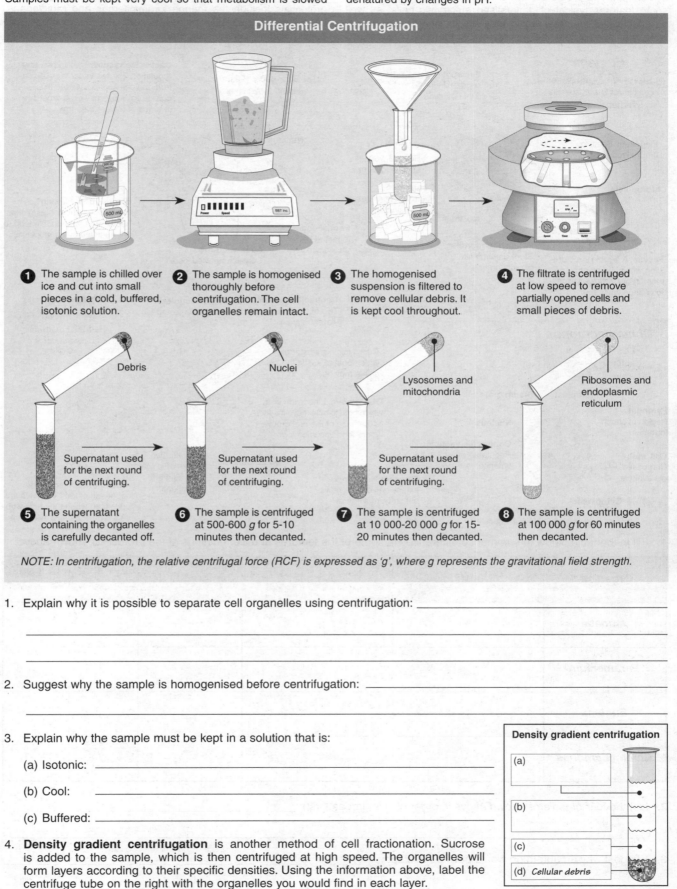

1. The sample is chilled over ice and cut into small pieces in a cold, buffered, isotonic solution.

2. The sample is homogenised thoroughly before centrifugation. The cell organelles remain intact.

3. The homogenised suspension is filtered to remove cellular debris. It is kept cool throughout.

4. The filtrate is centrifuged at low speed to remove partially opened cells and small pieces of debris.

Debris

Supernatant used for the next round of centrifuging.

Nuclei

Supernatant used for the next round of centrifuging.

Lysosomes and mitochondria

Supernatant used for the next round of centrifuging.

Ribosomes and endoplasmic reticulum

5. The supernatant containing the organelles is carefully decanted off.

6. The sample is centrifuged at 500-600 g for 5-10 minutes then decanted.

7. The sample is centrifuged at 10 000-20 000 g for 15-20 minutes then decanted.

8. The sample is centrifuged at 100 000 g for 60 minutes then decanted.

NOTE: In centrifugation, the relative centrifugal force (RCF) is expressed as 'g', where g represents the gravitational field strength.

Cell Structure

1. Explain why it is possible to separate cell organelles using centrifugation: _____

_____

_____

2. Suggest why the sample is homogenised before centrifugation: _____

_____

3. Explain why the sample must be kept in a solution that is:

(a) Isotonic: _____

(b) Cool: _____

(c) Buffered: _____

4. **Density gradient centrifugation** is another method of cell fractionation. Sucrose is added to the sample, which is then centrifuged at high speed. The organelles will form layers according to their specific densities. Using the information above, label the centrifuge tube on the right with the organelles you would find in each layer.

Density gradient centrifugation

(a)

(b)

(c)

(d) *Cellular debris*

Related activities: Enzyme Reaction Rates

EA 1

Unicellular Eukaryotes

Unicellular (single-celled) eukaryotes comprise the majority of the diverse kingdom, Protoctista. They are found almost anywhere there is water, including within larger organisms (as parasites or symbionts). The protoctists are a very diverse group, exhibiting some features typical of generalised eukaryotic cells, as well as specialised features, which may be specific to one genus. Note that even within the genera below there is considerable variation in size and appearance. *Amoeba* and *Paramecium* are both **heterotrophic**, ingesting food, which accumulates inside a **vacuole**. *Euglena* and *Chlamydomonas* are autotrophic algae, although *Euglena* is heterotrophic when deprived of light. Other protoctists include the marine foraminiferans and radiolarians, specialised intracellular parasites such as *Plasmodium*, and zooflagellates such as the parasites *Trypanosoma* and *Giardia*.

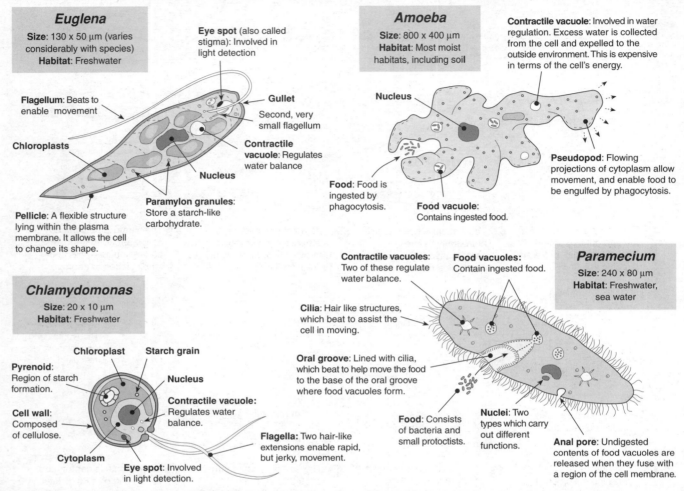

Euglena
Size: 130 x 50 µm (varies considerably with species)
Habitat: Freshwater

Eye spot (also called stigma): Involved in light detection

Flagellum: Beats to enable movement

Chloroplasts

Gullet
Second, very small flagellum

Contractile vacuole: Regulates water balance

Nucleus

Paramylon granules: Store a starch-like carbohydrate.

Pellicle: A flexible structure lying within the plasma membrane. It allows the cell to change its shape.

Amoeba
Size: 800 x 400 µm
Habitat: Most moist habitats, including soil

Contractile vacuole: Involved in water regulation. Excess water is collected from the cell and expelled to the outside environment. This is expensive in terms of the cell's energy.

Nucleus

Pseudopod: Flowing projections of cytoplasm allow movement, and enable food to be engulfed by phagocytosis.

Food: Food is ingested by phagocytosis.

Food vacuole: Contains ingested food.

Chlamydomonas
Size: 20 x 10 µm
Habitat: Freshwater

Chloroplast   **Starch grain**

Pyrenoid: Region of starch formation.

Nucleus

Cell wall: Composed of cellulose.

Contractile vacuole: Regulates water balance.

Cytoplasm

Eye spot: Involved in light detection.

Flagella: Two hair-like extensions enable rapid, but jerky, movement.

Contractile vacuoles: Two of these regulate water balance.

Food vacuoles: Contain ingested food.

Paramecium
Size: 240 x 80 µm
Habitat: Freshwater, sea water

Cilia: Hair like structures, which beat to assist the cell in moving.

Oral groove: Lined with cilia, which beat to help move the food to the base of the oral groove where food vacuoles form.

Food: Consists of bacteria and small protoctists.

Nuclei: Two types which carry out different functions.

Anal pore: Undigested contents of food vacuoles are released when they fuse with a region of the cell membrane.

1. Fill in the table below to summarise differences in some of the features and life functions of the protoctists shown above:

Organism	Nutrition	Movement	Osmoregulation	Eye spot present / absent	Cell wall present / absent
Amoeba					
Paramecium					
Euglena					
Chlamydomonas					

2. List the four organisms shown above in order of size (largest first): _____

_____

3. Suggest why an autotroph would have an eye spot: _____

_____

Prokaryotic Cells

Bacterial (prokaryotic) cells are much smaller and simpler than the cells of eukaryotes. They lack many eukaryotic features (e.g. a distinct nucleus and membrane-bound cellular organelles). The bacterial cell wall is an important feature. It is a complex, multi-layered structure and often has a role in virulence. These pages illustrate some features of bacterial structure and diversity.

Structure of a Generalised Bacterial Cell

Plasmids: Small, circular DNA molecules (accessory chromosomes) which can reproduce independently of the main chromosome. They can move between cells, and even between species, by **conjugation**. This property accounts for the transmission of antibiotic resistance between bacteria. Plasmids are also used as vectors in recombinant DNA technology.

Single, circular main chromosome: Makes them haploid for most genes. It is possible for some genes to be found on both the plasmid and chromosome and there may be several copies of a gene on a group of plasmids.

The cell lacks a nuclear membrane, so there is no distinct nucleus and the chromosomes are in direct contact with the cytoplasm. It is possible for free ribosomes to attach to mRNA while the mRNA is still in the process of being transcribed from the DNA.

Fimbriae: Hairlike structures that are shorter, straighter, and thinner than flagella. They are used for attachment, not movement. Pili are similar to fimbriae, but are longer and less numerous. They are involved in bacterial conjugation (below) and as phage receptors (opposite).

1 μm

Cytoplasm

Cell surface membrane: Similar in composition to eukaryotic membranes, although less rigid.

Glycocalyx. A viscous, gelatinous layer outside the cell wall. It is composed of polysaccharide and/or polypeptide. If it is firmly attached to the wall, it is called a **capsule**. If loosely attached, it is called a **slime layer**. Capsules may contribute to virulence in pathogenic species, e.g. by protecting the bacteria from the host's immune attack. In some species, the glycocalyx allows attachment to substrates.

Cell wall. A complex, semi-rigid structure that gives the cell shape, prevents rupture, and serves as an anchorage point for flagella. The cell wall is composed of a macromolecule called **peptidoglycan**; repeating disaccharides attached by polypeptides to form a lattice. The wall also contains varying amounts of lipopolysaccharides and lipoproteins. The amount of peptidoglycan present in the wall forms the basis of the diagnostic **gram stain**. In many species, the cell wall contributes to their virulence (disease-causing ability).

Flagellum (pl. flagella). Some bacteria have long, filamentous appendages, called flagella, that are used for locomotion. There may be a single polar flagellum (monotrichous), one or more flagella at each end of the cell, or the flagella may be distributed over the entire cell (peritrichous).

Cell Structure

Bacterial cell shapes

Most bacterial cells range between 0.20-2.0 μm in diameter and 2-10 μm length. Although they are a very diverse group, much of this diversity is in their metabolism. In terms of gross morphology, there are only a few basic shapes found (illustrated below). The way in which members of each group aggregate after division is often characteristic and is helpful in identifying certain species.

Bacilli
Rod-shaped

Bacilli: Rod-shaped bacteria that divide only across their short axis. Most occur as single rods, although pairs and chains are also found. The term bacillus can refer (as here) to shape. It may also denote a genus.

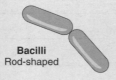

Cocci
Ball-shaped

Cocci: usually round, but sometimes oval or elongated. When they divide, the cells stay attached to each other and remain in aggregates e.g. pairs (diplococci) or clusters (staphylococci), that are usually a feature of the genus.

Spirilla
Spiral-shaped

Spirilla and vibrio: Bacteria with one or more twists. Spirilla bacteria have a helical (corkscrew) shape which may be rigid or flexible (as in spirochetes). Bacteria that look like curved rods (comma shaped) are called vibrios.

Bacterial conjugation

The two bacteria below are involved in conjugation: a one-way exchange of genetic information from a donor cell to a recipient cell. The plasmid, which must be of the 'conjugative' type, passes through a tube called a **sex pilus** to the other cell. Which is donor and which is recipient appears to be genetically determined. Conjugation should not be confused with sexual reproduction, as it does not involve the fusion of gametes or formation of a zygote.

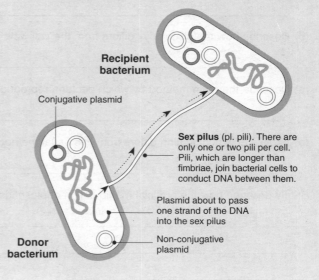

Recipient bacterium

Conjugative plasmid

Sex pilus (pl. pili). There are only one or two pili per cell. Pili, which are longer than fimbriae, join bacterial cells to conduct DNA between them.

Plasmid about to pass one strand of the DNA into the sex pilus

Non-conjugative plasmid

Donor bacterium

Related activities: Bacterial Diseases, Antimicrobial Drugs
Web links: Gram Stain Animation

RA 2

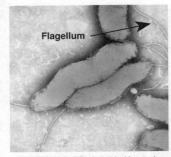

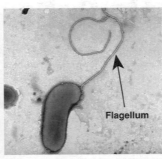

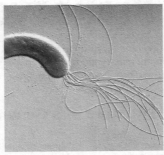

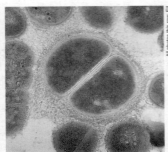

Campylobacter jejuni, a spiral bacterium responsible for foodborne intestinal disease. Note the single flagellum at each end (amphitrichous arrangement).

Helicobacter pylori, a comma-shaped vibrio bacterium that causes stomach ulcers in humans. This bacterium moves by means of multiple polar flagella.

A species of *Spirillum*, a spiral shaped bacterium with a tuft of polar flagella. Most of the species in this genus are harmless aquatic organisms.

Bacteria usually divide by binary fission. During this process, DNA is copied and the cell splits into two cells, as in these gram positive cocci.

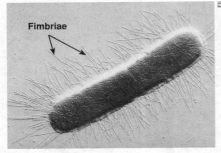

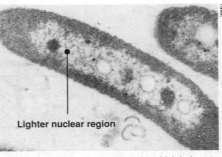

Escherichia coli, a common gut bacterium with **peritrichous** (around the entire cell) **fimbriae**. *E. coli* is a gram negative rod; it does not take up the gram stain but can be counter stained with safranin.

TEM showing *Enterobacter* bacteria, which belong to the family of gut bacteria commonly known as enterics. They are widely distributed in water, sewage, and soil. The family includes motile and non-motile species.

SEM of endospores of ***Bacillus anthracis*** bacteria, which cause the disease anthrax. These heat-resistant spores remain viable for many years and enable the bacteria to survive in a dormant state.

1. Describe three features distinguishing prokaryotic cells from eukaryotic cells:

   (a) _____

   (b) _____

   (c) _____

2. (a) Describe the function of flagella in bacteria: _____

   _____

   (b) Explain how fimbriae differ structurally and functionally from flagella: _____

   _____

   _____

3. (a) Describe the location and general composition of the bacterial cell wall: _____

   _____

   _____

   (b) Describe how the glycocalyx differs from the cell wall: _____

   _____

4. (a) Describe the main method by which bacteria reproduce: _____

   _____

   (b) Explain how conjugation differs from this usual method: _____

   _____

5. Briefly describe how the artificial manipulation of plasmids has been used for technological applications:

   _____

   _____

Production and Secretion of Proteins

Cells produce a range of organic polymers made up of repeating units of smaller molecules. The synthesis, packaging and movement of these **macromolecules** inside the cell involves a number of membrane bound organelles, as indicated below. These organelles provide compartments where the enzyme systems involved can be isolated. The example below shows a path for the modification of proteins after their production. After they pass into the interior of rough endoplasmic reticulum, some proteins may have carbohydrates added to them to form **glycoproteins**. Proteins may be further altered in the Golgi apparatus. The **Golgi apparatus** functions principally as a system for processing, sorting, and modifying proteins. Proteins that are to be secreted from the cell are synthesised by ribosomes on the rough endoplasmic reticulum and transported to the Golgi apparatus. At this stage, carbohydrates may be removed or added in a step-wise process. Other proteins may have fatty acids added to them to form **lipoproteins**. These modified proteins transport lipids in the plasma between various organs in the body (e.g. gut, liver, and adipose tissue).

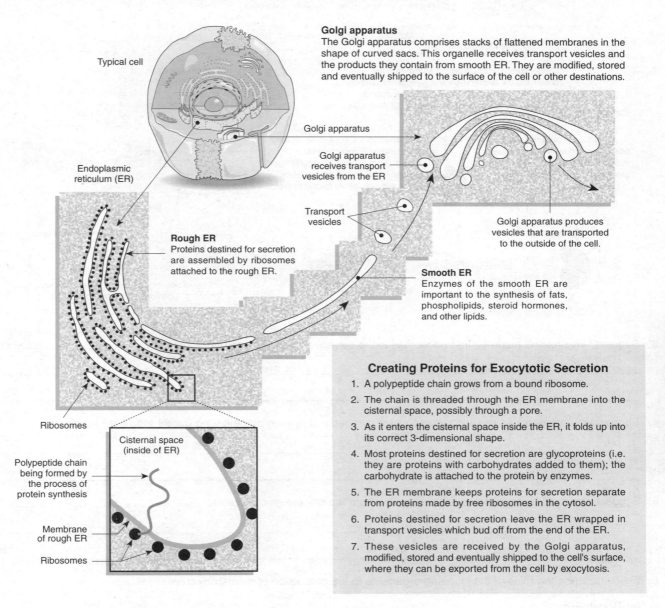

Golgi apparatus
The Golgi apparatus comprises stacks of flattened membranes in the shape of curved sacs. This organelle receives transport vesicles and the products they contain from smooth ER. They are modified, stored and eventually shipped to the surface of the cell or other destinations.

Typical cell

Endoplasmic reticulum (ER)

Golgi apparatus

Golgi apparatus receives transport vesicles from the ER

Transport vesicles

Golgi apparatus produces vesicles that are transported to the outside of the cell.

Rough ER
Proteins destined for secretion are assembled by ribosomes attached to the rough ER.

Smooth ER
Enzymes of the smooth ER are important to the synthesis of fats, phospholipids, steroid hormones, and other lipids.

Ribosomes

Cisternal space (inside of ER)

Polypeptide chain being formed by the process of protein synthesis

Membrane of rough ER

Ribosomes

Creating Proteins for Exocytotic Secretion

1. A polypeptide chain grows from a bound ribosome.
2. The chain is threaded through the ER membrane into the cisternal space, possibly through a pore.
3. As it enters the cisternal space inside the ER, it folds up into its correct 3-dimensional shape.
4. Most proteins destined for secretion are glycoproteins (i.e. they are proteins with carbohydrates added to them); the carbohydrate is attached to the protein by enzymes.
5. The ER membrane keeps proteins for secretion separate from proteins made by free ribosomes in the cytosol.
6. Proteins destined for secretion leave the ER wrapped in transport vesicles which bud off from the end of the ER.
7. These vesicles are received by the Golgi apparatus, modified, stored and eventually shipped to the cell's surface, where they can be exported from the cell by exocytosis.

Cell Structure

1. (a) Explain what a **glycoprotein** is: _____

   (b) Briefly describe the **roles** of glycoproteins: _____

   _____

2. (a) Explain what a **lipoprotein** is: _____

   (b) Briefly describe the **role** of lipoproteins: _____

   _____

   _____

Related activities: The Role of Membranes in Cells

RA 2

Possible Functions of Glycoproteins

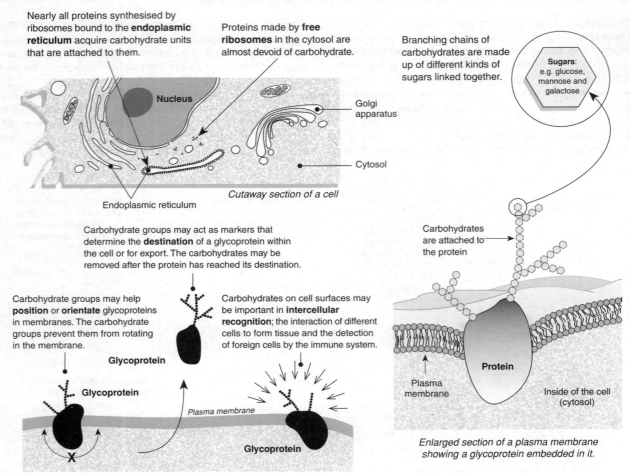

Nearly all proteins synthesised by ribosomes bound to the **endoplasmic reticulum** acquire carbohydrate units that are attached to them.

Proteins made by **free ribosomes** in the cytosol are almost devoid of carbohydrate.

Branching chains of carbohydrates are made up of different kinds of sugars linked together.

Sugars: e.g. glucose, mannose and galactose

Nucleus

Golgi apparatus

Cytosol

Cutaway section of a cell

Endoplasmic reticulum

Carbohydrate groups may act as markers that determine the **destination** of a glycoprotein within the cell or for export. The carbohydrates may be removed after the protein has reached its destination.

Carbohydrates are attached to the protein

Carbohydrate groups may help **position** or **orientate** glycoproteins in membranes. The carbohydrate groups prevent them from rotating in the membrane.

Carbohydrates on cell surfaces may be important in **intercellular recognition**; the interaction of different cells to form tissue and the detection of foreign cells by the immune system.

Glycoprotein

Glycoprotein

Plasma membrane

Glycoprotein

Protein

Plasma membrane

Inside of the cell (cytosol)

Enlarged section of a plasma membrane showing a glycoprotein embedded in it.

3. Suggest why proteins made by free ribosomes in the cytosol are usually free of carbohydrate: _____

_____

_____

4. Suggest why polypeptides requiring transport are synthesised by membrane-bound (rather than free) ribosomes:

_____

_____

5. Suggest why most proteins destined for secretion from the cell are glycoproteins: _____

_____

_____

6. Briefly describe the roles of the following organelles in the production of macromolecules:

(a) Rough ER: _____

(b) Smooth ER: _____

(c) Golgi apparatus: _____

(d) Transport vesicles: _____

7. Suggest why the orientation of a protein in the plasma membrane might be important: _____

_____

_____

_____

Optical Microscopes

The light microscope is one of the most important instruments used in biology practicals, and its correct use is a basic and essential skill of biology. High power light microscopes use a combination of lenses to magnify objects up to several hundred times. They are called **compound microscopes** because there are two or more separate lenses involved. A typical compound light microscope (bright field) is shown below (top photograph). The specimens viewed with these microscopes must be thin and mostly transparent. Light is focused up through the condenser and specimen; if the specimen is thick or opaque,

little or no detail will be visible. The microscope below has two eyepieces (**binocular**), although monocular microscopes, with a mirror rather than an internal light source, may still be encountered. Dissecting microscopes (lower photograph) are a type of binocular microscope used for observations at low total magnification (x4 to x50), where a large working distance between objective lenses and stage is required. A dissecting microscope has two separate lens systems, one for each eye. Such microscopes produce a 3-D view of the specimen and are sometimes called stereo microscopes for this reason.

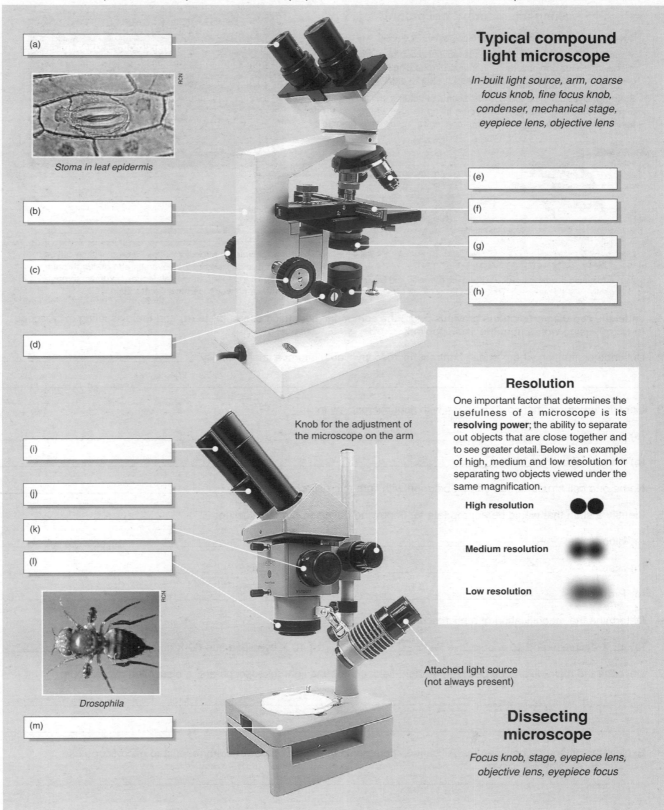

(a)

Stoma in leaf epidermis

(b)

(c)

(d)

(i)

(j)

(k)

(l)

Drosophila

(m)

Typical compound light microscope

In-built light source, arm, coarse focus knob, fine focus knob, condenser, mechanical stage, eyepiece lens, objective lens

(e)

(f)

(g)

(h)

Knob for the adjustment of the microscope on the arm

Resolution

One important factor that determines the usefulness of a microscope is its **resolving power**; the ability to separate out objects that are close together and to see greater detail. Below is an example of high, medium and low resolution for separating two objects viewed under the same magnification.

High resolution

Medium resolution

Low resolution

Attached light source (not always present)

Dissecting microscope

Focus knob, stage, eyepiece lens, objective lens, eyepiece focus

Cell Structure

Related Activities: Plant Cells, Animal Cells, Unicellular Eukaryotes

RDA 2

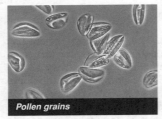

Pollen grains

Phase contrast illumination increases contrast of transparent specimens by producing interference effects.

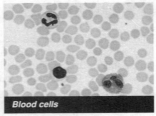

Blood cells

Leishman's stain is used to show red blood cells as red/pink, while staining the nucleus of white blood cells blue.

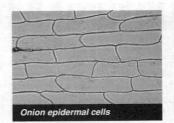

Onion epidermal cells

Standard **bright field** lighting shows cells with little detail; only cell walls, with the cell nuclei barely visible.

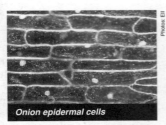

Onion epidermal cells

Dark field illumination is excellent for viewing near transparent specimens. The nucleus of each cell is visible.

Making a temporary wet mount

1. **Sectioning**: Very thin sections of fresh material are cut with a razorblade.

2. **Mounting**: The thin section(s) are placed in the centre of a clean glass microscope slide and covered with a drop of mounting liquid (e.g. water, glycerol or stain). A coverslip is placed on top to exclude air (below).

3. **Staining**: Dyes can be applied to stain some structures and leave others unaffected. The stains used in dyeing living tissues are called **vital stains** and they can be applied before or after the specimen is mounted.

Commonly used temporary stains

Stain	Final colour	Used for
Iodine solution	blue-black	Starch
Aniline sulfate	yellow	Lignin
Schultz's solution	blue	Starch
	blue or violet	Cellulose
	yellow	Protein, cutin, lignin, suberin
Methylene blue	blue	Nuclei

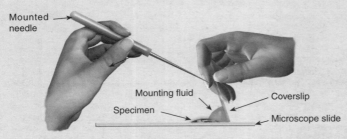

A mounted needle is used to support the coverslip and lower it gently over the specimen. This avoids including air in the mount.

Mounted needle

Mounting fluid

Specimen

Coverslip

Microscope slide

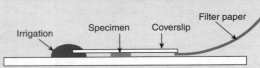

Irrigation — Specimen — Coverslip — Filter paper

If a specimen is already mounted, a drop of stain can be placed at one end of the coverslip and drawn through using filter paper (above). Water can be drawn through in the same way to remove excess stain.

1. Label the two diagrams on the previous page, the compound light microscope (a) to (h) and the dissecting microscope (i) to (m), using words from the lists supplied.

2. Describe a situation where phase contrast microscopy would improve image quality: _____
   _____

3. List two structures that could be seen with light microscopy in:

   (a) A plant cell: _____

   (b) An animal cell: _____

4. Name one cell structure that cannot be seen with light microscopy: _____

5. Identify a stain that would be appropriate for improving definition of the following:

   (a) Blood cells: _____   (d) Lignin: _____

   (b) Starch: _____   (e) Nuclei and DNA: _____

   (c) Protein: _____   (f) Cellulose: _____

6. Determine the magnification of a microscope using:

   (a) 15 X eyepiece and 40 X objective lens: _____   (b) 10 X eyepiece and 60 X objective lens: _____

7. Describe the main difference between a bright field, compound light microscope and a dissecting microscope:
   _____
   _____

8. Explain the difference between magnification and resolution (resolving power) with respect to microscope use:
   _____
   _____

Electron Microscopes

Electron microscopes (EMs) use a beam of electrons, instead of light, to produce an image. The higher resolution of EMs is due to the shorter wavelengths of electrons. There are two basic types of electron microscope: **scanning electron microscopes** (SEMs) and **transmission electron microscopes** (TEMs). In SEMs, the electrons are bounced off the surface of an object to produce detailed images of the external appearance. TEMs produce very clear images of specially prepared thin sections.

Transmission Electron Microscope (TEM)

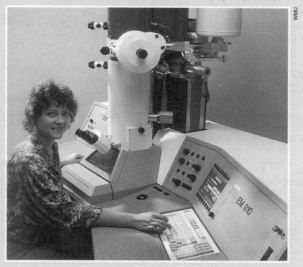

The transmission electron microscope is used to view extremely thin sections of material. Electrons pass through the specimen and are scattered. Magnetic lenses focus the image onto a fluorescent screen or photographic plate. The sections are so thin that they have to be prepared with a special machine, called an **ultramicrotome**, that can cut wafers to just 30 thousandths of a millimetre thick. It can magnify several hundred thousand times.

Electron gun
Electron beam
Electromagnetic condenser lens
Specimen
Electromagnetic objective lens
Vacuum pump
Electromagnetic projector lens
Eyepiece
TEM
Fluorescent screen or photographic plate

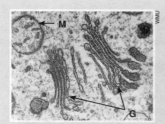

TEM photo showing the Golgi (**G**) and a mitochondrion (**M**).

Three HIV viruses budding out of a human lymphocyte (TEM).

Scanning Electron Microscope (SEM)

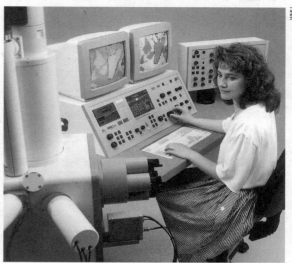

The scanning electron microscope scans a sample with a beam of primary electrons that knock electrons from its surface. These secondary electrons are picked up by a collector, amplified, and transmitted onto a viewing screen or photographic plate, producing a superb 3-D image. A microscope of this power can easily obtain clear pictures of organisms as small as bacteria and viruses. The image produced is of the outside surface only.

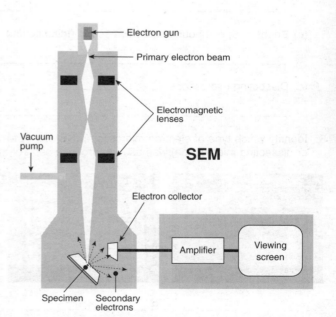

Electron gun
Primary electron beam
Electromagnetic lenses
Vacuum pump
SEM
Electron collector
Amplifier
Viewing screen
Specimen
Secondary electrons

SEM photo of stoma and epidermal cells on the upper surface of a leaf.

Image of hair louse clinging to two hairs on a Hooker's sealion (SEM).

Cell Structure

Related activities: Optical Microscopes, Interpreting Electron Micrographs

RA 2

	Light Microscope	Transmission Electron Microscope (TEM)	Scanning Electron Microscope (SEM)
Radiation source:	light	electrons	electrons
Wavelength:	400-700 nm	0.005 nm	0.005 nm
Lenses:	glass	electromagnetic	electromagnetic
Specimen:	living or non-living supported on glass slide	non-living supported on a small copper grid in a vacuum	non-living supported on a metal disc in a vacuum
Maximum resolution:	200 nm	1 nm	10 nm
Maximum magnification:	1500 x	250 000 x	100 000 x
Stains:	coloured dyes	impregnated with heavy metals	coated with carbon or gold
Type of image:	coloured	monochrome (black & white)	monochrome (black & white)

1. Explain why electron microscopes are able to resolve much greater detail than a light microscope:

   _____

   _____

   _____

2. Describe two typical applications for each of the following types of microscope:

   (a) Transmission electron microscope (TEM): _____

   _____

   (b) Scanning electron microscope (SEM): _____

   _____

   (c) Bright field, compound light microscope (thin section): _____

   _____

   (d) Dissecting microscope: _____

   _____

3. Identify which type of electron microscope (SEM or TEM) or optical microscope (bright field, compound light microscope or dissecting microscope) was used to produce each of the images in the photos below (A-H):

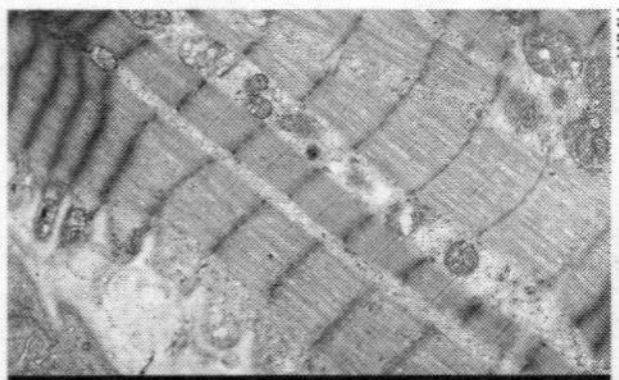

Cardiac muscle

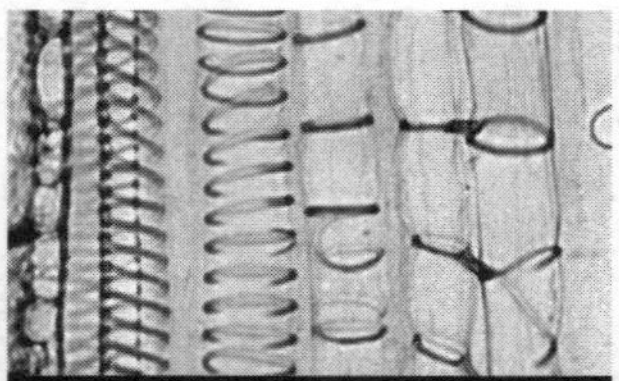

Plant vascular tissue

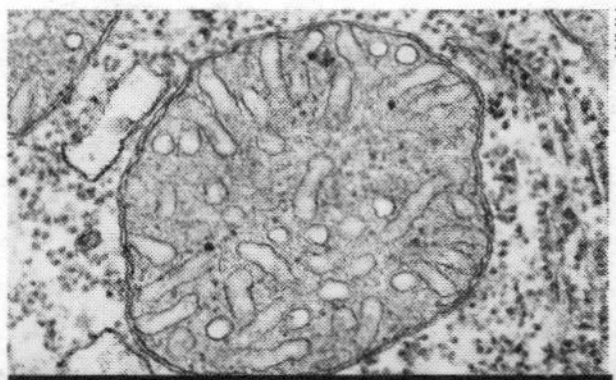

Mitochondrion

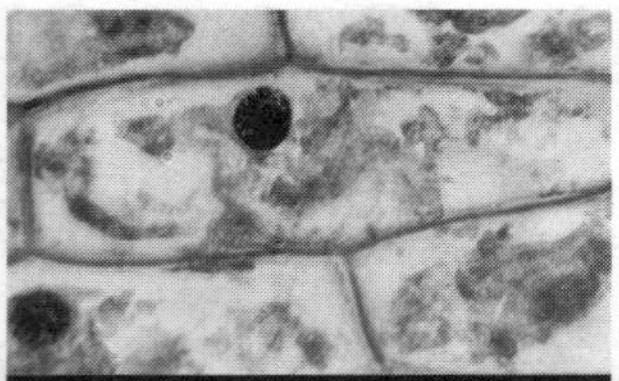

Plant epidermal cells

A _____ B _____ C _____ D _____

Head louse

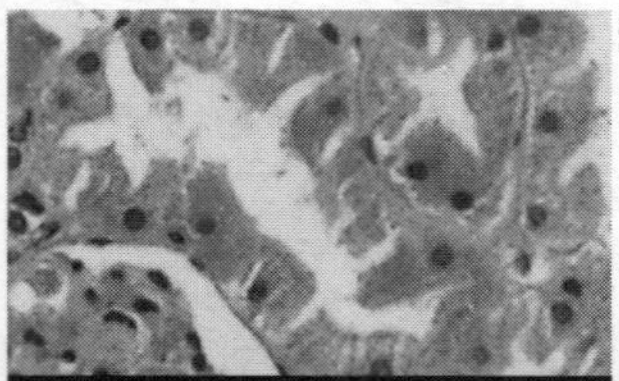

Kidney cells

Alderfly larva

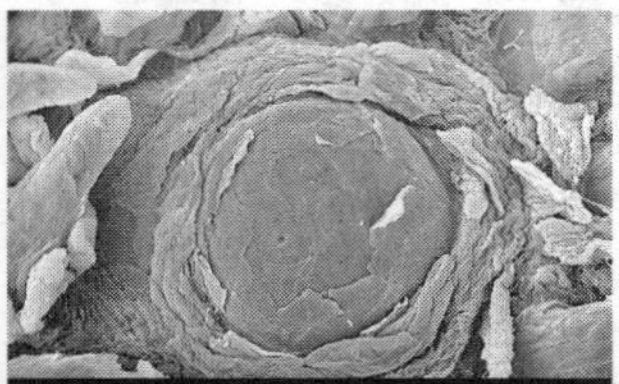

Tongue papilla

E _____ F _____ G _____ H _____

Interpreting Electron Micrographs

The photographs below were taken using a transmission electron microscope (TEM). They show some of the cell organelles in great detail. Remember that these photos are showing only **parts of cells, not whole cells**. Some of the photographs show more than one type of organelle. The questions refer to the main organelle in the centre of the photo.

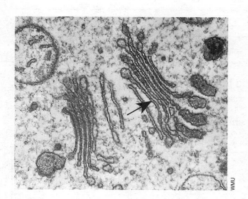

1. (a) Name this organelle (arrowed): _____

(b) State which kind of cell(s) this organelle would be found in:

_____

(c) Describe the function of this organelle: _____

_____

_____

(d) Label two structures that can be seen inside this organelle.

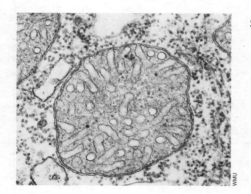

2. (a) Name this organelle (arrowed): _____

(b) State which kind of cell(s) this organelle would be found in:

_____

(c) Describe the function of this organelle: _____

_____

_____

_____

_____

3. (a) Name the large, circular organelle: _____

(b) State which kind of cell(s) this organelle would be found in:

_____

(c) Describe the function of this organelle: _____

_____

_____

(d) Label two regions that can be seen inside this organelle.

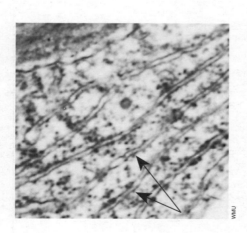

4. (a) Name and label the ribbon-like organelle in this photograph (arrowed):

_____

(b) State which kind of cell(s) this organelle is found in:

_____

(c) Describe the function of these organelles: _____

_____

_____

(d) Name the dark 'blobs' attached to the organelle you have labelled:

_____

Related activities: Electron Microscopes, Plant Cells, Animal Cells, Cell Structures and Organelles

RA 2

Cell Structure

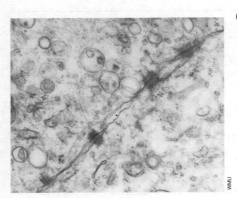

5. (a) Name this large circular structure (arrowed): _____

(b) State which kind of cell(s) this structure would be found in:

_____

(c) Describe the function of this structure: _____

_____

_____

(d) Label three features relating to this structure in the photograph.

6. The four dark structures shown in this photograph are called **desmosomes**. They cause the plasma membranes of neighbouring cells to stick together. Without desmosomes, animal cells would not combine together to form tissues.

(a) Describe the functions of the plasma membrane:

_____

_____

_____

(b) Label the plasma membrane and the four desmosomes in the photograph.

7. In the space below, draw a simple, labelled diagram of a **generalised cell** to show the **relative size** and **location** of these six structures and organelles (simple outlines of the organelles will do):

Cell Membranes and Transport

OCR: Unit F211, Module 1: Cells

1.1.2: Cell membranes

CIE: CORE SYLLABUS

D: Cell membranes and transport

Learning Objectives

☐ 1. Compile your own glossary from the **KEY WORDS** displayed in **bold type** in the learning objectives below.

Cell Membranes (pages 80-83)

☐ 2. Draw a simple labelled diagram of the structure of the **plasma membrane** (cell surface membrane), clearly identifying the arrangement of the lipids and proteins.

☐ 3. Describe and explain the current **fluid-mosaic model** of membrane structure, including the terms **lipid bilayer** and **partially permeable membrane**. Explain the roles of **phospholipids**, **cholesterol**, **glycolipids**, **proteins**, and **glycoproteins** in membrane structure. Recognise that the plasma membrane is essentially no different to the membranes of cellular organelles.

☐ 4. Describe the general functions of membranes (including the plasma membrane) in the cell, identifying their role in the structure of cellular organelles and their role in regulating the transport of materials within cells, as well as into and out of cells.

☐ 5. Outline the effect of changing temperature on membrane structure and permeability.

☐ 6. Explain the term **cell signalling** and identify the general role of signalling molecules in cellular communication. Explain the role of membrane-bound receptors as site where hormones and drugs can bind.

Cellular Transport (pages 84-91)

☐ 7. Summarise the types of movements that occur across membranes. Outline the role of proteins in membranes as receptors and carriers in membrane transport.

☐ 8. Describe **diffusion**, **facilitated diffusion**, and **osmosis**, identifying them as **passive transport** processes. Identify the types of substances moving in each case, and the role of membrane proteins and the **concentration gradient** in net movement.

☐ 9. Identify factors determining the rate of diffusion. Explain how **Fick's law** provides a framework for determining maximum diffusion rates across cell surfaces.

☐ 10. Suggest why cell size is limited by the rate of diffusion. Discuss the significance of **surface area to volume ratio** to cells. Explain why organisms without efficient transport mechanisms remain small.

☐ 11. Explain what is meant by **water potential** (ψ) and identify its significance to the net movement of water in cells. Define the components of water potential: **solute potential** and **pressure potential**.

☐ 12. With respect to plant cells, define the terms: **turgor** and **plasmolysis**. With respect to solutions of differing solute concentration, distinguish between: **hypotonic**, **isotonic**, **hypertonic**. Comment on the importance of ion concentrations in maintaining cell turgor.

☐ 13. Describe and explain the effects that solutions of different water potential have on plant and animal cells.

☐ 14. Distinguish between passive and **active transport** mechanisms. Understand the principles involved in active transport, clearly identifying the involvement of protein molecules and energy.

☐ 15. Describe the following active transport mechanisms: **ion-exchange pumps**, **exocytosis**, **endocytosis**, **phagocytosis**, and **pinocytosis**. Give examples of when and where (in the plant or animal body) each type of transport mechanism occurs.

 See the 'Textbook Reference Grid' on page 7 for textbook page references relating to material in this topic.

Supplementary Texts

See pages 5-6 for additional details of these texts:

■ Adds, J., *et al.*, 2003. **Molecules and Cells**, (NelsonThornes), chpt. 4 as reqd.

■ Harwood, R., 2002. **Biochemistry**, (Cambridge University Press), chpt. 5.

Presentation MEDIA to support this topic: **CELL BIO & BIOCHEM** Cell Membranes

See page 6 for details of publishers of periodicals:

STUDENT'S REFERENCE

■ **Cellular Factories** New Scientist, 23 Nov. 1996 (Inside Science). *An overview of cellular processes and the role of organelles in plant and animal cells.*

■ **Getting in and Out** Biol. Sci. Rev., 20(3), Feb. 2008, pp. 14-16. *An excellent account of diffusion: common misunderstandings and some adaptations.*

■ **Water Channels in the Cell Membrane** Biol. Sci. Rev., 9(2) November 1996, pp. 18-22. *The role of proteins in membrane transport, including the mechanisms involved in physiological processes.*

■ **Water, Water, Everywhere...** Biol. Sci. Rev., 7(5) May 1995, pp. 6-9. *The transport of water in plants (turgor, bulk flow and water potential).*

See pages 8-9 for details of how to access **Bio Links** from our web site: **www.biozone.co.uk**. From Bio Links, access sites under the topics:

GENERAL BIOLOGY ONLINE RESOURCES
• Biology I interactive animations • Instructional multimedia, University of Alberta • HowStuffWorks • Biointeractive ... *and others* > **Online Textbooks and Lecture Notes**: • S-Cool! A level biology revision guide Learn.co.uk ... *and others* > **Glossaries**: • Cellular biology: Glossary of terms • Kimball's biology glossary ... *and others*

CELL BIOLOGY AND BIOCHEMISTRY: • Cell and molecular biology online > **Cell Structure and Transport**: • Aquaporins • CELLS alive! • The virtual cell • Transport in and out of cells

The Role of Membranes in Cells

Many of the important structures and organelles in cells are composed of, or are enclosed by, membranes. These include: the endoplasmic reticulum, mitochondria, nucleus, Golgi apparatus, chloroplasts, lysosomes, vesicles and the plasma membrane itself. All membranes within eukaryotic cells share the same basic structure as the plasma membrane that encloses the entire cell.

They perform a number of critical functions in the cell: serving to compartmentalise regions of different function within the cell, controlling the entry and exit of substances, and fulfilling a role in recognition and communication between cells. Some of these roles are described below. The role of membranes in the production of macromolecules (e.g. proteins) is shown on the next page:

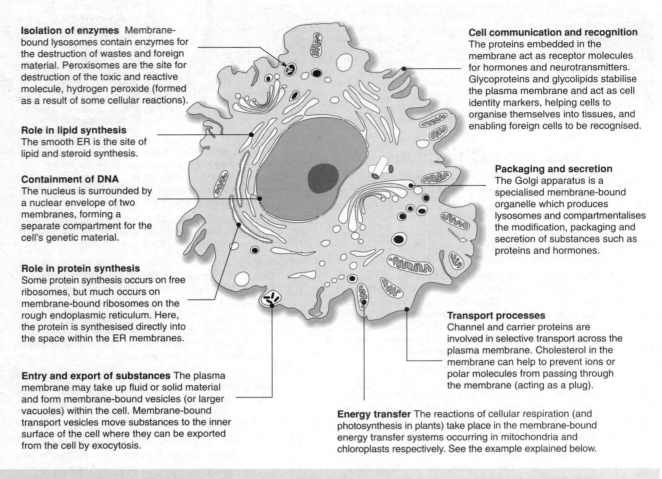

Isolation of enzymes Membrane-bound lysosomes contain enzymes for the destruction of wastes and foreign material. Peroxisomes are the site for destruction of the toxic and reactive molecule, hydrogen peroxide (formed as a result of some cellular reactions).

Role in lipid synthesis
The smooth ER is the site of lipid and steroid synthesis.

Containment of DNA
The nucleus is surrounded by a nuclear envelope of two membranes, forming a separate compartment for the cell's genetic material.

Role in protein synthesis
Some protein synthesis occurs on free ribosomes, but much occurs on membrane-bound ribosomes on the rough endoplasmic reticulum. Here, the protein is synthesised directly into the space within the ER membranes.

Entry and export of substances The plasma membrane may take up fluid or solid material and form membrane-bound vesicles (or larger vacuoles) within the cell. Membrane-bound transport vesicles move substances to the inner surface of the cell where they can be exported from the cell by exocytosis.

Cell communication and recognition
The proteins embedded in the membrane act as receptor molecules for hormones and neurotransmitters. Glycoproteins and glycolipids stabilise the plasma membrane and act as cell identity markers, helping cells to organise themselves into tissues, and enabling foreign cells to be recognised.

Packaging and secretion
The Golgi apparatus is a specialised membrane-bound organelle which produces lysosomes and compartmentalises the modification, packaging and secretion of substances such as proteins and hormones.

Transport processes
Channel and carrier proteins are involved in selective transport across the plasma membrane. Cholesterol in the membrane can help to prevent ions or polar molecules from passing through the membrane (acting as a plug).

Energy transfer The reactions of cellular respiration (and photosynthesis in plants) take place in the membrane-bound energy transfer systems occurring in mitochondria and chloroplasts respectively. See the example explained below.

Compartmentation within Membranes

Membranes play an important role in separating regions within the cell (and within organelles) where particular reactions occur. Specific enzymes are therefore often located in particular organelles. The reaction rate is controlled by controlling the rate at which substrates enter the organelle and therefore the availability of the raw materials required for the reactions.

Example (right): *The enzymes involved in cellular respiration are arranged in different parts of the mitochondria. Reactions are localised and separated by membrane systems.*

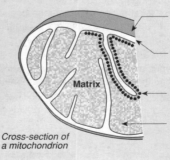

Amine oxidases and other enzymes on the outer membrane surface

Adenylate kinase and other *phosphorylases* between the membranes

Respiratory assembly enzymes embedded in the membrane (ATPase)

Many soluble enzymes of the *Krebs cycle* floating in the matrix, as well as enzymes for fatty acid degradation.

Matrix

Cross-section of a mitochondrion

1. Explain the crucial role of membrane systems and organelles in the following:

(a) Providing compartments within the cell: _____

_____

_____

(b) Increasing the total membrane surface area within the cell: _____

_____

_____

_____

Related activities: Cell Structures & Organelles, Active & Passive Transport
Web links: Cell Membranes

The Structure of Membranes

All cells have a plasma membrane that forms the outer limit of the cell. Bacteria, fungi, and plant cells have a cell wall outside this, but it is quite distinct and outside the cell. Membranes are also found inside eukaryotic cells as part of membranous **organelles**. Present day knowledge of membrane structure has been built up as a result of many observations and experiments. The original model of membrane structure, proposed by Davson and Danielli, was the unit membrane; a lipid bilayer coated with protein. This model was later modified after the discovery that the protein molecules were embedded within the bilayer rather than coating the outside. The now-accepted model of membrane structure is the **fluid-mosaic model** described below.

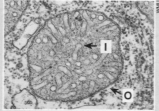
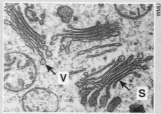
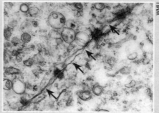

The **nuclear membrane** that surrounds the nucleus helps to control the passage of genetic information to the cytoplasm. It may also serve to protect the DNA.

Mitochondria have an outer membrane (**O**) which controls the entry and exit of materials involved in aerobic respiration. Inner membranes (**I**) provide attachment sites for enzyme activity.

The **Golgi apparatus** comprises stacks of membrane-bound sacs (**S**). It is involved in packaging materials for transport or export from the cell as secretory vesicles (**V**).

The cell is surrounded by a **plasma membrane** which controls the movement of most substances into and out of the cell. This photo shows two neighbouring cells (arrows).

The Fluid Mosaic Model

The currently accepted model for the structure of membranes is called the **fluid mosaic model**. In this model there is a double layer of lipids (fats) which are arranged with their 'tails' facing inwards. The double layer of lipids is thought to be quite fluid, with proteins 'floating' in this layer. The mobile proteins are thought to have a number of functions, including a role in active transport.

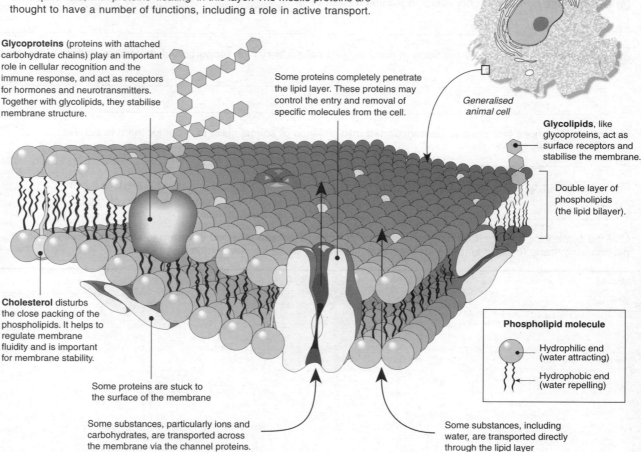

Glycoproteins (proteins with attached carbohydrate chains) play an important role in cellular recognition and the immune response, and act as receptors for hormones and neurotransmitters. Together with glycolipids, they stabilise membrane structure.

Some proteins completely penetrate the lipid layer. These proteins may control the entry and removal of specific molecules from the cell.

Generalised animal cell

Glycolipids, like glycoproteins, act as surface receptors and stabilise the membrane.

Double layer of phospholipids (the lipid bilayer).

Cholesterol disturbs the close packing of the phospholipids. It helps to regulate membrane fluidity and is important for membrane stability.

Some proteins are stuck to the surface of the membrane

Some substances, particularly ions and carbohydrates, are transported across the membrane via the channel proteins.

Some substances, including water, are transported directly through the lipid layer

Phospholipid molecule

Hydrophilic end (water attracting)

Hydrophobic end (water repelling)

1. (a) Describe the modern fluid mosaic model of membrane structure: _____

_____

_____

_____

_____

Related activities: Cell Membranes and Organelles, The Role of Membranes in Cells **Web links**: Membrane Structure Tutorial

RA 2

Cell Membranes and Transport

(b) Explain how the modern fluid mosaic model of membrane structure differs from the earlier Davson-Danielli model:

_____

_____

_____

_____

2. Discuss the various functional roles of membranes in cells: _____

_____

_____

_____

3. (a) Name a cellular organelle that possesses a membrane: _____

(b) Describe the membrane's purpose in this organelle: _____

_____

4. Identify three other cell organelles that are made up of membrane systems:

(a) _____

(b) _____

(c) _____

5. (a) Describe the purpose of cholesterol in plasma membranes: _____

_____

(b) Suggest why marine organisms living in polar regions have a very high proportion of cholesterol in their membranes:

_____

_____

6. List three substances that need to be transported **into** all kinds of animal cells, in order for them to survive:

(a) _____ (b) _____ (c) _____

7. List two substances that need to be transported **out** of all kinds of animal cells, in order for them to survive:

(a) _____ (b) _____

8. Use the symbol for a phospholipid molecule (below) to draw a **simple labelled diagram** to show the structure of a plasma membrane (include features such as lipid bilayer and various kinds of proteins):

Symbol for
phospholipid

Cell Signalling and Receptors

Cells use **signals** (chemical messengers) to gather information about, and respond to, changes in their cellular environment and for communication between cells. The reception of the signal by membrane receptors is followed by a **signal transduction pathway**. Signal transduction often involves a number of enzymes and molecules in a **signal cascade**, which results in a large response in the target cell. Cell signalling pathways are categorised primarily on the distance over which the signal molecule travels to reach its target cell, and generally fall into three categories. The **endocrine** pathway involves the transport of hormones varying distances through the circulatory system. During **paracrine** signalling, the signal acts locally upon neighbouring cells. Cells also produce and respond to their own signals in a process called autocrine signalling.

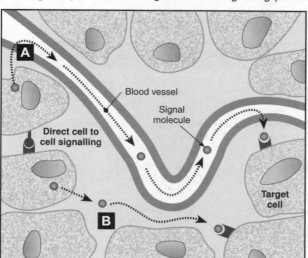

Cells communicate through a variety of mechanisms. Hormone or **endocrine signals** are released by ductless endocrine glands and carried long distances through the body by the circulatory system to the target cells. Examples include sex hormones, growth factors and neurohormones such as dopamine. Signal molecules can also act upon target cells within the immediate vicinity (this is called **paracrine signalling**). The chemical messenger can be transferred through the extracellular fluid (e.g. at synapses) or directly between cells, which is important during embryonic development.

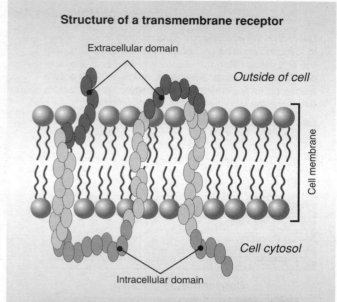

Structure of a transmembrane receptor

Transmembrane receptors span the cell membrane and bind signal molecules (ligands) which cannot cross the plasma membrane on their own. They have an extra-cellular domain outside the cell, and an intracellular domain within the cell cytosol. Ion channels and protein kinases are examples of transmembrane receptors.

1. Explain what is meant by cell signalling: _____

_____

_____

2. Identify the type of cell communication indicated by the letters A and B in the diagram, above left:

   (a) A: _____

   (b) B: _____

3. Describe the components that all cell signalling mechanisms have in common: _____

_____

_____

4. Explain the role of membrane-bound receptors in:

   (a) Hormonal responses: _____

   _____

   _____

   (b) Responses to drugs: _____

   _____

   _____

Cell Membranes and Transport

Related activities: Production and Secretion of Proteins, New Medicines
Web links: Cell Communication

A 2

Diffusion

The molecules that make up substances are constantly moving about in a random way. This random motion causes molecules to disperse from areas of high to low concentration; a process called **diffusion**. The molecules move along a **concentration gradient**. Diffusion and osmosis (diffusion of water molecules across a partially permeable membrane) are **passive** processes, and use no energy. Diffusion occurs freely across membranes, as long as the membrane is permeable to that molecule (partially permeable membranes allow the passage of some molecules but not others). Each type of molecule diffuses along its own concentration gradient. Diffusion of molecules in one direction does not hinder the movement of other molecules. Diffusion is important in allowing exchanges with the environment and in the regulation of cell water content.

Diffusion of Molecules Along Concentration Gradients

Diffusion is the movement of particles from regions of high to low concentration (the **concentration gradient**), with the end result being that the molecules become evenly distributed. In biological systems, diffusion often occurs across partially permeable membranes. Various factors determine the rate at which this occurs (see right).

Factors affecting rates of diffusion	
Concentration gradient:	Diffusion rates will be higher when there is a greater difference in concentration between two regions.
The distance involved:	Diffusion over shorter distances occurs at a greater rate than diffusion over larger distances.
The area involved:	The larger the area across which diffusion occurs, the greater the rate of diffusion.
Barriers to diffusion:	Thicker barriers slow diffusion rate. Pores in a barrier enhance diffusion.

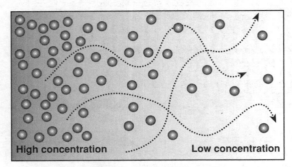

High concentration   **Low concentration**

Concentration gradient

If molecules are free to move, they move from high to low concentration until they are evenly dispersed.

These factors are expressed in **Fick's law**, which governs the rate of diffusion of substances within a system. It is described by:

$$\frac{\text{Surface area of membrane} \times \text{Difference in concentration across the membrane}}{\text{Length of the diffusion path (thickness of the membrane)}}$$

Diffusion through Membranes

Each type of diffusing molecule (gas, solvent, solute) moves **along its own concentration gradient**. Two-way diffusion (below) is common in biological systems, e.g. at the lung surface, carbon dioxide diffuses out and oxygen diffuses into the blood. Facilitated diffusion (below, right) increases the diffusion rate selectively and is important for larger molecules (e.g. glucose, amino acids) where a higher diffusion rate is desirable (e.g. transport of glucose into skeletal muscle fibres, transport of ADP into mitochondria). Neither type of diffusion requires energy expenditure because the molecules are not moving against their concentration gradient.

Unaided diffusion

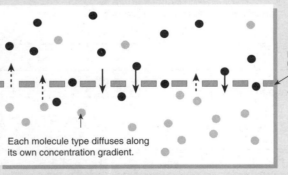

Each molecule type diffuses along its own concentration gradient.

Partially permeable membrane

Diffusion rates depend on the concentration gradient. Diffusion can occur in either direction but **net** movement is in the direction of the concentration gradient. An equilibrium is reached when concentrations are equal.

Facilitated diffusion

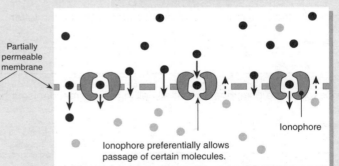

Ionophore

Ionophore preferentially allows passage of certain molecules.

Facilitated diffusion occurs when a substance is aided across a membrane by a special molecule called an **ionophore**. Ionophores allow some molecules to diffuse but not others, effectively speeding up the rate of diffusion of that molecule.

1. Describe two properties of an exchange surface that would facilitate rapid diffusion rates:

   (a) _____ (b) _____

2. Identify one way in which organisms maintain concentration gradients across membranes: _____

   _____

3. State how facilitated diffusion is achieved: _____

Related activities: Active and Passive Transport, Osmosis & Water Potential
Web links: Osmosis and Diffusion

Osmosis and Water Potential

Osmosis is the term describing the diffusion of water along its concentration gradient across a partially permeable membrane. It is the principal mechanism by which water enters and leaves cells in living organisms. As it is a type of diffusion, the rate at which osmosis occurs is affected by the same factors that affect all diffusion rates (see earlier). The tendency for water to move in any particular direction can be calculated on the basis of the water potential of the cell sap relative to its surrounding environment. The use of water potential to express the water relations of cells has replaced the terms osmotic potential and osmotic pressure although these are still frequently used in areas of animal physiology and medicine. The concepts of osmosis, water potential, cell turgor, and plasmolysis are explained below and on the next page.

Osmosis and the Water Potential of Cells

Osmosis is simply the diffusion of water molecules from high concentration to lower concentration, across a partially permeable membrane. The direction of this movement can be predicted on the basis of the water potential of the solutions involved. The **water potential** of a solution (denoted with the symbol ψ) is the term given to the tendency for water molecules to enter or leave a solution by osmosis. Pure water has the highest water potential, set at zero. Dissolving any solute into pure water lowers the water potential (makes it more negative). *Water always diffuses from regions of less negative to more negative water potential*. Water potential is determined by two components: the **solute potential**, ψs (of the cell sap) and the **pressure potential**, ψp. This is expressed as a simple equation:

$$\psi cell \;=\; \psi s \;+\; \psi p$$

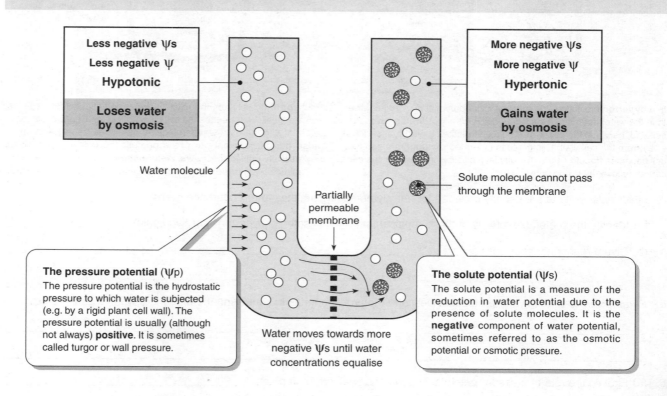

Less negative ψs
Less negative ψ
Hypotonic

Loses water by osmosis

Water molecule

The pressure potential (ψp)
The pressure potential is the hydrostatic pressure to which water is subjected (e.g. by a rigid plant cell wall). The pressure potential is usually (although not always) **positive**. It is sometimes called turgor or wall pressure.

Partially permeable membrane

Water moves towards more negative ψs until water concentrations equalise

More negative ψs
More negative ψ
Hypertonic

Gains water by osmosis

Solute molecule cannot pass through the membrane

The solute potential (ψs)
The solute potential is a measure of the reduction in water potential due to the presence of solute molecules. It is the **negative** component of water potential, sometimes referred to as the osmotic potential or osmotic pressure.

1. State the water potential of pure water at standard temperature and pressure: _____

2. The three diagrams below show the solute and pressure potential values for three hypothetical situations where two solutions are separated by a selectively permeable membrane. For each example (a) - (c) calculate ψ for the solutions on each side of the membrane, as indicated:

3. Draw arrows on each diagram to indicate the direction of net flow of water:

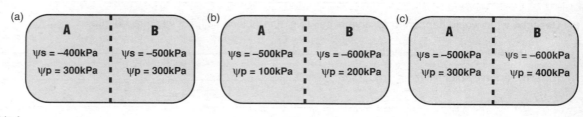

(a)

A	B
$\psi s = -400$kPa	$\psi s = -500$kPa
$\psi p = 300$kPa	$\psi p = 300$kPa

(b)

A	B
$\psi s = -500$kPa	$\psi s = -600$kPa
$\psi p = 100$kPa	$\psi p = 200$kPa

(c)

A	B
$\psi s = -500$kPa	$\psi s = -600$kPa
$\psi p = 300$kPa	$\psi p = 400$kPa

Calculate ψ for side A _____   _____   _____

Calculate ψ for side B _____   _____   _____

© Biozone International 2008

Related activities: Diffusion, Unicellular Eukaryotes
Web links: Osmosis and Diffusion, Cellular Transport

DA 2

Cell Membranes and Transport

Water Relations in Plant Cells

The plasma membrane of cells is a partially permeable membrane and osmosis is the principal mechanism by which water enters and leaves the cell. When the external water potential is the same as that of the cell there is no net movement of water. Two systems (cell and environment) with the same water potential are termed **isotonic**. The diagram below illustrates two different situations: when the external water potential is less negative than the cell (**hypotonic**) and when it is more negative than the cell (**hypertonic**).

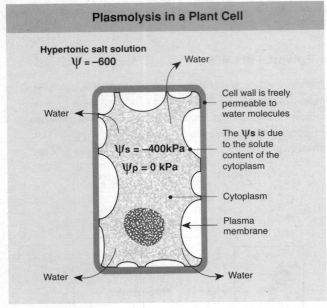

Plasmolysis in a Plant Cell

Hypertonic salt solution
$\Psi = -600$

Water

Water

Cell wall is freely permeable to water molecules

$\Psi s = -400kPa$
$\Psi p = 0$ kPa

The Ψs is due to the solute content of the cytoplasm

Cytoplasm

Plasma membrane

Water

Water

Turgor in a Plant Cell

Pure water (Hypotonic)
$\Psi = 0$

Water

Cell wall bulges outward

$\Psi s = -400kPa$
$\Psi p = 200$ kPa

Cytoplasm takes on water, putting pressure on the plasma membrane and cell wall. Ψp rises (offsetting Ψs at full turgor)

Water

Water

In a **hypertonic** solution, the external water potential is more negative than the water potential of the cell ($\Psi cell = \Psi s + \psi p$). Water leaves the cell and, because the cell wall is rigid, the plasma membrane shrinks away from the cell wall. This process is termed **plasmolysis** and the cell becomes **flaccid** ($\Psi p = 0$). Full plasmolysis is irreversible; the cell cannot recover by taking up water.

In a **hypotonic** solution, the external water potential is less negative than the $\Psi cell$. Water enters the cell causing it to swell tight. A pressure potential is generated when sufficient water has been taken up to cause the cell contents to press against the cell wall. Ψp rises progressively until it offsets Ψs. Water uptake stops when $\Psi cell = 0$. The rigid cell wall prevents cell rupture. Cells in this state are **turgid**.

4. Fluid replacements are usually provided for heavily perspiring athletes after endurance events.

   (a) Identify the preferable tonicity of these replacement drinks (isotonic, hypertonic, or hypotonic): _____

   (b) Give a reason for your answer: _____

   _____

5. *Paramecium* is a freshwater protozoan. Describe the problem it has in controlling the amount of water inside the cell:

   _____

   _____

6. (a) Explain the role of pressure potential in generating cell turgor in plants: _____

   _____

   (b) Explain the purpose of cell turgor to plants: _____

   _____

7. Explain how animal cells differ from plant cells with respect to the effects of net water movements: _____

   _____

8. Describe what would happen to an animal cell (e.g. a red blood cell) if it was placed into:

   (a) Pure water: _____

   (b) A hypertonic solution: _____

   (c) A hypotonic solution: _____

9. The malarial parasite lives in human blood. Relative to the tonicity of the blood, the parasite's cell contents would be hypotonic / isotonic / hypertonic (circle the correct answer).

Surface Area and Volume

When an object (e.g. a cell) is small it has a large surface area in comparison to its volume. In this case diffusion will be an effective way to transport materials (e.g. gases) into the cell. As an object becomes larger, its surface area compared to its volume is smaller. Diffusion is no longer an effective way to transport materials to the inside. For this reason, there is a physical limit for the size of a cell, with the effectiveness of diffusion being the controlling factor.

Diffusion in Organisms of Different Sizes

Respiratory gases and some other substances are exchanged with the surroundings by diffusion or active transport across the plasma membrane.

The **plasma membrane**, which surrounds every cell, functions as a selective barrier that regulates the cell's chemical composition. For each square micrometer of membrane, only so much of a particular substance can cross per second.

The surface area of an elephant is increased, for radiating body heat, by large flat ears.

The nucleus can control a smaller cell more efficiently.

Oxygen

Food

A specialised gas exchange surface (lungs) and circulatory (blood) system are required to speed up the movement of substances through the body.

Carbon dioxide

Wastes

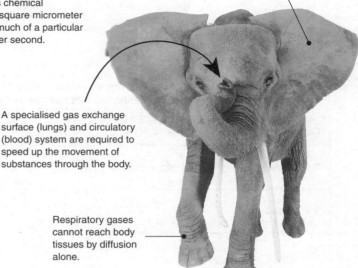

Respiratory gases cannot reach body tissues by diffusion alone.

Amoeba: The small size of single-celled protoctists, such as *Amoeba,* provides a large surface area relative to the cell's volume. This is adequate for many materials to be moved into and out of the cell by diffusion or active transport.

Multicellular organisms: To overcome the problems of small cell size, plants and animals became multicellular. They provide a small surface area compared to their volume but have evolved various adaptive features to improve their effective surface area.

Smaller is Better for Diffusion

One large cube

2 cm

2 cm

2 cm

Volume: = 8 cm^3

Surface area: = 24 cm^2

Eight small cubes

1 cm

1 cm

1 cm

Volume: = 8 cm^3 for 8 cubes

Surface area: = 6 cm^2 for 1 cube

= 48 cm^2 for 8 cubes

The eight small cells and the single large cell have the same total volume, but their surface areas are different. The small cells together have twice the total surface area of the large cell, because there are more exposed (inner) surfaces. Real organisms have complex shapes, but the same principles apply.

The surface-area volume relationship has important implications for processes involving transport into and out of cells across membranes. For activities such as gas exchange, the surface area available for diffusion is a major factor limiting the rate at which oxygen can be supplied to tissues.

Cell Membranes and Transport

Related activities: Diffusion, Cell Sizes

DA 1

The diagram below shows four hypothetical cells of different sizes (cells do not actually grow to this size, their large size is for the sake of the exercise). They range from a small 2 cm cube to a larger 5 cm cube. This exercise investigates the effect of cell size on the efficiency of diffusion.

2 cm cube   **3 cm cube**   **4 cm cube**   **5 cm cube**

1. Calculate the volume, surface area and the ratio of surface area to volume for each of the four cubes above (the first has been done for you). When completing the table below, show your calculations.

Cube size	Surface area	Volume	Surface area to volume ratio
2 cm cube	2 x 2 x 6 = 24 cm² (2 cm x 2 cm x 6 sides)	2 x 2 x 2 = 8 cm³ (height x width x depth)	24 to 8 = 3:1
3 cm cube			
4 cm cube			
5 cm cube			

2. Create a graph, plotting the surface area against the volume of each cube, on the grid on the right. Draw a line connecting the points and label axes and units.

3. State which increases the fastest with increasing size, the **volume** or **surface area**.

_____

4. Explain what happens to the ratio of surface area to volume with increasing size:

_____

_____

_____

_____

5. Diffusion of substances into and out of a cell occurs across the cell surface. Describe how increasing the size of a cell will affect the ability of diffusion to transport materials into and out of a cell:

_____

_____

_____

_____

_____

Ion Pumps

Diffusion alone cannot supply the cell's entire requirements for molecules (and ions). Some molecules (e.g. glucose) are required by the cell in higher concentrations than occur outside the cell. Others (e.g. sodium) must be removed from the cell in order to maintain cell fluid balance. These molecules must be moved across the plasma membrane by active transport mechanisms. **Active transport** requires the expenditure of energy because the molecules (or ions) must be moved **against** their concentration gradient. The work of active transport is performed by specific carrier proteins in the membrane. These transport proteins harness the energy of ATP to pump molecules from a low to a high concentration. When ATP transfers a phosphate group to the carrier protein, the protein changes its shape in such a way as to move the bound molecule across the membrane. Three types of membrane pump are illustrated below. The sodium-potassium pump (below, left) is almost universal in animal cells and is common in plant cells also. The concentration gradient created by ion pumps such as this and the proton pump (centre) is frequently coupled to the transport of other molecules such as glucose and sucrose (below, right).

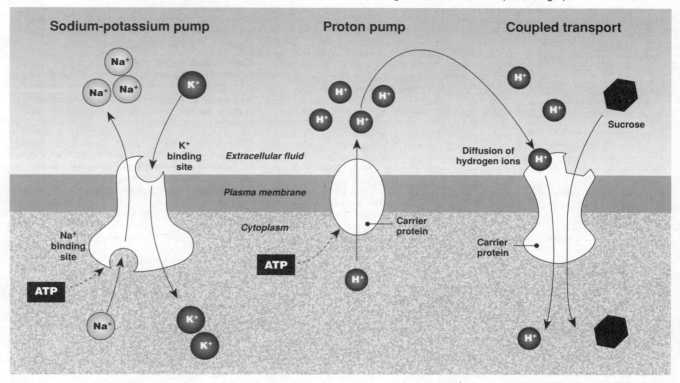

Sodium-potassium pump
The sodium-potassium pump is a specific protein in the membrane that uses energy in the form of ATP to exchange sodium ions (Na$^+$) for potassium ions (K$^+$) across the membrane. The unequal balance of Na$^+$ and K$^+$ across the membrane creates large concentration gradients that can be used to drive other active transport mechanisms.

Proton pumps
ATP driven proton pumps use energy to remove hydrogen ions (H$^+$) from inside the cell to the outside. This creates a large difference in the proton concentration either side of the membrane, with the inside of the plasma membrane being negatively charged. This potential difference can be coupled to the transport of other molecules.

Coupled transport (cotransport)
Plant cells use the gradient in hydrogen ions created by proton pumps to drive the active transport of nutrients into the cell. The specific transport protein couples the return of H$^+$ to the transport of sucrose into the phloem cells. The sucrose rides with the H$^+$ as it diffuses down the concentration gradient maintained by the proton pump.

1. The sodium-potassium pump plays an important role in the water balance of cells. In terms of osmosis, explain the consequences of the sodium-potassium pumps not working:

_____

_____

2. Explain how the transport of molecules such as sucrose can be coupled to the activity of an ion exchange pump:

_____

_____

_____

3. Explain why the ATP is required for membrane pump systems to operate: _____

_____

_____

4. Name a type of cell that relies on coupled transport to perform its function: _____

Related activities: Active and Passive Transport, Osmosis and Water Potential
Web links: Cellular Transport

A 2

Cell Membranes and Transport

Exocytosis and Endocytosis

Most cells carry out **cytosis**: a form of **active transport** involving the in- or outfolding of the plasma membrane. The ability of cells to do this is a function of the flexibility of the plasma membrane. Cytosis results in the bulk transport into or out of the cell and is achieved through the localised activity of microfilaments and microtubules in the cell cytoskeleton. Engulfment of material is

termed **endocytosis.** Endocytosis typically occurs in protozoans and certain white blood cells of the mammalian defence system (e.g. neutrophils, macrophages). **Exocytosis** is the reverse of endocytosis and involves the release of material from vesicles or vacuoles that have fused with the plasma membrane. Exocytosis is typical of cells that export material (secretory cells).

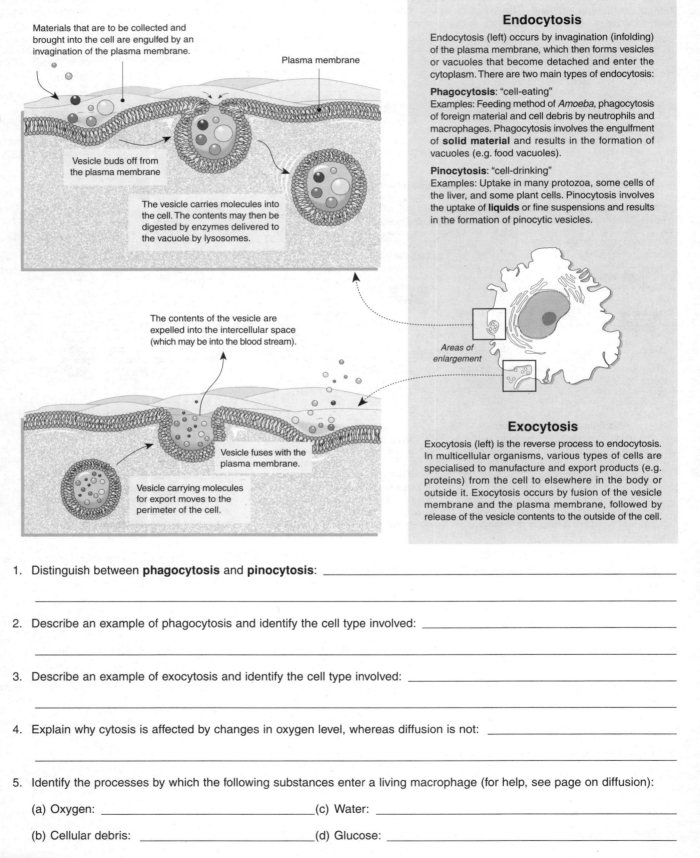

Materials that are to be collected and brought into the cell are engulfed by an invagination of the plasma membrane.

Plasma membrane

Vesicle buds off from the plasma membrane

The vesicle carries molecules into the cell. The contents may then be digested by enzymes delivered to the vacuole by lysosomes.

The contents of the vesicle are expelled into the intercellular space (which may be into the blood stream).

Vesicle fuses with the plasma membrane.

Vesicle carrying molecules for export moves to the perimeter of the cell.

Areas of enlargement

Endocytosis

Endocytosis (left) occurs by invagination (infolding) of the plasma membrane, which then forms vesicles or vacuoles that become detached and enter the cytoplasm. There are two main types of endocytosis:

Phagocytosis: "cell-eating"
Examples: Feeding method of *Amoeba*, phagocytosis of foreign material and cell debris by neutrophils and macrophages. Phagocytosis involves the engulfment of **solid material** and results in the formation of vacuoles (e.g. food vacuoles).

Pinocytosis: "cell-drinking"
Examples: Uptake in many protozoa, some cells of the liver, and some plant cells. Pinocytosis involves the uptake of **liquids** or fine suspensions and results in the formation of pinocytic vesicles.

Exocytosis

Exocytosis (left) is the reverse process to endocytosis. In multicellular organisms, various types of cells are specialised to manufacture and export products (e.g. proteins) from the cell to elsewhere in the body or outside it. Exocytosis occurs by fusion of the vesicle membrane and the plasma membrane, followed by release of the vesicle contents to the outside of the cell.

1. Distinguish between **phagocytosis** and **pinocytosis**: _____

_____

2. Describe an example of phagocytosis and identify the cell type involved: _____

_____

3. Describe an example of exocytosis and identify the cell type involved: _____

_____

4. Explain why cytosis is affected by changes in oxygen level, whereas diffusion is not: _____

_____

5. Identify the processes by which the following substances enter a living macrophage (for help, see page on diffusion):

   (a) Oxygen: _____   (c) Water: _____

   (b) Cellular debris: _____   (d) Glucose: _____

Related activities: Active and Passive Transport, Diffusion
Web links: Cellular Transport

Active and Passive Transport

Cells have a need to move materials both into and out of the cell. Raw materials and other molecules necessary for metabolism must be accumulated from outside the cell. Some of these substances are scarce outside of the cell and some effort is required to accumulate them. Waste products and molecules for use in other parts of the body must be 'exported' out of the cell.

Some materials (e.g. gases and water) move into and out of the cell by **passive transport** processes, without the expenditure of energy on the part of the cell. Other molecules (e.g. sucrose) are moved into and out of the cell using **active transport**. Active transport processes involve the expenditure of energy in the form of ATP, and therefore use oxygen.

Passive Transport

Active Transport

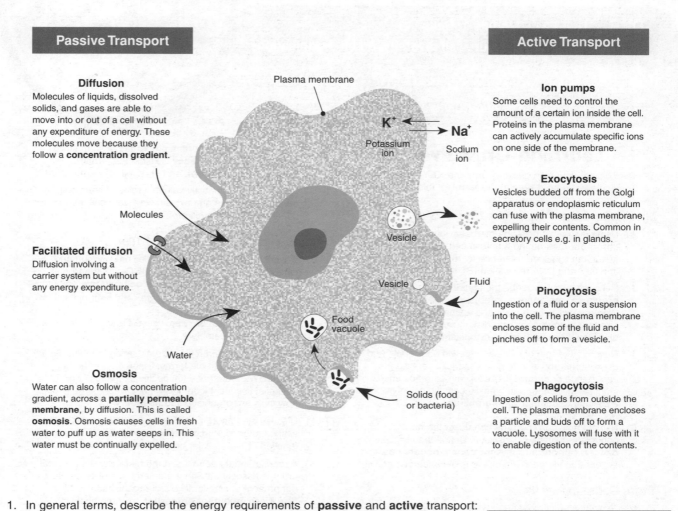

Diffusion
Molecules of liquids, dissolved solids, and gases are able to move into or out of a cell without any expenditure of energy. These molecules move because they follow a **concentration gradient**.

Facilitated diffusion
Diffusion involving a carrier system but without any energy expenditure.

Osmosis
Water can also follow a concentration gradient, across a **partially permeable membrane**, by diffusion. This is called **osmosis**. Osmosis causes cells in fresh water to puff up as water seeps in. This water must be continually expelled.

Ion pumps
Some cells need to control the amount of a certain ion inside the cell. Proteins in the plasma membrane can actively accumulate specific ions on one side of the membrane.

Exocytosis
Vesicles budded off from the Golgi apparatus or endoplasmic reticulum can fuse with the plasma membrane, expelling their contents. Common in secretory cells e.g. in glands.

Pinocytosis
Ingestion of a fluid or a suspension into the cell. The plasma membrane encloses some of the fluid and pinches off to form a vesicle.

Phagocytosis
Ingestion of solids from outside the cell. The plasma membrane encloses a particle and buds off to form a vacuole. Lysosomes will fuse with it to enable digestion of the contents.

Labels on diagram: Plasma membrane, Molecules, Water, Food vacuole, K^+ Potassium ion, Na^+ Sodium ion, Vesicle, Vesicle, Fluid, Solids (food or bacteria)

1. In general terms, describe the energy requirements of **passive** and **active** transport: _____

_____

_____

_____

2. Name two gases that move into or out of our bodies by **diffusion**: _____

_____

3. Name a gland which has cells where **exocytosis** takes place for the purpose of secretion: _____

_____

4. **Phagocytosis** is a process where solid particles are enveloped by the plasma membrane and drawn inside the cell.

(a) Name a protozoan (single-celled protoctist) that would use this technique for feeding: _____

(b) Describe how it uses the technique: _____

_____

(c) Name a type of cell found in human blood that uses this technique for capturing and destroying bacteria:

_____

Cell Membranes and Transport

Related activities: Diffusion, Osmosis and Water Potential, Ion Pumps, Exocytosis and Endocytosis, Unicellular Eukaryotes

RA 1

Cell Division

OCR: Unit F211, Module 1: Cells
1.1.3: Cell division, cell diversity, & cell organisation

CIE: CORE SYLLABUS
E: Cell and nuclear division

Learning Objectives

☐ 1. Compile your own glossary from the **KEY WORDS** displayed in **bold type** in the learning objectives below.

Mitosis and the Cell Cycle *(pages 93-97)*

☐ 2. Using diagrams, describe the behaviour of **chromosomes** during a mitotic **cell cycle** in eukaryotes. Include reference to: **mitosis**, **growth** (G_1 and G_2), and DNA replication (S).

☐ 3. Recognise and describe the following events in mitosis: **prophase**, **metaphase**, **anaphase**, and **telophase**. With respect to both plant and animal cells, understand the term **cytokinesis**, and distinguish between nuclear division and division of the cytoplasm.

☐ 4. Describe the role of mitosis in growth and repair, and asexual reproduction (e.g. in yeast). Recognise the importance of **daughter nuclei** with chromosomes identical in number and type. Recognise cell division as a prelude to **cellular differentiation**.

☐ 5. Explain how **carcinogens** can upset the normal controls regulating cell division. Define the terms: **cancer**, **tumour suppressor genes**, **oncogenes**. List factors that increase the chances of cancerous growth.

Stem Cells *(pages 98-99)*

☐ 6. Explain what is meant by a **stem cell** and distinguish between embryonic and adult stem cells. Describe the role of stem cells in multicellular organisms.

☐ 7. Describe the two important properties of stem cells: **self-renewal** and **potency**. Explain the terms: **totipotent**, **pluripotent**, and (if required) **multipotent**.

☐ 8. Describe the potentially valuable roles of stem cells in medical therapies and explain why stem cell technology offers such therapeutic promise.

Tissues and Organs *(pages 99-106)*

☐ 9. Describe how a **zygote** undergoes cell division and differentiation to produce an adult. Define the terms: **differentiation** and **specialised cell** with reference to:
  (a) The production of erythrocytes and neutrophils from bone marrow stem cells.
  (b) The production of xylem vessels and phloem sieve tubes from cambium.

☐ 10. Recognise the hierarchy of organisation in multicellular organisms. Explain the terms: tissue, organ, and organ system. With reference to specific examples (e.g. epithelial tissues, blood, xylem, and/or phloem), explain how cells are organised into **tissues**.

☐ 11. Discuss the importance of cooperation between cells, tissues, organs, and organ systems in the structure and function of multicellular organisms.

☐ 12. Appreciate that each step in the hierarchy of biological order is associated with the emergence of properties not present at simpler levels of organisation. Explain how these **emergent properties** (e.g. metabolism) result from the interactions of component parts.

 See the 'Textbook Reference Grid' on page 7 for textbook page references relating to material in this topic.

Supplementary Texts

See pages 5-6 for additional details of these texts:
■ Adds, J. *et al.*, 2003. **Molecules and Cells**, (NelsonThornes), pp. 48-49 and chpt. 5.
■ Jones, N., *et al.*, 2001. **The Essentials of Genetics**, (John Murray), pp. 9-16.

See page 6 for details of publishers of periodicals:

STUDENT'S REFERENCE

■ **To Divide or Not to Divide** Biol. Sci. Rev., 11(4) March 1999, pp. 2-5. *The cell cycle: cell growth and stages of cell division and their control.*

■ **The Cell Cycle and Mitosis** Biol. Sci. Rev., 14(4) April 2002, pp. 37-41. *Cell growth and division, key stages in the cell cycle, and the complex control over different stages of mitosis.*

■ **Rebels without a Cause** New Scientist, 13 July 2002, (Inside Science). *The causes of cancer: the uncontrolled division of cells that results in tumour formation. Breast cancer is a case example.*

■ **What is a Stem Cell?** Biol. Sci. Rev., 16(2) Nov. 2003, pp. 22-23. *The nature of stem cells and their therapeutic applications.*

■ **The Stem Cell Challenge** Scientific American, June 2004, pp. 60-67. *The scientific and political hurdles in the quest to understand and control embryonic stem cells.*

■ **Fast Tissue Culture** Biol. Sci. Rev., 10(3) Jan. 1998, pp. 2-6. *Techniques for plant propagation (includes design for a tissue culture project).*

■ **Human Cloning** Biol. Sci. Rev. 11(3) Jan. 1999, pp. 7-9. *Nuclear transfer and the ethics of the issues surrounding human and livestock cloning.*

■ **The Power to Divide** National Geographic, July 2005, pp. 2-27. *A series of case studies on different illnesses treated with therapeutic cloning.*

■ **Out of Control - Unlocking the Genetic Secrets of Cancer** Biol. Sci. Rev. 11(3) Jan. 1999, pp. 36-39. *The control of cell division: oncogenes and their role in the development of cancer.*

See pages 8-9 for details of how to access **Bio Links** from our web site: **www.biozone.co.uk**. From Bio Links, access sites under the topics:

GENERAL BIOLOGY ONLINE RESOURCES
• AP interactive animation • Ken's bio-web resources • Biology I interactive animations

CELL BIOLOGY AND BIOCHEMISTRY: • Mollecular biology web book > **Cell Division**: • Cell division: Binary fission and mitosis • Cell cycle and mitosis tutorial

BIOTECHNOLOGY > **Applications** > **Cloning and Tissue Culture:** • Contact the Stem Cell Research Foundation • Stem cells: gateway to 21st Century medicine… *and others*

Presentation MEDIA to support this topic: **CELL BIO & BIOCHEM** Processes in the Nucleus

Cell Division

The life cycle of **diploid sexually reproducing organisms** (such as humans) is illustrated in the diagram below. **Gametogenesis** is the process responsible for the production of male and female gametes for the purpose of sexual reproduction. The difference between meiosis in males and in females should be noted (see spermatogenesis and oogenesis in the box below).

Human embryos have cells which are rapidly dividing by **mitosis**. The term **somatic** means 'body', so the cell divisions are creating new body cells (as opposed to gametes or sex cells). The **2N** or **diploid** number refers to how many whole sets of chromosomes are present in each body cell. For a normal human embryo, all cells will have a diploid number of 46.

Adults still continue to produce somatic cells by mitosis for cell replacement and growth. Blood cells are replaced by the body at the astonishing rate of two million per second, and a layer of skin cells is constantly lost and replaced about every 28 days.

Gamete production begins at puberty, and lasts until menopause for women, and indefinitely for men. Gametes are **haploid cells** produced by the special type of cell division, called **meiosis**, which reduces the chromosome number to half. Human males produce about 200 million sperm per day (whether they are used or not), while females usually release a single egg only once a month.

Fertilisation involves fusion of the sperm and the egg to produce a single cell called the **zygote**. This cell has all the genetic information to build a human body as well as maintain it (metabolism).

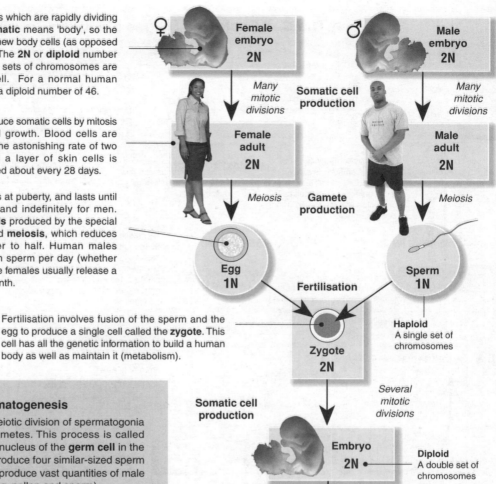

Spermatogenesis

Sperm production: Meiotic division of spermatogonia produces the male gametes. This process is called spermatogenesis. The nucleus of the **germ cell** in the male divides twice to produce four similar-sized sperm cells. Many organisms produce vast quantities of male gametes in this way (e.g. pollen and sperm).

Oogenesis

Egg production: In females, meiosis in the oogonium produces the egg cell or ovum. Unlike gamete production in males, the divison of the cytoplasm during oogenesis is unequal. Most of the cytoplasm and one of the four nuclei form the egg cell or **ovum**. The remainder of the cytoplasm, plus the other three nuclei, form much smaller **polar bodies** and are abortive (i.e. do not take part in fertilisation and formation of the zygote).

1. Describe the **purpose** of the following types of cell division:

   (a) Mitosis: _____

   _____

   (b) Meiosis: _____

   _____

2. Explain the significance of the **zygote**: _____

3. Describe the basic difference between the cell divisions involved in spermatogenesis and oogenesis:

   _____

   _____

Related activities: Mitosis and the Cell Cycle

A 1

Mitosis and the Cell Cycle

Mitosis is part of the 'cell cycle' in which an existing cell (the parent cell) divides into two (the daughter cells). Mitosis does not result in a change of chromosome numbers (unlike meiosis) and the daughter cells are identical to the parent cell. Although mitosis is part of a continuous cell cycle, it is divided into stages (below). The example below illustrates the cell cycle in a plant cell. Note that in animal cells, **cytokinesis** involves the formation of a constriction that divides the cell in two. It is usually well underway by the end of telophase and does not involve the formation of a cell plate.

The Cell Cycle and Stages of Mitosis

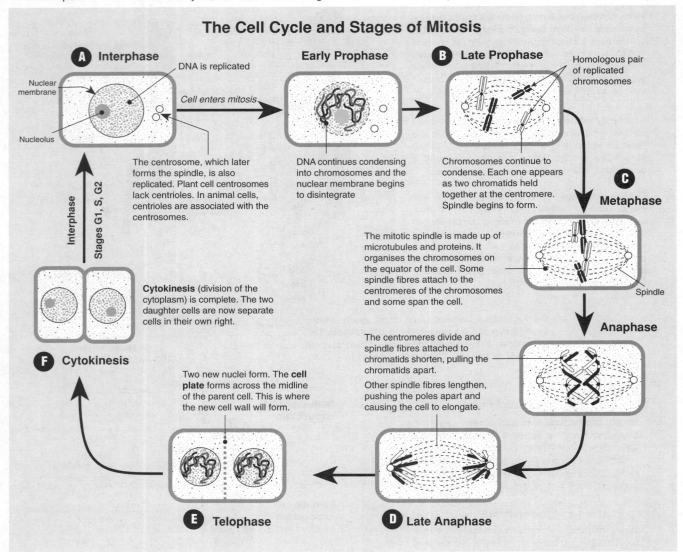

A Interphase

DNA is replicated

Nuclear membrane

Nucleolus

Cell enters mitosis

The centrosome, which later forms the spindle, is also replicated. Plant cell centrosomes lack centrioles. In animal cells, centrioles are associated with the centrosomes.

Early Prophase

DNA continues condensing into chromosomes and the nuclear membrane begins to disintegrate

B Late Prophase

Homologous pair of replicated chromosomes

Chromosomes continue to condense. Each one appears as two chromatids held together at the centromere. Spindle begins to form.

C Metaphase

The mitotic spindle is made up of microtubules and proteins. It organises the chromosomes on the equator of the cell. Some spindle fibres attach to the centromeres of the chromosomes and some span the cell.

Spindle

Anaphase

The centromeres divide and spindle fibres attached to chromatids shorten, pulling the chromatids apart.

Other spindle fibres lengthen, pushing the poles apart and causing the cell to elongate.

Interphase

Stages G1, S, G2

F Cytokinesis

Cytokinesis (division of the cytoplasm) is complete. The two daughter cells are now separate cells in their own right.

Two new nuclei form. The **cell plate** forms across the midline of the parent cell. This is where the new cell wall will form.

E Telophase

D Late Anaphase

The Cell Cycle Overview

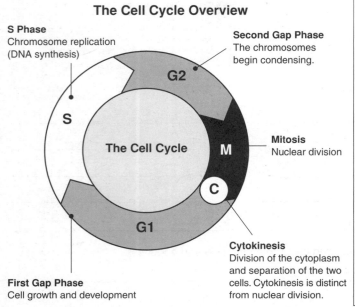

S Phase
Chromosome replication (DNA synthesis)

Second Gap Phase
The chromosomes begin condensing.

G2

S

The Cell Cycle

M

C

Mitosis
Nuclear division

G1

Cytokinesis
Division of the cytoplasm and separation of the two cells. Cytokinesis is distinct from nuclear division.

First Gap Phase
Cell growth and development

Homologous Chromosomes

In sexually reproducing organisms, the chromosomes of most cells are present as **homologous pairs**. One chromosome of a pair is supplied by the female parent and one by the male parent. Each homologue carries an identical assortment of genes, but the version of the gene (allele) from each parent may differ.

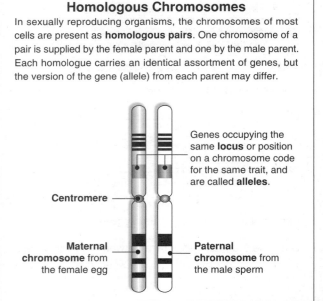

Genes occupying the same **locus** or position on a chromosome code for the same trait, and are called **alleles**.

Centromere

Maternal chromosome from the female egg

Paternal chromosome from the male sperm

Related activities: The Genetic Origins of Cancer, Root Cell Development

Mitotic cell division has several purposes (below left). In multicellular organisms, mitosis repairs damaged cells and tissues, and produces the growth in an organism that allows it to reach its adult size. In unicellular organisms, and some small multicellular organisms, cell division allows organisms to reproduce asexually (as in the budding yeast cell cycle below).

The Functions of Mitosis

① Growth

In plants, cell division occurs in regions of **meristematic tissue**. In the plant root tip (right), the cells in the root apical meristem are dividing by mitosis to produce new cells. This elongates the root, resulting in **plant growth**.

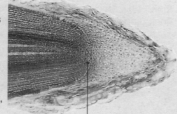

Root apical meristem

② Repair

Photo: AB Sheldon

Some animals, such as this skink (left), detach their limbs as a defence mechanism in a process called autotomy. The limbs can be **regenerated** via the mitotic process, although the tissue composition of the new limb differs slightly from that of the original.

③ Reproduction

Mitotic division enables some animals to reproduce **asexually**. The cells of this Hydra (left) undergo mitosis, forming a 'bud' on the side of the parent organism. Eventually the bud, which is genetically identical to its parent, detaches to continue the life cycle.

Parent

The Budding Yeast Cell Cycle

Yeasts can reproduce asexually through **budding**. In *Saccharomyces cerevisiae* (baker's yeast), budding involves mitotic division in the parent cell, with the formation of a daughter cell (or bud). As budding begins, a ring of chitin stabilises the area where the bud will appear and enzymatic activity and turgor pressure act to weaken and extrude the cell wall. New cell wall material is incorporated during this phase. The nucleus of the parent cell also divides in two, to form a daughter nucleus, which migrates into the bud. The daughter cell is genetically identical to its parent cell and continues to grow, eventually separating from the parent cell.

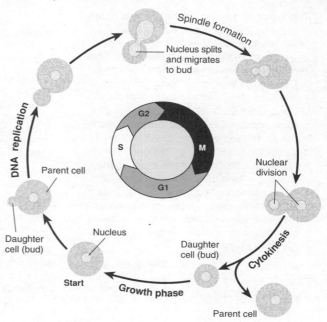

Spindle formation

Nucleus splits and migrates to bud

DNA replication

Parent cell

Nucleus

Daughter cell (bud)

Start

Growth phase

G2

S

M

G1

Nuclear division

Daughter cell (bud)

Cytokinesis

Parent cell

1. The photographs below were taken at various stages through mitosis in a plant cell. They are not in any particular order. Study the diagram on the previous page and determine the stage represented in each photograph (e.g. anaphase).

Photos: RCN

 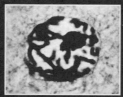 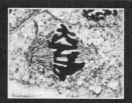 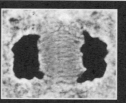 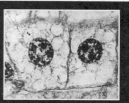

(a) _____   (b) _____   (c) _____   (d) _____   (e) _____

2. State two important changes that chromosomes must undergo before cell division can take place: _____

_____

3. Briefly summarise the stages of the cell cycle by describing what is happening at the points (**A-F**) in the diagram on the previous page:

A. _____

B. _____

C. _____

D. _____

E. _____

F. _____

The Genetic Origins of Cancer

Normal cells do not live forever. Under certain circumstances, cells are programmed to die, particularly during development. Cells that become damaged beyond repair will normally undergo this programmed cell death (called **apoptosis** or **cell suicide**). Cancer cells evade this control and become immortal, continuing to divide regardless of any damage incurred. **Carcinogens** are agents capable of causing cancer. Roughly 90% of carcinogens are also mutagens, i.e. they damage DNA. Chronic exposure to carcinogens accelerates the rate at which dividing cells make errors. Susceptibility to cancer is also influenced by genetic make-up. Any one or a number of cancer-causing factors (including defective genes) may interact to induce cancer.

Cancer: Cells out of Control

Cancerous transformation results from changes in the genes controlling normal cell growth and division. The resulting cells become immortal and no longer carry out their functional role. Two types of gene are normally involved in controlling the cell cycle: proto-oncogenes, which start the cell division process and are essential for normal cell development, and **tumour-suppressor** genes, which switch off cell division. In their normal form, both kinds of genes work as a team, enabling the body to perform vital tasks such as repairing defective cells and replacing dead ones. But mutations in these genes can disrupt these finely tuned checks and balances. Proto-oncogenes, through mutation, can give rise to **oncogenes**; genes that lead to uncontrollable cell division. Mutations to tumour-suppressor genes initiate most human cancers. The best studied tumour-suppressor gene is **p53**, which encodes a protein that halts the cell cycle so that DNA can be repaired before division.

The panel, right, shows the mutagenic action of some selected carcinogens on four of five codons of the **p53 gene**.

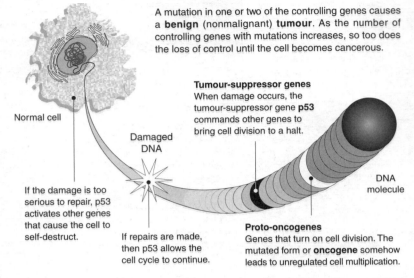

Normal cell

Damaged DNA

If the damage is too serious to repair, p53 activates other genes that cause the cell to self-destruct.

If repairs are made, then p53 allows the cell cycle to continue.

A mutation in one or two of the controlling genes causes a **benign** (nonmalignant) **tumour**. As the number of controlling genes with mutations increases, so too does the loss of control until the cell becomes cancerous.

Tumour-suppressor genes
When damage occurs, the tumour-suppressor gene **p53** commands other genes to bring cell division to a halt.

DNA molecule

Proto-oncogenes
Genes that turn on cell division. The mutated form or **oncogene** somehow leads to unregulated cell multiplication.

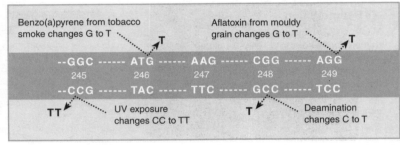

Benzo(a)pyrene from tobacco smoke changes G to T

Aflatoxin from mouldy grain changes G to T

--GGC	ATG	AAG	CGG	AGG
245	246	247	248	249
--CCG	TAC	TTC	GCC	TCC

UV exposure changes CC to TT

Deamination changes C to T

Features of Cancer Cells

The diagram right shows a single **lung cell** that has become cancerous. It no longer carries out the role of a lung cell, and instead takes on a parasitic lifestyle, taking from the body what it needs in the way of nutrients and contributing nothing in return. The rate of cell division is greater than in normal cells in the same tissue because there is no *resting phase* between divisions.

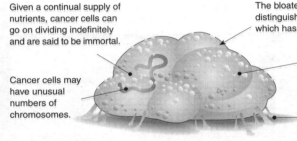

Given a continual supply of nutrients, cancer cells can go on dividing indefinitely and are said to be immortal.

Cancer cells may have unusual numbers of chromosomes.

The bloated, lumpy shape is readily distinguishable from a healthy cell, which has a flat, scaly appearance.

Metabolism is disrupted and the cell ceases to function constructively.

Cancerous cells lose their attachments to neighbouring cells.

1. Explain how cancerous cells differ from normal cells: _____

_____

2. Explain how the cell cycle is normally controlled, including reference to the role of **tumour-suppressor genes**:

_____

_____

_____

_____

3. With reference to the role of **oncogenes**, explain how the normal controls over the cell cycle can be lost:

_____

_____

_____

Related activities: Mitosis and the Cell Cycle, Cell Growth and Cancer

Cell Growth and Cancer

Cancer is a term describing a large group of diseases characterised by the progressive and uncontrolled growth of abnormal cells. There is no single cause for all the forms of cancer; environmental, genetic, and biological factors are usually implicated. Certain risk factors increase a person's chance of getting cancer. Some risk factors, such as exposure to tobacco smoke, are controllable, while others, such as gender, are not. Because cancers arise as a result of damage to DNA, those factors that cause cellular damage, e.g. exposure to the chemicals in cigarette smoke, increase the risk of cancers developing.

Stages in the Formation of Cancer

The growth of a cancer begins when the genes controlling cell growth and multiplication (**oncogenes**) are transformed by agents known as **carcinogens**. Most well studied is the p53 gene which normally acts to prevent cell division in damaged cells. Scientists have found that the p53 gene is altered in 40% of all cancers. Once a cell is transformed into a tumour-forming type (**malignant**), the change in its oncogenes is passed on to all offspring cells:

Cancer cells ignore density-dependent inhibition and continue to multiply even after contacting one another, piling up until the nutrient supply becomes limiting.

1. Benign tumour cells
Defects (mutations) in one or two controlling genes cause the formation of a benign tumour. This is a localised population of proliferating cells where formation of new cells is matched by cell death.

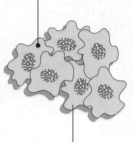

2. Malignant tumour cells
More mutations may cause the cells to become malignant. These cells stop producing a chemical that prevents blood vessels from forming. New capillaries grow into the tumour, providing it with nutrients.

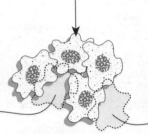

3. Metastasis
The new capillaries also provide a route for the malignant cells to break away from the tumour and travel to other parts of the body where they start new cancers.

Malignant cells break away from tumour mass and spread through the body through the **blood** or **lymphatic systems**.

Risk Factors for Cancer

The greatest **uncontrollable risk factor** for cancer is **ageing**; most cancers occur in people over the age of 65. Others include **genetic predisposition** (family history) and gender. **Controllable risk factors** include **lifestyle factors**, such as **tobacco use**. Not unexpectedly, different kinds of cancer are associated with different risk factors. For example, sunlight exposure increases the risk of skin cancers. Some major risk factors include the following:

Tobacco use is related to a wide range of cancers; smoking alone causes one third of all cancer deaths.

Excessive alcohol intake, especially when associated with tobacco use, is associated with oral cancers.

A highly processed, high fat diet is associated with higher risk of various cancers, including colon cancer.

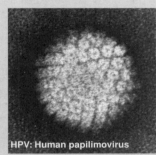

HPV: Human papilimovirus

Certain Infections are associated with the development of cancers. HPV is strongly linked to cervical cancer.

Ionising radiation and hazardous substances, such as asbestos and formaldehyde, cause cell damage that can lead to cancer.

Unprotected exposure to ultraviolet light causes early ageing of the skin and damage that can lead to the development of skin cancers.

1. Explain the mechanism by which the risk factors described above increase the chance of developing cancer:

_____

2. Explain why it can be difficult to determine the causative role of a single risk factor in the development of a cancer:

_____

_____

Related activities: The Genetic Origins of Cancer

RA 2

Stem Cells

Stem cells are undifferentiated cells found in multicellular organisms. They are characterised by two features. The first, **self renewal**, is the ability to undergo numerous cycles of cell division while maintaining an unspecialised state. The second, **potency**, is the ability to differentiate into specialised cells. **Totipotent** cells, produced in the first few divisions of a fertilized egg, can differentiate into any cell type, embryonic or extra-embryonic. **Pluripotent cells** are descended from totipotent cells and can give rise to any of the cells derived from the three germ layers (endoderm, mesoderm, and ectoderm). Embryonic stem cells at the blastocyst stage and foetal stem cells are pluripotent. Adult (somatic) stem cells are termed **multipotent**. They are undifferentiated cells found among differentiated cells in a tissue or organ. These cells can give rise to several other cell types, but those types are limited mainly to the cells of the blood, heart, muscle and nerves. The primary roles of adult stem cells are to maintain and repair the tissue in which they are found. A potential use of stem cells is making cells and tissues for medical therapies, such as **cell replacement therapy** and **tissue engineering** (for example, for bone and skin grafts).

Stem Cells and Blood Cell Production

New blood cells are produced in the red bone marrrow, which becomes the main site of blood production after birth, taking over from the foetal liver. All types of blood cells develop from a single cell type: called a **multipotent stem cell** or haemocytoblast. These cells are capable of mitosis and of differentiation into 'committed' precursors of each of the main types of blood cell.

Each of the different cell lines is controlled by a specific **growth factor**. When a stem cell divides, one of its daughters remains a stem cell, while the other becomes a precursor cell, either a **lymphoid cell** or **myeloid cell**. These cells continue to mature into the various type of blood cells, developing their specialised features and characteristic roles as they do so.

Lymphoid precursor cell — Matures in thymus — T lymphocyte, Natural killer (NK) lymphocyte, B lymphocyte

Multipotent stem cell

Monocytes and macrophages

Red bone marrow

Myeloid precursor cell

Neutrophil, Basophil, Eosinophil — Granulocytes

Red blood cells

Platelets

Megakaryocyte

1. Describe the two defining features of stem cells:

   (a) _____

   (b) _____

2. Distinguish between embryonic stem cells and adult stem cells with respect to their **potency** and their potential applications in medical technologies:

   _____
   _____
   _____

3. Using an example, explain the purpose of stem cells in an adult: _____

   _____
   _____

4. Describe one potential advantage of using embryonic stem cells for tissue engineering technology: _____

   _____
   _____
   _____

Related activities: Differentiation of Human Cells
Web links: Stem Cells in the Spotlight, Stem Cell Resources

Differentiation of Human Cells

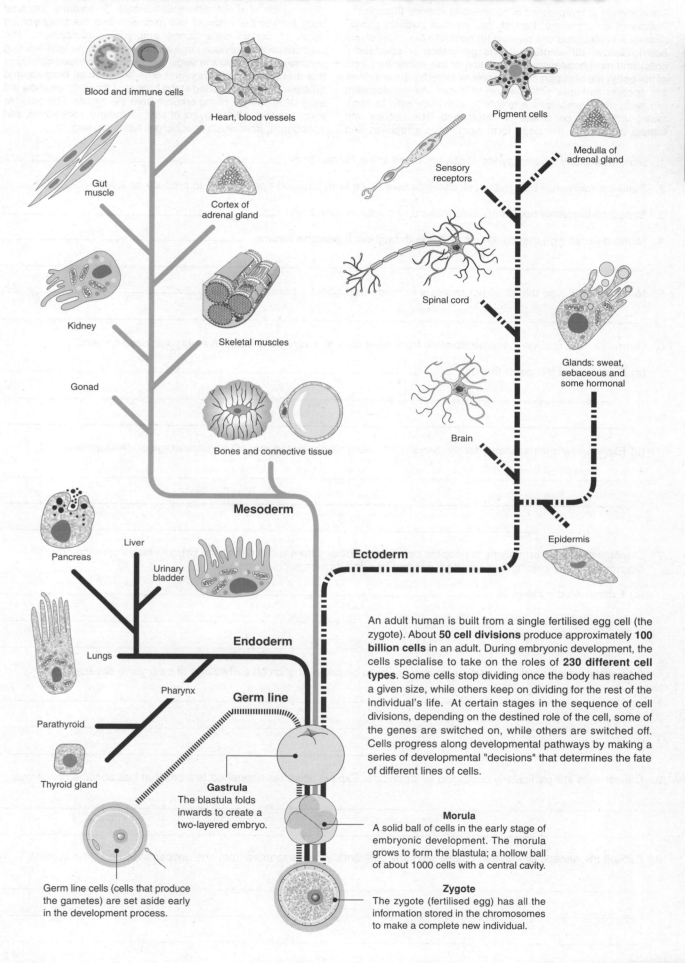

Blood and immune cells

Heart, blood vessels

Gut muscle

Cortex of adrenal gland

Kidney

Skeletal muscles

Gonad

Bones and connective tissue

Mesoderm

Pigment cells

Medulla of adrenal gland

Sensory receptors

Spinal cord

Glands: sweat, sebaceous and some hormonal

Brain

Epidermis

Ectoderm

Pancreas

Liver

Urinary bladder

Endoderm

Lungs

Pharynx

Germ line

Parathyroid

Thyroid gland

Gastrula
The blastula folds inwards to create a two-layered embryo.

An adult human is built from a single fertilised egg cell (the zygote). About **50 cell divisions** produce approximately **100 billion cells** in an adult. During embryonic development, the cells specialise to take on the roles of **230 different cell types**. Some cells stop dividing once the body has reached a given size, while others keep on dividing for the rest of the individual's life. At certain stages in the sequence of cell divisions, depending on the destined role of the cell, some of the genes are switched on, while others are switched off. Cells progress along developmental pathways by making a series of developmental "decisions" that determines the fate of different lines of cells.

Morula
A solid ball of cells in the early stage of embryonic development. The morula grows to form the blastula; a hollow ball of about 1000 cells with a central cavity.

Zygote
The zygote (fertilised egg) has all the information stored in the chromosomes to make a complete new individual.

Germ line cells (cells that produce the gametes) are set aside early in the development process.

Related activities: Cell Growth and Cancer, Stem Cells

RA 2

Development is the process of progressive change through the lifetime of an organism. Part of this process involves growth (increase in size) and cell division (to generate the multicellular body). Cellular **differentiation** (the generation of specialised cells) and morphogenesis (the creation of the shape and form of the body) are also part of development. Differentiation defines the specific structure and function of a cell. As development proceeds, the possibilities available to individual cells become fewer, until each cell's **fate** is determined. The tissues and organs making up the body form from the aggregation and organisation of these differentiated cells. In animals, the final body form is the result of cell migration and the programmed death of certain cells during embryonic development. The diagram on the previous page shows how a single fertilised egg (zygote) gives rise to the large number of specialised cell types that make up the adult human body. The morula, blastula, and gastrula stages mentioned at the bottom of the diagram show the early development of the embryo from the zygote. The gastrula gives rise to the three layers of cells (ectoderm, mesoderm, and endoderm), from which specific cell types develop.

1. State how many different types of cell are found in the human body: _____

2. State approximately how many cell divisions take place from fertilised egg (zygote) to produce an adult: _____

3. State approximately how many cells make up an adult human body: _____

4. Name one cell type that continues to divide throughout a person's lifetime: _____

_____

5. Name one cell type that does not continue to divide throughout a person's lifetime: _____

_____

6. Germ line cells diverge (become isolated) from other cells at a very early stage in embryonic development.

   (a) Explain what the **germ line** is: _____

_____

_____

   (b) Explain why it is necessary for the germ line to become separated at such an early stage of development:

_____

_____

_____

7. Cloning whole new organisms is possible by taking a nucleus from a cell during the blastula stage of embryonic development and placing it into an egg cell that has had its own nucleus removed.

   (a) Explain what a **clone** is: _____

_____

_____

   (b) Explain why the cell required for cloning needs to be taken at such an early stage of embryonic development:

_____

_____

_____

8. Cancer cells are particularly damaging to organisms. Explain what has happened to a cell that has become cancerous:

_____

_____

9. Explain the genetic events that enable so many different cell types to arise from one unspecialised cell (the zygote):

_____

_____

_____

Human Cell Specialisation

Animal cells are often specialised to perform particular functions. The eight specialised cell types shown below are representative of some 230 different cell types in humans. Each has specialised features that suit it to performing a specific role.

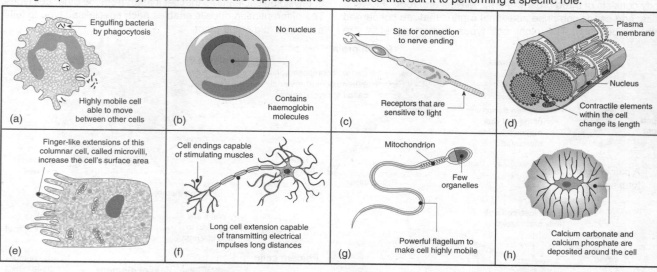

1. Identify each of the cells (b) to (h) pictured above, and describe their **specialised features** and **role** in the body:

(a) Type of cell: _Phagocytic white blood cell (neutrophil)_

   Specialised features: _Engulfs bacteria and other foreign material by phagocytosis_

   Role of cell within body: _Destroys pathogens and other foreign material as well as cellular debris_

(b) Type of cell: _____

   Specialised features: _____

   Role of cell within body: _____

(c) Type of cell: _____

   Specialised features: _____

   Role of cell within body: _____

(d) Type of cell: _____

   Specialised features: _____

   Role of cell within body: _____

(e) Type of cell: _____

   Specialised features: _____

   Role of cell within body: _____

(f) Type of cell: _____

   Specialised features: _____

   Role of cell within body: _____

(g) Type of cell: _____

   Specialised features: _____

   Role of cell within body: _____

(h) Type of cell: _____

   Specialised features: _____

   Role of cell within body: _____

Related activities: Animal Cells   RA 2

Plant Cell Specialisation

Plants show a wide variety of cell types. The vegetative plant body consists of three organs: stems, leaves, and roots. Flowers, fruits, and seeds comprise additional organs that are concerned with reproduction. The eight cell types illustrated below are representatives of these plant organ systems. Each has structural or physiological features that set it apart from the other cell types. The differentiation of cells enables each specialised type to fulfill a specific role in the plant.

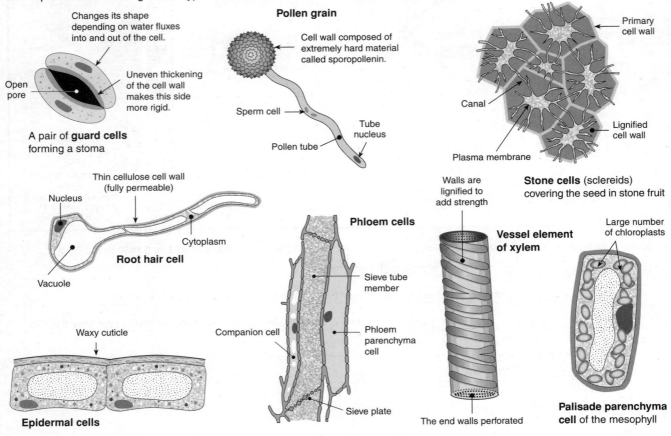

1. Using the information given above, describe the **specialised features** and **role** of each of the cell types (b)-(h) below:

(a) **Guard cell**: Features: _Curved, sausage shaped cell, unevenly thickened._

  Role in plant: _Turgor changes alter the cell shape to open or close the stoma._

(b) **Pollen grain**: Features: _____

  Role in plant: _____

(c) **Palisade parenchyma cell**: Features: _____

  Role in plant: _____

(d) **Epidermal cell**: Features: _____

  Role in plant: _____

(e) **Vessel element**: Features: _____

  Role in plant: _____

(f) **Stone cell**: Features: _____

  Role in plant: _____

(g) **Sieve tube member** (of phloem): Features: _____

  Role in plant: _____

(h) **Root hair cell**: Features: _____

  Role in plant: _____

Related activities: Plant Cells

Root Cell Development

In plants, cell division for growth (mitosis) is restricted to growing tips called **meristematic** tissue. These are located at the tips of every stem and root. This is unlike mitosis in a growing animal where cell divisions can occur all over the body. The diagram below illustrates the position and appearance of developing and growing cells in a plant root. Similar zones of development occur in the growing stem tips, which may give rise to specialised structures such as leaves and flowers.

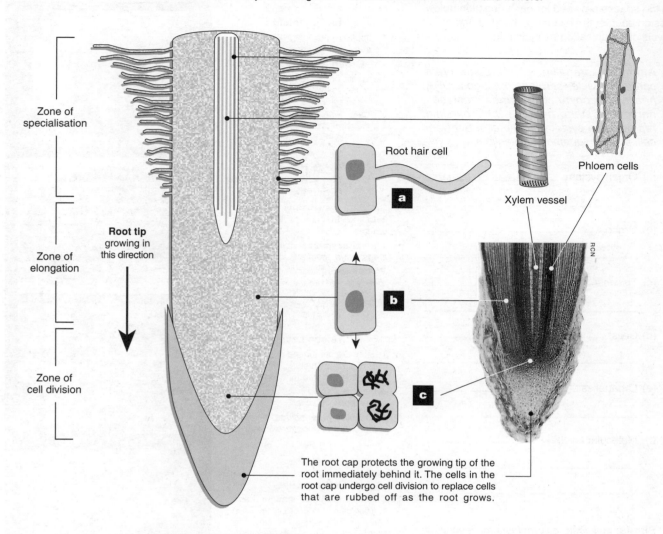

Zone of specialisation

Root hair cell

Phloem cells

Xylem vessel

a

Root tip
growing in
this direction

Zone of elongation

b

Zone of cell division

c

The root cap protects the growing tip of the root immediately behind it. The cells in the root cap undergo cell division to replace cells that are rubbed off as the root grows.

1. Briefly describe what is happening to the plant cells at each of the points labelled (**a**) to (**c**) in the diagram above:

   (a) _____

   (b) _____

   (c) _____

2. The light micrograph (below) shows a section of the cells of an onion root tip, stained to show up the chromosomes.

   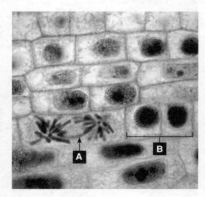

   (a) State the mitotic stage of the cell labelled A and explain your answer:

   _____

   (b) State the mitotic stage just completed in the cells labelled B and explain:

   _____

   (c) If, in this example, 250 cells were examined and 25 were found to be in the process of mitosis, state the proportion of the cell cycle occupied by mitosis:

   _____

   _____

3. Identify the cells that divide and specialise when a tree increases its girth (diameter): _____

Levels of Organisation

Organisation and the emergence of novel properties in complex systems are two of the defining features of living organisms. Organisms are organised according to a hierarchy of structural levels (below), each level building on the one below it. At each level, novel properties emerge that were not present at the simpler level. Hierarchical organisation allows specialised cells to group together into tissues and organs to perform a particular function. This improves efficiency of function in the organism.

In the spaces provided for each question below, assign each of the examples listed to one of the levels of organisation as indicated.

1. **Animals**: *adrenaline, blood, bone, brain, cardiac muscle, cartilage, collagen, DNA, heart, leucocyte, lysosome, mast cell, nervous system, neurone, phospholipid, reproductive system, ribosomes, Schwann cell, spleen, squamous epithelium.*

(a) Organ system: _____

_____

(b) Organs: _____

_____

(c) Tissues: _____

_____

(d) Cells: _____

_____

(e) Organelles: _____

_____

(f) Molecular level: _____

_____

_____

2. **Plants**: *cellulose, chloroplasts, collenchyma, companion cells, DNA, epidermal cell, fibres, flowers, leaf, mesophyll, parenchyma, pectin, phloem, phospholipid, ribosomes, roots, sclerenchyma, tracheid.*

(a) Organs: _____

_____

(b) Tissues: _____

_____

(c) Cells: _____

_____

(d) Organelles: _____

_____

(e) Molecular level: _____

_____

_____

The Organism
A complex, functioning whole that is the sum of all its component parts.

Organ System Level
In animals, organs form parts of even larger units known as organ systems. An organ system is an association of organs with a common function e.g. digestive system, cardiovascular system, and the urinogenital system.

Organ Level
Organs are structures of definite form and structure, comprising two or more tissues.
Animal examples include: heart, lungs, brain, stomach, kidney.
Plant examples include: leaves, roots, storage organs, ovary.

Tissue Level
Tissues are composed of groups of cells of similar structure that perform a particular, related function.
Animal examples include: epithelial tissue, bone, muscle.
Plant examples include: phloem, chlorenchyma, endodermis, xylem.

Cellular Level
Cells are the basic structural and functional units of an organism. Each cell type has a different structure and function; the result of cellular differentiation during development.
Animal examples include: epithelial cells, osteoblasts, muscle fibres.
Plant examples include: sclereids, xylem vessels, sieve tubes.

Organelle Level
Many diverse molecules may associate together to form complex, highly specialised structures within cells called cellular organelles e.g. mitochondria, Golgi apparatus, endoplasmic reticulum, chloroplasts.

Chemical and Molecular Level
Atoms and molecules form the most basic, level of organisation. This level includes all the chemicals essential for maintaining life e.g. water, ions, fats, carbohydrates, amino acids, proteins, and nucleic acids.

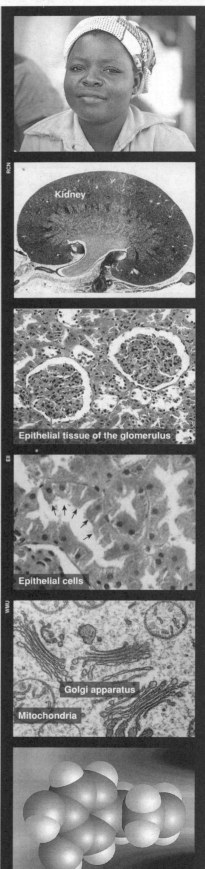

Kidney

Epithelial tissue of the glomerulus

Epithelial cells

Golgi apparatus

Mitochondria

Related activities: Animal Tissues, Plant Tissues

Animal Tissues

The study of tissues (plant or animal) is called **histology**. The cells of a tissue, and their associated intracellular substances, e.g. collagen, are grouped together to perform particular functions. Tissues improve the efficiency of operation because they enable tasks to be shared amongst various specialised cells. **Animal tissues** can be divided into four broad groups: **epithelial tissues**, **connective tissues**, **muscle**, and **nervous**

tissues. Organs usually consist of several types of tissue. The heart mostly consists of cardiac muscle tissue, but also has epithelial tissue, which lines the heart chambers to prevent leaking, connective tissue for strength and elasticity, and nervous tissue, in the form of neurones, which direct the contractions of the cardiac muscle. The features of some of he more familiar animal tissues are described below.

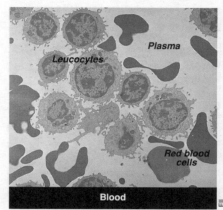

Blood

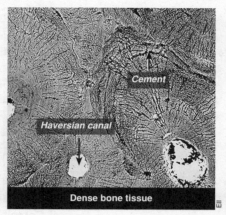

Dense bone tissue

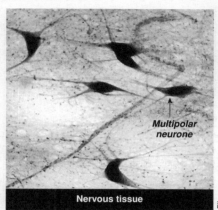

Nervous tissue

Connective tissue is the major supporting tissue of the animal body. It comprises cells, widely dispersed in a semi-fluid matrix. Connective tissues bind other structures together and provide support, and protection against damage, infection, or heat loss. Connective tissues include dentine (teeth), adipose (fat) tissue, bone (above) and cartilage, and the tissues around the body's organs and blood vessels. Blood (above, left) is a special type of liquid tissue, comprising cells floating in a liquid matrix.

Nervous tissue contains densely packed nerve cells (neurones) which are specialised for the transmission of nerve impulses. Associated with the neurones there may also be supporting cells and connective tissue containing blood vessels.

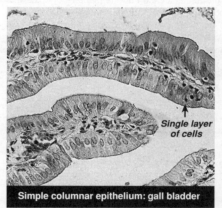

Simple columnar epithelium: gall bladder

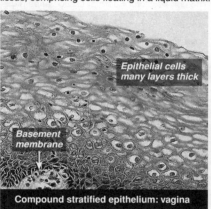

Compound stratified epithelium: vagina

Skeletal (striated) muscle fibres

Epithelial tissue is organised into single (above, left) or layered (above) sheets. It lines internal and external surfaces (e.g. blood vessels, ducts, gut lining) and protects the underlying structures from wear, infection, and/or pressure. Epithelial cells rest on a basement membrane of fibres and collagen and are held together by a carbohydrate-based "glue". The cells may also be specialised for absorption, secretion, or excretion. Examples: stratified (compound) epithelium of vagina, ciliated epithelium of respiratory tract, cuboidal epithelium of kidney ducts, and the columnar epithelium of the intestine.

Muscle tissue consists of very highly specialised cells called fibres, held together by connective tissue. The three types of muscle in the body are cardiac muscle, skeletal muscle (above), and smooth muscle. Muscles bring about both voluntary and involuntary (unconscious) body movements.

1. Explain how the development of tissues improves functional efficiency: _____

_____

_____

2. Describe the general functional role of each of the following broad tissue types:

   (a) Epithelial tissue: _____   (c) Muscle tissue: _____

   (b) Nervous tissue: _____   (d) Connective tissue: _____

3. Identify the particular features that contribute to the particular functional role of each of the following tissue types:

   (a) Muscle tissue: _____

   _____

   (b) Nervous tissue: _____

   _____

Plant Tissues

Plant tissues are divided into two groups: simple and complex. **Simple tissues** contain only one cell type and form packing and support tissues. **Complex tissues** contain more than one cell type and form the conducting and support tissues of plants. Tissues are in turn grouped into tissue systems which make up the plant body. Vascular plants have three systems; the dermal, vascular, and ground tissue systems. The **dermal system** is the outer covering of the plant providing protection and reducing water loss. **Vascular tissue** provides the transport system by which water and nutrients are moved through the plant. The **ground tissue** system, which makes up the bulk of a plant, is made up mainly of simple tissues such as parenchyma, and carries out a wide variety of roles within the plant including photosynthesis, storage, and support.

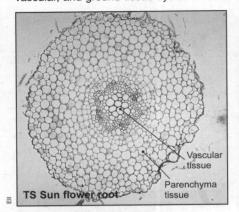

TS Sun flower root — Vascular tissue / Parenchyma tissue

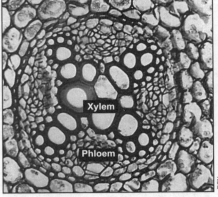

Xylem / Phloem

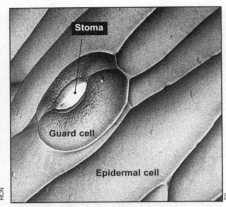

Stoma / Guard cell / Epidermal cell

Simple Tissues

Simple tissues consists of only one or two cell types. **Parenchyma tissue** is the most common and involved in storage, photosynthesis, and secretion. **Collenchyma tissue** comprises thick-walled collenchyma cells alternating with layers of intracellular substances (pectin and cellulose) to provide flexible support. The cells of **sclerenchyma** tissue (fibres and sclereids) have rigid cell walls which provide support.

Complex Tissues

Xylem and phloem tissue (above left), which together make up the plant **vascular tissue** system, are complex tissues. Each comprises several tissue types including tracheids, vessel members, parenchyma and fibres in xylem, and sieve tube members, companion cells, parenchyma and sclerenchyma in phloem. **Dermal tissue** is also complex tissue and covers the outside of the plant. The composition of dermal tissue varies depending upon its location on the plant. Root epidermal tissue consist of epidermal cells which extend to root hairs (**trichomes**) for increasing surface area. In contrast, the epidermal tissue of leaves (above right) are covered by a waxy cuticle to reduce water loss, and specialised guard cells regulate water intake via the stomata (pores in the leaf through which gases enter and leave the leaf tissue).

1. The table below lists the major types of simple and complex plant tissue. Complete the table by filling in the role each of the tissue types plays within the plant. The first example has been completed for you.

Simple Tissue	Cell Type(s)	Role within the Plant
Parenchyma	Parenchyma cells	Involved in respiration, photosynthesis, storage and secretion.
Collenchyma		
Sclerenchyma		
Root endodermis	Endodermal cells	
Pericycle		
Complex Tissue		
Leaf mesophyll	Spongy mesophyll cells, palisade mesophyll cells	
Xylem		
Phloem		
Epidermis		

Related activities: Levels of Organisation, Xylem, Phloem

Gas Exchange in Animals

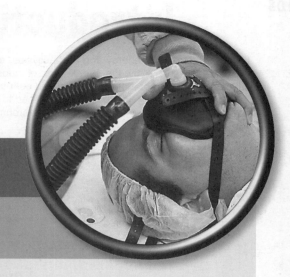

Learning Objectives

☐ 1. Compile your own glossary from the **KEY WORDS** displayed in **bold type** in the learning objectives below.

The Basics of Gas Exchange *(pages 108-110)*

☐ 2. Distinguish between **cellular respiration** and **gas exchange** and explain why organisms need to exchange materials with their environment.

☐ 3. Describe the relationship between an organism's size and its surface area (the **surface area: volume ratio** or **SA:V**). Explain why multicellular organisms need specialised exchange surfaces whereas single-celled organisms do not.

☐ 4. Explain how **respiratory gases** are exchanged across gas exchange surfaces. Describe the essential features of an efficient gas exchange surface. With reference to **Fick's law**, explain the significance of these features.

☐ 5. Recognise that gas exchange systems in organisms are adapted to meet the metabolic demands of the organism in the environment in which it lives. Relate this to the different types of gas exchange systems and **respiratory pigments** seen in different phyla.

☐ 6. Explain what is meant by **ventilation** of the gas exchange surface. Recognise the need for ventilation mechanisms in animals and explain how the ventilation mechanism is related to the organism's environment.

Gas Exchange in Humans *(pages 108-110, 131)*
Humans are provided as the mammalian example

☐ 7. Describe the structure, location, adaptations, and function of the gas exchange surfaces and related structures in humans (**trachea**, **bronchi**, **bronchioles**, **lungs**, and **alveoli**). Explain how these features contribute to efficient gas exchange.

☐ 8. Describe the distribution of the following tissues and cells in the **trachea**, **bronchi**, and **bronchioles**:

cartilage, **ciliated epithelium**, **goblet cells**, and **smooth muscle cells**. Describe the function of the **cartilage**, **cilia**, **goblet cells**, **smooth muscle**, and **elastic fibres** in the gas exchange system.

☐ 9. Recognise the relationship between gas exchange surfaces (alveoli) and the blood vessels in the lung tissue. Draw a simple diagram of an **alveolus** (air sac) to illustrate the movement of O_2 and CO_2, into and out of the blood in the surrounding capillary.

☐ 10. Describe the mechanism of ventilation (**breathing**) in humans. Include reference to the following:

　(a) The role of the rib cage, **diaphragm**, **intercostal muscles**, and **pleural membranes** in breathing.

　(b) The role of **surfactants** in lung function.

　(c) The distinction between **inspiration** (inhalation) as an active process and **expiration** (exhalation) as a passive process (during normal, quiet breathing).

☐ 11. Describe how a **spirometer** is used to measure **vital capacity**, **tidal volume**, breathing rate, and oxygen uptake in humans.

☐ 12. Explain how the breathing (ventilation) rate and **pulmonary ventilation** (PV) rate are calculated and expressed. Provide some typical values for **breathing rate**, **tidal volume**, and **PV**. Describe how each of these is affected by strenuous exercise.

Extension: Controlling Breathing *(page 115)*

☐ 13. Explain how basic rhythm of breathing is controlled through the **respiratory centre** in the medulla.

☐ 14. Identify influences on the respiratory centre and describe how these reflect changes in the body's demand for oxygen. Include reference to the activity of the **chemoreceptors** in the carotid arteries and the aorta and their response to low blood pH.

Material on the effects of cigarette smoking on the gas exchange system is covered in "Human Disease".

 **Textbooks**

 See the 'Textbook Reference Grid' on page 7 for textbook page references relating to material in this topic.

Supplementary Texts

See pages 5-6 for additional details of these texts:

■ Adds, J. *et al.*, 2004. **Exchange & Transport, Energy & Ecosystems** (NelsonThornes), pp. 2-26.

■ Clegg, C.J., 1998. **Mammals: Structure and Function** (John Murray), pp. 24-31.

 Periodicals

See page 6 for details of publishers of periodicals:

STUDENT'S REFERENCE

■ **Lungs and the Control of Breathing** Bio. Sci. Rev. 14(4) April 2002, pp. 2-5. *The mechanisms, control, and measurement of breathing. This article includes good, clear diagrams and useful summaries of the important points.*

■ **Gas Exchange in the Lungs** Bio. Sci. Rev. 16(1) Sept. 2003, pp. 36-38. *The structure and function of the alveoli of the lungs, with an account of respiratory problems and diseases such as respiratory distress syndrome and emphysema.*

 **Internet**

See pages 8-9 for details of how to access **Bio Links** from our web site: **www.biozone.co.uk**. From Bio Links, access sites under the topics:

GENERAL BIOLOGY ONLINE RESOURCES

• Biology I interactive animations　*… and others*
> **Online Textbooks and Lecture Notes**:
Human biology help • Learn.co.uk • S-Cool! A level biology revision guide *… and others*

ANIMAL BIOLOGY: • Anatomy and physiology •
Human physiology lecture notes *… and others* >
Gas Exchange: • Gas exchange • Lesson 11: The respiratory system • Respiratory system • Respiratory system: Chpt 41

Introduction to Gas Exchange

Living cells require energy for the activities of life. Energy is released in cells by the breakdown of sugars and other substances in the metabolic process called **cellular respiration**. As a consequence of this process, gases need to be exchanged between the respiring cells and the environment. In most organisms (with the exception of some bacterial groups) these gases are carbon dioxide (CO_2) and oxygen (O_2). The diagram below illustrates this process for an animal. Plant cells also respire, but their gas exchange budget is different because they also produce O_2 and consume CO_2 in photosynthesis.

The Need for Gas Exchange

Gas exchange is the process by which oxygen is acquired and carbon dioxide is removed. Cellular respiration creates a constant demand for oxygen (O_2) and a need to eliminate carbon dioxide gas (CO_2).

Gas exchange surfaces provide a means for gases to enter and leave the body. Some organisms use the body surface as the sole gas exchange surface, but many have specialised gas exchange structures (e.g. lungs, gills, or stomata). Amphibians use the body surface and simple lungs to provide for their gas exchange requirements.

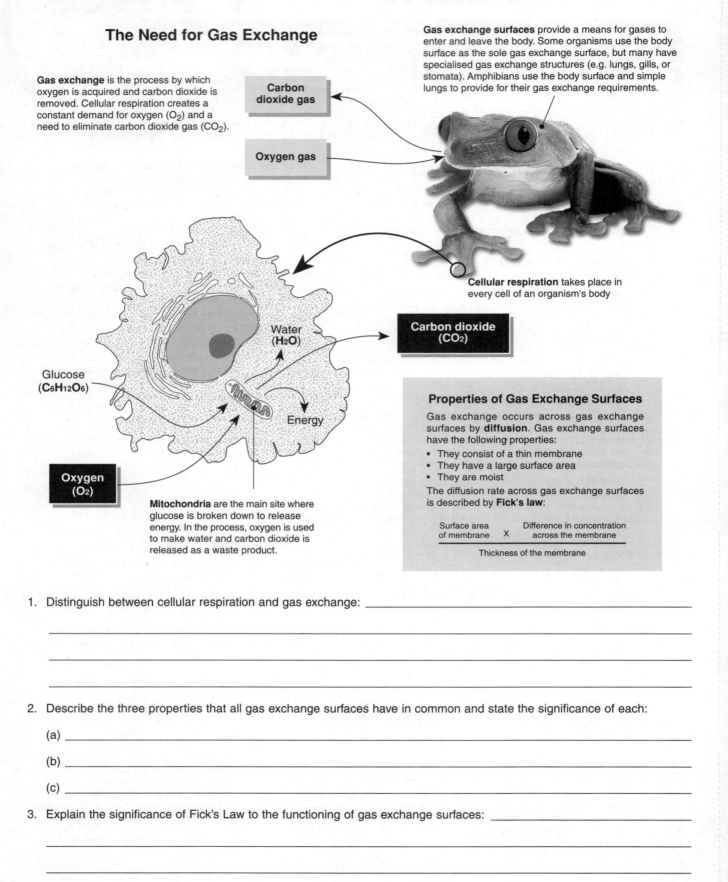

Carbon dioxide gas

Oxygen gas

Cellular respiration takes place in every cell of an organism's body

Water (H_2O)

Glucose ($C_6H_{12}O_6$)

Energy

Carbon dioxide (CO_2)

Oxygen (O_2)

Mitochondria are the main site where glucose is broken down to release energy. In the process, oxygen is used to make water and carbon dioxide is released as a waste product.

Properties of Gas Exchange Surfaces

Gas exchange occurs across gas exchange surfaces by **diffusion**. Gas exchange surfaces have the following properties:

- They consist of a thin membrane
- They have a large surface area
- They are moist

The diffusion rate across gas exchange surfaces is described by **Fick's law**:

$$\frac{\text{Surface area of membrane} \quad X \quad \text{Difference in concentration across the membrane}}{\text{Thickness of the membrane}}$$

1. Distinguish between cellular respiration and gas exchange: _____

_____

_____

2. Describe the three properties that all gas exchange surfaces have in common and state the significance of each:

(a) _____

(b) _____

(c) _____

3. Explain the significance of Fick's Law to the functioning of gas exchange surfaces: _____

_____

_____

Related activities: Diffusion, Surface Area and Volume

Gas Exchange in Animals

The way in which gas exchange is achieved is influenced by the animal's general body form and by the environment in which the animal lives. Small, aquatic organisms such as sponges, flatworms and cnidarians, require no specialised respiratory structures. Gases are exchanged between the surrounding water (or moist environment) and the body's cells by diffusion directly across the organism's surface. Larger animals require specialised gas exchange systems. The complexity of these is related to the efficiency of gas exchange required, which is determined by the oxygen demands of the organism.

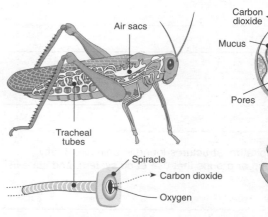

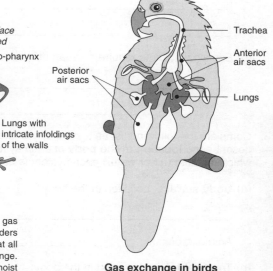

Gas exchange in insects

Insects, and sometimes spiders, transport gases via a system of branching tubes called **tracheae** or **tracheal tubes**. The gases move by diffusion across the moist lining directly to and from the tissues. The end of each tube contains a small amount of fluid which regulates the movement of gases by changing the surface area of air in contact with the cells.

Gas exchange in amphibians

All amphibians make some use of surface gas exchange. There are even some salamanders (a type of amphibian) that have no lungs at all and rely completely on surface gas exchange. This is only possible if the surface is kept moist by secretions from mucous glands. Frogs carry out gas exchange through the skin and in the lungs. At times of inactivity, the skin alone is a sufficient surface with either water or air.

Gas exchange in birds

A bird has air sacs in addition to lungs. The air sacs function in ventilating the lungs, where gas exchange takes place. Together, the anterior and posterior air sacs function as bellows that keep air flowing through the lungs continuously and in one direction.

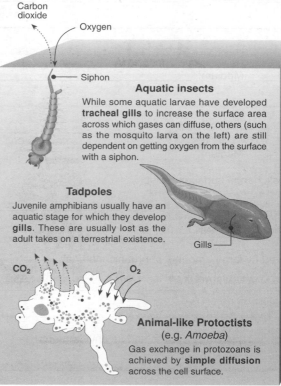

Aquatic insects

While some aquatic larvae have developed **tracheal gills** to increase the surface area across which gases can diffuse, others (such as the mosquito larva on the left) are still dependent on getting oxygen from the surface with a siphon.

Tadpoles

Juvenile amphibians usually have an aquatic stage for which they develop **gills**. These are usually lost as the adult takes on a terrestrial existence.

Animal-like Protoctists
(e.g. *Amoeba*)

Gas exchange in protozoans is achieved by **simple diffusion** across the cell surface.

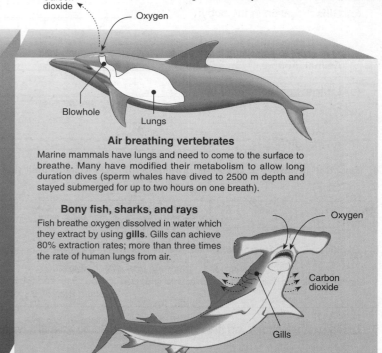

Air breathing vertebrates

Marine mammals have lungs and need to come to the surface to breathe. Many have modified their metabolism to allow long duration dives (sperm whales have dived to 2500 m depth and stayed submerged for up to two hours on one breath).

Bony fish, sharks, and rays

Fish breathe oxygen dissolved in water which they extract by using **gills**. Gills can achieve 80% extraction rates; more than three times the rate of human lungs from air.

Jellyfish increase their surface area for gas exchange by having ruffles.

Nudibranch snails have elaborate exposed gills to assist gas exchange.

Some salamanders have no lungs and breathe solely through their skin.

Tube worms carry out gas exchange with feathery extensions in the water.

Related activities: Diffusion

ERA 2

1. Suggest two reasons for the development of gas exchange structures and systems in animals:

   (a) _____

   (b) _____

2. (a) Explain why the air sacs of birds provide more efficient use of the air taken in with each breath:

   _____

   _____

   (b) Explain why birds require such an efficient method of gas exchange: _____

   _____

   _____

3. Complete the following list as a summary of the main features of the respiratory structures found in animals. Briefly describe the **location in the body** of each system, name the animal group or groups that use each system, and state in which medium (air or water) each system is used:

   (a) **Body surface**: Location in the body: _____

   _____

   Animal groups: _____ Medium: _____

   (b) **Tracheal tubes**: Location in the body: _____

   _____

   Animal groups: _____ Medium: _____

   (c) **Gills**: Location in the body: _____

   _____

   Animal groups: _____ Medium: _____

   (d) **Lungs**: Location in the body: _____

   _____

   Animal groups: _____ Medium: _____

4. Describe two ways in which air breathers manage to keep their gas exchange surfaces moist:

   (a) _____

   (b) _____

5. Explain why organisms with gills are at risk when their water is polluted by large amounts of organic material:

   _____

   _____

6. Using examples, discuss the relationship between an animal's type of gas exchange system and its environment:

   _____

   _____

   _____

   _____

   _____

   _____

The Human Respiratory System

Lungs are internal sac-like organs found in most amphibians, and all reptiles, birds, and mammals. The paired lungs of mammals are connected to the outside air by way of a system of tubular passageways: the trachea, bronchi, and bronchioles. Ciliated, mucus secreting epithelium lines this system of tubules, trapping and removing dust and pathogens before they reach the gas exchange surfaces. Each lung is divided into a number of lobes, each receiving its own bronchus. Each bronchus divides many times, terminating in the respiratory bronchioles from which arise 2-11 alveolar ducts and numerous **alveoli** (air sacs). These provide a very large surface area (70 m^2) for the exchange of respiratory gases by diffusion between the alveoli and the blood in the capillaries. The details of this exchange across the **respiratory membrane** are described opposite.

Morphology of the Respiratory System

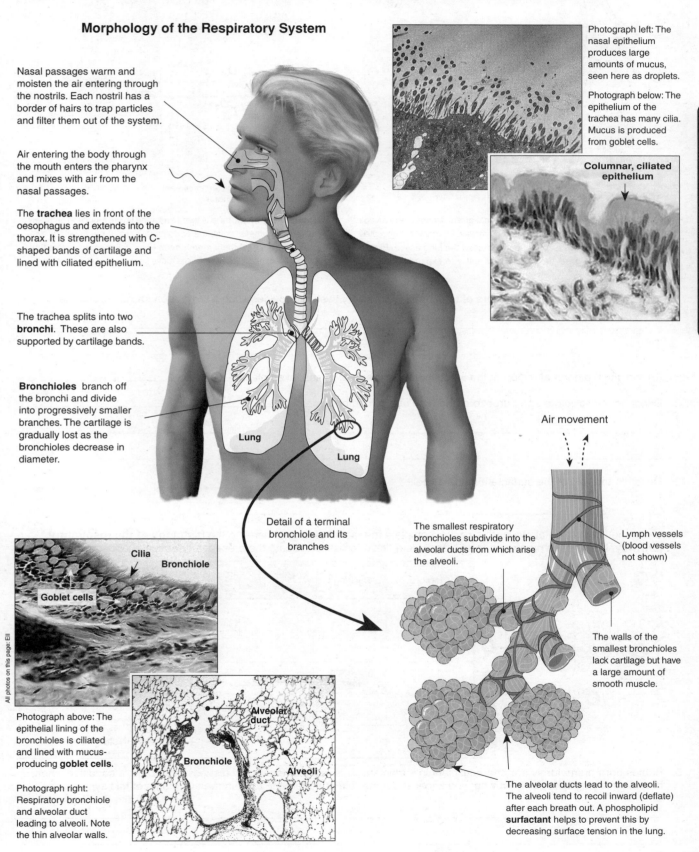

Nasal passages warm and moisten the air entering through the nostrils. Each nostril has a border of hairs to trap particles and filter them out of the system.

Air entering the body through the mouth enters the pharynx and mixes with air from the nasal passages.

The **trachea** lies in front of the oesophagus and extends into the thorax. It is strengthened with C-shaped bands of cartilage and lined with ciliated epithelium.

The trachea splits into two **bronchi**. These are also supported by cartilage bands.

Bronchioles branch off the bronchi and divide into progressively smaller branches. The cartilage is gradually lost as the bronchioles decrease in diameter.

Lung

Lung

Photograph left: The nasal epithelium produces large amounts of mucus, seen here as droplets.

Photograph below: The epithelium of the trachea has many cilia. Mucus is produced from goblet cells.

Columnar, ciliated epithelium

Cilia
Bronchiole

Goblet cells

All photos on this page: EII

Photograph above: The epithelial lining of the bronchioles is ciliated and lined with mucus-producing **goblet cells**.

Photograph right: Respiratory bronchiole and alveolar duct leading to alveoli. Note the thin alveolar walls.

Alveolar duct

Bronchiole

Alveoli

Detail of a terminal bronchiole and its branches

Air movement

The smallest respiratory bronchioles subdivide into the alveolar ducts from which arise the alveoli.

Lymph vessels (blood vessels not shown)

The walls of the smallest bronchioles lack cartilage but have a large amount of smooth muscle.

The alveolar ducts lead to the alveoli. The alveoli tend to recoil inward (deflate) after each breath out. A phospholipid **surfactant** helps to prevent this by decreasing surface tension in the lung.

Related activities: Gas Transport in Humans, Breathing in Humans, Review of Lung Function

RA 2

Gas Exchange in Animals

An Alveolus

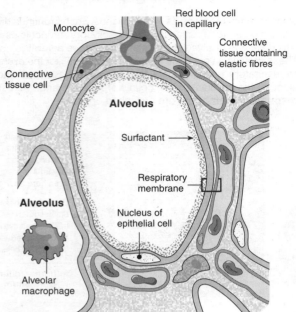

Monocyte

Red blood cell in capillary

Connective tissue containing elastic fibres

Connective tissue cell

Alveolus

Surfactant

Respiratory membrane

Alveolus

Nucleus of epithelial cell

Alveolar macrophage

The diagram above illustrates the physical arrangement of the alveoli to the capillaries through which the blood moves. Phagocytic monocytes and macrophages are also present to protect the lung tissue. Elastic connective tissue gives the alveoli their ability to expand and recoil.

The Respiratory Membrane

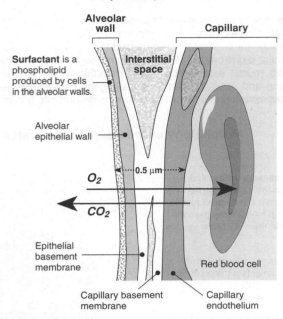

Alveolar wall

Capillary

Surfactant is a phospholipid produced by cells in the alveolar walls.

Interstitial space

Alveolar epithelial wall

O_2

0.5 µm

CO_2

Epithelial basement membrane

Red blood cell

Capillary basement membrane

Capillary endothelium

The **respiratory membrane** is the term for the layered junction between the alveolar epithelial cells, the endothelial cells of the capillary, and their associated basement membranes (thin, collagenous layers that underlie the epithelial tissues). Gases move freely across this membrane.

1. (a) Explain how the basic structure of the human respiratory system provides such a large area for gas exchange:

_____

_____

(b) Identify the general region of the lung where exchange of gases takes place: _____

2. Describe the structure and purpose of the respiratory membrane: _____

_____

_____

3. Describe the role of the surfactant in the alveoli: _____

_____

4. Using the information above and opposite, complete the table below summarising the **histology of the respiratory pathway**. Name each numbered region and use a tick or cross to indicate the presence or absence of particular tissues.

	Region	Cartilage	Ciliated epithelium	Goblet cells (mucus)	Smooth muscle	Connective tissue
1						✓
2						
3		gradually lost				
4	Alveolar duct		✗	✗		
5					very little	

5. Babies born prematurely are often deficient in surfactant. This causes respiratory distress syndrome; a condition where breathing is very difficult. From what you know about the role of surfactant, explain the symptoms of this syndrome:

_____

_____

Breathing in Humans

In mammals, the mechanism of breathing (ventilation) provides a continual supply of fresh air to the lungs and helps to maintain a large diffusion gradient for respiratory gases across the gas exchange surface. Oxygen must be delivered regularly to supply the needs of respiring cells. Similarly, carbon dioxide, which is produced as a result of cellular metabolism, must be quickly eliminated from the body. Adequate lung ventilation is essential to these exchanges. The cardiovascular system participates by transporting respiratory gases to and from the cells of the body. The volume of gases exchanged during breathing varies according to the physiological demands placed on the body (e.g. by exercise). These changes can be measured using spirometry.

Gas Exchange in Animals

Inspiration (inhalation or breathing in)

During quiet breathing, inspiration is achieved by increasing the space (therefore decreasing the pressure) inside the lungs. Air then flows into the lungs to fill the space. Inspiration is always an active process involving muscle contraction.

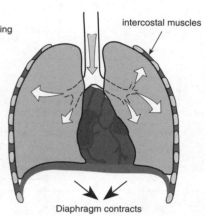

1a External intercostal muscles contract causing the ribcage to expand and move up

1b Diaphragm contracts and drops downwards

2 Thoracic volume increases, lungs expand, and the pressure inside the lungs decreases

3 Air flows into the lungs in response to the pressure gradient

intercostal muscles

Diaphragm contracts

Expiration (exhalation or breathing out)

During quiet breathing, expiration is achieved passively by decreasing the space (thus increasing the pressure) inside the lungs. Air then flows passively out of the lungs to equalize with the air pressure. In active breathing, muscle contraction is involved in bringing about both inspiration and expiration.

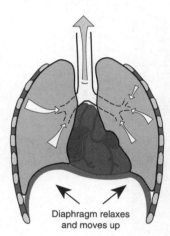

1 In **quiet breathing**, external intercostal muscles and diaphragm relax. Elasticity of the lung tissue causes recoil.

In **forced breathing**, the internal intercostals and abdominal muscles also contract to increase the force of the expiration

2 Thoracic volume decreases and the pressure inside the lungs increases

3 Air flows passively out of the lungs in response to the pressure gradient

Diaphragm relaxes and moves up

Using spirometry to determine changes in lung volume

The apparatus used to measure the amount of air exchanged during breathing and the rate of breathing is a **spirometer** (also called a respirometer). A simple spirometer consists of a weighted drum, containing oxygen or air, inverted over a chamber of water. A tube connects the air-filled chamber with the subject's mouth, and soda lime in the system absorbs the carbon dioxide breathed out. Breathing results in a trace called a spirogram, from which lung volumes can be measured directly.

During inspiration
Air is removed from the chamber, the drum sinks, and an upward deflection is recorded on the paper on the rotating drum.

During expiration
Air is added to the chamber, the drum rises, and a downward deflection is recorded.

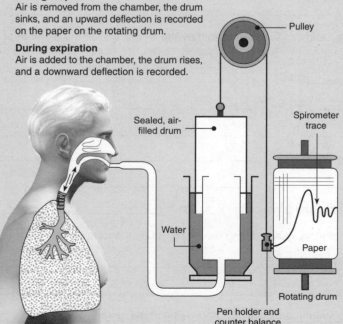

Pulley

Sealed, air-filled drum

Spirometer trace

Water

Paper

Pen holder and counter balance

Rotating drum

Lung Volumes and Capacities

The air in the lungs can be divided into volumes. Lung capacities are combinations of volumes.

Description of volume	Vol / dm³
Tidal volume (TV) Volume of air breathed in and out in a single breath	0.5
Inspiratory reserve volume (IRV) Volume breathed in by a maximum inspiration at the end of a normal inspiration	3.3
Expiratory reserve volume (ERV) Volume breathed out by a maximum effort at the end of a normal expiration	1.0
Residual volume (RV) Volume of air remaining in the lungs at the end of a maximum expiration	1.2
Description of capacity	
Inspiratory capacity (IC) = TV + IRV Volume breathed in by a maximum inspiration at the end of a normal expiration	3.8
Vital capacity (VC) = IRV + TV + ERV Volume breathed in by a maximum inspiration following a maximum expiration	4.8
Total lung capacity (TLC) = VC + RV The total volume of the lungs. Only a fraction of TLC is used in normal breathing	6.0

Only about 70% of the air that is inhaled reaches the alveoli. The rest remains in the air spaces of the nose, throat, larynx, trachea and bronchi. This air is unavailable for gas exchange and is called the **dead air volume (dead space air)**.

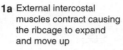

Related activities: The Human Respiratory System
Web links: Effects of Training, Respiratory Basics Learning Activity

DA 2

Measuring Changes in Lung Volume

Changes in lung volume can be measured using spirometry (see opposite). Total adult lung volume varies between 4 and 6 litres (dm^3) (it is greater in males). The **vital capacity** is somewhat less than this because of the residual volume of air that remains in the lungs even after expiration. The exchange between fresh air and the residual volume is a slow process and the composition of gases in the lungs remains relatively constant (table, right). Once measured, the **tidal volume** can be used to calculate the pulmonary ventilation rate or **PV**: the amount of air exchanged with the environment per minute. During exercise, the breathing rate, tidal volume, and PV increase up to a maximum (as indicated below).

Respiratory gas	Approximate percentages of O_2 and CO_2		
	Inhaled air	Air in lungs	Exhaled air
O_2	21.0	13.8	16.4
CO_2	0.04	5.5	3.6

Above: The percentages of respiratory gases in air (by volume) during normal breathing. The percentage volume of oxygen in the alveolar air (in the lung) is lower than that in the exhaled air because of the influence of the dead air volume in the airways (air unavailable for gas exchange).

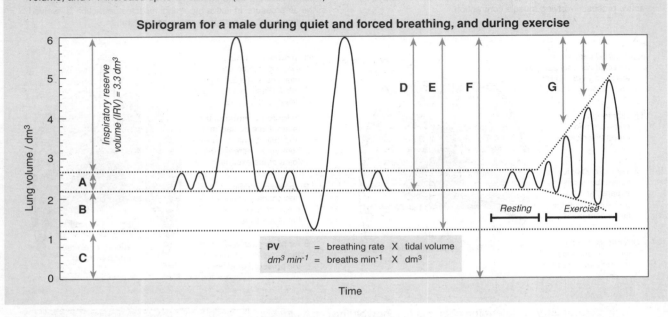

Spirogram for a male during quiet and forced breathing, and during exercise

PV $=$ breathing rate $\times$ tidal volume
$dm^3\ min^{-1}$ $=$ breaths min^{-1} $\times$ dm^3

1. (a) Briefly outline the sequence of events involved in quiet breathing: _____

_____

_____

(b) Explain the essential difference between this and the situation during heavy exercise or forced breathing: _____

_____

_____

2. Using the definitions given opposite, identify the volumes and capacities indicated by the letters **A-F** on the diagram of a spirogram above. For each, indicate the volume (vol) in dm^3. The inspiratory reserve volume has been identified for you:

(a) A: _____ Vol: _____   (d) D: _____ Vol: _____

(b) B: _____ Vol: _____   (e) E: _____ Vol: _____

(c) C: _____ Vol: _____   (f) F: _____ Vol: _____

3. Explain what is happening in the sequence indicated by the letter **G**: _____

_____

4. Calculate PV when breathing rate is 15 breaths per minute and tidal volume is 4.0 dm^3: _____

5. The table above gives approximate percentages for respiratory gases during breathing. Study the data and then:

(a) Calculate the difference in CO_2 between inhaled and exhaled air: _____

(b) Explain where this 'extra' CO_2 comes from: _____

(c) Explain why the dead air volume raises the oxygen content of exhaled air above that in the lungs: _____

_____

Control of Breathing

The basic rhythm of breathing is controlled by the **respiratory centre**, a cluster of neurones located in the medulla oblongata. This rhythm is adjusted in response to the physical and chemical changes that occur when we carry out different activities.

Although the control of breathing is involuntary, we can exert some degree of conscious control over it. The diagram below illustrates how breathing is regulated by these voluntary and involuntary controls.

The Control of Breathing

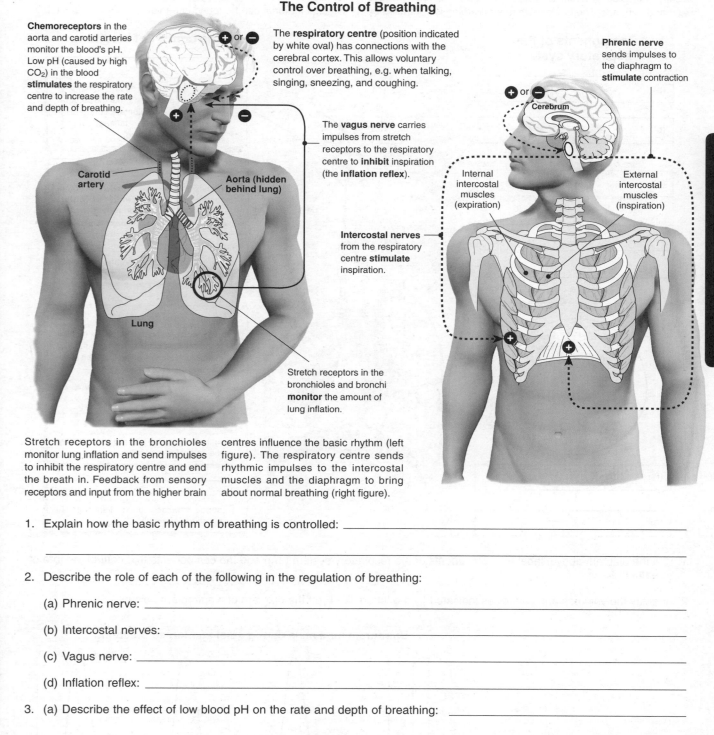

Chemoreceptors in the aorta and carotid arteries monitor the blood's pH. Low pH (caused by high CO_2) in the blood **stimulates** the respiratory centre to increase the rate and depth of breathing.

The **respiratory centre** (position indicated by white oval) has connections with the cerebral cortex. This allows voluntary control over breathing, e.g. when talking, singing, sneezing, and coughing.

Phrenic nerve sends impulses to the diaphragm to **stimulate** contraction

The **vagus nerve** carries impulses from stretch receptors to the respiratory centre to **inhibit** inspiration (the **inflation reflex**).

Intercostal nerves from the respiratory centre **stimulate** inspiration.

Stretch receptors in the bronchioles and bronchi **monitor** the amount of lung inflation.

Carotid artery

Aorta (hidden behind lung)

Lung

Cerebrum

Internal intercostal muscles (expiration)

External intercostal muscles (inspiration)

Gas Exchange in Animals

Stretch receptors in the bronchioles monitor lung inflation and send impulses to inhibit the respiratory centre and end the breath in. Feedback from sensory receptors and input from the higher brain centres influence the basic rhythm (left figure). The respiratory centre sends rhythmic impulses to the intercostal muscles and the diaphragm to bring about normal breathing (right figure).

1. Explain how the basic rhythm of breathing is controlled: _____

   _____

2. Describe the role of each of the following in the regulation of breathing:

   (a) Phrenic nerve: _____

   (b) Intercostal nerves: _____

   (c) Vagus nerve: _____

   (d) Inflation reflex: _____

3. (a) Describe the effect of low blood pH on the rate and depth of breathing: _____

   _____

   (b) Explain how this effect is mediated: _____

   _____

   (c) Suggest why blood pH is a good mechanism by which to regulate breathing rate: _____

   _____

   _____

Review of Lung Function

The respiratory system in humans and other air breathing vertebrates includes the lungs and the system of tubes through which the air reaches them. Breathing (ventilation) provides a continual supply of fresh air to the lungs and helps to maintain a large diffusion gradient for respiratory gases across the gas exchange surface. The basic rhythm of breathing is controlled by the respiratory centre in the medulla of the hindbrain. The volume of gases exchanged during breathing varies according to the physiological demands placed on the body. These changes can be measured using spirometry. The following activity summarises the key features of respiratory system structure and function. The stimulus material can be found in earlier exercises in this topic.

Components of the respiratory system

(a)

(b)

(c)

(d)

(e)

(f)

(g)

The control of breathing

(i) _____ controls the rate and depth of breathing. It also has connections with the cerebral cortex that allow voluntary control over breathing (e.g. when talking, singing, sneezing, and coughing).

(ii) _____ carries impulses from stretch receptors to the respiratory centre to **inhibit** inspiration (the **inflation reflex**).

(iii) _____ from the respiratory centre, **stimulate** inspiration.

(iv) _____ in the aorta and carotid arteries, monitor blood pH. Low pH (caused by high CO_2) in the blood stimulates an increase in the rate and depth of breathing.

(v) _____ in the bronchioles and bronchi, **monitor** the amount of lung inflation.

(vi) _____ sends impulses to the diaphragm to **stimulate** contraction.

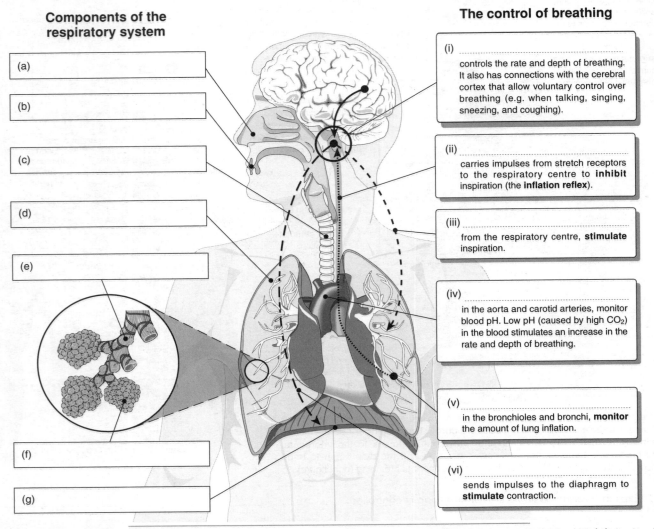

1. On the diagram above, label the components of the respiratory system (a-g) and the components that control the rate of breathing (i - vi).

2. Identify the volumes and capacities indicated by the letters **A - E** on the diagram of a spirogram below.

A = _____

B = _____

C = _____

D = _____

E = _____

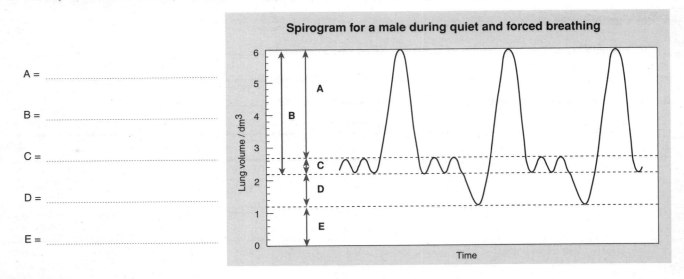

Spirogram for a male during quiet and forced breathing

Lung volume / dm³

Time

Related activities: The Human Respiratory System, Breathing in Humans, Control of Breathing, Gas Transport in Humans

Respiratory Pigments

Regardless of the gas exchange system present, the amount of oxygen that can be carried in solution in the blood is small. The efficiency of gas exchange in animals is enhanced by the presence of **respiratory pigments**. All respiratory pigments consist of proteins complexed with iron or copper. They combine reversibly with oxygen and greatly increase the capacity of blood to transport oxygen and deliver it to the tissues. For example, the amount of oxygen dissolved in the plasma in mammals is only about 2 cm³ O_2 per litre. However the amount carried bound to haemoglobin is 100 times this. Haemoglobin is the most widely distributed respiratory pigment and is characteristic of all vertebrates and many invertebrate taxa. Other respiratory pigments include chlorocruorin, haemocyanin, and haemerythrin. Note that the precise structure and carrying capacity of any one particular pigment type varies between taxa (see the range of haemoglobins in the table below).

Respiratory Pigments

Respiratory pigments are coloured proteins capable of combining reversibly with oxygen, hence increasing the amount of oxygen that can be carried by the blood. Pigments typical of representative taxa are listed below. Note that the polychaetes are very variable in terms of the pigment possessed.

Taxon	Oxygen capacity / cm³ O_2 per 100 cm³ blood	Pigment
Oligochaetes	1 - 10	Haemoglobin
Polychaetes	1 - 10	Haemoglobin, chlorocruorin, or haemerythrin
Crustaceans	1 - 6	Haemocyanin
Molluscs	1 - 6	Haemocyanin
Fishes	2 - 4	Haemoglobin
Reptiles	7 - 12	Haemoglobin
Birds	20 - 25	Haemoglobin
Mammals	15 - 30	Haemoglobin

Mammalian Haemoglobin

Haemoglobin is a globular protein consisting of 574 amino acids arranged in four polypeptide sub-units: two identical **beta chains** and two identical **alpha chains**. The four sub-units are held together as a functional unit by bonds. Each sub-unit has an iron-containing haem group at its centre and binds one molecule of oxygen.

Chemical formula:
$$C_{3032}H_{4816}O_{872}N_{780}S_8Fe_4$$

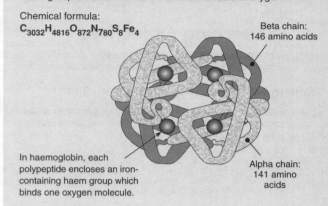

Beta chain: 146 amino acids

Alpha chain: 141 amino acids

In haemoglobin, each polypeptide encloses an iron-containing haem group which binds one oxygen molecule.

Aquatic polychaete fanworms e.g. *Sabella*, possess **chlorocruorin**.

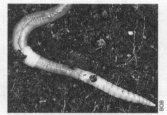

Oligochaete annelids, such as earthworms, have **haemoglobin**.

Aquatic crustaceans e.g. crabs, possess **haemocyanin** pigment.

Vertebrates such as this fish have **haemoglobin** pigment.

Cephalopod molluscs such as *Nautilus* contain **haemocyanin**.

Birds, being vertebrates contain the pigment **haemoglobin**.

Many large active polychaetes, e.g. *Nereis*, contain **haemoglobin**.

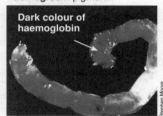

Dark colour of haemoglobin

Chironomus is one of only two insect genera to contain a pigment.

1. (a) Explain how respiratory pigments increase the carrying capacity of the blood: _____

   _____

   (b) Identify which feature of a respiratory pigment determines its oxygen carrying capacity: _____

   _____

2. With reference to haemoglobin, suggest how oxygen carrying capacity is related to metabolic activity: _____

   _____

   _____

3. Suggest why larger molecular weight respiratory pigments are carried dissolved in the plasma rather than within cells:

   _____

Animal Transport Systems

OCR: Unit F211, Module 2: Exchange & Transport

1.2.2: Transport in animals

CIE: CORE SYLLABUS

G(l)-(w): mammalian transport system (including heart)

Learning Objectives

☐ 1. Compile your own glossary from the **KEY WORDS** displayed in **bold type** in the learning objectives below.

Transport Systems in Animals *(page 119-122)*

☐ 2. Explain the need for **transport systems** in multicellular animals in relation to size, level of activity, and **surface area to volume ratio**.

☐ 3. Identify the main components and functions of animal transport systems. With reference to insects and fish, describe the characteristics of **open circulatory systems** and **closed circulatory systems**.

☐ 4. Describe the features of a typical closed, **single circulatory system** (as in fish) and a closed, **double circulatory system** (as in mammals).

☐ 5. Describe the blood flow in the double circulatory system of a mammal indicating the **heart**, the **pulmonary** and **systemic** circulation, the direction of blood flow, and where in the circuit the blood is oxygenated and deoxygenated.

Heart Structure & Function *(pages 128, 133-138)*

☐ 6. Describe the internal and external gross structure of the human **heart** in relation to its function. On diagrams identify **atria**, **ventricles**, **atrioventricular valves**, and **semilunar valves**, as well as the major vessels and the coronary circulation. Relate the differences in the thickness of the heart chambers to their functions.

☐ 7. Describe the **cardiac cycle**, relating stages in the cycle (**atrial systole**, **ventricular systole**, and **diastole**) to the maintenance of blood flow through the heart. Describe the changes in pressure and volume, and associated valve movements during the cycle.

☐ 8. Describe how the heart beat is initiated and maintained, identifying the role of the **sinoatrial node** (SAN), the **atrioventricular node** (AVN), the **bundle of His**, and the **Purkinje fibres**. Relate the activity of the SAN to the **intrinsic heart rate**.

☐ 9. If required, describe the extrinsic regulation of **heart rate** through the **autonomic nervous system**.

☐ 10. Interpret and explain an electrocardiogram (ECG) with respect to both normal and abnormal heart activity.

Blood Vessels & Gas Transport *(pages 123-132)*

☐ 11. Recognise **arteries**, **veins**, and **capillaries** using a light microscope. Describe and contrast the structure of **arteries**, **arterioles**, **veins**, and **capillaries** in humans. Relate the structure of each type of blood vessel to its specific function in the circulatory system.

☐ 12. Use a diagram to show the relative positions of blood vessels in a capillary network and their relationship to the **lymphatic vessels**. Distinguish between **blood**, **lymph**, **plasma**, and **tissue fluid**.

☐ 13. Describe the formation of **tissue fluid** and explain how and where it is returned to the blood circulatory system.

☐ 14. Describe the nature and/or composition of **blood** including reference to the role of each of the following: *Non-cellular components*: **plasma** (water, mineral ions, blood proteins, hormones, nutrients, urea, vitamins). *Cellular components*: **erythrocytes**, **leucocytes** (**lymphocytes**, **monocytes**, **granulocytes**), **platelets**.

☐ 15. Describe the structure of **erythrocytes** relating their structure to their transport function. Describe the role of **respiratory pigments** (**myoglobin** and **haemoglobin**) in the transport and delivery of oxygen to the tissues.

☐ 16. Explain the ways in which CO_2 is carried in the blood (including the role of haemoglobin).

☐ 17. Describe the transport (including loading/unloading) of oxygen in relation to the **oxygen-haemoglobin** (O_2-Hb) **dissociation curve**. Compare the oxygen affinities and dissociation curves of adult and **foetal haemoglobin** and explain the significance of these differences.

☐ 18. Describe the effect of pH (CO_2 level) on the oxygen-haemoglobin dissociation curve (the **Bohr effect**) and explain its significance.

☐ 19. Describe and explain the short and long term effects of **high altitude** on blood composition of humans.

 See the 'Textbook Reference Grid' on page 7 for textbook page references relating to material in this topic.

Supplementary Texts

See pages 5-6 for additional details of these texts:

■ Adds, J. *et al.*, 2004. **Exchange & Transport, Energy & Ecosystems** (Nelson Thornes), chpt. 2.

■ Clegg, C.J., 1998. **Mammals: Structure and Function** (John Murray), pp. 24-47.

See page 6 for details of publishers of periodicals:

STUDENT'S REFERENCE

■ **Keeping Pace - Cardiac Muscle and Heartbeat** Biol. Sci. Rev., 19(3), Feb. 2007, pp. 21-24. *Cardiac muscle cells generate electrical activity like nerve impulses, and these impulses produce smooth contraction of the heart muscle.*

■ **A Fair Exchange** Biol. Sci. Rev., 13(1), Sept. 2000, pp. 2-5. *Formation and reabsorption of tissue fluid (includes disorders of fluid balance).*

See pages 8-9 for details of how to access **Bio Links** from our web site: **www.biozone.co.uk**. From Bio Links, access sites under the topics:

GENERAL BIOLOGY ONLINE RESOURCES
• AP Interactive animation • Biology I interactive animations ... *and others* **ANIMAL BIOLOGY**: • Anatomy and physiology • Human physiology lecture notes... *and others* > **Circulatory System**: • How the heart works • The circulatory system • The matter of the human heart ... *and others*

Internal Transport

Animal cells require a constant supply of nutrients and oxygen, and continuous removal of wastes. Simple, small organisms (e.g. sponges, cnidarians, flatworms, nematodes) can achieve this through simple diffusion across moist body surfaces without requiring a specialised system (below). Larger, more complex organisms require a circulatory system to transport materials because diffusion is too inefficient and slow to supply all the cells of the body adequately. The principal components of a circulatory system are blood, a heart, and blood vessels. Circulatory systems transport nutrients, oxygen, carbon dioxide, wastes, and hormones. They also help to maintain fluid balance, regulate body temperature, and may assist in the defence of the body against invading microorganisms. In the diagram below, simple diffusion is compared with transport by a circulatory system.

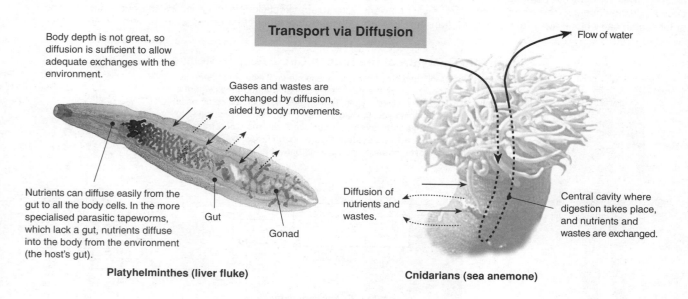

Transport via Diffusion

Body depth is not great, so diffusion is sufficient to allow adequate exchanges with the environment.

Gases and wastes are exchanged by diffusion, aided by body movements.

Nutrients can diffuse easily from the gut to all the body cells. In the more specialised parasitic tapeworms, which lack a gut, nutrients diffuse into the body from the environment (the host's gut).

Gut

Gonad

Platyhelminthes (liver fluke)

Flow of water

Diffusion of nutrients and wastes.

Central cavity where digestion takes place, and nutrients and wastes are exchanged.

Cnidarians (sea anemone)

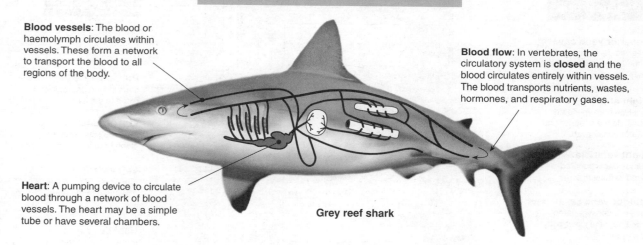

Transport via a Circulatory System

Blood vessels: The blood or haemolymph circulates within vessels. These form a network to transport the blood to all regions of the body.

Blood flow: In vertebrates, the circulatory system is **closed** and the blood circulates entirely within vessels. The blood transports nutrients, wastes, hormones, and respiratory gases.

Heart: A pumping device to circulate blood through a network of blood vessels. The heart may be a simple tube or have several chambers.

Grey reef shark

1. Explain why animals above a certain size require an internal transport system of some kind:

   _____

2. Briefly describe the function of each of the three major components of a circulatory system in an animal:

   (a) Blood vessels: _____

   (b) Heart: _____

   (c) Blood or haemolymph: _____

   _____

3. For simple aquatic organisms, diffusion presents no problem because they are surrounded in a fluid medium. Explain how similar organisms living on land are able to use diffusion to obtain nutrients and dispose of wastes:

   _____

   _____

Animal Transport Systems

Related activities: Circulatory Systems

A 1

Mammalian Transport

Animal cells require a constant supply of nutrients and oxygen, and continuous removal of wastes. Simple, small organisms achieve this through simple diffusion across moist body surfaces. Larger, more complex organisms require a circulatory system to transport materials because diffusion is too inefficient and slow to supply all the cells of the body adequately. Circulatory systems transport materials, but also help to maintain fluid balance, regulate body temperature, and assist in defending the body against pathogens. The blood vessels form a vast network of tubes that carry blood away from the heart, transport it to the tissues, and then return it to the heart. The arteries, arterioles, capillaries, venules, and veins are organised into specific routes to circulate blood throughout the body. The figure below shows some of the **circulatory routes** through which the blood travels. The **pulmonary system** (or circulation) carries blood between the heart and lungs, and the **systemic system** (circulation) carries blood between the heart and the rest of the body. Two important subdivisions of the systemic circuit are the coronary (cardiac) circulation, which supplies the heart muscle, and the **hepatic portal circulation**, which runs from the gut to the liver.

Schematic Overview of the Human Circulatory System

Deoxygenated blood (coloured grey below) travels to the right side of the heart via the vena cavae. The heart pumps the deoxygenated blood to the lungs where it releases carbon dioxide and receives oxygen. The oxygenated blood (coloured white below) travels via the pulmonary vein back to the heart from where it is pumped to all parts of the body. The **venous system** (figure, left) returns blood from the capillaries to the heart. The **arterial system** (figure right) carries blood from the heart to the capillaries. **Portal systems** carry blood between two capillary beds.

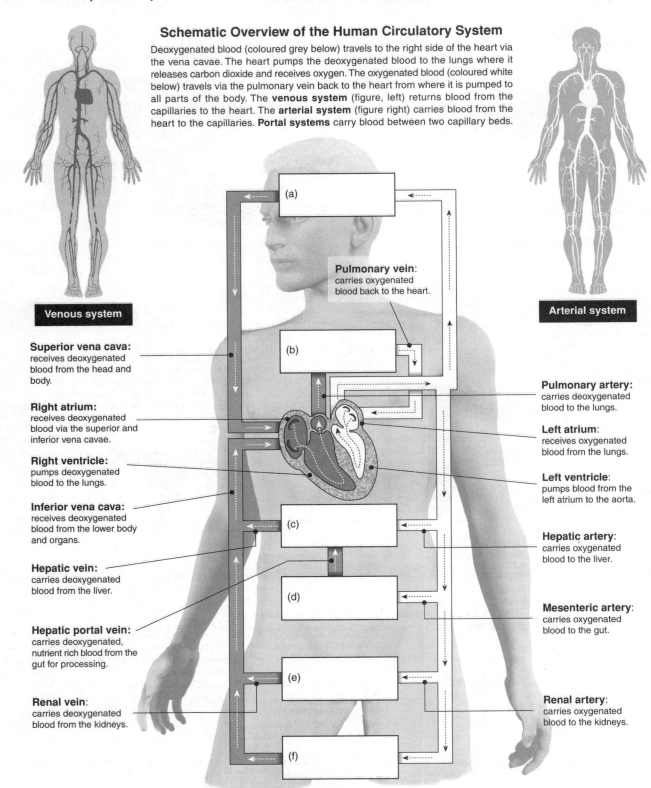

Venous system

Arterial system

Superior vena cava: receives deoxygenated blood from the head and body.

Right atrium: receives deoxygenated blood via the superior and inferior vena cavae.

Right ventricle: pumps deoxygenated blood to the lungs.

Inferior vena cava: receives deoxygenated blood from the lower body and organs.

Hepatic vein: carries deoxygenated blood from the liver.

Hepatic portal vein: carries deoxygenated, nutrient rich blood from the gut for processing.

Renal vein: carries deoxygenated blood from the kidneys.

Pulmonary vein: carries oxygenated blood back to the heart.

Pulmonary artery: carries deoxygenated blood to the lungs.

Left atrium: receives oxygenated blood from the lungs.

Left ventricle: pumps blood from the left atrium to the aorta.

Hepatic artery: carries oxygenated blood to the liver.

Mesenteric artery: carries oxygenated blood to the gut.

Renal artery: carries oxygenated blood to the kidneys.

1. Complete the diagram above by labelling the boxes with the organs or structures they represent.

A 1   **Related activities:** The Human Heart

Circulatory Systems

Two basic types of circulatory systems have evolved in animals. Many invertebrates have an **open circulatory system**, while vertebrates (including humans) have a **closed circulatory system**. The latter is often called a cardiovascular system because it consists of a heart and a network of tube-like vessels. The circulatory systems of arthropods are open but quite varied. Insects, unlike most other arthropods, do not use a circulatory system to transport oxygen around the body. Instead, oxygen is delivered directly to the tissues via a system of "air tubes" (the tracheal system) which carries oxygen directly to all tissues. In addition to its usual transport functions, the circulatory system may also be important in hydraulic movements of the whole body (as in many molluscs) or its component parts (e.g. newly emerged butterflies expand their wings through hydraulic pressure).

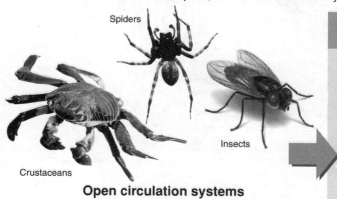

Spiders

Insects

Crustaceans

Open circulation systems

Arthropods and molluscs (except squid and octopus) have open circulatory systems in which the blood is pumped by a tubular, or sac-like, heart through short vessels into large spaces in the body cavity. The blood bathes the cells before reentering the heart through holes (**ostia**). Muscle action may assist the circulation of the blood.

Bony fish

Rays

Sharks

Closed, single circuit systems

In closed circulation systems, the blood is contained within vessels and is returned to the heart after every circulation of the body. Exchanges between the blood and the fluids bathing the cells occurs by diffusion across capillaries. In single circuit systems, typical of fish, the blood goes directly from the gills to the body. The blood loses pressure at the gills and flows at low pressure around the body.

Birds

Reptiles

Amphibians

Closed, double circuit systems

Double circulation systems occur in all vertebrates other than fish. The blood is pumped through a pulmonary circuit to the lungs, where it is oxygenated. The blood returns to the heart, which pumps the oxygenated blood, through a systemic circuit, to the body. In amphibians and most reptiles, the heart is not completely divided and there is some mixing of oxygenated and deoxygenated blood. In birds and mammals, the heart is fully divided and there is no mixing.

Types of Circulatory Systems

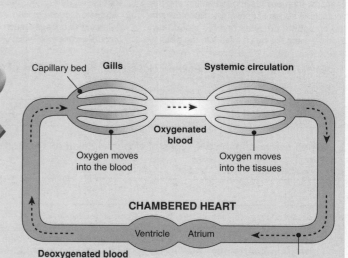

Tubular heart on the dorsal (top) surface of the animal. Circulating fluids are pumped towards the head.

Ostium (hole) for the uptake of blood

One way valves ensure the blood flows in the forward direction.

Head

TUBULAR HEART

Abdomen

Body fluids flow freely within the body cavity

Capillary bed **Gills**

Systemic circulation

Oxygenated blood

Oxygen moves into the blood

Oxygen moves into the tissues

CHAMBERED HEART

Ventricle   Atrium

Deoxygenated blood

Direction of blood flow

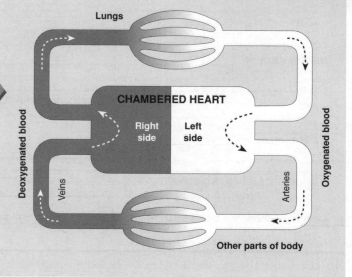

Lungs

Deoxygenated blood

CHAMBERED HEART

Right side

Left side

Oxygenated blood

Veins

Arteries

Other parts of body

Animal Transport Systems

Related activities: Veins, Arteries

A 1

Fish Heart

Amphibian Heart

Mammalian Heart

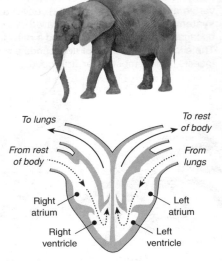

Fish Heart diagram labels: Conus arteriosus, Ventricle, Atrium, Sinus venosus, From rest of body, To gills, Ventral aorta, Atrioventricular valves, Sinoatrial valves, From rest of body

Amphibian Heart diagram labels: To lungs, To rest of body, From rest of body, From lungs, Right atrium, Left atrium, Ventricle (single chamber)

Mammalian Heart diagram labels: To lungs, To rest of body, From rest of body, From lungs, Right atrium, Left atrium, Right ventricle, Left ventricle

The fish heart is linear, with a sequence of three chambers in series (the conus may be included as a fourth chamber). Blood from the body first enters the heart through the sinus venosus, then passes into the atrium and the ventricle. A series of one-way valves between the chambers prevents reverse blood flow. Blood leaving the heart travels to the gills.

Amphibian hearts are three chambered. The atrium is divided into left and right chambers, but the ventricle lacks an internal dividing wall. Although this allows mixing of oxygenated and deoxygenated blood, the spongy nature of the ventricle reduces mixing. Amphibians are able to tolerate this because much of their oxygen uptake occurs across their moist skin, and not their lungs.

In birds and mammals, the heart is fully partitioned into two halves, resulting in four chambers. Blood circulates through two circuits, with no mixing of the two. Oxygenated blood from the lungs is kept separated from the deoxygenated blood returning from the rest of the body.

1. Explain the difference between closed and open systems of circulation: _____

_____

_____

2. When comparing the two types of closed circulatory systems, explain why a double is more efficient than a single circuit:

_____

_____

_____

3. Vertebrate hearts have evolved from relatively simple structures (as in fish) to more complex organs such as those found in mammals. Describe the number and arrangement of heart chambers in:

(a) Fish: _____

_____

_____

_____

(b) Amphibians: _____

_____

_____

(c) Mammals: _____

_____

_____

4. Describe where the blood flows to after it passes through the gills in a fish: _____

_____

_____

Arteries

In vertebrates, arteries are the blood vessels that carry blood away from the heart to the capillaries within the tissues. The large arteries that leave the heart divide into medium-sized (distributing) arteries. Within the tissues and organs, these distribution arteries branch to form very small vessels called **arterioles**, which deliver blood to capillaries. Arterioles lack the thick layers of arteries and consist only of an endothelial layer wrapped by a few smooth muscle fibres at intervals along their length. Resistance to blood flow is altered by contraction (**vasoconstriction**) or relaxation (**vasodilation**) of the blood vessel walls, especially in the arterioles. Vasoconstriction increases resistance and leads to an increase in blood pressure whereas vasodilation has the opposite effect. This mechanism is important in regulating the blood flow into tissues.

Arteries

Arteries have an elastic, stretchy structure that gives them the ability to withstand the high pressure of blood being pumped from the heart. At the same time, they help to maintain pressure by having some contractile ability themselves (a feature of the central muscle layer). Arteries nearer the heart have more elastic tissue, giving greater resistance to the higher blood pressures of the blood leaving the left ventricle. Arteries further from the heart have more muscle to help them maintain blood pressure. Between heartbeats, the arteries undergo elastic recoil and contract. This tends to smooth out the flow of blood through the vessel.

Arteries comprise three main regions (right):

1. A thin inner layer of epithelial cells called the **endothelium** lines the artery.

2. A central layer (the **tunica media**) of elastic tissue and smooth muscle that can stretch and contract.

3. An outer connective tissue layer (the **tunica externa**) has a lot of elastic tissue.

Artery Structure

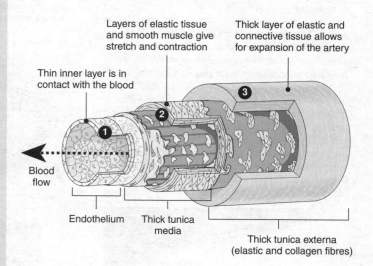

Layers of elastic tissue and smooth muscle give stretch and contraction

Thick layer of elastic and connective tissue allows for expansion of the artery

Thin inner layer is in contact with the blood

Blood flow

Endothelium   Thick tunica media

Thick tunica externa (elastic and collagen fibres)

Cross section through a large artery

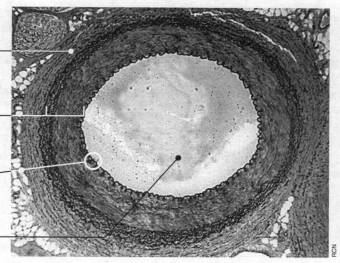

(a)

(b)

(c)

(d)

1. Using the diagram to help you, label the photograph (a)-(d) of the cross section through an artery (above).

2. (a) Explain why the walls of arteries need to be thick with a lot of elastic tissue: _____

   _____

   (b) Explain why arterioles lack this elastic tissue layer: _____

   _____

3. Explain the purpose of the smooth muscle in the artery walls: _____

   _____

4. (a) Describe the effect of vasodilation on the diameter of an arteriole: _____

   (b) Describe the effect of vasodilation on blood pressure: _____

Related activities: Veins, Capillaries and Tissue Fluid
Web links: Arteries

A 1

Animal Transport Systems

Veins

Veins are the blood vessels that return blood to the heart from the tissues. The smallest veins (**venules**) return blood from the capillary beds to the larger veins. Veins and their branches contain about 59% of the blood in the body. The structural differences between veins and arteries are mainly associated with differences in the relative thickness of the vessel layers and the diameter of the lumen. These, in turn, are related to the vessel's functional role.

Veins

When several capillaries unite, they form small veins called **venules**. The venules collect the blood from capillaries and drain it into **veins**. Veins are made up of essentially the same three layers as arteries but they have less elastic and muscle tissue and a larger **lumen**. The venules closest to the capillaries consist of an **endothelium** and a tunica externa of connective tissue. As the venules approach the veins, they also contain the tunica media characteristic of veins (right). Although veins are less elastic than arteries, they can still expand enough to adapt to changes in the pressure and volume of the blood passing through them. Blood flowing in the veins has lost a lot of pressure because it has passed through the narrow capillary vessels. The low pressure in veins means that many veins, especially those in the limbs, need to have valves to prevent backflow of the blood as it returns to the heart.

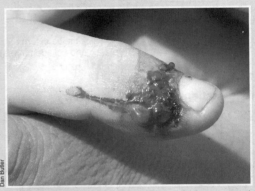

If a vein is cut, as is shown in this severe finger wound, the blood oozes out slowly in an even flow, and usually clots quickly as it leaves. In contrast, arterial blood spurts rapidly and requires pressure to staunch the flow.

Vein Structure

Inner thin layer of simple squamous epithelium lines the vein (**endothelium** or **tunica intima**).

Central thin layer of elastic and muscle tissue (**tunica media**). The smaller venules lack this inner layer.

Thin layer of elastic connective tissue (**tunica externa**)

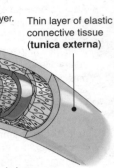

One-way valves are located along the length of veins to prevent the blood from flowing backwards.

Blood flow

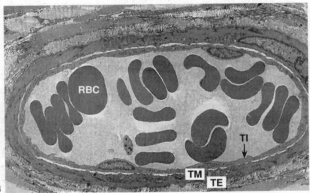

Above: TEM of a vein showing red blood cells (RBC) in the lumen, and the tunica intima (TI), tunica media (TM), and tunica externa (TE).

1. Contrast the structure of veins and arteries for each of the following properties:

   (a) Thickness of muscle and elastic tissue: _____

   _____

   (b) Size of the lumen (inside of the vessel): _____

   _____

2. With respect to their functional roles, give a reason for the differences you have described above: _____

   _____

   _____

3. Explain the role of the valves in assisting the veins to return blood back to the heart: _____

   _____

4. Blood oozes from a venous wound, rather than spurting as it does from an arterial wound. Account for this difference:

   _____

   _____

   _____

© Biozone International 2008

Related activities: Arteries, Capillaries and Tissue Fluid
Web links: Veins

Capillaries and Tissue Fluid

In vertebrates, capillaries are very small vessels that connect arterial and venous circulation and allow efficient exchange of nutrients and wastes between the blood and tissues. Capillaries form networks or beds and are abundant where metabolic rates are high. Fluid that leaks out of the capillaries has an essential role in bathing the tissues. The movement of fluid into and out of capillaries depends on the balance between the blood (hydrostatic) pressure (HP) and the solute potential (ψs) at each end of a capillary bed. Not all the fluid is returned to the capillaries and this extra fluid must be returned to the general circulation. This is the role of the **lymphatic system**; a system of vessels that parallels the system of arteries and veins. The lymphatic system also has a role in internal defence, and in transporting lipids absorbed from the digestive tract. Note: A version of this activity (without reference to solute potential terminology), is available on the web and the Teacher Resource CD-ROM.

Exchanges in Capillaries

Blood passes from the arterioles into capillaries: small blood vessels with a diameter of just 4-10 µm. Red blood cells are 7-8 µm and only just squeeze through. The only tissue present is an **endothelium** of squamous epithelial cells. Capillaries form networks of vessels that penetrate all parts of the body. They are so numerous that no cell is more than 25 µm from any capillary. It is in the capillaries that the exchange of materials between the body cells and the blood takes place. Blood pressure causes fluid to leak from capillaries through small gaps where the endothelial cells join. This fluid bathes the tissues, supplying nutrients and oxygen, and removing wastes (right). The density of capillaries in a tissue is an indication of that tissue's metabolic activity. For example, cardiac muscle relies heavily on oxidative metabolism. It has a high demand for blood flow and is well supplied with capillaries. Smooth muscle is far less active than cardiac muscle, relies more on anaerobic metabolism, and does not require such an extensive blood supply.

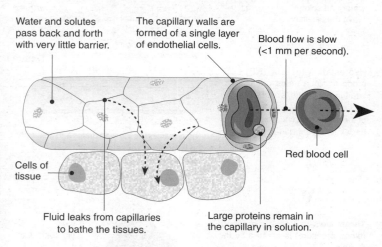

Water and solutes pass back and forth with very little barrier.

The capillary walls are formed of a single layer of endothelial cells.

Blood flow is slow (<1 mm per second).

Red blood cell

Cells of tissue

Fluid leaks from capillaries to bathe the tissues.

Large proteins remain in the capillary in solution.

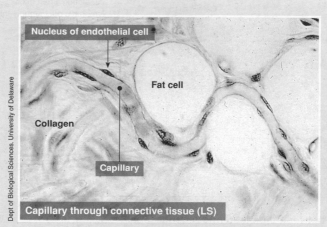

Nucleus of endothelial cell

Fat cell

Collagen

Capillary

Dept of Biological Sciences, University of Delaware

Capillary through connective tissue (LS)

Capillaries are found near almost every cell in the body. In many places, the capillaries form extensive branching networks. In most tissues, blood normally flows through only a small portion of a capillary network when the metabolic demands of the tissue are low. When the tissue becomes active, the entire capillary network fills with blood.

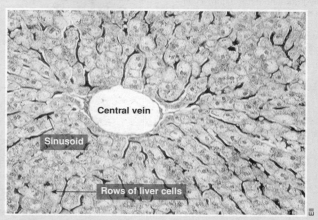

Central vein

Sinusoid

Rows of liver cells

Microscopic blood vessels in some dense organs, such as the liver (above), are called **sinusoids**. They are wider than capillaries and follow a more convoluted path through the tissue. Instead of the usual endothelial lining, they are lined with phagocytic cells. Like capillaries, sinusoids transport blood from arterioles to venules.

Animal Transport Systems

1. Describe the structure of a capillary, contrasting it with the structure of a vein and an artery:

   _____

   _____

   _____

   _____

2. Sinusoids provide a functional replacement for capillaries in some organs:

   (a) Describe how sinusoids differ structurally from capillaries: _____

   _____

   (b) Describe in what way capillaries and sinusoids are similar: _____

   _____

Related activities: The Lymphatic System, Arteries, Veins
Web links: Microcirculation, Capillaries and Tissue Fluid

RA 2

The Formation of Tissue Fluid

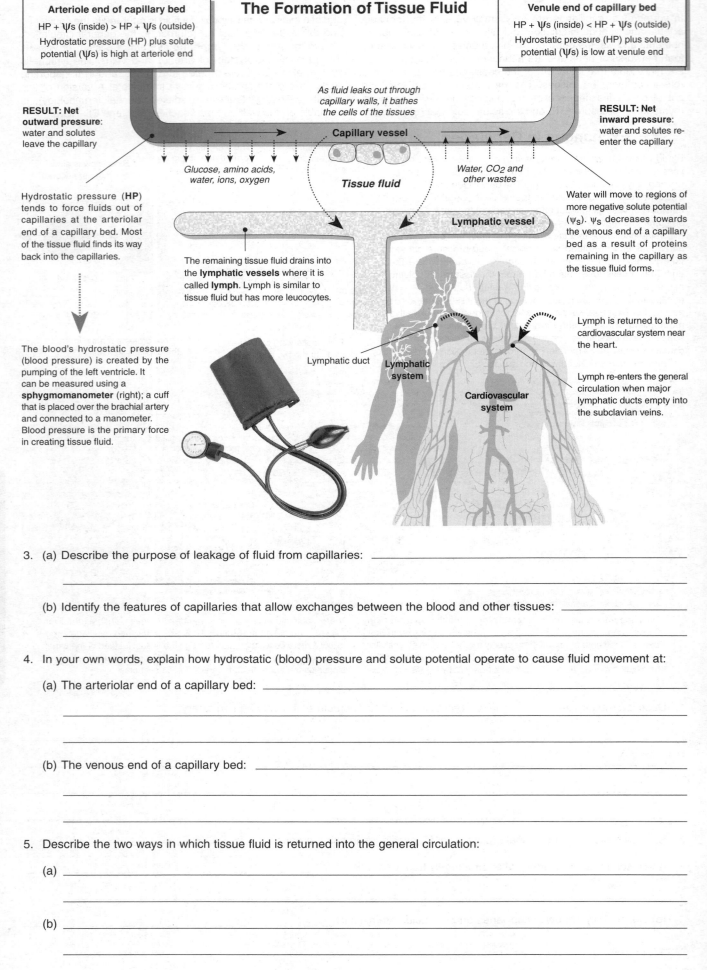

Arteriole end of capillary bed

HP + Ψs (inside) > HP + Ψs (outside)

Hydrostatic pressure (HP) plus solute potential (Ψs) is high at arteriole end

Venule end of capillary bed

HP + Ψs (inside) < HP + Ψs (outside)

Hydrostatic pressure (HP) plus solute potential (Ψs) is low at venule end

As fluid leaks out through capillary walls, it bathes the cells of the tissues

RESULT: Net outward pressure: water and solutes leave the capillary

Capillary vessel

RESULT: Net inward pressure: water and solutes re-enter the capillary

Glucose, amino acids, water, ions, oxygen

Tissue fluid

Water, CO_2 and other wastes

Hydrostatic pressure (HP) tends to force fluids out of capillaries at the arteriolar end of a capillary bed. Most of the tissue fluid finds its way back into the capillaries.

Water will move to regions of more negative solute potential (ψ_S). ψ_S decreases towards the venous end of a capillary bed as a result of proteins remaining in the capillary as the tissue fluid forms.

Lymphatic vessel

The remaining tissue fluid drains into the **lymphatic vessels** where it is called **lymph**. Lymph is similar to tissue fluid but has more leucocytes.

Lymph is returned to the cardiovascular system near the heart.

The blood's hydrostatic pressure (blood pressure) is created by the pumping of the left ventricle. It can be measured using a **sphygmomanometer** (right); a cuff that is placed over the brachial artery and connected to a manometer. Blood pressure is the primary force in creating tissue fluid.

Lymphatic duct

Lymphatic system

Cardiovascular system

Lymph re-enters the general circulation when major lymphatic ducts empty into the subclavian veins.

3. (a) Describe the purpose of leakage of fluid from capillaries: _____

    _____

    (b) Identify the features of capillaries that allow exchanges between the blood and other tissues: _____

    _____

4. In your own words, explain how hydrostatic (blood) pressure and solute potential operate to cause fluid movement at:

    (a) The arteriolar end of a capillary bed: _____

    _____

    _____

    (b) The venous end of a capillary bed: _____

    _____

    _____

5. Describe the two ways in which tissue fluid is returned into the general circulation:

    (a) _____

    _____

    (b) _____

    _____

The Effects of High Altitude

The air at high altitudes contains less oxygen than the air at sea level. Air pressure decreases with altitude so the pressure (therefore amount) of oxygen in the air also decreases. Sudden exposure to an altitude of 2000 m would make you breathless on exertion and above 7000 m most people would become unconscious. The effects of altitude on physiology are related to this lower oxygen availability. Humans and other animals can make some physiological adjustments to life at altitude; this is called acclimatisation. Some of the changes to the cardiovascular and respiratory systems to high altitude are outlined below.

Mountain Sickness

Altitude sickness or mountain sickness is usually a mild illness associated with trekking to altitudes of 5000 metres or so. Common symptoms include headache, insomnia, poor appetite and nausea, vomiting, dizziness, tiredness, coughing, and breathlessness. The best way to avoid mountain sickness is to ascend to altitude slowly (no more than 300 m per day above 3000 m). Continuing to ascend with mountain sickness can result in more serious illnesses: accumulation of fluid on the brain (cerebral oedema) and accumulation of fluid in the lungs (pulmonary oedema). These complications can be fatal if not treated with oxygen and a rapid descent to lower altitude.

People who live permanently at high altitude, e.g. Tibetans, Nepalese, and Peruvian Indians, have physiologies adapted (genetically, through evolution) to high altitude. Their blood volumes and red blood cell counts are high, and they can carry heavy loads effortlessly despite a small build. In addition, their metabolism uses oxygen very efficiently.

Physiological Adjustment to Altitude

Effect	Minutes	Days	Weeks
Increased heart rate	← →		
Increased breathing		← →	
Concentration of blood		← →	
Increased red blood cell production			← →
Increased capillary density			← →

The human body can make adjustments to life at altitude. Some of these changes take place almost immediately: breathing and heart rates increase. Other adjustments may take weeks (see above). These responses are all aimed at improving the rate of supply of oxygen to the body's tissues. When more permanent adjustments to physiology are made (increased blood cells and capillary networks) heart and breathing rates can return to normal.

Llamas, vicunas, and Bactrian camels are well suited to high altitude life. Vicunas and llamas, which live in the Andes, have high blood cell counts and their red blood cells live almost twice as long as those in humans. Their haemoglobin also picks up and offloads oxygen more efficiently than the haemoglobin of most mammals.

Animal Transport Systems

1. (a) Describe the general effects of high altitude on the body: _____
   _____

   (b) Name the general term given to describe these effects: _____

2. (a) Identify one short term physiological adaptation that humans make to high altitude: _____
   _____

   (b) Explain how this adaptation helps to increase the amount of oxygen the body receives: _____
   _____

3. (a) Describe one longer term adaptation that humans can make to living at high altitude: _____
   _____

   (b) Explain how this adaptation helps to increase the amount of oxygen the body receives: _____
   _____

Related activities: Blood, Gas Transport in Humans

A 2

Exercise and Blood Flow

Exercise promotes health by improving the rate of blood flow back to the heart (called the venous return). This is achieved by strengthening all types of muscle and by increasing the efficiency of the heart. During exercise blood flow to different parts of the body changes in order to cope with the extra demands of the muscles, the heart, and the lungs.

1. The following table gives data for the **rate** of blood flow to various parts of the body at rest and during strenuous exercise. **Calculate** the **percentage** of the total blood flow that each organ or tissue receives under each regime of activity.

Organ or tissue	At rest		Strenuous exercise	
	$cm^3\ min^{-1}$	% of total	$cm^3\ min^{-1}$	% of total
Brain	700	14	750	4.2
Heart	200		750	
Lung tissue	100		200	
Kidneys	1100		600	
Liver	1350		600	
Skeletal muscles	750		12 500	
Bone	250		250	
Skin	300		1900	
Thyroid gland	50		50	
Adrenal glands	25		25	
Other tissue	175		175	
TOTAL	5000	100	17 800	100

2. Explain how the body increases the rate of blood flow during exercise: _____

_____

_____

3. (a) State approximately how many times the total rate of blood flow increases between rest and exercise: _____

   (b) Explain why the increase is necessary: _____

_____

_____

4. (a) Identify which organs or tissues show no change in the rate of blood flow with exercise: _____

_____

   (b) Explain why this is the case: _____

_____

_____

5. (a) Identify which organs or tissues show the most change in the rate of blood flow with exercise: _____

_____

   (b) Explain why this is the case: _____

_____

_____

Related activities: Control of Heart Activity

Blood

Blood makes up about 8% of body weight. Blood is a complex liquid tissue comprising cellular components suspended in plasma. If a blood sample is taken, the cells can be separated from the plasma by centrifugation. The cells (formed elements) settle as a dense red pellet below the transparent, straw-coloured plasma. Blood performs many functions: it transports nutrients, respiratory gases, hormones, and wastes; it has a role in thermoregulation through the distribution of heat; it defends against infection; and its ability to clot protects against blood loss. The examination of blood is also useful in diagnosing disease. The cellular components of blood are normally present in particular gas specified ratios. A change in the morphology, type, or proportion of different blood cells can therefore be used to indicate a specific disorder or infection (right).

Non-Cellular Blood Components

The non-cellular blood components form the plasma. Plasma is a watery matrix of ions and proteins and makes up 50-60% of the total blood volume.

Water
The main constituent of blood and lymph.
Role: Transports dissolved substances. Provides body cells with water. Distributes heat and has a central role in thermoregulation. Regulation of water content helps to regulate blood pressure and volume.

Mineral ions
Sodium, bicarbonate, magnesium, potassium, calcium, chloride.
Role: Osmotic balance, pH buffering, and regulation of membrane permeability. They also have a variety of other functions, e.g. Ca^{2+} is involved in blood clotting.

Plasma proteins
7-9% of the plasma volume.
Serum albumin
Role: Osmotic balance and pH buffering, Ca^{2+} transport.
Fibrinogen and prothrombin
Role: Take part in blood clotting.
Immunoglobulins
Role: Antibodies involved in the immune response.
α-globulins
Role: Bind/transport hormones, lipids, fat soluble vitamins.
β-globulins
Role: Bind/transport iron, cholesterol, fat soluble vitamins.
Enzymes
Role: Take part in and regulate metabolic activities.

Substances transported by non-cellular components
Products of digestion
Examples: sugars, fatty acids, glycerol, and amino acids.
Excretory products
Example: urea
Hormones and vitamins
Examples: insulin, sex hormones, vitamins A and B_{12}.
Importance: These substances occur at varying levels in the blood. They are transported to and from the cells dissolved in the plasma or bound to plasma proteins.

Cellular Blood Components

The cellular components of the blood (also called the formed elements) float in the plasma and make up 40-50% of the total blood volume.

Erythrocytes (red blood cells or RBCs)
5-6 million per mm^3 blood; 38-48% of total blood volume.
Role: RBCs transport oxygen (O_2) and a small amount of carbon dioxide (CO_2). The oxygen is carried bound to haemoglobin (Hb) in the cells. Each Hb molecule can bind four molecules of oxygen.

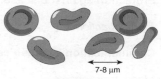

7-8 μm

Platelets

Small, membrane bound cell fragments derived from bone marrow cells; about 1/4 the size of RBCs.
2 μm
0.25 million per mm^3 blood.
Role: To start the blood clotting process.

Leucocytes (white blood cells)
5-10 000 per mm^3 blood
2-3% of total blood volume.
Role: Involved in internal defence. There are several types of white blood cells (see below).

Lymphocytes
T and B cells.
24% of the white cell count.
Role: Antibody production and cell mediated immunity.

Neutrophils

Phagocytes.
70% of the white cell count.
Role: Engulf foreign material.

Eosinophils

Rare leucocytes; normally 1.5% of the white cell count.
Role: Mediate allergic responses such as hayfever and asthma.

Basophils

Rare leucocytes; normally 0.5% of the white cell count.
Role: Produce heparin (an anti-clotting protein), and histamine. Involved in inflammation.

Animal Transport Systems

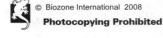
Related activities: Gas Transport in Humans, The Body's Defences

A 2

The Examination of Blood

Different types of microscopy give different information about blood. A SEM (right) shows the detailed external morphology of the blood cells. A fixed smear of a blood sample viewed with a light microscope (far right) can be used to identify the different blood cell types present, and their ratio to each other. Determining the types and proportions of different white blood cells in blood is called a **differential white blood cell count**. Elevated counts of particular cell types indicate allergy or infection.

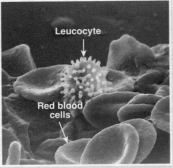

SEM of red blood cells and a leucocyte.

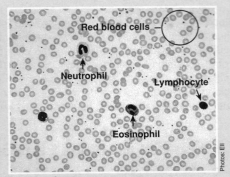

Light microscope view of a fixed blood smear.

1. For each of the following blood functions, identify the component(s) of the blood responsible and state how the function is carried out (the mode of action). The first one is done for you:

   (a) **Temperature regulation**. *Blood component involved:* <u>Water component of the plasma</u>

   Mode of action: <u>Water absorbs heat and dissipates it from sites of production (e.g. organs)</u>

   (b) **Protection against disease**. *Blood component:* _____

   Mode of action: _____

   (c) **Communication between cells, tissues, and organs**. *Blood component:* _____

   Mode of action: _____

   (d) **Oxygen transport**. *Blood component:* _____

   Mode of action: _____

   (e) **CO_2 transport**. *Blood components:* _____

   Mode of action: _____

   (f) **Buffer against pH changes**. *Blood components:* _____

   Mode of action: _____

   (g) **Nutrient supply**. *Blood component:* _____

   Mode of action: _____

   (h) **Tissue repair**. *Blood components:* _____

   Mode of action: _____

   (i) **Transport of hormones, lipids, and fat soluble vitamins**. *Blood component:* _____

   Mode of action: _____

2. Identify a feature that distinguishes red and white blood cells: _____

3. Explain two physiological advantages of red blood cell structure (lacking nucleus and mitochondria):

   (a) _____

   (b) _____

4. Suggest what each of the following results from a differential white blood cell count would suggest:

   (a) Elevated levels of eosinophils (above the normal range): _____

   (b) Elevated levels of neutrophils (above the normal range): _____

   (c) Elevated levels of basophils (above the normal range): _____

   (d) Elevated levels of lymphocytes (above the normal range): _____

Gas Transport in Humans

The transport of respiratory gases around the body is the role of the blood and its respiratory pigments. Oxygen is transported throughout the body chemically bound to the respiratory pigment **haemoglobin** inside the red blood cells. In the muscles, oxygen from haemoglobin is transferred to and retained by **myoglobin**, a molecule that is chemically similar to haemoglobin except that it consists of only one haem-globin unit. Myoglobin has a greater affinity for oxygen than haemoglobin and acts as an oxygen store within muscles, releasing the oxygen during periods of prolonged or extreme muscular activity. If the myoglobin store is exhausted, the muscles are forced into oxygen debt and must respire anaerobically. The waste product of this, lactic acid, accumulates in the muscle and is transported (as lactate) to the liver where it is metabolised under aerobic conditions.

Gas Exchange and Transport

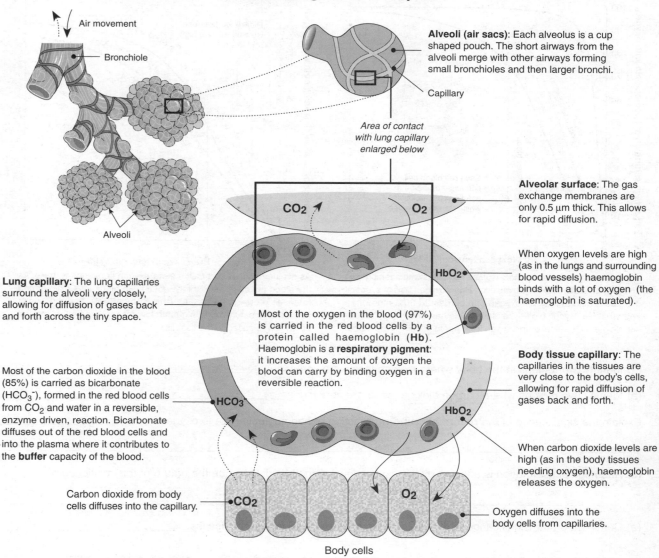

Air movement

Bronchiole

Alveoli

Alveoli (air sacs): Each alveolus is a cup shaped pouch. The short airways from the alveoli merge with other airways forming small bronchioles and then larger bronchi.

Capillary

Area of contact with lung capillary enlarged below

CO_2 O_2

Alveolar surface: The gas exchange membranes are only 0.5 μm thick. This allows for rapid diffusion.

HbO_2

When oxygen levels are high (as in the lungs and surrounding blood vessels) haemoglobin binds with a lot of oxygen (the haemoglobin is saturated).

Lung capillary: The lung capillaries surround the alveoli very closely, allowing for diffusion of gases back and forth across the tiny space.

Most of the oxygen in the blood (97%) is carried in the red blood cells by a protein called haemoglobin (**Hb**). Haemoglobin is a **respiratory pigment**: it increases the amount of oxygen the blood can carry by binding oxygen in a reversible reaction.

Most of the carbon dioxide in the blood (85%) is carried as bicarbonate (HCO_3^-), formed in the red blood cells from CO_2 and water in a reversible, enzyme driven, reaction. Bicarbonate diffuses out of the red blood cells and into the plasma where it contributes to the **buffer** capacity of the blood.

HCO_3^-

Body tissue capillary: The capillaries in the tissues are very close to the body's cells, allowing for rapid diffusion of gases back and forth.

HbO_2

When carbon dioxide levels are high (as in the body tissues needing oxygen), haemoglobin releases the oxygen.

Carbon dioxide from body cells diffuses into the capillary.

CO_2 O_2

Oxygen diffuses into the body cells from capillaries.

Body cells

Transport of carbon dioxide in the blood

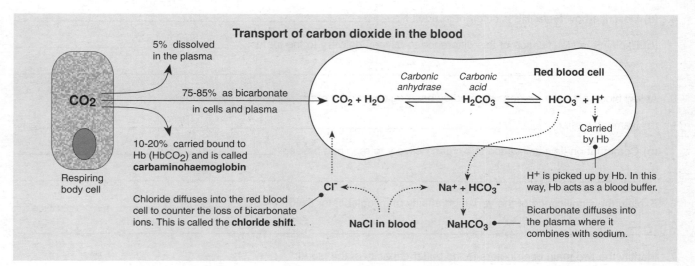

CO_2

5% dissolved in the plasma

75-85% as bicarbonate in cells and plasma

10-20% carried bound to Hb ($HbCO_2$) and is called **carbaminohaemoglobin**

Respiring body cell

Chloride diffuses into the red blood cell to counter the loss of bicarbonate ions. This is called the **chloride shift**.

Carbonic anhydrase   Carbonic acid   **Red blood cell**

$CO_2 + H_2O \rightleftharpoons H_2CO_3 \rightleftharpoons HCO_3^- + H^+$

Carried by Hb

H^+ is picked up by Hb. In this way, Hb acts as a blood buffer.

Cl^- $Na^+ + HCO_3^-$

NaCl in blood $NaHCO_3$

Bicarbonate diffuses into the plasma where it combines with sodium.

Oxygen does not easily dissolve in blood, but is carried in chemical combination with haemoglobin (Hb) in red blood cells. The most important factor determining how much oxygen is carried by Hb is the level of oxygen in the blood. The greater the oxygen tension, the more oxygen will combine with Hb. This relationship can be illustrated with an oxygen-haemoglobin dissociation curve as shown below (Fig. 1). In the lung capillaries, (high O_2), a lot of oxygen is picked up and bound by Hb. In the tissues, (low O_2), oxygen is released. In skeletal muscle, myoglobin picks up oxygen from haemoglobin and therefore serves as an oxygen store when oxygen tensions begin to fall. The release of oxygen is enhanced by the **Bohr effect** (Fig. 2).

Respiratory Pigments and the Transport of Oxygen

Fig. 1: Dissociation curves for haemoglobin and myoglobin at normal body temperature for foetal and adult human blood.

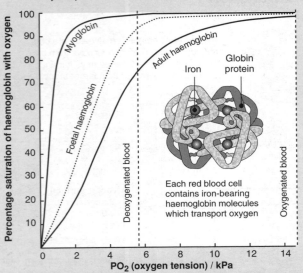

As oxygen level increases, more oxygen combines with haemoglobin (Hb). Hb saturation remains high, even at low oxygen tensions. Foetal Hb has a high affinity for oxygen and carries 20-30% more than maternal Hb. Myoglobin in skeletal muscle has a very high affinity for oxygen and will take up oxygen from haemoglobin in the blood.

Fig. 2: Oxygen-haemoglobin dissociation curves for human blood at normal body temperature at different blood pH.

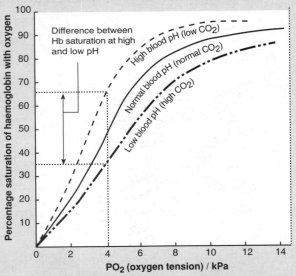

As pH increases (lower CO_2), more oxygen combines with Hb. As the blood pH decreases (higher CO_2), Hb binds less oxygen and releases more to the tissues (**the Bohr effect**). The difference between Hb saturation at high and low pH represents the amount of oxygen released to the tissues.

1. (a) Identify two regions in the body where oxygen levels are very high: _____

   (b) Identify two regions where carbon dioxide levels are very high: _____

2. Explain the significance of the **reversible binding** reaction of haemoglobin (Hb) to oxygen: _____

   _____

3. (a) Haemoglobin saturation is affected by the oxygen level in the blood. Describe the nature of this relationship:

   _____

   (b) Comment on the significance of this relationship to oxygen delivery to the tissues: _____

   _____

4. (a) Describe how foetal Hb is different to adult Hb: _____

   (b) Explain the significance of this difference to oxygen delivery to the foetus: _____

   _____

5. At low blood pH, less oxygen is bound by haemoglobin and more is released to the tissues:

   (a) Name this effect: _____

   (b) Comment on its significance to oxygen delivery to respiring tissue: _____

   _____

6. Explain the significance of the very high affinity of myoglobin for oxygen: _____

   _____

7. Identify the two main contributors to the buffer capacity of the blood: _____

The Human Heart

The heart is the centre of the human cardiovascular system. It is a hollow, muscular organ, weighing on average 342 grams. Each day it beats over 100 000 times to pump 3780 litres of blood through 100 000 kilometres of blood vessels. It comprises a system of four muscular chambers (two **atria** and two **ventricles**) that alternately fill and empty of blood, acting as a double pump.

The left side pumps blood to the body tissues and the right side pumps blood to the lungs. The heart lies between the lungs, to the left of the body's midline, and it is surrounded by a double layered **pericardium** of tough fibrous connective tissue. The pericardium prevents overdistension of the heart and anchors the heart within the **mediastinum**.

Human Heart Structure

(sectioned, anterior view)

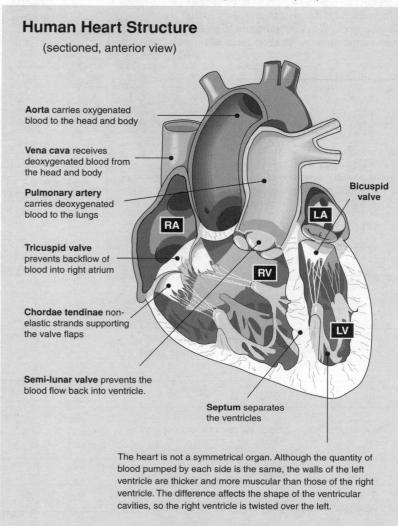

Aorta carries oxygenated blood to the head and body

Vena cava receives deoxygenated blood from the head and body

Pulmonary artery carries deoxygenated blood to the lungs

Tricuspid valve prevents backflow of blood into right atrium

Chordae tendinae non-elastic strands supporting the valve flaps

Semi-lunar valve prevents the blood flow back into ventricle.

Bicuspid valve

Septum separates the ventricles

The heart is not a symmetrical organ. Although the quantity of blood pumped by each side is the same, the walls of the left ventricle are thicker and more muscular than those of the right ventricle. The difference affects the shape of the ventricular cavities, so the right ventricle is twisted over the left.

Key to abbreviations

RA Right atrium; receives deoxygenated blood via anterior and posterior vena cavae

RV Right ventricle; pumps deoxygenated blood to the lungs via the pulmonary artery

LA Left atrium; receives blood returning to the heart from the lungs via the pulmonary veins

LV Left ventricle; pumps oxygenated blood to the head and body via the aorta

Top view of a heart in section, showing valves

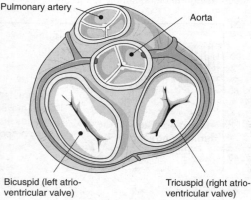

Pulmonary artery

Aorta

Bicuspid (left atrio-ventricular valve)

Tricuspid (right atrio-ventricular valve)

Posterior view of heart

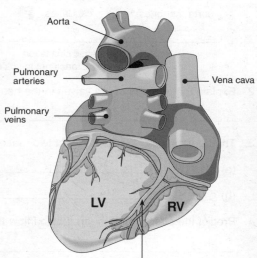

Aorta

Pulmonary arteries

Vena cava

Pulmonary veins

LV

RV

Coronary arteries: The high oxygen demands of the heart muscle are met by a dense capillary network. Coronary arteries arise from the aorta and spread over the surface of the heart supplying the cardiac muscle with oxygenated blood. Deoxygenated blood is collected by cardiac veins and returned to the right atrium via a large coronary sinus.

Animal Transport Systems

1. In the schematic diagram of the heart, below, label the four chambers and the main vessels entering and leaving them. The arrows indicate the direction of blood flow. Use large coloured circles to mark the position of each of the four valves.

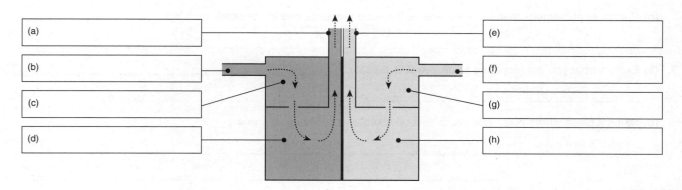

(a)   (b)   (c)   (d)   (e)   (f)   (g)   (h)

Related activities: Review of the Human Heart
Web links: Anatomy of the Heart

RA 2

Pressure Changes and the Asymmetry of the Heart

aorta, 100 mg Hg

The heart is not a symmetrical organ. The left ventricle and its associated arteries are thicker and more muscular than the corresponding structures on the right side. This asymmetry is related to the necessary pressure differences between the pulmonary (lung) and systemic (body) circulations (not to the distance over which the blood is pumped per se). The graph below shows changes blood pressure in each of the major blood vessel types in the systemic and pulmonary circuits (the horizontal distance not to scale). The pulmonary circuit must operate at a much lower pressure than the systemic circuit to prevent fluid from accumulating in the alveoli of the lungs. The left side of the heart must develop enough "spare" pressure to enable increased blood flow to the muscles of the body and maintain kidney filtration rates without decreasing the blood supply to the brain.

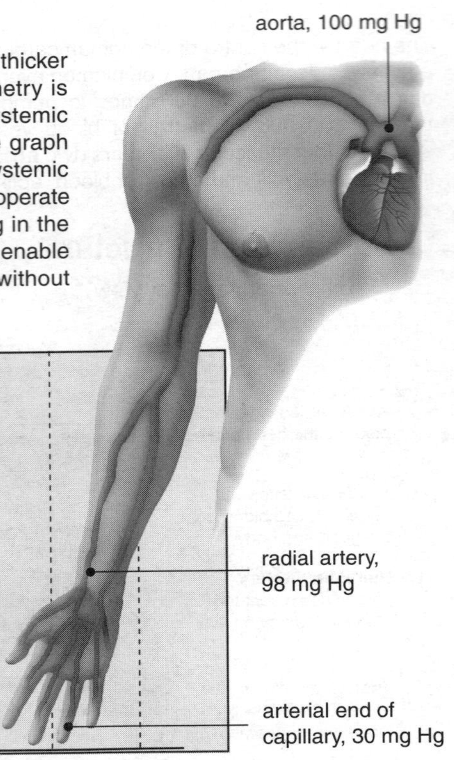

Blood pressure during contraction (systole)

The greatest fall in pressure occurs when the blood moves into the capillaries, even though the distance through the capillaries represents only a tiny proportion of the total distance travelled.

Blood pressure during contraction (diastole)

Pressure /mm Hg

radial artery, 98 mg Hg

arterial end of capillary, 30 mg Hg

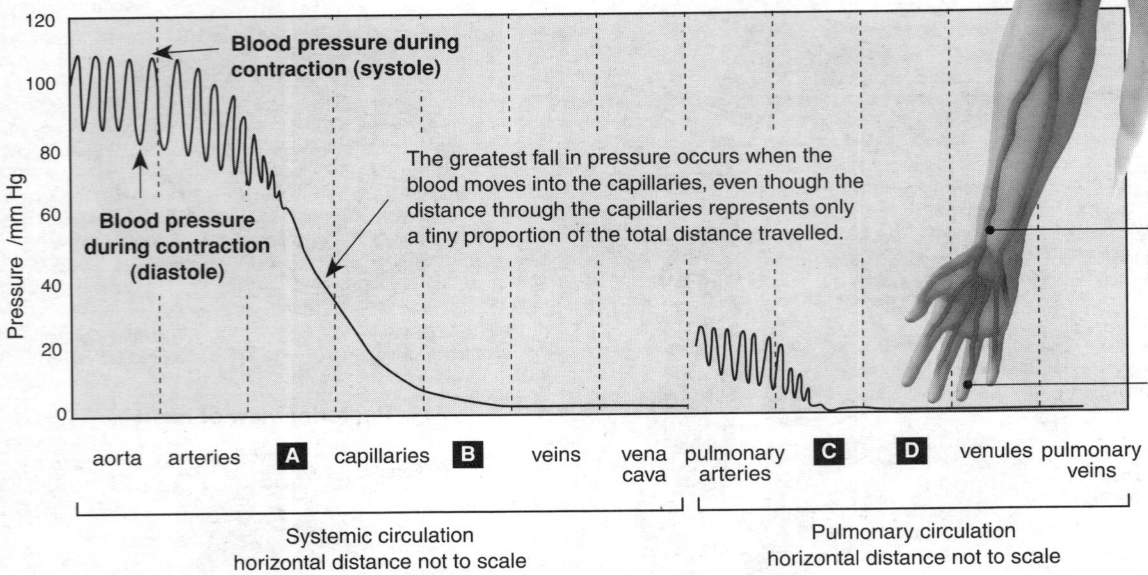

aorta   arteries   **A**   capillaries   **B**   veins   vena cava   pulmonary arteries   **C**   **D**   venules   pulmonary veins

Systemic circulation
horizontal distance not to scale

Pulmonary circulation
horizontal distance not to scale

2. Explain the purpose of the valves in the heart: _____

_____

3. The heart is full of blood. Suggest two reasons why, despite this, it needs its own blood supply:

(a) _____

(b) _____

4. Predict the effect on the heart if blood flow through a coronary artery is restricted or blocked: _____

_____

_____

5. Identify the vessels corresponding to the letters **A-D** on the graph above:

A: _____ B: _____ C: _____ D: _____

6. (a) Find out what is meant by the pulse pressure and explain how it is calculated: _____

_____

(b) Predict what happens to the pulse pressure between the aorta and the capillaries: _____

_____

7. (a) Explain what you are recording when you take a pulse: _____

_____

(b) Name a place where pulse rate could best be taken and briefly explain why: _____

_____

_____

Control of Heart Activity

When removed from the body the cardiac muscle continues to beat. Therefore, the origin of the heartbeat is **myogenic**: the contractions arise as an intrinsic property of the cardiac muscle itself. The heartbeat is regulated by a special conduction system consisting of the pacemaker (**sinoatrial node**) and specialised conduction fibres called **Purkinje fibres**. The pacemaker sets a basic rhythm for the heart, but this rate is influenced by the cardiovascular control centre in the medulla in response to sensory information from pressure receptors in the walls of the heart and blood vessels, and by higher brain functions. Changing the rate and force of heart contraction is the main mechanism for controlling cardiac output in order to meet changing demands.

Generation of the Heartbeat

The basic rhythmic heartbeat is **myogenic**. The nodal cells (SAN and atrioventricular node) spontaneously generate rhythmic action potentials without neural stimulation. The normal resting rate of self-excitation of the SAN is about 50 beats per minute.

The amount of blood ejected from the left ventricle per minute is called the **cardiac output**. It is determined by the **stroke volume** (the volume of blood ejected with each contraction) and the **heart rate** (number of heart beats per minute).

> **Cardiac output**
> = **stroke volume** x **heart rate**

Cardiac muscle responds to stretching by contracting more strongly. The greater the blood volume entering the ventricle, the greater the force of contraction. This relationship is known as **Starling's Law.**

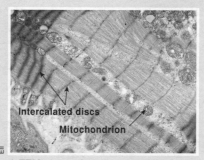

A TEM photo of cardiac muscle showing branched fibres (muscle cells). Each muscle fibre has one or two nuclei and many large mitochondria. **Intercalated discs** are specialised electrical junctions that separate the cells and allow the rapid spread of impulses through the heart muscle.

Sinoatrial node (SAN) is also called the **pacemaker**. It is a mass of specialised muscle cells near the opening of the superior vena cava. The pacemaker initiates the cardiac cycle, spontaneously generating action potentials that cause the atria to contract. The SAN sets the basic pace of the heart rate, although this rate is influenced by hormones and impulses from the autonomic nervous system.

Atrioventricular node (AVN) at the base of the atrium briefly delays the impulse to allow time for the atrial contraction to finish before the ventricles contract.

Bundle of His (atrioventricular bundle) containing Purkinje tissue. A tract of conducting fibres that distribute the action potentials over the ventricles causing ventricular contraction.

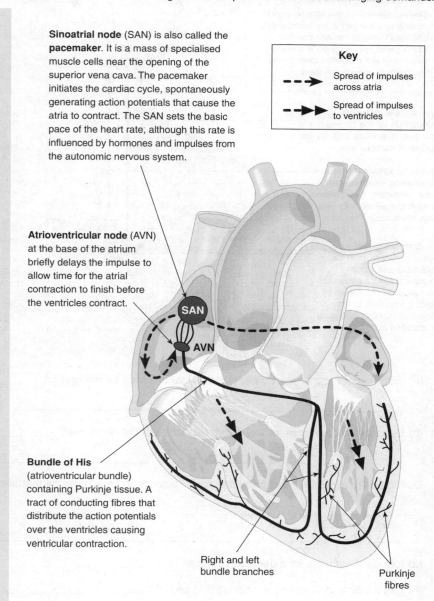

Key

- - -> Spread of impulses across atria

- - ->> Spread of impulses to ventricles

Right and left bundle branches

Purkinje fibres

SAN

AVN

1. Identify the role of each of the following in heart activity:

   (a) The sinoatrial node: _____

   (b) The atrioventricular node: _____

   (c) The bundle of His: _____

2. Explain the significance of the delay in impulse conduction at the AVN: _____

   _____

3. (a) Calculate the cardiac output when stroke volume is 70 cm³ and the heart rate is 70 beats per minute:

   _____

   (b) Trained endurance athletes have a very high cardiac output. Suggest how this is achieved: _____

   _____

Autonomic Nervous System
Control of Heartbeat

Cardiovascular control centre comprises the **accelerator centre** (which acts to speed heart rate and force of contraction) and the **inhibitory centre** (which acts to decrease heart rate and force of contraction).

The accelerator centre also responds directly to adrenalin in the blood and to changes in blood composition (low blood pH or low oxygen). These responses are mediated through the sympathetic nervous system.

Cerebral hemispheres may send impulses (e.g. in sexual arousal).

Hypothalamus may send impulses (e.g. anger or alarm).

The carotid reflex: Pressure receptors in the carotid sinus detect stretch caused by increased arterial flow (blood flow leaving the heart). They send impulses to the inhibitory centre to mediate decrease in heart rate via the vagus nerve (parasympathetic stimulation).

Sympathetic nervous stimulation via the cardiac nerve increases heart rate through the release of noradrenalin.

Parasympathetic nervous stimulation via the vagus nerve decreases heart rate through the release of acetylcholine.

The Bainbridge reflex: Pressure receptors in the vena cava and atrium respond to stretch caused by increased venous return by sending impulses to the accelerator centre, mediating an increase in heart rate.

The aortic reflex: Pressure receptors in the aorta detect stretch caused by increased arterial flow. They send impulses to the inhibitory centre to mediate decrease in heart rate via the vagus nerve.

●······▶ Parasympathetic motor nerve (vagus)

●– –▶ Sympathetic motor nerve (cardiac nerve)

●——▶ Sensory nerve

4. (a) With respect to the heart beat, explain what is meant by **myogenic**: _____

_____

(b) Describe the evidence for the myogenic nature of the heart beat: _____

_____

5. During heavy exercise, heart rate increases. Describe the mechanisms that are involved in bringing about this increase:

_____

_____

6. (a) Identify a stimulus for a decrease in heart rate: _____

(b) Explain how this change in heart rate is brought about: _____

_____

7. Identify two pressure receptors involved in control of heart rate and state what they respond to:

(a) _____

(b) _____

8. Guarana is a chemical which is found in many energy drinks. A group of students designed an experiment to test whether guarana stimulates a cardiovascular response. The test subjects had their pulses recorded before and after drinking an energy drink containing a known amount of guarana.

(a) Suggest two reasons why the test subjects may respond in different ways: _____

_____

(b) Describe a suitable control for this experiment: _____

_____

The Cardiac Cycle

The **cardiac cycle** refers to the sequence of events of a heartbeat The pumping of the heart consists of alternate contractions (**systole**) and relaxations (**diastole**). During a complete cycle, each chamber undergoes a systole and a diastole. For a heart beating at 75 beats per minute, one cardiac cycle lasts about 0.8 seconds. Pressure changes within the heart's chambers generated by the cycle of contraction and relaxation are responsible for blood movement and cause the heart valves to open and close, preventing the backflow of blood. The noise of the blood when the valves open and close produces the heartbeat sound (**lubb-dupp**).

The Cardiac Cycle

The **pulse** results from the rhythmic expansion of the arteries as the blood spurts from the left ventricle. Pulse rate therefore corresponds to heart rate.

Stage 1: Atrial systole and ventricular filling The ventricles relax and blood flows into them from the atria. Note that 70% of the blood from the atria flows passively into the ventricles. It is during the last third of ventricular filling that the atria contract.

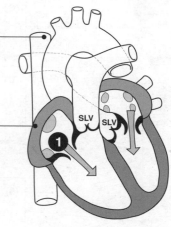

Heart during ventricular filling

Stage 2: Ventricular systole The atria relax, the ventricles contract, and blood is pumped from the ventricles into the aorta and the pulmonary artery. The start of ventricular contraction coincides with the first heart sound.

Stage 3: (not shown) There is a short period of atrial and ventricular relaxation (diastole). Semilunar valves (**SLV**) close to prevent backflow into the ventricles (see diagram, left). The cycle begins again.

Atrio-ventricular valves closed

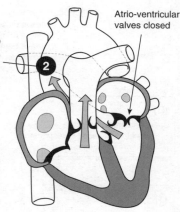

Heart during ventricular contraction

The Cardiac Cycle and the ECG

The electrical impulses transmitted through the heart generate electrical currents that can be detected by placing metal electrodes on the body's surface. They can be recorded on a heart monitor as a trace, called an **electrocardiogram** or ECG. The ECG pattern is the result of the different impulses produced at each phase of the **cardiac cycle**. A normal ECG (below) shows a regular repeating pattern of electrical pulses. Each wave of electrical activity brings about a corresponding contraction in the part of the heart receiving the electrical impulse. Each part of the ECG is given a letter according to an international code (below). An ECG provides a useful method of monitoring changes in heart rate and activity and detection of heart disorders.

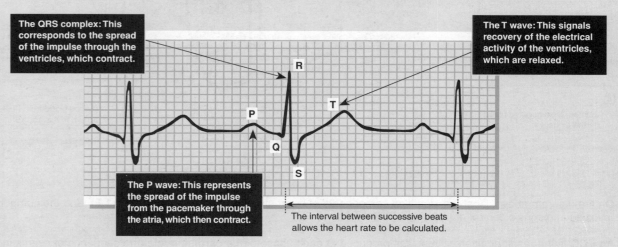

The QRS complex: This corresponds to the spread of the impulse through the ventricles, which contract.

The T wave: This signals recovery of the electrical activity of the ventricles, which are relaxed.

The P wave: This represents the spread of the impulse from the pacemaker through the atria, which then contract.

The interval between successive beats allows the heart rate to be calculated.

1. Identify each of the following phases of an ECG by its international code:

   (a) Excitation of the ventricles and ventricular systole: _____

   (b) Electrical recovery of the ventricles and ventricular diastole: _____

   (c) Excitation of the atria and atrial systole: _____

2. Suggest the physiological reason for the period of electrical recovery experienced each cycle (the T wave):

   _____

   _____

   _____

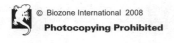

Review of the Human Heart

Large, complex organisms require a circulatory system to transport materials because diffusion is too inefficient and slow to supply all the cells of the body adequately. The circulatory system in humans transports nutrients, respiratory gases, wastes, and hormones, aids in regulating body temperature and maintaining fluid balance, and has a role in internal defence. All circulatory systems comprise a network of vessels, a circulatory fluid (blood), and a heart. This activity summarises key features of the structure and function of the human heart. The information for this activity can be found in the pages earlier in this topic.

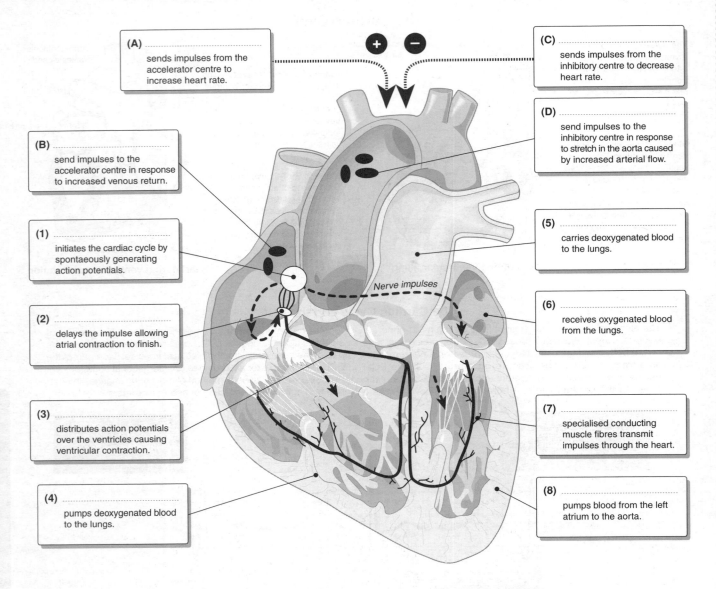

(A) .... sends impulses from the accelerator centre to increase heart rate.

(C) .... sends impulses from the inhibitory centre to decrease heart rate.

(B) .... send impulses to the accelerator centre in response to increased venous return.

(D) .... send impulses to the inhibitory centre in response to stretch in the aorta caused by increased arterial flow.

(1) .... initiates the cardiac cycle by spontaeously generating action potentials.

(5) .... carries deoxygenated blood to the lungs.

(2) .... delays the impulse allowing atrial contraction to finish.

(6) .... receives oxygenated blood from the lungs.

Nerve impulses

(3) .... distributes action potentials over the ventricles causing ventricular contraction.

(7) .... specialised conducting muscle fibres transmit impulses through the heart.

(4) .... pumps deoxygenated blood to the lungs.

(8) .... pumps blood from the left atrium to the aorta.

1. On the diagram above, label the identified components of heart structure and intrinsic control (**1-8**), and the components involved in extrinsic control of heart rate (**A-D**).

2. An **ECG** is the result of different impulses produced at each phase of the **cardiac cycle** (the sequence of events in a heartbeat). For each electrical event indicated in the ECG below, describe the corresponding event in the cardiac cycle:

A --
The spread of the impulse from the pacemaker (sinoatrial node) through the atria.

B --
The spread of the impulse through the ventricles.

C --
Recovery of the electrical activity of the ventricles.

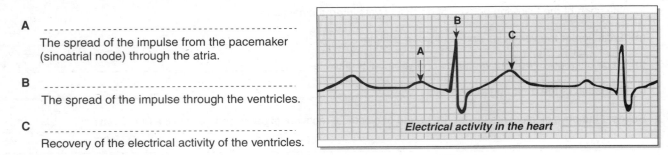

Electrical activity in the heart

3. Describe one treatment that may be indicated when heart rhythm is erratic or too slow: _____

_____

138

Plant Transport Systems

OCR: Unit F211, Module 2: Exchange & Transport
1.2.3: Transport in plants

CIE: CORE SYLLABUS
G(a)-(k): Transport in multicellar plants

Learning Objectives

☐ 1. Compile your own glossary from the **KEY WORDS** displayed in **bold type** in the learning objectives below.

☐ 2. Explain the need for **transport systems** in multicellular plants in relation to size and **surface area to volume ratio**. Relate the presence of structural tissues in plants to the presence of an organised transport system. Recognise the relationship between the transport systems and the specialised exchange systems at the roots and leaves.

Transport Tissues *(pages 140-145)*

☐ 3. Describe the composition and function of the transport tissues in angiosperms: **xylem** (**vessels**, **tracheids**, fibres, xylem parenchyma) and **phloem** (**companion cells**, **sieve elements**, fibres, phloem parenchyma).

☐ 4. Using diagrams, describe the distribution of **xylem** and **phloem** in a dicotyledonous **stem**, **leaf**, and **root**.

☐ 5. Describe adaptations for function in a dicot primary root, including the structure and role of **root hairs** and the **endodermis**, as well as xylem, and phloem.

Transport Mechanisms *(pages 146-152)*

☐ 6. Describe the mechanism and pathways for water uptake in plant roots. Include reference to the role of **osmosis**, gradients in **water potential**, and the **symplastic**, **apoplastic**, and **vacuolar pathways** through the root. Explain the role of the **endodermis** in the movement of water into the **symplast**.

☐ 7. Describe the ways in which mineral uptake occurs in plant roots (passive and active transport mechanisms).

☐ 8. Define the terms **transpiration** and **transpiration stream**. Recognise transpiration as an inevitable consequence of gas exchange and explain the role of **stomata** in these processes. Identify two benefits of transpiration to plants.

☐ 9. Draw a labelled diagram to show the transpiration stream in a flowering plant. Describe how water and dissolved minerals are moved up the plant from the roots to the leaves. Explain the roles of **cohesion-tension** (capillary action), **root pressure**, and **transpiration pull** in the movement of water up the plant, identifying the relative importance of each.

☐ 10. Explain the effect of humidity, light, air movement, temperature, and water availability on transpiration rate. Describe how the factors affecting transpiration could be investigated experimentally.

☐ 11. Understand that species are adapted to survive in particular environmental conditions. Describe structural and/or physiological adaptations in **xerophytes**. Explain how these adaptations reduce transpiration rate and thereby enhance survival in dry conditions.

☐ 12. Explain **translocation**, identifying it as an **active** (energy requiring) process. Draw a labelled diagram to show the movement of dissolved food molecules (especially sucrose) in the phloem. Identify **sources** and **sinks** in the transport of sucrose.

☐ 13. Describe the **mass flow (pressure-flow) hypothesis** for the mechanism of translocation in plants. Evaluate the evidence for and against the mass flow hypothesis.

☐ 14. Interpret and evaluate the evidence for the occurrence and rate of ion and solute transport in plants.

See the 'Textbook Reference Grid' on page 7 for textbook page references relating to material in this topic.

Supplementary Texts
See pages 5-6 for additional details of these texts:

■ Adds, J. *et al.*, 2004. **Exchange & Transport, Energy & Ecosystems** (NelsonThornes), chpt. 2

References to software and videos for this topic are provided on the Teacher Resource CD-ROM

See page 6 for details of publishers of periodicals:

STUDENT'S REFERENCE

■ **How Trees Lift Water** Biol. Sci. Rev., 18(1), Sept. 2005, pp. 33-37. *An excellent account of the cohesion-tension mechanism by which plants move water through their tissues against gravity.*

■ **High Tension** Biol. Sci. Rev., 13(1), Sept. 2000, pp. 14-18. *An excellent account of the mechanisms by which plants transport water and solutes.*

■ **Cacti** Biol. Sci. Rev., 20(1), Sept. 2007, pp. 26-30. *The growth forms and structural and physiological adaptations of cacti.*

■ **Plants in the Greenhouse World** New Scientist, 6 May 1989 (Inside Science). *An easy-to-read account explaining how a plant's many functions are affected by the availability of water.*

■ **Plants, Water and Climate** New Scientist, 25 Feb. 1989, (Inside Science). *Aspects of plant transport: osmosis and turgor, transport from the root to the leaf, transpiration, and stomatal control.*

See pages 8-9 for details of how to access **Bio Links** from our web site: **www.biozone.co.uk**. From Bio Links, access sites under the topics:

PLANT BIOLOGY: • Plant biology for non-science majors ... *and others* **Structure and Function**: • Angiosperm structure and function tutorials • Plant structure • Plant structure II > **Nutrition and Gas Exchange:** • Gas exchange in plants > **Support and Transport:** • LAB: Measuring plant transpiration • Plant structure and growth • Plant transport lecture

Transport in Plants

The support and transport systems in plants are closely linked; many of the same tissues are involved in both systems. Primitive plants (e.g. mosses and liverworts) are small and low growing, and have no need for support and transport systems. If a plant is to grow to any size, it must have ways to hold itself up against gravity and to move materials around its body. The body of a flowering plant has three parts: **roots** anchor the plant and absorb nutrients from the soil, **leaves** produce sugars by photosynthesis, and **stems** link the roots to the leaves and provide support for the leaves and reproductive structures. Stems have distinct points, called **nodes**, at which leaves and buds attach. The region of the stem between two nodes is called the **internode**. Regardless of their shape or location, all stems can be distinguished as such by the presence of nodes and internodes. Vascular tissues (xylem and phloem) link all plant parts so that water, minerals, and manufactured food can be transported between different regions. All plants rely on fluid pressure within their cells (turgor) to give some support to their structure.

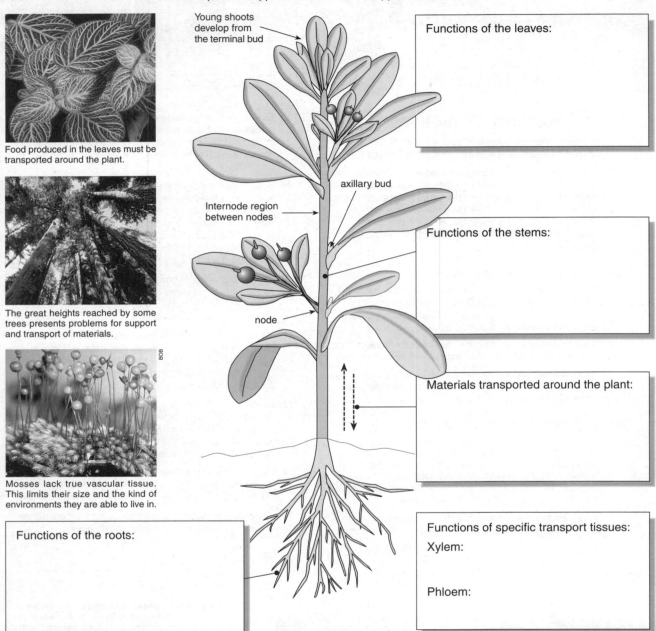

Food produced in the leaves must be transported around the plant.

The great heights reached by some trees presents problems for support and transport of materials.

Mosses lack true vascular tissue. This limits their size and the kind of environments they are able to live in.

Young shoots develop from the terminal bud

axillary bud

Internode region between nodes

node

Functions of the leaves:

Functions of the stems:

Materials transported around the plant:

Functions of the roots:

Functions of specific transport tissues:
Xylem:

Phloem:

1. In the boxes provided in the diagram above:

   (a) List the main functions of the leaves, roots and stems (remember that the leaves themselves have leaf veins).

   (b) List the materials that are transported around the plant body.

   (c) Describe the functions of the transport tissues: xylem and phloem.

2. Name the solvent for all the materials that are transported around the plant: _____

3. State what processes are involved in the transport of sap in the following tissues:

   (a) The xylem: _____

   (b) The phloem: _____

RA 1   **Related activities**: Stems and Roots, Xylem, Phloem, Uptake at the Root, Translocation

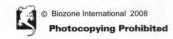

Stems and Roots

The stem and root systems of plants are closely linked. Stems are the primary organs for supporting the plant, whereas roots anchor the plant in the ground, absorb water and minerals from the soil, and transport these materials to other parts of the plant body. Roots may also act as storage organs, storing excess carbohydrate reserves until they are required by the plant. Like most parts of the plant, stems and roots contain vascular tissues. These take the form of bundles containing the xylem and phloem

and strengthening fibres. The entire plant body, including the roots and stems is covered in an epidermis but, unlike most of the plant, the root epidermis has only a thin cuticle that presents no barrier to water entry. Young roots are also covered with **root hairs**. Compared with stems, roots are relatively simple and uniform in structure, and their features are associated with aeration of the tissue and transport of water and minerals form the soil. Dicot stems and roots are described below.

Dicot Stem Structure

In dicots, the vascular bundles are arranged in an orderly fashion around the stem. Each vascular bundle contains **xylem** (to the inside) and **phloem** (to the outside). Between the phloem and the xylem is the **vascular cambium**; a layer of cells that divide to produce the thickening of the stem. The middle of the stem, called the **pith**, is filled with thin-walled parenchyma cells. The vascular bundles in dicots are arranged in an orderly way around the periphery of the stem (below).

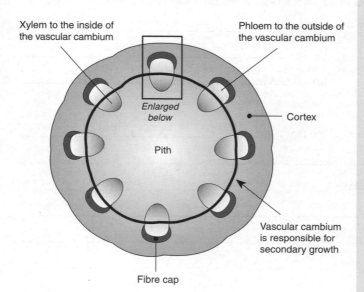

Xylem to the inside of the vascular cambium · Phloem to the outside of the vascular cambium · *Enlarged below* · Cortex · Pith · Vascular cambium is responsible for secondary growth · Fibre cap

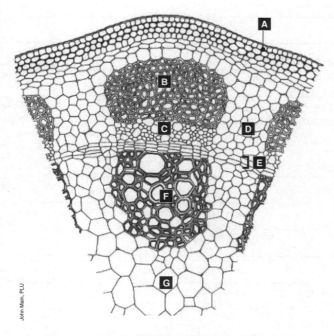

Cross section through a typical dicot stem

Dicot Root Structure

The primary tissues of a dicot root are simple in structure. The large cortex is made up of parenchyma (packing) cells, which store starch and other substances. The air spaces between the cells are essential for aeration of the root tissue, which is non-photosynthetic. The vascular tissue, xylem (X) and phloem (P) forms a central cylinder through the root and is surrounded by the **pericycle**, a ring of cells from which lateral roots arise.

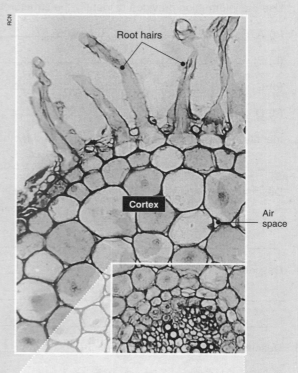

Root hairs · Cortex · Air space

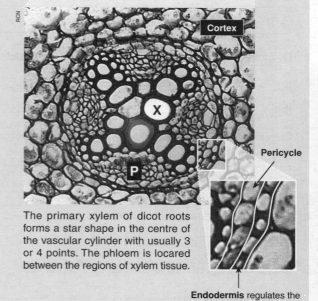

Cortex · X · P · Pericycle

The primary xylem of dicot roots forms a star shape in the centre of the vascular cylinder with usually 3 or 4 points. The phloem is locared between the regions of xylem tissue.

Endodermis regulates the flow of water into the root

Plant Transport Systems

Related activities: Xylem, Phloem, Uptake at the Root · RA 2

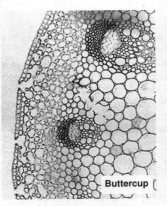

Buttercup

University of Florida

RCN

In plants with photosynthetic stems, CO_2 enters the stem through stomata in the epidermis. The air spaces in the cortex are more typical of leaf mesophyll than stem cortex.

Strawberry plants send out runners. These are above-ground, trailing stems that form roots at their nodes. The plant uses this mechanism to spread vegetatively over a wide area.

Root hairs are located just behind the region of cell elongation in the root tip. The root tip is covered by a slimy root cap. This protects the dividing cells of the tip and lubricates root movement.

The roots and their associated root hairs provide a very large surface area for the uptake of water and ions, as shown in this photograph of the roots of a hydroponically grown plant.

1. Use the information provided to identify the structures **A-G** in the photograph of the dicot stem on the previous page:

   (a) A: _____

   (b) B: _____

   (c) C: _____

   (d) D: _____

   (e) E: _____

   (f) F: _____

   (g) G: _____

2. Identify the feature that distinguishes stems from other parts of the plant: _____

   _____

3. Describe a distinguishing feature of stem structure in dicots: _____

   _____

   _____

4. Describe the role of the vascular cambium: _____

   _____

   _____

5. Describe three functions of roots: _____

   _____

   _____

6. Describe two distinguishing features of internal anatomy of a primary dicot root:

   (a) _____

   (b) _____

7. Describe the role of the parenchyma cells of the root cortex: _____

   _____

   _____

8. Explain the purpose of the root hairs: _____

   _____

9. Explain why the root tip is covered by a cap of cells: _____

   _____

   _____

Leaf Structure

The main function of leaves is as photosynthetic organs in which the sun's radiant energy is collected and used to drive the fixation of carbon dioxide. Regardless of their varying forms, foliage leaves comprise epidermal, mesophyll, and vascular (xylem and phloem) tissues. These tissues are organised in such a way as to maximise photosynthesis by maximising capture of sunlight energy and facilitating diffusion of gases into and out of the leaf tissue. Gases enter and leave the leaf by way of **stomata**. Inside the leaf (as illustrated below), the large air spaces and loose arrangement of the spongy mesophyll provide a large surface area for gas exchange. The basic structure of a dicot leaf is described below. However, the mesophyll (the packing tissue of the leaf) may be variously arranged according to the particular photosynthetic adaptations of the leaf.

Dicot Leaf Structure

Respiring plant cells use oxygen (O_2) and produce carbon dioxide (CO_2). These gases move in and out of the plant and through the air spaces by diffusion. Angiosperms have many air spaces between the cells of the stems, leaves, and roots. These air spaces are continuous and gases are able to move freely through them and into the plant s cells via the **stomata** (*sing.* stoma).

When the plant is photosynthesising, the situation is more complex. Overall there is a net consumption of CO_2 and a net production of oxygen. CO_2 fixation maintains a gradient in CO_2 concentration between the inside of the leaf and the atmosphere. Oxygen is produced in excess of respiratory needs and diffuses out of the leaf. These **net** exchanges are indicated by the arrows on the diagram.

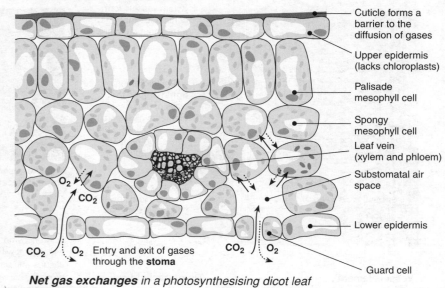

- Cuticle forms a barrier to the diffusion of gases
- Upper epidermis (lacks chloroplasts)
- Palisade mesophyll cell
- Spongy mesophyll cell
- Leaf vein (xylem and phloem)
- Substomatal air space
- Lower epidermis
- Guard cell

CO_2 / O_2 Entry and exit of gases through the **stoma**

Net gas exchanges in a photosynthesising dicot leaf

The surface of the leaf epidermis of a dicot illustrating the density and scattered arrangement of the pores or **stomata**. In dicots, stomata are usually present only on the lower leaf surface.

The leaves of dicots can be distinguished from those of monocots by their netted pattern of leaf veins. Monocots, in contrast, generally have leaves with parallel venation.

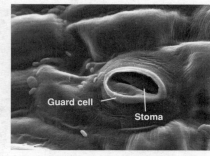

Guard cells on each side of a stoma (pl. stomata) regulate the entry and exit of gases and water vapour. Stomata permit gas exchange but are also the major routes for water loss.

1. Describe two adaptive features of leaves:

   (a) _____

   (b) _____

2. Identify the region of a dicot leaf where most of the chloroplasts are found: _____

3. Explain the purpose of the air spaces in the leaf tissue: _____
   _____
   _____

4. (a) Describe how gases enter and leave the leaf tissue: _____
   _____

   (b) Explain how this movement is regulated: _____
   _____
   _____

Related activities: Transpiration, Adaptations of Xerophytes

RA 2

Plant Transport Systems

Xylem

Xylem is the principal **water conducting tissue** in vascular plants. It is also involved in conducting dissolved minerals, in food storage, and in supporting the plant body. As in animals, tissues in plants are groupings of different cell types that work together for a common function. Xylem is a **complex tissue**. In angiosperms, it is composed of five cell types: tracheids, vessels, xylem parenchyma, sclereids (short sclerenchyma cells), and fibres. The tracheids and vessel elements form the bulk of the tissue. They are heavily strengthened and are the conducting cells of the xylem. Parenchyma cells are involved in storage, while fibres and sclereids provide support. When mature, xylem is dead.

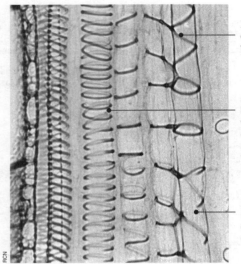

Xylem vessels form continuous tubes throughout the plant.

Spiral thickening of **lignin** around the walls of the vessel elements give extra strength allowing the vessels to remain rigid and upright.

Xylem is dead when mature. Note how the cells have lost their cytoplasm.

The Structure of Xylem Tissue

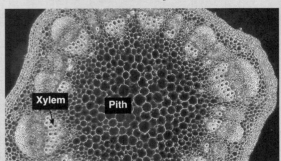

This cross section through the stem, *Helianthus* (sunflower) shows the central pith, surrounded by a peripheral ring of vascular bundles. Note the xylem vessels with their thick walls.

Fibres are a type of sclerenchyma cell. They are associated with vascular tissues and usually occur in groups. The cells are very elongated and taper to a point and the cell walls are heavily thickened. Fibres give mechanical support to tissues, providing both strength and elasticity.

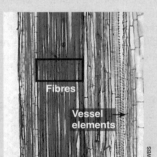

Vessel elements are found only in the xylem of angiosperms. They are large diameter cells that offer very low resistance to water flow. The possession of vessels (stacks of vessel elements) provides angiosperms with a major advantage over gymnosperms and ferns as they allow for very rapid water uptake and transport.

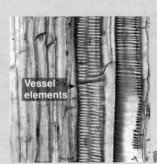

Vessel element

Tip of tracheid cell

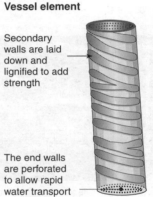

Secondary walls are laid down and lignified to add strength

Pits and bordered pits that allow transfer of water between cells

The end walls are perforated to allow rapid water transport

No cytoplasm or nucleus in mature cell

Vessel elements and tracheids are the two conducting cells types in xylem. Tracheids are long, tapering hollow cells. Water passes from one tracheid to another through thin regions in the wall called **pits**. Vessel elements have pits, but the end walls are also perforated and water flows unimpeded through the stacked elements.

1. Describe the function of **xylem**: _____

    _____

2. Identify the four main cell types in xylem and explain their role in the tissue:

    (a) _____

    (b) _____

    (c) _____

    (d) _____

3. Describe one way in which xylem is strengthened in a mature plant: _____

4. Describe a feature of vessel elements that increases their efficiency of function: _____

    _____

Related activities: Plant Cell Specialisation, Plant Tissues, Uptake at the Root, Transpiration

Phloem

Like xylem, **phloem** is a complex tissue, comprising a variable number of cell types. Phloem is the principal **food (sugar) conducting tissue** in vascular plants, transporting dissolved sugars around the plant. The bulk of phloem tissue comprises the **sieve tubes** (sieve tube members and sieve cells) and their companion cells. The sieve tubes are the principal conducting cells in phloem and are closely associated with the **companion cells** (modified parenchyma cells) with which they share a mutually dependent relationship. Other parenchyma cells, concerned with storage, occur in phloem, and strengthening fibres and sclereids (short sclerenchyma cells) may also be present. Unlike xylem, phloem is alive when mature.

LS through a sieve tube end plate

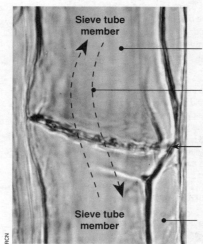

Sieve tube member

The sieve tube members lose most of their organelles but are still alive when mature

Sugar solution flows in both directions

Sieve tube end plate
Tiny holes (arrowed in the photograph below) perforate the sieve tube elements allowing the sugar solution to pass through.

Sieve tube member

Companion cell: a cell adjacent to the sieve tube member, responsible for keeping it alive

TS through a sieve tube end plate

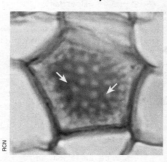

Adjacent sieve tube members are connected via **sieve plates** through which the phloem sap flows.

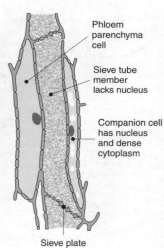

Phloem parenchyma cell

Sieve tube member lacks nucleus

Companion cell has nucleus and dense cytoplasm

Sieve plate

The Structure of Phloem Tissue

Phloem is alive at maturity and functions in the transport of sugars and minerals around the plant. Like xylem, it forms part of the structural vascular tissue of plants.

Fibres are associated with phloem as they are in xylem. Here they are seen in cross section where you can see the extremely thick cell walls and the way the fibres are clustered in groups. See the previous page for a view of fibres in longitudinal section.

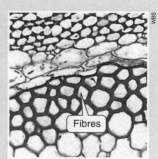

Fibres

In this cross section through a buttercup root, the smaller companion cells can be seen lying alongside the sieve tube members. It is the sieve tube members that, end on end, produce the **sieve tubes**. They are the conducting tissue of phloem.

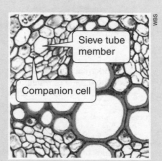

Sieve tube member

Companion cell

In this longitudinal section of a buttercup root, each sieve tube member has a thin **companion cell** associated with it. Companion cells retain their nucleus and control the metabolism of the sieve tube member next to them. They also have a role in the loading and unloading of sugar into the phloem.

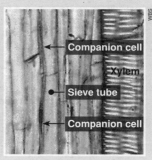

Companion cell
Xylem
Sieve tube
Companion cell

1. Describe the function of **phloem**: _____

2. Describe two differences between xylem and phloem: _____

_____

3. Explain the purpose of the **sieve plate** at the ends of each sieve tube member: _____

_____

4. (a) Name the conducting cell type in phloem: _____

   (b) Explain two roles of the companion cell in phloem: _____

   _____

5. State the purpose of the phloem parenchyma cells: _____

6. Identify a type of cell that provides strengthening in phloem: _____

Plant Transport Systems

Related activities: Plant Cell Specialisation, Plant Tissues, Translocation

RA 2

Uptake in the Root

Plants need to take up water and minerals constantly. They must compensate for the continuous loss of water from the leaves and provide the materials they need for the manufacture of food. The uptake of water and minerals is mostly restricted to the younger, most recently formed cells of the roots and the root hairs. Some water moves through the plant tissues via the plasmodesmata of the cells (the **symplastic route**), but most passes through the free spaces between cell walls (the **apoplast**). Water uptake is assisted by root pressure, which arises because the soil and root tissue has a higher water potential than other plant tissues. Two processes are involved in water and ion uptake: diffusion (osmosis in the case of water) and active transport. Note: An alternative version of this activity, without reference to water potential, is available in *Uptake in the Root* on the TRC (or see web links below).

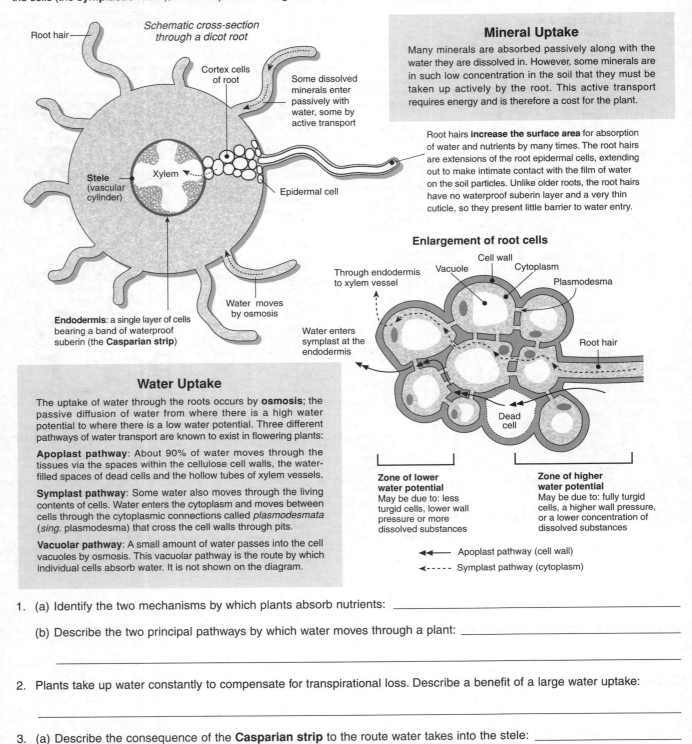

Mineral Uptake

Many minerals are absorbed passively along with the water they are dissolved in. However, some minerals are in such low concentration in the soil that they must be taken up actively by the root. This active transport requires energy and is therefore a cost for the plant.

Root hairs **increase the surface area** for absorption of water and nutrients by many times. The root hairs are extensions of the root epidermal cells, extending out to make intimate contact with the film of water on the soil particles. Unlike older roots, the root hairs have no waterproof suberin layer and a very thin cuticle, so they present little barrier to water entry.

Schematic cross-section through a dicot root

- Root hair
- Cortex cells of root
- Some dissolved minerals enter passively with water, some by active transport
- Stele (vascular cylinder)
- Xylem
- Epidermal cell
- Water moves by osmosis
- **Endodermis**: a single layer of cells bearing a band of waterproof suberin (the **Casparian strip**)

Enlargement of root cells

- Through endodermis to xylem vessel
- Cell wall
- Vacuole
- Cytoplasm
- Plasmodesma
- Root hair
- Water enters symplast at the endodermis
- Dead cell

Zone of lower water potential
May be due to: less turgid cells, lower wall pressure or more dissolved substances

Zone of higher water potential
May be due to: fully turgid cells, a higher wall pressure, or a lower concentration of dissolved substances

◄── Apoplast pathway (cell wall)
◄---- Symplast pathway (cytoplasm)

Water Uptake

The uptake of water through the roots occurs by **osmosis**; the passive diffusion of water from where there is a high water potential to where there is a low water potential. Three different pathways of water transport are known to exist in flowering plants:

Apoplast pathway: About 90% of water moves through the tissues via the spaces within the cellulose cell walls, the water-filled spaces of dead cells and the hollow tubes of xylem vessels.

Symplast pathway: Some water also moves through the living contents of cells. Water enters the cytoplasm and moves between cells through the cytoplasmic connections called *plasmodesmata* (*sing.* plasmodesma) that cross the cell walls through pits.

Vacuolar pathway: A small amount of water passes into the cell vacuoles by osmosis. This vacuolar pathway is the route by which individual cells absorb water. It is not shown on the diagram.

1. (a) Identify the two mechanisms by which plants absorb nutrients: _____

   (b) Describe the two principal pathways by which water moves through a plant: _____

   _____

2. Plants take up water constantly to compensate for transpirational loss. Describe a benefit of a large water uptake:

   _____

3. (a) Describe the consequence of the **Casparian strip** to the route water takes into the stele: _____

   _____

   (b) Suggest why this feature might be advantageous in terms of selective mineral uptake: _____

   _____

   _____

Related activities: Root Structure
Web links: Uptake in the Root

Transpiration

Plants lose water all the time, despite the adaptations they have to help prevent it (e.g. waxy leaf cuticle). Approximately 99% of the water a plant absorbs from the soil is lost by evaporation from the leaves and stem. This loss, mostly through stomata, is called **transpiration** and the flow of water through the plant is called the **transpiration stream**. Plants rely on a gradient in water potential (ψ) from the roots to the air to move water through their cells. Water flows passively from soil to air along a gradient of decreasing water potential. The gradient in water potential is the driving force in the ascent of water up a plant. A number of processes contribute to water movement up the plant: transpiration pull, cohesion, and root pressure. Transpiration may seem to be a wasteful process, but it has benefits. Evaporative water loss cools the plant and the transpiration stream helps the plant to maintain an adequate mineral uptake, as many essential minerals occur in low concentrations in the soil.

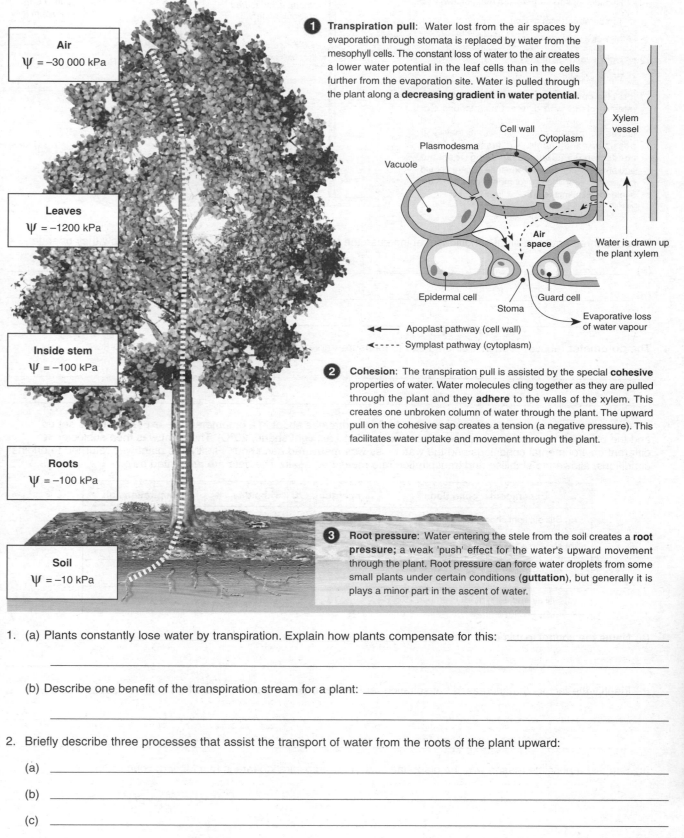

Air
ψ = −30 000 kPa

Leaves
ψ = −1200 kPa

Inside stem
ψ = −100 kPa

Roots
ψ = −100 kPa

Soil
ψ = −10 kPa

1 **Transpiration pull**: Water lost from the air spaces by evaporation through stomata is replaced by water from the mesophyll cells. The constant loss of water to the air creates a lower water potential in the leaf cells than in the cells further from the evaporation site. Water is pulled through the plant along a **decreasing gradient in water potential**.

Xylem vessel

Cell wall

Cytoplasm

Plasmodesma

Vacuole

Air space

Water is drawn up the plant xylem

Epidermal cell

Guard cell

Stoma

Evaporative loss of water vapour

◄◄──── Apoplast pathway (cell wall)
◄----- Symplast pathway (cytoplasm)

2 **Cohesion**: The transpiration pull is assisted by the special **cohesive** properties of water. Water molecules cling together as they are pulled through the plant and they **adhere** to the walls of the xylem. This creates one unbroken column of water through the plant. The upward pull on the cohesive sap creates a tension (a negative pressure). This facilitates water uptake and movement through the plant.

3 **Root pressure**: Water entering the stele from the soil creates a **root pressure;** a weak 'push' effect for the water's upward movement through the plant. Root pressure can force water droplets from some small plants under certain conditions (**guttation**), but generally it is plays a minor part in the ascent of water.

1. (a) Plants constantly lose water by transpiration. Explain how plants compensate for this: _____

_____

(b) Describe one benefit of the transpiration stream for a plant: _____

_____

2. Briefly describe three processes that assist the transport of water from the roots of the plant upward:

(a) _____

(b) _____

(c) _____

Related activities: Osmosis and Water Potential
Web links: Transpiration, Transpiration Animation

DA 3

Plant Transport Systems

The Potometer

A potometer is a simple instrument for investigating transpiration rate (water loss per unit time). The equipment is simple and easy to obtain. A basic potometer, such as the one shown right, can easily be moved around so that transpiration rate can be measured under different environmental conditions

Some of the physical conditions investigated are:

- Humidity or vapour pressure (high or low)

- Temperature (high or low)

- Air movement (still or windy)

- Light level (high or low)

- Water supply

It is also possible to compare the transpiration rates of plants with different adaptations e.g. comparing transpiration rates in plants with rolled leaves vs rates in plants with broad leaves. If possible, experiments like these should be conducted simultaneously using replicate equipment. If conducted sequentially, care should be taken to keep the environmental conditions the same for all plants used.

The progress of an air bubble along the pipette is measured at regular intervals

1 cm³ pipette

Clamp stand

Fresh, leafy shoot

Sealed with petroleum jelly

Rubber bung

Flask filled with water

3. Describe three environmental conditions that increase the rate of transpiration in plants, explaining how they operate:

(a) _____

(b) _____

(c) _____

4. The **potometer** (above) is an instrument used to measure transpiration rate. Briefly explain how it works:

_____

_____

5. An experiment was conducted on transpiration from a hydrangea shoot in a potometer. The experiment was set up and the plant left to stabilise (environmental conditions: still air, light shade, 20°C). The plant was then subjected to different environmental conditions and the water loss was measured each hour. Finally, the plant was returned to original conditions, allowed to stabilise and transpiration rate measured again. The data are presented below:

Experimental conditions	Temperature / °C	Humidity / %	Transpiration / gh⁻¹
(a) Still air, light shade, 20°C	18	70	1.20
(b) Moving air, light shade, 20°C	18	70	1.60
(c) Still air, bright sunlight, 23°C	18	70	3.75
(d) Still air and dark, moist chamber, 19.5°C	18	100	0.05

(a) Name the control in this experiment: _____

_____

(b) Identify the factors that increased transpiration rate, explaining how each has its effect: _____

_____

_____

(c) Suggest a possible reason why the plant had such a low transpiration rate in humid, dark conditions:

_____

_____

Adaptations of Xerophytes

Plants adapted to dry conditions are called **xerophytes** and they show structural (xeromorphic) and physiological adaptations for water conservation. These typically include small, hard leaves, and epidermis with a thick cuticle, sunken stomata, succulence, and permanent or temporary absence of leaves. Xerophytes may live in humid environments, provided that their roots are in dry microenvironments (e.g. the roots of epiphytic plants that grow on tree trunks or branches). The nature of the growing environment is important in many other situations too. **Halophytes** (salt tolerant plants) and alpine species may also show xeromorphic features in response to the scarcity of obtainable water and high transpirational losses in these environments.

Leaves modified into spines or hairs to reduce water loss. Light coloured spines reflect solar radiation.

Squat, rounded shape reduces surface area. The surface tissues of many cacti are tolerant of temperatures in excess of 50¡C.

Shallow, but extensive fibrous root system.

Stem becomes the major photosynthetic organ, plus a reservoir for water storage.

Water table low

Seaweeds, which are protoctists, not plants, tolerate drying between tides even though they have no xeromorphic features.

A waxy coating of **suberin** on mangrove roots excludes 97% of salt from the water.

Dry Desert Plant

Desert plants, such as cacti, must cope with low or sporadic rainfall and high transpiration rates. A number of structural adaptations (diagram left) reduce water losses, and enable them to access and store available water. Adaptations such as waxy leaves also reduce water loss and, in many desert plants, germination is triggered only by a certain quantity of rainfall.

Acacia trees have **deep root systems**, allowing them to draw water from lower water table systems.

Hairs

The outer surface of many succulents are coated in fine hairs, which traps air close to the surface reducing transpiration rate.

Ocean Margin Plant

Land plants that colonise the shoreline must have adaptations to obtain water from their saline environment while maintaining their osmotic balance. In addition, the shoreline is often a windy environment, so they frequently show xeromorphic adaptations that enable them to reduce transpirational water losses.

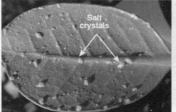

Salt crystals

To maintain osmotic balance, mangroves can secrete absorbed salt as salt crystals (above), or accumulate salt in old leaves which are subsequently shed.

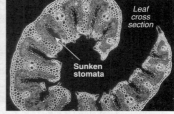

Leaf cross section

Sunken stomata

Grasses found on shoreline coasts (where it is often windy), curl their leaves and have sunken stomata to reduce water loss by transpiration.

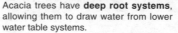

Methods of water conservation in various plant species

Adaptation for water conservation	Effect of adaptation	Example
Thick, waxy cuticle to stems and leaves	Reduces water loss through the cuticle.	*Pinus* sp. ivy (*Hedera*), sea holly (*Eryngium*), prickly pear (*Opuntia*).
Reduced number of stomata	Reduces the number of pores through which water loss can occur.	Prickly pear (*Opuntia*), *Nerium* sp.
Stomata sunken in pits, grooves, or depressions Leaf surface covered with fine hairs Massing of leaves into a rosette at ground level	Moist air is trapped close to the area of water loss, reducing the diffusion gradient and therefore the rate of water loss.	**Sunken stomata**: *Pinus* sp., *Hakea* sp. **Hairy leaves**: lamb s ear. **Leaf rosettes**: dandelion (*Taraxacum*), daisy.
Stomata closed during the light, open at night	CAM metabolism: CO_2 is fixed during the night, water loss in the day is minimised.	**CAM plants**, e.g. American aloe, pineapple, *Kalanchoe*, *Yucca*.
Leaves reduced to scales, stem photosynthetic Leaves curled, rolled, or folded when flaccid	Reduction in surface area from which transpiration can occur.	**Leaf scales**: broom (*Cytisus*). **Rolled leaf**: marram grass (*Ammophila*), *Erica* sp.
Fleshy or succulent stems Fleshy or succulent leaves	When readily available, water is stored in the tissues for times of low availability.	**Fleshy stems**: *Opuntia*, candle plant (*Kleinia*). **Fleshy leaves**: *Bryophyllum*.
Deep root system below the water table	Roots tap into the lower water table.	Acacias, oleander.
Shallow root system absorbing surface moisture	Roots absorb overnight condensation.	Most cacti

Plant Transport Systems

Related activities: Transpiration

A 1

Adaptations in halophytes and drought tolerant plants

Ice plant (*Carpobrotus*): The leaves of many desert and beach dwelling plants are fleshy or succulent. The leaves are triangular in cross section and crammed with water storage cells. The water is stored after rain for use in dry periods. The shallow root system is able to take up water from the soil surface, taking advantage of any overnight condensation.

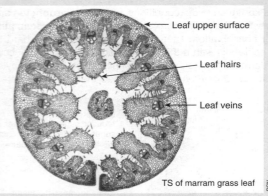

TS of marram grass leaf

Leaf upper surface

Leaf hairs

Leaf veins

Marram grass (*Ammophila*): The long, wiry leaf blades of this beach grass are curled downwards with the stomata on the inside. This protects them against drying out by providing a moist microclimate around the stomata. Plants adapted to high altitude often have similar adaptations.

Ball cactus (*Echinocactus grusonii*): In many cacti, the leaves are modified into long, thin spines which project outward from the thick fleshy stem. This reduces the surface area over which water loss can occur. The stem stores water and takes over as the photosynthetic organ. As in succulents, a shallow root system enables rapid uptake of surface water.

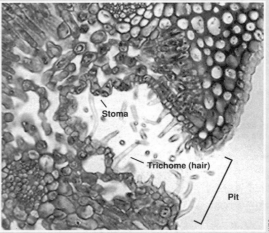

Stoma

Trichome (hair)

Pit

Oleander is a xerophyte from the mediterranean region with many water conserving features. It has a thick multi-layered epidermis and the stomata are sunken in trichome-filled pits on the leaf underside. The pits restrict water loss to a greater extent than they reduce uptake of carbon dioxide.

1. Explain the purpose of **xeromorphic** adaptations: _____

_____

2. Describe three xeromorphic adaptations of plants:

   (a) _____

   (b) _____

   (c) _____

3. Describe a physiological mechanism by which plants can reduce water loss during the daylight hours:

   _____

   _____

4. Explain why creating a moist microenvironment around the areas of water loss reduces transpiration rate:

   _____

5. Explain why seashore plants (halophytes) exhibit many desert-dwelling adaptations: _____

   _____

   _____

Translocation

Phloem transports the organic products of photosynthesis (sugars) through the plant in a process called **translocation**. In angiosperms, the sugar moves through the sieve elements, which are arranged end-to-end and perforated with sieve plates. Apart from water, phloem sap comprises mainly sucrose (up to 30%). It may also contain minerals, hormones, and amino acids, in transit around the plant. Movement of sap in the phloem is from a **source** (a plant organ where sugar is made or mobilised) to a **sink** (a plant organ where sugar is stored or used). Loading sucrose into the phloem at a source involves energy expenditure; it is slowed or stopped by high temperatures or respiratory inhibitors. In some plants, unloading the sucrose at the sinks also requires energy, although in others, diffusion alone is sufficient to move sucrose from the phloem into the cells of the sink organ.

Transport in the Phloem by Pressure-Flow

Phloem sap moves from source (region where sugar is produced or mobilised) to sink (region where sugar is used or stored) at rates as great as 100 m h^{-1}: too fast to be accounted for by cytoplasmic streaming. The most acceptable model for phloem movement is the **pressure-flow** (bulk flow) hypothesis. Phloem sap moves by bulk flow, which creates a pressure (hence the term "pressure-flow"). The key elements in this model are outlined below and in steps 1-4 right. For simplicity, the cells that lie between the source or sink cells and the phloem sieve-tube have been omitted.

1 Loading sugar into the phloem from a source (e.g. leaf cell) increases the solute concentration (decreases the water potential, ψ) inside the sieve-tube cells. This causes the sieve-tubes to take up water from the surrounding tissues by osmosis.

2 The water absorption creates a hydrostatic pressure that forces the sap to move along the tube (bulk flow), just as pressure pushes water through a hose.

3 The gradient of pressure in the sieve tube is reinforced by the active unloading of sugar and consequent loss of water by osmosis at the sink (e.g. root cell).

4 Xylem recycles the water from sink to source.

Measuring Phloem Flow

Experiments investigating flow of phloem often use aphids. Aphids feed on phloem sap (left) and act as natural **phloem probes**. When the mouthparts (stylet) of an aphid penetrate a sieve-tube cell, the pressure in the sieve-tube force-feeds the aphid. While the aphid feeds, it can be severed from its stylet, which remains in place in the phloem. The stylet serves as a tiny tap that exudes sap. Using different aphids, the rate of flow of this sap can be measured at different locations on the plant.

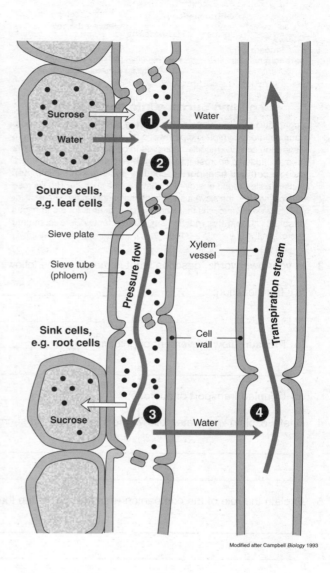

Modified after Campbell *Biology* 1993

1. (a) Explain what is meant by '**source to sink**' flow in phloem transport: _____

_____

(b) Name the usual **source** and **sink** in a growing plant:

Source: _____ Sink: _____

(c) Name another possible **source** region in the plant and state when it might be important: _____

_____

(d) Name another possible **sink** region in the plant and state when it might be important: _____

_____

2. Explain why energy is required for translocation and where it is used: _____

_____

Related activities: Xylem, Phloem, Active and Passive Transport
Web links: Translocation, Sucrose Transport

RA 3

Plant Transport Systems

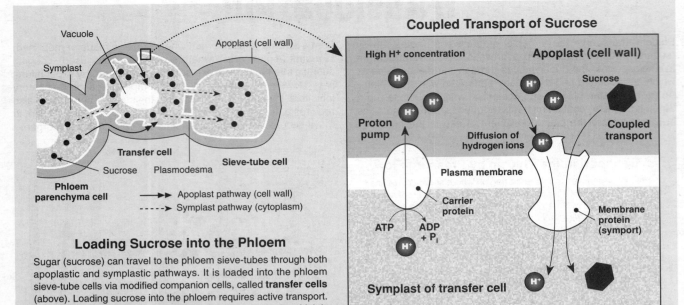

Loading Sucrose into the Phloem

Sugar (sucrose) can travel to the phloem sieve-tubes through both apoplastic and symplastic pathways. It is loaded into the phloem sieve-tube cells via modified companion cells, called **transfer cells** (above). Loading sucrose into the phloem requires active transport. Using a **coupled transport** (secondary pump) mechanism (right), transfer cells expend energy to accumulate the sucrose. The sucrose then passes into the sieve tube through plasmodesmata. The transfer cells have wall ingrowths that increase surface area for the transport of solutes. Using this mechanism, some plants can accumulate sucrose in the phloem to 2-3 times the concentration in the mesophyll.

Above: Proton pumps generate a hydrogen ion gradient across the membrane of the transfer cell. This process requires expenditure of energy. The gradient is then used to drive the transport of sucrose, by coupling the sucrose transport to the diffusion of H+ back into the cell.

3. In your own words, describe what is meant by the following:

(a) Translocation: _____

_____

(b) Pressure-flow movement of phloem: _____

_____

(c) Coupled transport of sucrose: _____

4. Briefly explain why water follows the sucrose as the sucrose is loaded into the phloem sieve-tube cell:

_____

_____

5. Explain the role of the companion (transfer) cell in the loading of sucrose into the phloem: _____

_____

_____

6. Contrast the composition of phloem sap and xylem sap (see the activities on xylem and phloem if you need help):

_____

_____

7. Explain why it is necessary for phloem to be alive to be functional, whereas xylem can function as a dead tissue:

_____

_____

8. The sieve plate represents a significant barrier to effective mass flow of phloem sap. Suggest why the presence of the sieve plate is often cited as evidence against the pressure-flow model for phloem transport:

_____

_____

_____

Biological Molecules

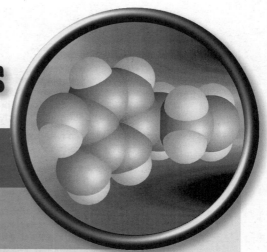

OCR: Unit F212, Module 1: Biological Molecules
2.1.1: Biological molecules and 2.1.3: Enzymes

CIE: CORE SYLLABUS
B: Biological molecules and C: Enzymes

Learning Objectives

The learning objectives relating to the structure and function of nucleic acids are provided in the topic "The Genetic Code".

☐ 1.   Compile your own glossary from the **KEY WORDS** displayed in **bold type** in the learning objectives below.

Basic Organic Chemistry *(pages 155-157)*

☐ 2.   Identify the four most common elements found in living things. Provide examples of where these elements occur in cells. Explain what is meant by **organic chemistry** and explain its importance in biology.

☐ 3.   Distinguish between ionic bonds and covalent bonds and understand the importance of **covalent bonds** in carbon-based compounds.

☐ 4.   Distinguish between **monomers** and **polymers** and provide examples of each type. Explain clearly what is meant by a **macromolecule** and give examples.

☐ 5.   EXTENSION: Explain how **chromatography** is used to separate and identify biological molecules. Describe the calculation and use of **Rf values**.

Water and Inorganic Ions *(pages 155, 158)*

☐ 6.   Describe the structure of water, including reference to the polar nature of the water molecule, the nature of the bonding within the molecule, and the importance of **hydrogen bonding** between water molecules.

☐ 7.   Relate the structure and physical properties of water to its various roles in living organisms. Explain why water is termed the **universal solvent**.

☐ 8.   Using examples, describe the role of **inorganic ions** (mineral ions) in biological systems. Examples could include: Na^+, K^+, Mg^{2+}, Cl^-, NO_3^-, and PO_4^{3-}.

Carbohydrates *(pages 157, 159-160)*

☐ 9.   Describe the basic composition and general formula of **carbohydrates**. Describe the roles of carbohydrates in biological systems.

☐ 10. Describe the molecular structure of a **monosaccharide** (e.g. α glucose). Provide examples of **triose**, **pentose**, and **hexose sugars** (including fructose and galactose). For each, identify its biological role.

☐ 11. Distinguish between **structural** and **optical isomers** in monosaccharides, explaining the basis for the isomerism in each case. Describe structural isomers of glucose (α and β **glucose**) and their biological significance.

☐ 12. Describe what is meant by a **disaccharide**. Explain how disaccharides are formed by a **condensation** reaction and broken apart by **hydrolysis**. Identify the **glycosidic bond** formed and broken in each case. Give examples of disaccharides and their functions, and name the monosaccharides involved in each case.

☐ 13. Identify examples of **reducing** and **non-reducing sugars**, and describe the **Benedict's test** for distinguishing these. Explain the basis of the test and its result. Describe a test for a non-reducing sugar.

☐ 14. Explain what is meant by a **polysaccharide** and describe how polysaccharides are formed. Compare and contrast the structure of starch, cellulose and/or glycogen, and relate their structure to their function in biological systems.

☐ 15. Describe the I_2/KI (iodine in potassium iodide solution) **test** for starch. Explain its basis and result.

Lipids *(pages 157, 161-162)*

☐ 16. Describe the general properties of lipids. Recognise the diversity of lipids in biological systems (e.g. steroids, phospholipids, waxes, and fats and oils and describe their functional roles.

☐ 17. Describe the **emulsion test** for lipids. Explain the basis of the test and its result.

☐ 18. Recognise that most lipids are **triglycerides** (triacylglycerols). Describe how triglycerides are classified as **fats** or **oils** and explain the basis of the classification.

☐ 19. Describe the basic structure of a triglyceride. Explain their formation by **condensation** reactions between glycerol and three fatty acids. Identify the **ester bonds** that result from this. Distinguish between **saturated** and **unsaturated fatty acids** and relate this difference to the properties of the fat or oil that results.

☐ 20. Using a diagram, describe the basic structure of a **phospholipid** and explain how it differs from the structure of a triglyceride. Explain how the structure of phospholipids is important to their role in membranes.

Amino Acids & Proteins *(pages 71-72, 157, 163-66)*

☐ 21. Draw or describe the general structure and formula of an **amino acid**. Explain the basis for the different properties of amino acids.

☐ 22. Recognise that, of over 170 amino acids, only 20 are commonly found in proteins. Distinguish between **essential** and **non-essential amino acids**.

☐ 23. Recognise the property of **optical isomerism** in amino acids and explain its basis. Distinguish L- and D- forms and identify which isomer is active in biological systems.

☐ 24. Using a diagram, describe how amino acids are joined together in a **condensation reaction** to form **dipeptides** and **polypeptides**. Describe the nature of **peptide bonds** that result. Describe how polypeptides are broken down by **hydrolysis**.

☐ 25. Describe the **biuret test** for proteins. Explain the basis of the test and its result.

26. Recall where (in the cell) proteins are made and recognise the ways in which they can be modified after production. Distinguish between the **primary structure** of a protein and its **secondary structure**.

27. Recognise the two main types of secondary structure found in proteins: **alpha-helix** and **beta-pleated sheet**.

28. Explain what is meant by the **tertiary structure** of a protein and explain how it arises. Describe the relationship between the tertiary structure of a **globular protein** and its biological function.

29. With reference to examples (e.g. collagen and insulin or haemoglobin), distinguish between **globular** and **fibrous proteins**. Consider the structure, properties, and biological functions of the protein.

30. With reference to specific examples (e.g. collagen, insulin, haemoglobin), describe the role of different types of bonds in proteins: hydrogen bonds, ionic bonds, disulfide bonds, hydrophobic interactions.

31. Explain what is meant by protein **denaturation** and explain why it destroys the activity of proteins. Describe how different agents denature proteins.

32. Explain what is meant by the **quaternary structure** of a protein. In a named example (e.g. **haemoglobin**, *a globular protein*) describe how the quaternary structure arises and relate it to the protein's function.

33. Recognise the ways in which proteins can be classified:
    - By their structure (e.g. globular or fibrous)
    - By their functional role: structural, contractile, immunological, as enzymes, hormones, or respiratory pigments, in transport, in storage.

Enzymes *(pages 167-170)*

34. Define: **enzyme**, **catalyst**, and **substrate**. Describe the general properties of enzymes and explain their role in metabolism. Distinguish between the **intracellular** and **extracellular** activity of enzymes and give examples.

35. Use diagrams to describe the mechanism by which enzymes work as catalysts to bring about reactions in cells. Include reference to the **active site**, **enzyme-substrate complex**, **enzyme-product complex**, and lowering of **activation energy**.

36. Contrast the **induced fit** and the **lock and key** models of enzyme function, clearly explaining how they differ.

37. Describe ways in which the time course of an enzyme-catalysed reaction can be followed: by measuring the rate of product formation (e.g. catalase) or by measuring the rate of substrate use (e.g. amylase).

38. Describe and explain the effect of the following factors on enzyme activity: substrate concentration, enzyme concentration, pH, and temperature. Describe or demonstrate how the effect of each of these could be investigated experimentally. Identify the **optimum conditions** for some named enzymes. Recognise that enzymes (being proteins) can be **denatured**.

39. Distinguish between **coenzymes** and **cofactors**. Explain how cofactors enable an enzyme to work.

40. Explain the effects of **competitive** and **non-competitive inhibitors** on the rate of enzyme-controlled reactions, with reference to both **reversible** and **irreversible inhibition**. Recognise that metabolic poisons may operate as enzyme inhibitors and describe at least one example.

See the 'Textbook Reference Grid' on page 7 for textbook page references relating to material in this topic.

Supplementary Texts

See pages 5-6 for additional details of these texts:
- Adds, J. *et al.*, 2003. **Molecules and Cells**, (NelsonThornes), chpt. 1 & 3.
- Clegg, C.J., 2002. **Microbes in Action**, (John Murray), 50-53 (enzyme technology).
- Harwood, R., 2002. **Biochemistry**, (Cambridge University Press), entire text.

See page 6 for details of publishers of periodicals:

STUDENT'S REFERENCE
Water, ions, and carbon chemistry

- **Biochemistry** Biol. Sci. Rev., 20(2) Nov. 2007, pp. 21-24. *An outline of what constitutes biochemistry and its role as a essential discipline within science.*
- **Water** Biol. Sci. Rev., 8(3) Jan. 1996, pp. 38-40. *The important properties and roles of water.*
- **Of Hydrogen Bondage** Biol. Sci. Rev., 10(1) Sept. 1997, pp. 36-38. *The critical role of hydrogen bonding in biological molecules and water.*

- **Why Life Chose Carbon** Biol. Sci. Rev., 10(2) November 1997, pp. 15-17. *The structure of the carbon atom and its role in biological chemistry.*
- **D-Glucose: A Shapely, Stable Molecule** Biol. Sci. Rev., 16(2) Nov. 2003, pp. 15-20. *Properties of glucose: a small, six carbon sugar.*
- **Designer Starches** Biol. Sci. Rev., 19(3) Feb. 2007, pp. 18-20. *The composition of starch, and an excellent account of its properties and functions.*
- **Glucose & Glucose-Containing Carbohydrates** Biol. Sci. Rev., 19(1) Sept. 2006, pp. 12-15. *The structure of glucose and its polymers.*
- **Stuck with Structures?** Biol. Sci. Rev., 15(2) Nov. 2002, pp. 28-29. *A guide to interpreting the structural formulae of common organic compounds.*
- **Foetal Haemoglobin** Biol. Sci. Rev., 16(1) Sept. 2003, pp. 15-17. *The complex quaternary structure of haemoglobin molecules.*
- **Making Proteins Work (I)** Biol. Sci. Rev., 15(1) Sept. 2002, pp. 22-25. *A synopsis of how a globular and a fibrous protein each become functional.*
- **Making Proteins Work (II)** Biol. Sci. Rev., 15(2) Nov. 2002, pp. 24-27. *How carbohydrates are added to proteins to make them functional.*
- **Exploring Proteins** Biol. Sci. Rev., 16(4) April 2004, pp. 32-36. *Understanding how proteins function as complexes within the cell. Chromatographic techniques are also described.*
- **Universal Body Builder** New Scientist, 23 May 1998 (Inside Science). *The structure and role of collagen, the most common protein in animals.*

Enzymes and enzyme technology

- **Enzymes** Biol. Sci. Rev., 15(1) Sept. 2002, pp. 2-5. *Enzymes as catalysts: how they work, models of enzyme function, and cofactors and inhibitors.*
- **Enzymes: Fast and Flexible** Biol. Sci. Rev., 19(1) Sept. 2006, pp. 2-5. *The structure of enzymes and how they work so efficiently at relatively low temperatures.*

- **Enzyme Technology** Biol. Sci. Rev., 12 (5) May 2000, pp. 26-27. *The range and importance of industrial enzymes in modern biotechnology.*
- **Enzymes from Fungi** Biol. Sci. Rev., 13(3) Jan. 2001, pp. 19-21. *A discussion of the production and applications of fungal enzymes.*

See pages 8-9 for details of how to access **Bio Links** from our web site: **www.biozone.co.uk**. From Bio Links, access sites under the topics:
BIOTECHNOLOGY > Applications in Biotechnology > Industrial Biotechnology: • About industrial enzymes • Chapter 19: industrial microbiology • Discover enzymes ... *and others*
CELL BIOLOGY AND BIOCHEMISTRY: • Cell & molecular biology online • Molecular biology web book ... *and others* > **Biochemistry and Metabolic Pathways:** • Enzymes • Energy and enzymes • Energy, enzymes and catalysis problem set • Reactions and enzymes • The Biology project: Biochemistry

Presentation MEDIA to support this topic:
CELL BIO & BIOCHEM:
• Molecules of Life

The Biochemical Nature of the Cell

The molecules that make up living things can be grouped into five classes: water, carbohydrates, lipids, proteins, and nucleic acids. Water is the main component of organisms and provides an environment in which metabolic reactions can occur. Water molecules attract each other, forming large numbers of hydrogen bonds. It is this feature that gives water many of its unique properties, including its low viscosity and its chemical behaviour as a **universal solvent**. Apart from water, most other substances in cells are compounds of carbon, hydrogen, oxygen, and nitrogen. The combination of carbon atoms with the atoms of other elements provides a huge variety of molecular structures. These are described on the following pages.

Important Properties of Water

Water is a liquid at room temperature and many substances dissolve in it. It is a medium inside cells and for aquatic life.

A lot of energy is required before water will change state so aquatic environments are thermally stable and sweating and transpiration cause rapid cooling.

Ice is less dense than water. Consequently ice floats, insulating the underlying water and providing valuable habitat.

Water has a high surface tension and low viscosity. It forms droplets on surfaces and can flow freely through narrow vessels.

Water is colourless, with a high transmission of visible light, so light penetrates tissue and aquatic environments.

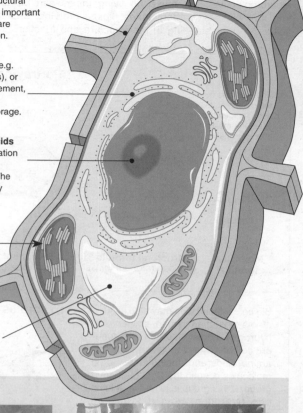

Carbohydrates form the structural components of cells, they are important in energy storage, and they are involved in cellular recognition.

Proteins may be structural (e.g. collagen), catalytic (enzymes), or they may be involved in movement, message signalling, internal defence and transport, or storage.

Nucleotides and nucleic acids Nucleic acids encode information for the construction and functioning of an organism. The nucleotide, ATP, is the energy currency of the cell.

Lipids provide insulation and a concentrated source of energy. Phospholipids are a major component of cellular membranes.

Water is a major component of cells: many substances dissolve in it, metabolic reactions occur in it, and it provides support and turgor.

1. Explain the biological significance of each of the following physical properties of water:

   (a) Low viscosity: _____

   (b) Colourless and transparent: _____

   (c) Universal solvent: _____

   (d) Ice is less dense than water: _____

2. Identify the biologically important role of each of the following molecules:

   (a) Lipids: _____

   (b) Carbohydrates: _____

   (c) Proteins: _____

   (d) Nucleic acids: _____

Related activities: Organic Molecules, Water and Inorganic Ions

A 1

Organic Molecules

Organic molecules are those chemical compounds containing carbon that are found in living things. Specific groups of atoms, called **functional groups**, attach to a carbon-hydrogen core and confer specific chemical properties on the molecule. Some organic molecules in organisms are small and simple, containing only one or a few functional groups, while others are large complex assemblies called **macromolecules**. The macromolecules that make up living things can be grouped into four classes: carbohydrates, lipids, proteins, and nucleic acids. An understanding of the structure and function of these

molecules is necessary to many branches of biology, especially biochemistry, physiology, and molecular genetics. The diagram below illustrates some of the common ways in which biological molecules are portrayed. Note that the **molecular formula** expresses the number of atoms in a molecule, but does not convey its structure; this is indicated by the **structural formula**. Molecules can also be represented as **models**. A ball and stick model shows the arrangement and type of bonds while a space filling model gives a more realistic appearance of a molecule, showing how close the atoms really are.

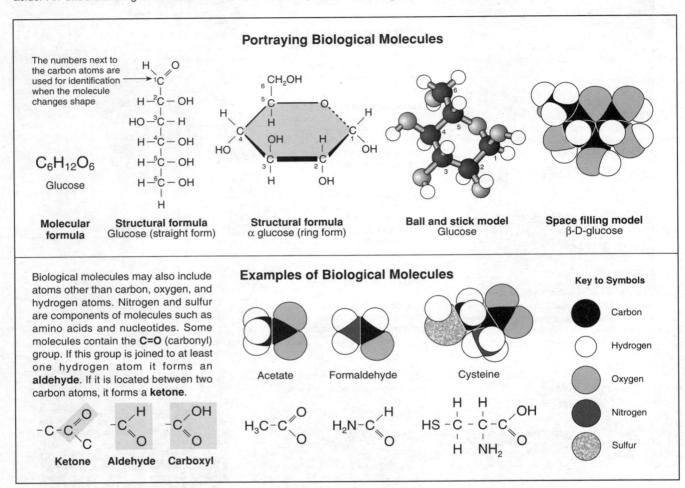

1. Identify the three main elements comprising the structure of organic molecules: _____

2. Name two other elements that are also frequently part of organic molecules: _____

3. State how many covalent bonds a carbon atom can form with neighbouring atoms: _____

4. Distinguish between molecular and structural formulae for a given molecule: _____

   _____

   _____

5. Describe what is meant by a functional group: _____

   _____

6. Classify formaldehyde according to the position of the C=O group: _____

7. Identify a functional group always present in amino acids: _____

8. Identify the significance of cysteine in its formation of disulfide bonds: _____

   _____

Related activities: Biochemical Nature of the Cell, Amino Acids, Proteins

Biochemical Tests

Biochemical tests are used to detect the presence of nutrients such as lipids, proteins, and carbohydrates (sugar and starch) in various foods. These simple tests are useful for detecting nutrients when large quantities are present. A more accurate technique by which to separate a mixture of compounds involves **chromatography**. Chromatography is used when only a small sample is available or when you wish to distinguish between nutrients. Simple biochemical food tests will show whether sugar is present, whereas chromatography will distinguish between the different types of sugars (e.g. fructose or glucose).

Paper Chromatography

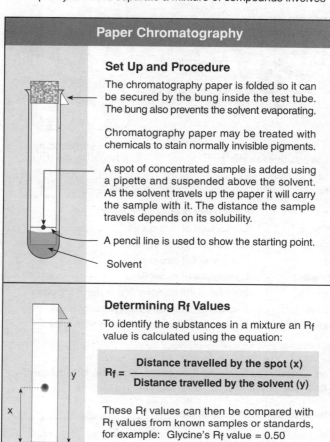

Set Up and Procedure

The chromatography paper is folded so it can be secured by the bung inside the test tube. The bung also prevents the solvent evaporating.

Chromatography paper may be treated with chemicals to stain normally invisible pigments.

A spot of concentrated sample is added using a pipette and suspended above the solvent. As the solvent travels up the paper it will carry the sample with it. The distance the sample travels depends on its solubility.

A pencil line is used to show the starting point.

Solvent

Determining R_f Values

To identify the substances in a mixture an R_f value is calculated using the equation:

$$R_f = \frac{\text{Distance travelled by the spot (x)}}{\text{Distance travelled by the solvent (y)}}$$

These R_f values can then be compared with R_f values from known samples or standards, for example: Glycine's R_f value = 0.50

Alanine's R_f value = 0.70

Arginine's R_f value = 0.72

Leucine's R_f value = 0.91

Simple Food Tests

Proteins: The Biuret Test

Reagent: Biuret solution.

Procedure: A sample is added to biuret solution and gently heated.

Positive result: Solution turns from blue to lilac.

Starch: The Iodine Test

Reagent: Iodine.

Procedure: Iodine solution is added to the sample.

Positive result: Blue-black staining occurs.

Lipids: The Emulsion Test

Reagent: Ethanol.

Procedure: The sample is shaken with ethanol. After settling, the liquid portion is distilled and mixed with water.

Positive result: The solution turns into a cloudy-white emulsion of suspended lipid molecules.

Sugars: The Benedict's Test

Reagent: Benedict's solution.

Procedure: *Non reducing sugars*: The sample is boiled with dilute hydrochloric acid, then cooled and neutralised. A test for reducing sugars is then performed.

Reducing sugar: Benedict's solution is added, and the sample is placed in a water bath.

Positive result: Solution turns from blue to orange.

1. Calculate the R_f value for the example given above (show your working): _____

_____

2. Explain why the R_f value of a substance is always less than 1: _____

_____

3. Discuss when it is appropriate to use chromatography instead of a simple food test: _____

_____

_____

4. Predict what would happen if a sample was immersed in the chromatography solvent, instead of suspended above it:

_____

_____

5. With reference to their R_f values, rank the four amino acids (listed above) in terms of their solubility: _____

_____

6. Outline why lipids must be mixed in ethanol before they will form an emulsion in water: _____

_____

Related activities: Proteins, Carbohydrates, Lipids

RDA 2

Water and Inorganic Ions

The Earth's crust contains approximately 100 elements but only 16 are essential for life (see the table of inorganic ions below). Of the smaller molecules making up living things water is the most abundant typically making up about two-thirds of any organism's body. Water has a simple molecular structure and the molecule is very polar, with ends that exhibit partial positive and negative charges. Water molecules have a weak attraction for each other and inorganic ions, forming weak hydrogen bonds.

Water and Inorganic Ions

Water provides an environment in which metabolic reactions can happen. Water takes part in, and is a common product of, many reactions. The most important feature of the chemical behaviour of water is its **dipole** nature. It has a small positive charge on each of the two hydrogens and a small negative charge on the oxygen.

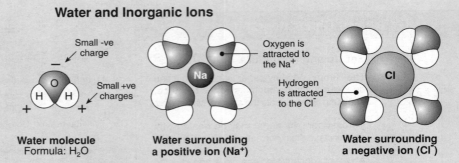

Small -ve charge

Small +ve charges

Water molecule
Formula: H_2O

Oxygen is attracted to the Na^+

Hydrogen is attracted to the Cl^-

Water surrounding a positive ion (Na^+)

Water surrounding a negative ion (Cl^-)

Inorganic ions are important for the structure and metabolism of all living organisms. An ion is simply an atom (or group of atoms) that has gained or lost one or more electrons. Many of these ions are soluble in water. Some of the inorganic ions required by organisms and their biological roles are listed in the table on the right.

Ion	Name	Biological role
Ca^{2+}	Calcium	Component of bones and teeth
Mg^{2+}	Magnesium	Component of chlorophyll
Fe^{2+}	Iron (II)	Component of hemoglobin
NO_3^-	Nitrate	Component of amino acids
PO_4^{3-}	Phosphate	Component of nucleotides
Na^+	Sodium	Involved in the transmission of nerve impulses
K^+	Potassium	Involved in controlling plant water balance
Cl^-	Chloride	Involved in the removal of water from urine

1. On the diagram above, showing a positive and a negative ion surrounded by water molecules, draw the positive and negative charges on the water molecules (as shown in the example provided).

2. Explain the importance of the **dipole nature** of water molecules to the chemistry of life: _____

_____

_____

3. Distinguish between inorganic and organic compounds: _____

_____

4. Describe a role of the following elements in living organisms (plants, animals and prokaryotes) and a consequence of the element being deficient in an organism's diet:

(a) Calcium: _____

_____

(b) Iron: _____

_____

(c) Phosphorus: _____

_____

(d) Sodium: _____

_____

(e) Sulfur: _____

_____

(f) Nitrogen: _____

_____

RA 2

Related activities: Biochemical Nature of the Cell, Organic Molecules
Web links: Hydrogen Bonds and Water, Water and pH

Carbohydrates

Carbohydrates are a family of organic molecules made up of carbon, hydrogen, and oxygen atoms with the general formula $(CH_2O)_x$. The most common arrangements found in sugars are hexose (6 sided) or pentose (5 sided) rings. Simple sugars, or monosaccharides, may join together to form compound sugars (disaccharides and polysaccharides), releasing water in the process (**condensation**). Compound sugars can be broken down into their constituent monosaccharides by the opposite reaction (**hydrolysis**). Sugars play a central role in cells, providing energy and, in some cells, contributing to support. They are the major component of most plants (60-90% of the dry weight) and are used by humans as a cheap food source, and a source of fuel, housing, and clothing. In all carbohydrates, the structure is closely related to their functional properties (below).

Monosaccharides

Monosaccharides are used as a primary energy source for fuelling cell metabolism. They are **single-sugar** molecules and include glucose (grape sugar and blood sugar) and fructose (honey and fruit juices). The commonly occurring monosaccharides contain between three and seven carbon atoms in their carbon chains and, of these, the 6C hexose sugars occur most frequently. All monosaccharides are classified as **reducing** sugars (i.e. they can participate in reduction reactions).

Single sugars (monosaccharides)

Triose

C
|
C
|
C

e.g. glyceraldehyde

Pentose

e.g. ribose, deoxyribose

Hexose

e.g. glucose, fructose, galactose

Disaccharides

Disaccharides are **double-sugar** molecules and are used as energy sources and as building blocks for larger molecules. The type of disaccharide formed depends on the monomers involved and whether they are in their α- or β- form. Only a few disaccharides (e.g. lactose) are classified as reducing sugars.

Sucrose = α-glucose + β-fructose (simple sugar found in plant sap)
Maltose = α-glucose + α-glucose (a product of starch hydrolysis)
Lactose = β-glucose + β-galactose (milk sugar)
Cellobiose = β-glucose + β-glucose (from cellulose hydrolysis)

Double sugars (disaccharides)

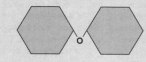

Examples
sucrose,
lactose,
maltose,
cellobiose

Polysaccharides

Cellulose: Cellulose is a structural material in plants and is made up of unbranched chains of β-**glucose** molecules held together by **1, 4 glycosidic links**. As many as 10 000 glucose molecules may be linked together to form a straight chain. Parallel chains become cross-linked with hydrogen bonds and form bundles of 60-70 molecules called microfibrils. Cellulose microfibrils are very strong and are a major component of the structural components of plants, such as the cell wall (photo, right).

Starch: Starch is also a polymer of glucose, but it is made up of long chains of α-**glucose** molecules linked together. It contains a mixture of 25-30% **amylose** (unbranched chains linked by α-1, 4 glycosidic bonds) and 70-75% **amylopectin** (branched chains with α-1, 6 glycosidic bonds every 24-30 glucose units). Starch is an energy storage molecule in plants and is found concentrated in insoluble **starch granules** within plant cells (see photo, right). Starch can be easily hydrolysed by enzymes to soluble sugars when required.

Glycogen: Glycogen, like starch, is a branched polysaccharide. It is chemically similar to amylopectin, being composed of α-**glucose** molecules, but there are more α-1,6 glycosidic links mixed with α-1,4 links. This makes it more highly branched and water-soluble than starch. Glycogen is a storage compound in animal tissues and is found mainly in **liver** and **muscle** cells (photo, right). It is readily hydrolysed by enzymes to form glucose.

Chitin: Chitin is a tough modified polysaccharide made up of chains of β-**glucose** molecules. It is chemically similar to cellulose but each glucose has an amine group (–NH$_2$) attached. After cellulose, chitin is the second most abundant carbohydrate. It is found in the cell walls of fungi and is the main component of the **exoskeleton** of insects (right) and other arthropods.

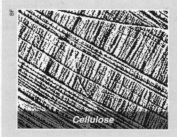

Cellulose

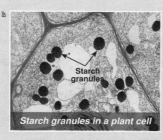

Starch granules in a plant cell

Starch granules

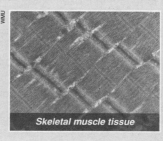

Skeletal muscle tissue

Chitinous insect exoskeleton

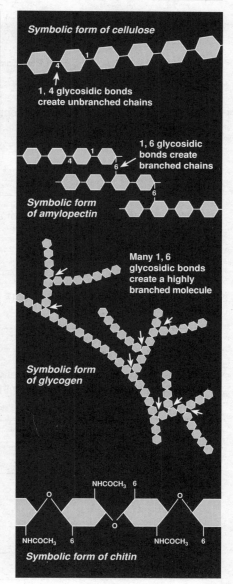

Symbolic form of cellulose

1, 4 glycosidic bonds create unbranched chains

1, 6 glycosidic bonds create branched chains

Symbolic form of amylopectin

Many 1, 6 glycosidic bonds create a highly branched molecule

Symbolic form of glycogen

NHCOCH$_3$ 6

NHCOCH$_3$ 6   NHCOCH$_3$ 6

Symbolic form of chitin

Related activities: Organic Molecules, Biochemical Tests
Web links: Condensation and Hydrolysis

A 2

Isomerism

Compounds with the same chemical formula (same types and numbers of atoms) may differ in the arrangement of their atoms. Such variations in the arrangement of atoms in molecules are called **isomers**. In **structural isomers** (such as fructose and glucose, and the α and β glucose, right), the atoms are linked in different sequences. **Optical isomers** are identical in every way but are mirror images of each other.

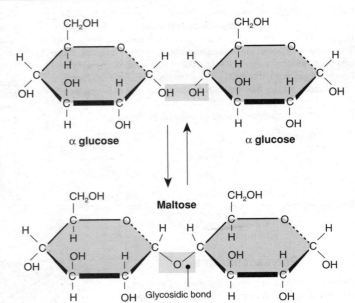

α glucose   β glucose

Condensation and Hydrolysis Reactions

Monosaccharides can combine to form compound sugars in what is called a **condensation** reaction. Compound sugars can be broken down by **hydrolysis** to simple monosaccharides.

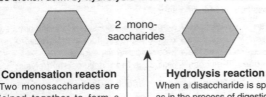

2 mono-saccharides

Condensation reaction
Two monosaccharides are joined together to form a disaccharide with the release of a water molecule (hence its name). Energy is supplied by a nucleotide sugar (e.g. ADP-glucose).

Hydrolysis reaction
When a disaccharide is split, as in the process of digestion, a water molecule is used as a source of hydrogen and a hydroxyl group. The reaction is catalysed by enzymes.

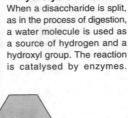

+
H_2O —— Glycosidic bond

Disaccharide + water

α glucose   α glucose

Maltose

Glycosidic bond

Disaccharide + water

1. Distinguish between structural and optical isomers in carbohydrates, describing examples of each:

_____

_____

_____

2. Explain how the isomeric structure of a carbohydrate may affect its chemical behaviour: _____

_____

_____

3. Explain briefly how compound sugars are formed and broken down: _____

_____

_____

4. Discuss the structural differences between the polysaccharides cellulose, starch, and glycogen, explaining how the differences in structure contribute to the functional properties of the molecule:

_____

_____

_____

_____

_____

_____

Lipids

Lipids are a group of organic compounds with an oily, greasy, or waxy consistency. They are relatively insoluble in water and tend to be water-repelling (e.g. cuticle on leaf surfaces). Lipids are important biological fuels, some are hormones, and some serve as structural components in plasma membranes. Proteins and carbohydrates may be converted into fats by enzymes and stored within cells of adipose tissue. During times of plenty, this store is increased, to be used during times of food shortage.

Neutral Fats and Oils

The most abundant lipids in living things are **neutral fats**. They make up the fats and oils found in plants and animals. Fats are an economical way to store fuel reserves, since they yield more than twice as much energy as the same quantity of carbohydrate. Neutral fats are composed of a glycerol molecule attached to one (monoglyceride), two (diglyceride) or three (triglyceride) fatty acids. The fatty acid chains may be saturated or unsaturated (see below). **Waxes** are similar in structure to fats and oils, but they are formed with a complex alcohol instead of glycerol.

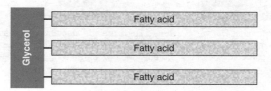

Triglyceride: an example of a neutral fat

Saturated and Unsaturated Fatty Acids

Fatty acids are a major component of neutral fats and phospholipids. About 30 different kinds are found in animal lipids. **Saturated fatty acids** contain the maximum number of hydrogen atoms. **Unsaturated fatty acids** contain some carbon atoms that are double-bonded with each other and are not fully saturated with hydrogens. Lipids containing a high proportion of saturated fatty acids tend to be solids at room temperature (e.g. butter). Lipids with a high proportion of unsaturated fatty acids are oils and tend to be liquid at room temperature. This is because the unsaturation causes kinks in the straight chains so that the fatty acids do not pack closely together. Regardless of their degree of saturation, fatty acids yield a large amount of energy when oxidised.

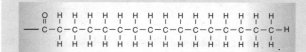

Formula (above) and molecular model (below)
for **palmitic acid** (a saturated fatty acid)

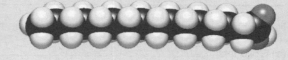

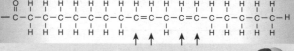

Formula (above) and molecular model (below)
for **linoleic acid** (an unsaturated fatty acid)

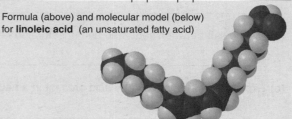

Condensation

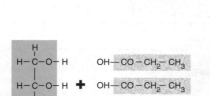

Glycerol   Fatty acids

Triglycerides form when glycerol bonds with three fatty acids. Glycerol is an alcohol containing three carbons. Each of these carbons is bonded to a hydroxyl (-OH) group.

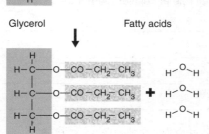

Triglyceride   Water

When glycerol bonds with the fatty acid, an **ester bond** is formed and water is released. Three separate condensation reactions are involved in producing a triglyceride.

Phospholipids

Phospholipids are the main component of cellular membranes. They consist of a glycerol attached to two fatty acid chains and a phosphate (PO_4^{3-}) group. The phosphate end of the molecule is attracted to water (it is hydrophilic) while the fatty acid end is repelled (hydrophobic). The hydrophobic ends turn inwards in the membrane to form a **phospholipid bilayer**.

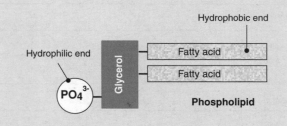

Steroids

Although steroids are classified as lipids, their structure is quite different from that of other lipids. Steroids have a basic structure of three rings made of 6 carbon atoms each and a fourth ring containing 5 carbon atoms. Examples of steroids include the male and female sex hormones (testosterone and oestrogen), and the hormones cortisol and aldosterone. Cholesterol, while not a steroid itself, is a sterol lipid and is a precursor to several steroid hormones.

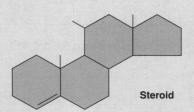

Steroid

Important Biological Functions of Lipids

Lipids are concentrated sources of energy and provide fuel for aerobic respiration.

Phospholipids form the structural framework of cellular membranes.

Waxes and oils secreted on to surfaces provide waterproofing in plants and animals.

Fat absorbs shocks. Organs that are prone to bumps and shocks (e.g. kidneys) are cushioned with a relatively thick layer of fat.

Lipids are a source of metabolic water. During respiration, stored lipids are metabolised for energy, producing water and carbon dioxide.

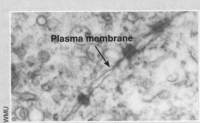

Stored lipids provide insulation. Increased body fat reduces the amount of heat lost to the environment (e.g. in winter or in water).

1. Outline the key **chemical** difference between a phospholipid and a triglyceride: _____

_____

_____

2. Name the type of fatty acids found in lipids that form the following at room temperature:

   (a) Solid fats: _____ (b) Oils: _____

3. Relate the structure of phospholipids to their chemical properties and their functional role in cellular membranes:

_____

_____

4. (a) Distinguish between saturated and unsaturated fatty acids: _____

_____

   (b) Explain how the type of fatty acid present in a neutral fat or phospholipid is related to that molecule's properties:

_____

_____

   (c) Suggest how the cell membrane structure of an Arctic fish might differ from that of tropical fish species:

_____

_____

5. Identify two examples of steroids. For each example, describe its physiological function:

   (a) _____

   (b) _____

6. Explain how fats can provide an animal with:

   (a) Energy: _____

   (b) Water: _____

   (c) Insulation: _____

Amino Acids

Amino acids are the basic units from which proteins are made. Plants can manufacture all the amino acids they require from simpler molecules, but animals must obtain a certain number of ready-made amino acids (called **essential amino acids**) from their diet. The distinction between essential and non-essential amino acids is somewhat unclear though, as some amino acids can be produced from others and some are interconvertible by the urea cycle. Amino acids can combine to form peptide chains in a **condensation reaction**. The reverse reaction, the hydrolysis of peptide chains, releases free water and single amino acids.

Structure of Amino Acids

There are over 150 amino acids found in cells, but only 20 occur commonly in proteins. The remaining, non-protein amino acids have specialised roles as intermediates in metabolic reactions, or as neurotransmitters and hormones. All amino acids have a common structure (see right). The only difference between the different types lies with the 'R' group in the general formula. This group is variable, which means that it is different in each kind of amino acid.

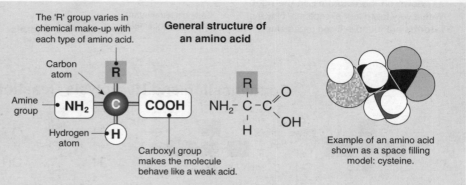

The 'R' group varies in chemical make-up with each type of amino acid.

General structure of an amino acid

Carbon atom

R

Amine group — NH₂

COOH

Hydrogen atom — H

Carboxyl group makes the molecule behave like a weak acid.

Example of an amino acid shown as a space filling model: cysteine.

Properties of Amino Acids

Three examples of amino acids with different chemical properties are shown right, with their specific 'R' groups outlined. The 'R' groups can have quite diverse chemical properties.

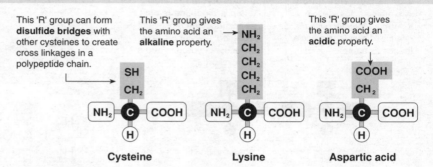

This 'R' group can form **disulfide bridges** with other cysteines to create cross linkages in a polypeptide chain.

This 'R' group gives the amino acid an **alkaline** property.

This 'R' group gives the amino acid an **acidic** property.

Cysteine   **Lysine**   **Aspartic acid**

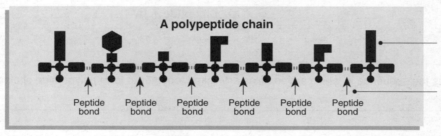

A polypeptide chain

Peptide bond   Peptide bond   Peptide bond   Peptide bond   Peptide bond   Peptide bond

The order of amino acids in a protein is directed by the order of nucleotides in DNA and mRNA.

Peptide bonds link amino acids together in long polymers called polypeptide chains. These may form part or all of a protein.

The amino acids are linked together by peptide bonds to form long chains of up to several hundred amino acids (called polypeptide chains). These chains may be functional units (complete by themselves) or they may need to be joined to other polypeptide chains before they can carry out their function. In humans, not all amino acids can be manufactured by our body: ten must be taken in with our diet (eight in adults). These are the 'essential amino acids'. They are indicated by the symbol ◆ on the right. Those indicated with as asterisk are also required by infants.

Amino acids occurring in proteins

Alanine	Glycine	Proline
Arginine *	Histidine *	Serine
Asparagine	Isoleucine ◆	Threonine ◆
Aspartic acid	Leucine ◆	Tryptophan ◆
Cysteine	Lysine ◆	Tyrosine
Glutamine	Methionine ◆	Valine ◆
Glutamic acid	Phenylalanine ◆	

1. Describe the biological function of amino acids: _____

_____

_____

_____

2. Describe what makes each of the 20 amino acids found in proteins unique: _____

_____

_____

_____

Related activities: Organic Molecules, Proteins, Translation
Web links: Amino Acids and Proteins

Optical Isomers of Amino Acids

All amino acids, apart from the simplest one (glycine) show optical isomerism. The two forms that these optical isomers can take relate to the arrangement of the four bonding sites on the carbon atom. This can result in two different arrangements as shown on the diagrams on the right. With a very few minor exceptions, only the **L-forms** are found in living organisms.

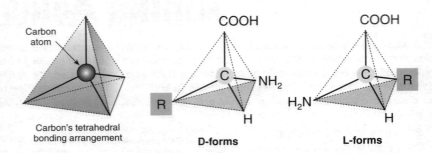

Carbon atom

Carbon's tetrahedral bonding arrangement

D-forms

L-forms

Condensation and Hydrolysis Reactions

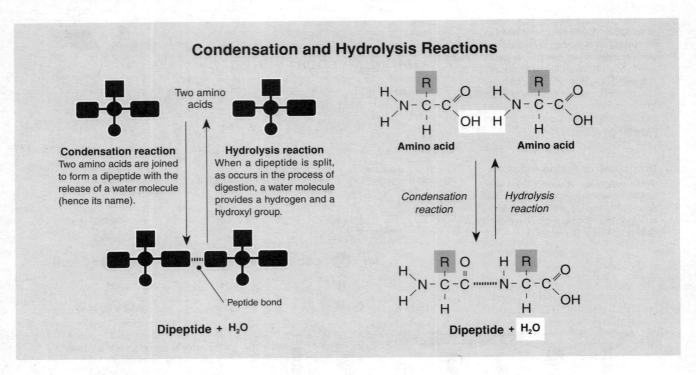

Condensation reaction
Two amino acids are joined to form a dipeptide with the release of a water molecule (hence its name).

Hydrolysis reaction
When a dipeptide is split, as occurs in the process of digestion, a water molecule provides a hydrogen and a hydroxyl group.

Two amino acids

Peptide bond

Dipeptide + H₂O

Amino acid   Amino acid

Condensation reaction   Hydrolysis reaction

Dipeptide + H₂O

3. Describe the process that determines the sequence in which amino acids are linked together to form polypeptide chains:

_____

_____

4. Explain what is meant by **essential amino acids**: _____

_____

_____

5. Describe briefly the process of the **condensation** reaction for amino acids: _____

_____

_____

_____

_____

6. Describe briefly the process of the **hydrolysis** reaction for amino acids: _____

_____

_____

_____

7. Name the optical isomeric form that occurs in nearly all amino acids in living things: _____

Proteins

The precise folding up of a protein into its **tertiary structure** creates a three dimensional arrangement of the active 'R' groups. The way each 'R' group faces with respect to the others gives the protein its unique chemical properties. If a protein loses this precise structure (denaturation), it is usually unable to carry out its biological function. Proteins are often classified on the basis of structure (globular vs fibrous). Some of the properties used for the basis of structural classification are outlined over the page.

Primary Structure - 1° *(amino acid sequence)*

Strings of hundreds of amino acids link together with peptide bonds to form molecules called polypeptide chains. There are 20 different kinds of amino acids that can be linked together in a vast number of different combinations. This sequence is called the **primary structure**. It is the arrangement of attraction and repulsion points in the amino acid chain that determines the higher levels of organisation in the protein and its biological function.

Secondary Structure - 2° *(α-helix or ß pleated sheet)*

Polypeptides become folded in various ways, referred to as the secondary (2°) structure. The most common types of 2° structures are a coiled α-**helix** and a β-**pleated sheet**. Secondary structures are maintained with hydrogen bonds between neighbouring CO and NH groups. H-bonds, although individually weak, provide considerable strength when there are a large number of them. The example, right, shows the two main types of secondary structure. In both, the **'R' side groups** (not shown) project out from the structure. Most globular proteins contain regions of α-helices together with β-sheets. Keratin (a fibrous protein) is composed almost entirely of α-helices. Fibroin (silk protein), is another fibrous protein, almost entirely in β-sheet form.

Tertiary Structure - 3° *(folding)*

Every protein has a precise structure formed by the folding of the secondary structure into a complex shape called the **tertiary structure**. The protein folds up because various points on the secondary structure are attracted to one another. The strongest links are caused by bonding between neighbouring *cysteine* amino acids which form disulfide bridges. Other interactions that are involved in folding include weak ionic and hydrogen bonds as well as hydrophobic interactions.

Quaternary Structure - 4°

Some proteins (such as enzymes) are complete and functional with a tertiary structure only. However, many complex proteins exist as aggregations of polypeptide chains. The arrangement of the polypeptide chains into a functional protein is termed the **quaternary structure**. The example (right) shows a molecule of haemoglobin, a globular protein composed of 4 polypeptide sub-units joined together; two identical *beta chains* and two identical *alpha chains*. Each has a haem (iron containing) group at the centre of the chain, which binds oxygen. Proteins containing non-protein material are **conjugated proteins**. The non-protein part is the **prosthetic group**.

Denaturation of Proteins

Denaturation refers to the loss of the three-dimensional structure (and usually also the biological function) of a protein. Denaturation is often, although not always, permanent. It results from an alteration of the bonds that maintain the secondary and tertiary structure of the protein, even though the sequence of amino acids remains unchanged. Agents that cause denaturation are:

- **Strong acids and alkalis**: Disrupt ionic bonds and result in coagulation of the protein. Long exposure also breaks down the primary structure of the protein.
- **Heavy metals**: May disrupt ionic bonds, form strong bonds with the carboxyl groups of the R groups, and reduce protein charge. The general effect is to cause the precipitation of the protein.
- **Heat and radiation** (e.g. UV): Cause disruption of the bonds in the protein through increased energy provided to the atoms.
- **Detergents and solvents**: Form bonds with the non-polar groups in the protein, thereby disrupting hydrogen bonding.

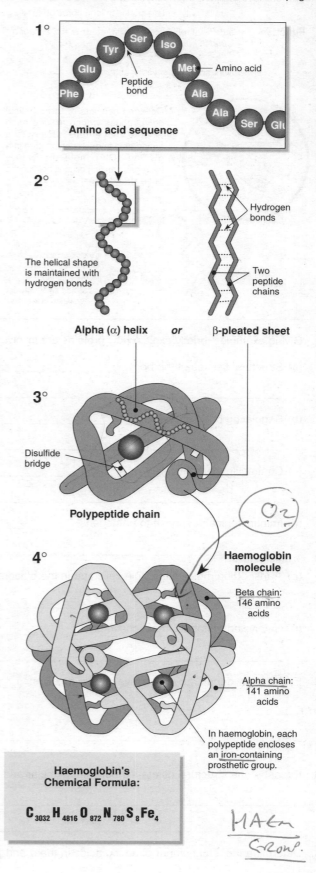

Amino acid sequence

Peptide bond — Amino acid

The helical shape is maintained with hydrogen bonds

Hydrogen bonds

Two peptide chains

Alpha (α) helix *or* **β-pleated sheet**

Disulfide bridge

Polypeptide chain

O₂

Haemoglobin molecule

Beta chain: 146 amino acids

Alpha chain: 141 amino acids

In haemoglobin, each polypeptide encloses an iron-containing prosthetic group.

Haemoglobin's Chemical Formula:

$$C_{3032} H_{4816} O_{872} N_{780} S_8 Fe_4$$

HAEm GROUP.

Related activities: Amino Acids, Enzymes, Biochemical Tests, Production and Secretion of Proteins   **Web links**: Amino Acids and Proteins

RA 2

Structural Classification of Proteins

Fibrous Proteins

Properties
- Water insoluble
- Very tough physically; may be supple or stretchy
- Parallel polypeptide chains in long fibres or sheets

Function
- Structural role in cells and organisms *e.g. collagen found in connective tissue, cartilage, bones, tendons, and blood vessel walls.*
- Contractile *e.g. myosin, actin*

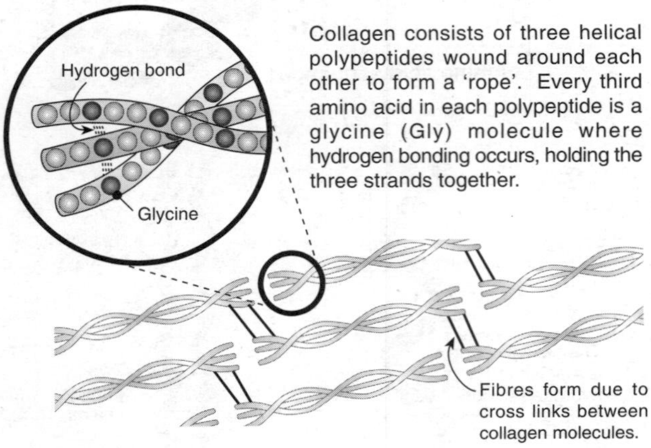

Globular Proteins

Properties
- Easily water soluble
- Tertiary structure critical to function
- Polypeptide chains folded into a spherical shape

Function
- Catalytic *e.g. enzymes*
- Regulatory *e.g. hormones (insulin)*
- Transport *e.g. haemoglobin*
- Protective *e.g. antibodies*

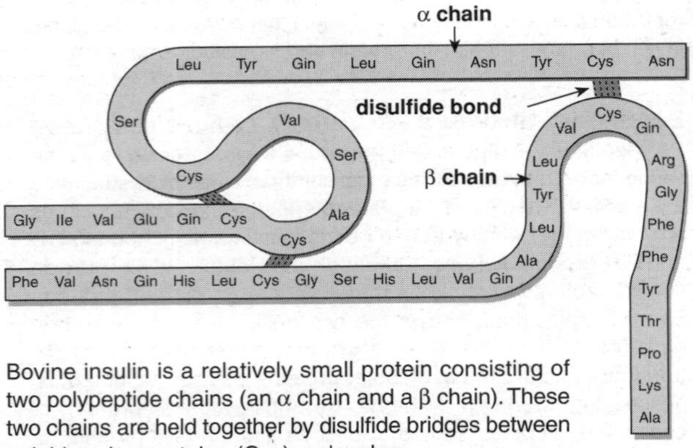

Collagen consists of three helical polypeptides wound around each other to form a 'rope'. Every third amino acid in each polypeptide is a glycine (Gly) molecule where hydrogen bonding occurs, holding the three strands together.

Hydrogen bond

Glycine

Fibres form due to cross links between collagen molecules.

α chain

disulfide bond

β chain

Bovine insulin is a relatively small protein consisting of two polypeptide chains (an α chain and a β chain). These two chains are held together by disulfide bridges between neighbouring cysteine (Cys) molecules.

1. Giving examples, briefly explain how proteins are involved in the following functional roles:

(a) Structural tissues of the body: _____

_____

(b) Regulating body processes: _____

_____

(c) Contractile elements: _____

_____

(d) Immunological response to pathogens: _____

_____

(e) Transporting molecules within cells and in the bloodstream: _____

_____

(f) Catalysing metabolic reactions in cells: _____

_____

2. Explain how denaturation destroys protein function: _____

_____

_____

3. Describe one structural difference between globular and fibrous proteins: _____

_____

_____

4. Determine the total number of amino acids in the α and β chains of the insulin molecule illustrated above:

(a) α chain: _____   (b) β chain: _____

Enzymes

Most enzymes are proteins. They are capable of catalysing (speeding up) biochemical reactions and are therefore called biological **catalysts**. Enzymes act on one or more compounds (called the **substrate**). They may break a single substrate molecule down into simpler substances, or join two or more substrate molecules chemically together. The enzyme itself is unchanged in the reaction; its presence merely allows the reaction to take place more rapidly. When the substrate attains the required **activation energy** to enable it to change into the product, there is a 50% chance that it will proceed forward to form the product, otherwise it reverts back to a stable form of the reactant again. The part of the enzyme's surface into which the substrate is bound and undergoes reaction is known as the **active site**. This is made of different parts of polypeptide chain folded in a specific shape so they are closer together. For some enzymes, the complexity of the binding sites can be very precise, allowing only a single kind of substrate to bind to it. Some other enzymes have lower **specificity** and will accept a wide range of substrates of the same general type (e.g. lipases break up any fatty acid chain length of lipid). This is because the enzyme is specific for the type of chemical bond involved and not an exact substrate.

Enzyme Structure

The model on the right is of an enzyme called *Ribonuclease S*, that breaks up RNA molecules. It is a typical enzyme, being a globular protein and composed of up to several hundred atoms. The darkly shaded areas are called **active sites** and make up the **cleft**; the region into which the substrate molecule(s) are drawn. The correct positioning of these sites is critical for the catalytic reaction to occur. The substrate (RNA in this case) is drawn into the cleft by the active sites. By doing so, it puts the substrate molecule under stress, causing the reaction to proceed more readily.

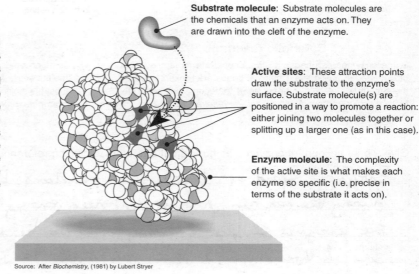

Substrate molecule: Substrate molecules are the chemicals that an enzyme acts on. They are drawn into the cleft of the enzyme.

Active sites: These attraction points draw the substrate to the enzyme's surface. Substrate molecule(s) are positioned in a way to promote a reaction: either joining two molecules together or splitting up a larger one (as in this case).

Enzyme molecule: The complexity of the active site is what makes each enzyme so specific (i.e. precise in terms of the substrate it acts on).

Source: After *Biochemistry*, (1981) by Lubert Stryer

How Enzymes Work

The **lock and key** model proposed earlier this century suggested that the substrate was simply drawn into a closely matching cleft on the enzyme molecule. More recent studies have revealed that the process more likely involves an **induced fit** (see diagram on the right), where the enzyme or the reactants change their shape slightly. The reactants become bound to enzymes by weak chemical bonds. This binding can weaken bonds within the reactants themselves, allowing the reaction to proceed more readily.

The presence of an enzyme simply makes it easier for a reaction to take place. All **catalysts** speed up reactions by influencing the stability of bonds in the reactants. They may also provide an alternative reaction pathway, thus lowering the activation energy needed for a reaction to take place (see the graph below).

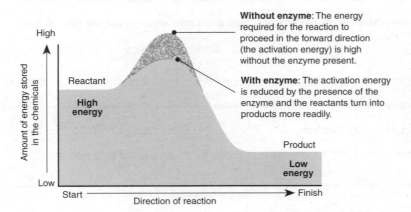

Without enzyme: The energy required for the reaction to proceed in the forward direction (the activation energy) is high without the enzyme present.

With enzyme: The activation energy is reduced by the presence of the enzyme and the reactants turn into products more readily.

Induced Fit Model

An enzyme fits to its substrate somewhat like a lock and key. The shape of the enzyme changes when the substrate fits into the cleft (called the **induced fit**):

1 Two substrate molecules are drawn into the cleft of the enzyme.

2 The enzyme changes shape, forcing the substrate molecules to combine.

3 The resulting end product is released by the enzyme which returns to its normal shape, ready to receive more.

Related activities: Enzyme Reaction Rates
Web links: How Enzymes Work

RA 2

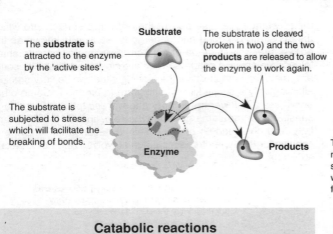

The **substrate** is attracted to the enzyme by the 'active sites'.

Substrate

The substrate is cleaved (broken in two) and the two **products** are released to allow the enzyme to work again.

The substrate is subjected to stress which will facilitate the breaking of bonds.

Enzyme

Products

The two substrate molecules are attracted to the enzyme by the 'active sites'.

Substrates

The two substrate molecules form a single product and are released to allow the enzyme to work again.

Product

The substrate molecules are subjected to stress which will aid the formation of bonds.

Enzyme

Catabolic reactions

Some enzymes can cause a single substrate molecule to be drawn into the active site. Chemical bonds are broken, causing the substrate molecule to break apart to become two separate molecules. **Examples**: *digestion, cellular respiration*.

Anabolic reactions

Some enzymes can cause two substrate molecules to be drawn into the active site. Chemical bonds are formed, causing the two substrate molecules to form bonds and become a single molecule. **Examples**: *protein synthesis, photosynthesis*.

1. Give a brief account of enzymes as **biological catalysts**, including reference to the role of the **active site**:

- Lower activation energy.

Enzymes "speed up" biochemical reactions by simply being present during the reaction, & most don't need energy to do so. The part of the enzymes surface that the substrate binds to is called the Active site, & the more of these ~~mxggxhg~~ increases the rate of reaction, and so enzymes are referred to as biological catalysts.

- Enzyme remain unchanged by reaction.

2. Distinguish between **catabolism** and **anabolism**, giving an example of each and identifying each reaction as **endergonic** or **exergonic**:

Catabolic cleave products in two (digestion) (exergonic?)

Anabolic forms two products into one (photosynthesis) (endergonic).

3. Outline the key features of the '**lock and key**' model of enzyme action: _____

Specificity of enzyme to substrate.

The substrate is placed into a closely matching cleft on the enzyme molecule where the reaction takes place.

4. Outline the '**induced fit**' model of enzyme action, explaining how it differs from the lock and key model:

The induced fit model is similar however the shape of the enzyme & active site changes when the substrate fits into the cleft.

5. Identify two factors that could cause enzyme denaturation, explaining how they exert their effects (see the next activity):

(a) Increase or decrease in temperature could cause bonds to form within the enzyme, shifting the active site.

(b) Changes in the pH can do the same as above. Conc^n H+ ion effect properties of R group in active site.

6. Explain what might happen to the functioning of an enzyme if the gene that codes for it was altered by a mutation:

The enzyme may be denatured when it's created or changed to react with a different substrate.

different amino acid, so alters 3° structure, ∴ maybe 3D structure of active site altered.

Enzyme Reaction Rates

Enzymes are sensitive molecules. They often have a narrow range of conditions under which they operate properly. For most of the enzymes associated with plant and animal metabolism, there is little activity at low temperatures. As the temperature increases, so too does the enzyme activity, until the point is reached where the temperature is high enough to damage the enzyme's structure. At this point, the enzyme ceases to function; a phenomenon called enzyme or protein **denaturation**.

Extremes in acidity (pH) can also cause the protein structure of enzymes to denature. Poisons often work by denaturing enzymes or occupying the enzyme's active site so that it does not function. In some cases, enzymes will not function without cofactors, such as vitamins or trace elements. In the four graphs below, the rate of reaction or degree of enzyme activity is plotted against each of four factors that affect enzyme performance. Answer the questions relating to each graph:

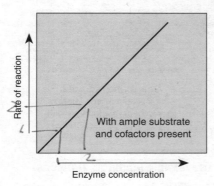

With ample substrate and cofactors present

Rate of reaction

Enzyme concentration

1. **Enzyme concentration**
   (a) Describe the change in the rate of reaction when the enzyme concentration is increased (assuming there is plenty of the substrate present):

   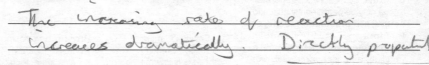
   The increasing rate of reaction increases dramatically. Directly proportional

   (b) Suggest how a cell may vary the amount of enzyme present in a cell:

   Inc. Protein Synthesis.

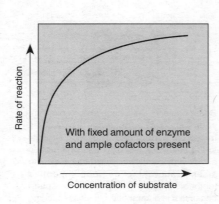

With fixed amount of enzyme and ample cofactors present

Rate of reaction

Concentration of substrate

2. **Substrate concentration**
   (a) Describe the change in the rate of reaction when the substrate concentration is **increased** (assuming a fixed amount of enzyme and ample cofactors):

   A sharp increase then slowly decreases levels off / plateaus / rate of inc slows.

   (b) Explain why the rate changes the way it does: 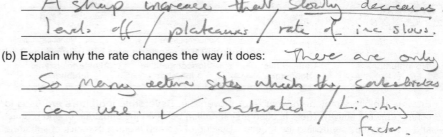 There are only so many active sites which the substrates can use. ✓ Saturated / Limiting factor.

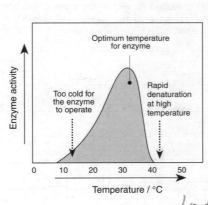

Optimum temperature for enzyme

Too cold for the enzyme to operate

Rapid denaturation at high temperature

Enzyme activity

0   10   20   30   40   50
Temperature / °C

3. **Temperature**
   Higher temperatures speed up all reactions, but few enzymes can tolerate temperatures higher than 50–60°C. The rate at which enzymes are **denatured** (change their shape and become inactive) increases with higher temperatures.

   (a) Describe what is meant by an optimum temperature for enzyme activity:

   The temperature at which the enzyme functions at the best.

   (b) Explain why most enzymes perform poorly at low temperatures:

   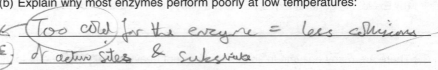
   Too cold for the enzyme = less collisions
   Low K.E. of active sites & substrate

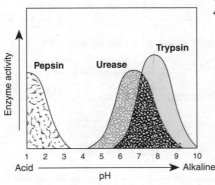

Pepsin   Urease   Trypsin

Enzyme activity

1 2 3 4 5 6 7 8 9 10
Acid   Alkaline
pH

4. **pH (acidity/alkalinity)**
   Like all proteins, enzymes are **denatured** by extremes of **pH** (very acid or alkaline). Within these extremes, most enzymes are still influenced by pH. Each enzyme has a preferred pH range for optimum activity.

   (a) State the optimum pH for each of the enzymes:

   Pepsin: _____ 1 _____   Trypsin: _____ 6.5 _____   Urease: _____ 8 _____

   (b) Pepsin acts on proteins in the stomach. Explain how its optimum pH is suited to its working environment:

   Acids need to digest / break down what's ingested ...? HCl in stomach

Enzyme Cofactors and Inhibitors

Enzyme activity is often influenced by the presence of other chemicals. Some of these may enhance an enzyme's activity. Called **cofactors**, they are a nonprotein component of an enzyme and may be organic molecules (**coenzymes**) or inorganic ions (e.g. Ca^{2+}, Zn^{2+}). Enzymes may also be deactivated, temporarily or permanently, by chemicals called enzyme **inhibitors**.

Types of Enzyme

Nearly all enzymes are made of protein, although RNA has been demonstrated to have enzymatic properties. Some enzymes consist of just protein, while others require the addition of extra components to complete their catalytic properties. These may be permanently attached parts called **prosthetic groups**, or temporarily attached pieces (**coenzymes**) that detach after a reaction, and may participate with another enzyme in other reactions.

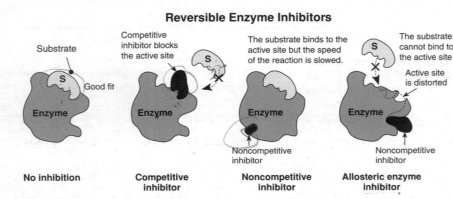

Protein-only enzymes

Active site

enzyme

Enzyme comprises only protein, e.g. lysozyme

Conjugated protein enzymes

Active site

Prosthetic group is more or less permanently attached

Apoenzyme

Prosthetic group required
Contains apoenzyme (protein) plus a prosthetic group, e.g. flavoprotein + FAD

Active site

Coenzyme becomes detached after the reaction

Apoenzyme

Coenzyme required
Contains apoenzyme (protein) plus a coenzyme (non-protein) e.g. dehydrogenases + NAD

Reversible Enzyme Inhibitors

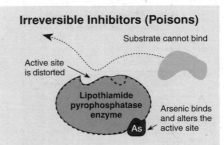

Substrate

S

Good fit

Enzyme

No inhibition

Competitive inhibitor blocks the active site

S

Enzyme

Competitive inhibitor

The substrate binds to the active site but the speed of the reaction is slowed.

S

Enzyme

Noncompetitive inhibitor

Noncompetitive inhibitor

The substrate cannot bind to the active site

S

×

Active site is distorted

Enzyme

Noncompetitive inhibitor

Allosteric enzyme inhibitor

Enzyme inhibitors may be reversible or irreversible. **Reversible inhibitors** are used to control enzyme activity. There is often an interaction between the substrate or end product and the enzymes controlling the reaction. Buildup of the end product or a lack of substrate may deactivate the enzyme. This deactivation may take the form of **competitive** (competes for the active site) or **noncompetitive** inhibition. While noncompetitive inhibitors have the effect of slowing down the rate of reaction, **allosteric inhibitors** block the active site altogether and prevent its functioning.

Irreversible Inhibitors (Poisons)

Substrate cannot bind

Active site is distorted

Lipothiamide pyrophosphatase enzyme

As

Arsenic binds and alters the active site

Some heavy metals, such as arsenic (As), cadmium (Cd), and lead (Pb) act as **irreversible inhibitors**. They bind strongly to the sulfhydryl (-SH) groups of a protein and destroy catalytic activity. Most, including arsenic (above), act as **noncompetitive** inhibitors. Mercury (Hg) is an exception because it is a competitive inhibitor, binding to the sulfhydryl group in the active site of the papain enzyme. Heavy metals are retained in the body and lost slowly.

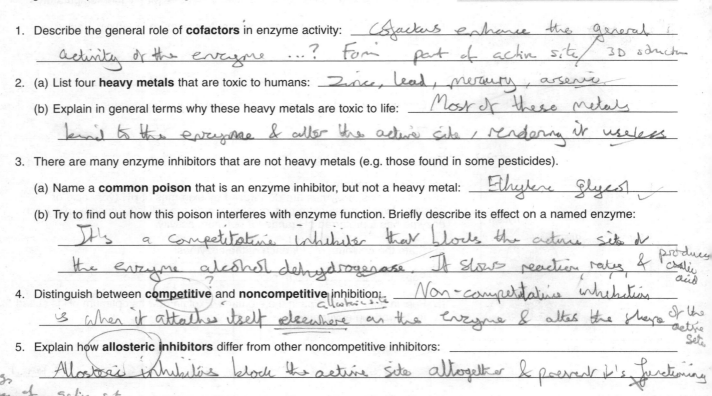

1. Describe the general role of **cofactors** in enzyme activity: _Cofactors enhance the general activity of the enzyme ...? Form part of active site / 3D structure_

2. (a) List four **heavy metals** that are toxic to humans: _Zinc, lead, mercury, arsenic_

   (b) Explain in general terms why these heavy metals are toxic to life: _Most of these metals bind to the enzyme & alter the active site, rendering it useless_

3. There are many enzyme inhibitors that are not heavy metals (e.g. those found in some pesticides).

   (a) Name a **common poison** that is an enzyme inhibitor, but not a heavy metal: _Ethylene glycol_

   (b) Try to find out how this poison interferes with enzyme function. Briefly describe its effect on a named enzyme: _It's a competitive inhibitor that blocks the active site of the enzyme alcohol dehydrogenase. It slows reaction rates & produces oxalic acid_

4. Distinguish between **competitive** and **noncompetitive** inhibition: _Non-competitive inhibition allosteric site is when it attaches itself elsewhere on the enzyme & alters the shape of the active site_

5. Explain how **allosteric inhibitors** differ from other noncompetitive inhibitors: _Allosteric inhibitors block the active site altogether & prevent it's functioning_ _Changes shape of active site_

The Genetic Code

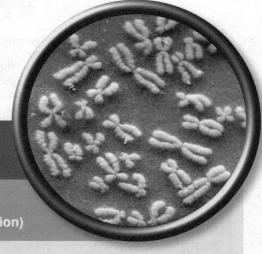

OCR: Unit F212, Module 1: Biological Molecules
2.1.2: Nucleic acids

CIE: CORE SYLLABUS
F: Genetic control (nucleic acid structure and function)

Learning Objectives

☐ 1. Compile your own glossary from the **KEY WORDS** displayed in **bold type** in the learning objectives below.

Chromosome Structure *(pages 173-174)*

☐ 2. EXTENSION: Describe the structure and morphology of eukaryote **chromosomes**, explaining how DNA is packaged and organised in the nucleus.

Nucleic Acids *(pages 172, 175-180)*

☐ 3. Recognise examples of **nucleic acids** and describe their role in biological systems.

☐ 4. Describe the components of a (mono)**nucleotide**: a 5C sugar (**ribose** or **deoxyribose**), a nitrogenous base (**purine** or **pyrimidine**), and a phosphate. Identify the purines and pyrimidines that form **nucleotides**.

☐ 5. Understand the role of **condensation** reactions in the formation of **polynucleotides** (nucleic acids).

☐ 6. Describe the Watson-Crick **double-helix** model of DNA structure. Include reference to the **base pairing rule**, the **antiparallel strands**, and the role of **hydrogen bonding** between **purines** and **pyrimidines**. Contrast the structure and function of **DNA** and **RNA**.

DNA Replication *(pages 181-182)*

☐ 7. Explain the **semi-conservative** replication of DNA during interphase, including the role of **DNA polymerase**, **helicase**, and **DNA ligase**.

☐ 8. Explain the significance of DNA replication in the **5' to 3' direction**. Relate this to the formation of the **leading strand** and the **lagging strand**.

The Genetic Code *(pages 183-189)*

OCR students should consider this material in outline only. It is covered in A2 Unit F215: Module 1: 5.1.1 Cellular Control

☐ 9. Explain the features of the **genetic code**, including:
   • The 4-letter alphabet and the 3-letter **triplet code** (**codon**) of base sequences.
   • The **non-overlapping**, linear nature of the code which is read from start to finish point in one direction.
   • Specific punctuation codons and their significance.
   • The **universal nature** and **degeneracy** of the code.

☐ 10. Outline the basis by which information is transferred from DNA to protein. Distinguish between **allele** and **gene**. Explain what is meant by **gene expression** and define its two stages: **transcription** and **translation**. *NOTE: Gene expression can refer just to transcription (expression of the gene as its mRNA product.)*

☐ 11. Describe **transcription**, including reference to the role of mRNA, the direction of transcription (5' → 3') and the role of **RNA polymerase**. Distinguish between the **coding** (**sense**) **strand** and the **template** (**antisense**) **strand** and understand the significance of introns with the respect to the production of functional mRNA.

☐ 12. Recall the structure of **proteins** as **polypeptides** with a complex (post-translational) structure. Explain how the 4-letter alphabet of bases provides the code for the 20 amino acids needed to assemble proteins.

☐ 13. Describe **translation**, including the role of mRNA, transfer RNA (**tRNA**), **anticodons**, and **ribosomes**.

☐ 14. Recognise **enzymes** as proteins whose synthesis is controlled by DNA. Understand the role of enzymes in the control of metabolic pathways.

Textbooks

See the 'Textbook Reference Grid' on page 7 for textbook page references relating to material in this topic.

Supplementary Texts

See pages 5-6 for additional details of these texts:

■ Adds, J., *et al.*, 2003. **Molecules and Cells**, (NelsonThornes), chpt. 2.

■ Jones, N., *et al.*, 2001. **The Essentials of Genetics**, (John Murray), pp. 123-188, 257.

Presentation MEDIA to support this topic:
GENES AND INHERITANCE
• The Genetic Code

Periodicals

See page 6 for details of publishers of periodicals:

STUDENT'S REFERENCE

■ **Gene Structure and Expression** Biol. Sci. Rev., 12 (5) May 2000, pp. 22-25. *An account of gene function, including a comparison of gene regulation in pro- and eukaryotes.*

■ **What is a Gene?** Biol. Sci. Rev., 15(2) Nov. 2002, pp. 9-11. *A good synopsis of genes and their role in heredity, mutations, and transcriptional control of gene expression.*

■ **Transfer RNA** Biol. Sci. Rev., 15(3) Feb. 2003, pp. 26-29. *tRNAs and their role in protein synthesis.*

■ **Control Centre** New Scientist, 17 July 1999, (Inside Science). *The organisation of DNA in eukaryotic cells, how genes code for proteins, and the role of ribosomes and RNA in translation.*

TEACHER'S REFERENCE

■ **The Hidden Genetic Program** Scientific American, Oct. 2004, pp. 30-37. *Large portions of the DNA of complex organisms may encode RNA molecules with important regulatory functions.*

■ **DNA: 50 Years of the Double Helix** New Scientist, 15 March 2003, pp. 35-51. *A special issue on DNA: structure and function, repair, the new-found role of histones, and the functional significance of chromosome position in the nucleus.*

See pages 8-9 for details of how to access **Bio Links** from our web site: **www.biozone.co.uk**. From Bio Links, access sites under the topics:

GENETICS: • DNA glossary • Virtual library on genetics > **Molecular Genetics (DNA):** • Beginners guide to molecular biology • DNA and molecular genetics • Molecular genetics • Primer on molecular genetics • Protein synthesis

DNA Molecules

Even the smallest DNA molecules are extremely long. The DNA from the small *Polyoma* virus, for example, is 1.7 µm long; about three times longer than the longest proteins. The DNA comprising a bacterial chromosome is 1000 times longer than the cell into which it has to fit. The amount of DNA present in the nucleus of the cells of eukaryotic organisms varies widely from one species to another. In vertebrate sex cells, the quantity of DNA ranges from 40 000 **kb** to 80 000 000 **kb**, with humans about in the middle of the range. The traditional focus of DNA research has been on those DNA sequences that code for proteins, yet protein-coding DNA accounts for less than 2% of the DNA in human chromosomes. The rest of the DNA, once dismissed as non-coding 'evolutionary junk', is now recognised as giving rise to functional RNA molecules, many of which have already been identified as having important regulatory functions. While there is no clear correspondence between the complexity of an organism and the number of protein-coding genes in its genome, this is not the case for non-protein-coding DNA. The genomes of more complex organisms contain much more of this so-called "non-coding" DNA. These RNA-only 'hidden' genes tend to be short and difficult to identify, but the sequences are highly conserved and clearly have a role in inheritance, development, and health.

Sizes of DNA Molecules			
Group	**Organism**	**Base pairs** (in 1000s, or kb)	**Length**
Viruses	Polyoma or SV40	5.1	1.7 µm
	Lambda phage	48.6	17 µm
	T2 phage	166	56 µm
	Vaccinia	190	65 µm
Bacteria	Mycoplasma	760	260 µm
	E. coli (from human gut)	4600	1.56 mm
Eukaryotes	Yeast	13 500	4.6 mm
	Drosophila (fruit fly)	165 000	5.6 cm
	Human	2 900 000	99 cm

Kilobase (kb)

A kilobase is unit of length equal to 1000 base pairs of a double-stranded nucleic acid molecule (or 1000 bases of a single-stranded molecule). One kb of double stranded DNA has a length of 0.34 µm. (1 µm = 1/1000 mm)

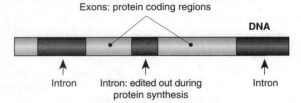

Exons: protein coding regions

DNA

Intron   Intron: edited out during protein synthesis   Intron

Most protein-coding genes in eukaryotic DNA are not continuous and may be interrupted by 'intrusions' of other pieces of DNA. Protein-coding regions (**exons**) are interrupted by non-protein-coding regions called **introns**. Introns range in frequency from 1 to over 30 in a single 'gene' and also in size (100 to more than 10 000 bases). Introns are edited out of the protein-coding sequence during protein synthesis, but probably, after processing, go on to serve a regulatory function.

Giant lampbrush chromosomes

Lampbrush chromosomes are large chromosomes found in amphibian eggs, with lateral loops of DNA that produce a brushlike appearance under the microscope. The two scanning electron micrographs (below and right) show minute strands of DNA giving a fuzzy appearance in the high power view.

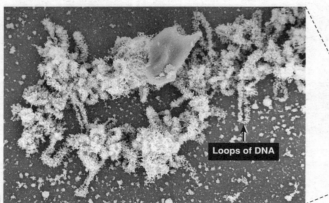

Loops of DNA

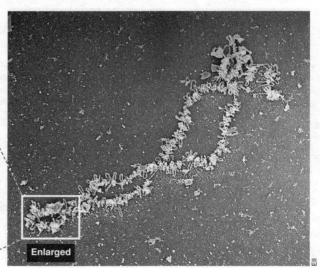

Enlarged

1. Consult the table above and make the following comparisons. Determine how much more DNA is present in:

   (a) The bacterium *E. coli* compared to the Lambda Phage virus: _____

   (b) Human cells compared to the bacteria *E. coli*: _____

2. State what proportion of DNA in a eukaryotic cell is used to code for proteins or structural RNA: _____

3. Describe two reasons why geneticists have reevaluated their traditional view that one gene codes for one polypeptide:

   (a) _____

   _____

   (b) _____

   _____

Related activities: The Simplest Case: Genes to Proteins, Gene Expression

Eukaryote Chromosome Structure

The chromosomes of eukaryote cells (such as those from plants and animals) are complex in their structure compared to those of prokaryotes. The illustration below shows a chromosome during the early stage of meiosis. Here it exists as a chromosome consisting of two chromatids. A non-dividing cell would have chromosomes with the 'equivalent' of a single chromatid only. The chromosome consists of a protein coated strand which coils in three ways during the time when the cell prepares to divide.

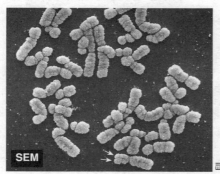

SEM

A cluster of human chromosomes seen during metaphase of cell division. Individual chromatids (arrowed) are difficult to discern on these double chromatid chromosomes.

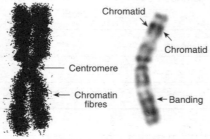

Chromatid
Chromatid
Centromere
Chromatin fibres
Banding

Chromosome TEM   Human chromosome 3

A human chromosome from a dividing white blood cell (above left). Note the compact organisation of the chromatin in the two chromatids. The LM photograph (above right) shows the banding visible on human chromosome 3.

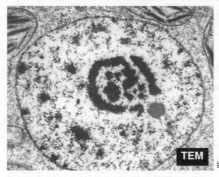

TEM

In non-dividing cells, chromosomes exist as single-armed structures. They are not visible as coiled structures, but are 'unwound' to make the genes accessible for transcription (above).

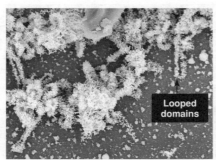

Looped domains

The evidence for the existence of looped domains comes from the study of giant lampbrush chromosomes in amphibian oocytes (above). Under electron microscopy, the lateral loops of the DNA-protein complex have a brushlike appearance.

The Packaging of Chromatin

Chromatin structure is based on successive levels of DNA packing. **Histone proteins** are responsible for packing the DNA into a compact form. Without them, the DNA could not fit into the nucleus. Five types of histone proteins form a complex with DNA, in a way that resembles "beads on a string". These beads, or **nucleosomes**, form the basic unit of DNA packing.

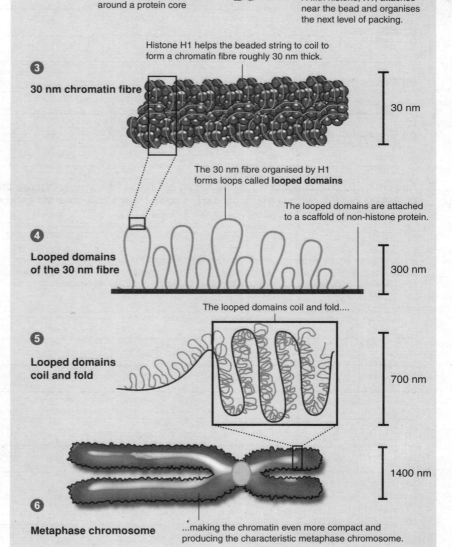

① **DNA molecule** — 2 nm

Each bead has two molecules of each of four types of histone (H2A, H2B, H3, and H4)

② **Nucleosomes** — DNA — 10 nm

The nucleosome bead consists of DNA wrapped around a protein core

A fifth histone, **H1**, attaches near the bead and organises the next level of packing.

Histone H1 helps the beaded string to coil to form a chromatin fibre roughly 30 nm thick.

③ **30 nm chromatin fibre** — 30 nm

The 30 nm fibre organised by H1 forms loops called **looped domains**

The looped domains are attached to a scaffold of non-histone protein.

④ **Looped domains of the 30 nm fibre** — 300 nm

The looped domains coil and fold....

⑤ **Looped domains coil and fold** — 700 nm

⑥ **Metaphase chromosome** — 1400 nm

...making the chromatin even more compact and producing the characteristic metaphase chromosome.

The Genetic Code

Related activities: DNA Molecules
Web links: Chromosome Structure

EA 2

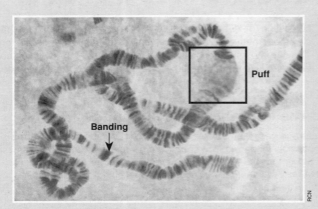

Banded chromosome: This light microscope photo is a view of the polytene chromosomes in a salivary gland cell of a sandfly. It shows a banding pattern that is thought to correspond to groups of genes. Regions of chromosome **puffing** are thought to occur where the genes are being transcribed into mRNA (see SEM on right).

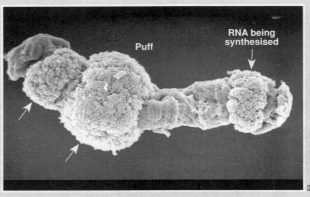

A **polytene chromosome** viewed with a scanning electron microscope (SEM). The arrows indicate localised regions of the chromosome that are uncoiling to expose their genes (puffing) to allow transcription of those regions. Polytene chromosomes are a special type of chromosome consisting of a large bundle of chromatids bound tightly together.

1. Explain the significance of the following terms used to describe the structure of chromosomes:

   (a) DNA: _____

   _____

   (b) Chromatin: _____

   _____

   (c) Histone: _____

   _____

   (d) Centromere: _____

   _____

   (e) Chromatid: _____

   _____

2. Each human cell has about a 1 metre length of DNA in its nucleus. Discuss the mechanisms by which this DNA is packaged into the nucleus and organised in such a way that it does not get ripped apart during cell division:

   _____

   _____

   _____

   _____

   _____

   _____

   _____

   _____

   _____

   _____

   _____

   _____

   _____

Nucleic Acids

Nucleic acids are a special group of chemicals in cells concerned with the transmission of inherited information. They have the capacity to store the information that controls cellular activity. The central nucleic acid is called **deoxyribonucleic acid** (DNA). DNA is a major component of chromosomes and is found primarily in the nucleus, although a small amount is found in mitochondria and chloroplasts. Other **ribonucleic acids** (RNA) are involved in the 'reading' of the DNA information. All nucleic acids are made up of simple repeating units called **nucleotides**, linked together to form chains or strands, often of great length. The strands vary in the sequence of the bases found on each nucleotide. It is this sequence which provides the 'genetic code' for the cell. In addition to nucleic acids, certain nucleotides and their derivatives are also important as suppliers of energy (**ATP**) or as hydrogen ion and electron carriers in respiration and photosynthesis (NAD, NADP, and FAD).

Chemical Structure of a Nucleotide

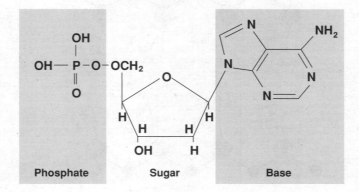

Phosphate | Sugar | Base

Bases

Purines:

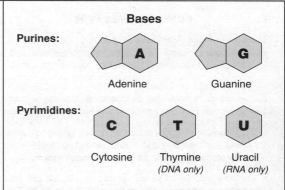

Adenine | Guanine

Pyrimidines:

Cytosine | Thymine *(DNA only)* | Uracil *(RNA only)*

The two-ringed bases above are **purines** and make up the longer bases. The single-ringed bases are **pyrimidines**. Although only one of four kinds of base can be used in a nucleotide, **uracil** is found only in RNA, replacing **thymine**. DNA contains: A, T, G, and C, while RNA contains A, U, G, and C.

Symbolic Form of a Nucleotide

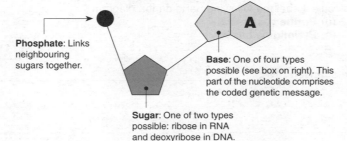

Phosphate: Links neighbouring sugars together.

Base: One of four types possible (see box on right). This part of the nucleotide comprises the coded genetic message.

Sugar: One of two types possible: ribose in RNA and deoxyribose in DNA.

Nucleotides are the building blocks of DNA. Their precise sequence in a DNA molecule provides the genetic instructions for the organism to which it governs. Accidental changes in nucleotide sequences are a cause of mutations, usually harming the organism, but occasionally providing benefits.

Sugars

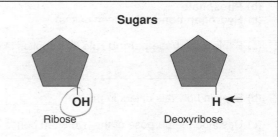

Ribose | Deoxyribose

Deoxyribose sugar is found only in DNA. It differs from **ribose** sugar, found in RNA, by the lack of a single oxygen atom (arrowed).

RNA Molecule

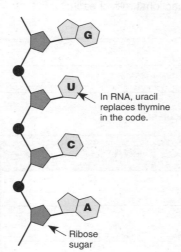

In RNA, uracil replaces thymine in the code.

Ribose sugar

DNA Molecule

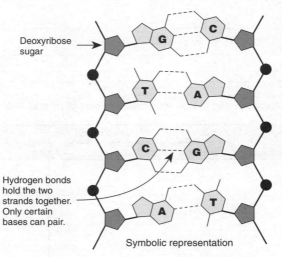

Deoxyribose sugar

Hydrogen bonds hold the two strands together. Only certain bases can pair.

Symbolic representation

DNA Molecule

Space filling model

Ribonucleic acid (RNA) comprises a *single strand* of nucleotides linked together.

Deoxyribonucleic acid (DNA) comprises a *double strand* of nucleotides linked together. It is shown unwound in the symbolic representation (left). The DNA molecule takes on a twisted, double helix shape as shown in the space filling model on the right.

Formation of a nucleotide

Condensation
(water removed)

A nucleotide is formed when phosphoric acid and a base are chemically bonded to a sugar molecule. In both cases, water is given off, and they are therefore condensation reactions. In the reverse reaction, a nucleotide is broken apart by the addition of water (**hydrolysis**).

Formation of a dinucleotide

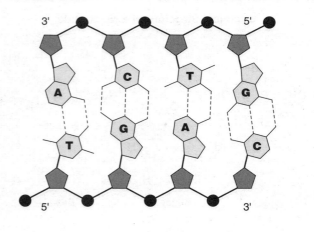

Two nucleotides are linked together by a condensation reaction between the phosphate of one nucleotide and the sugar of another.

Double-Stranded DNA

The **double-helix** structure of DNA is like a ladder twisted into a corkscrew shape around its longitudinal axis. It is 'unwound' here to show the relationships between the bases.

- The way the correct pairs of bases are attracted to each other to form hydrogen bonds is determined by the number of bonds they can form and the shape (length) of the base.

- The **template strand** the side of the DNA molecule that stores the information that is transcribed into mRNA. The template strand is also called the **antisense strand**.

- The other side (often called the **coding strand**) has the same nucleotide sequence as the mRNA except that T in DNA substitutes for U in mRNA. The coding strand is also called the **sense strand**.

1. The diagram above depicts a double-stranded DNA molecule. Label the following parts on the diagram:
   (a) **Sugar** (deoxyribose)   (d) **Purine** bases
   (b) **Phosphate**   (e) **Pyrimidine** bases
   (c) **Hydrogen bonds** (between bases)

2. (a) Explain the **base-pairing rule** that applies in double-stranded DNA: _____

   _____

   (b) Explain how this differs in mRNA: _____

   (c) Describe the purpose of the hydrogen bonds in double-stranded DNA: _____

   _____

3. Describe the functional role of nucleotides: _____

   _____

4. Distinguish between the **template strand** and **coding strand** of DNA, identifying the functional role of each:

   _____

   _____

   _____

5. Complete the following table summarising the differences between DNA and RNA molecules:

	DNA	RNA
Sugar present		
Bases present		
Number of strands		
Relative length		

Creating a DNA Model

Although DNA molecules can be enormous in terms of their molecular size, they are made up of simple repeating units called **nucleotides**. A number of factors control the way in which these nucleotide building blocks are linked together. These factors cause the nucleotides to join together in a predictable way. This is referred to as the **base pairing rule** and can be used to construct a complementary DNA strand from a template strand, as illustrated in the exercise below:

DNA Base Pairing Rule			
Adenine	is always attracted to	**Thymine**	A ⟷ T
Thymine	is always attracted to	**Adenine**	T ⟷ A
Cytosine	is always attracted to	**Guanine**	C ⟷ G
Guanine	is always attracted to	**Cytosine**	G ⟷ C

1. Cut around the nucleotides on page 139 and separate each of the 24 nucleotides by cutting along the columns and rows (see arrows indicating two such cutting points). Although drawn as geometric shapes, these symbols represent chemical structures.

2. Place one of each of the four kinds of nucleotide on their correct spaces below:

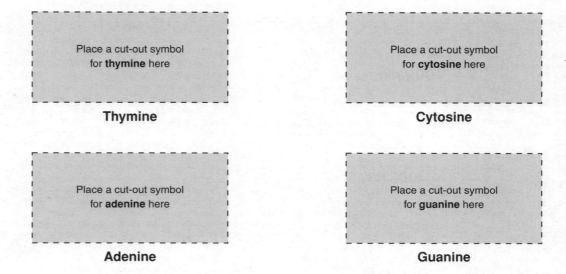

Place a cut-out symbol for **thymine** here

Thymine

Place a cut-out symbol for **cytosine** here

Cytosine

Place a cut-out symbol for **adenine** here

Adenine

Place a cut-out symbol for **guanine** here

Guanine

3. Identify and **label** each of the following features on the *adenine* nucleotide immediately above: **phosphate**, **sugar**, **base**, **hydrogen bonds**

4. Create one strand of the DNA molecule by placing the 9 correct 'cut out' nucleotides in the labelled spaces on the following page (DNA molecule). Make sure these are the right way up (with the **P** on the left) and are aligned with the left hand edge of each box. Begin with thymine and end with guanine.

5. Create the complementary strand of DNA by using the base pairing rule above. Note that the nucleotides have to be arranged upside down.

6. Under normal circumstances, it is not possible for adenine to pair up with guanine or cytosine, nor for any other mismatches to occur. Describe the two factors that prevent a mismatch from occurring:

   (a) Factor 1: _____

   _____

   (b) Factor 2: _____

   _____

7. Once you have checked that the arrangement is correct, you may glue, paste or tape these nucleotides in place.

NOTE: There may be some value in keeping these pieces loose in order to practise the base pairing rule. For this purpose, *removable tape* would be best.

The Genetic Code

Related activities: Nucleic Acids, The DNA Molecule

PA 2

DNA Molecule

Put the named nucleotides on the left hand side to create the template strand

Put the matching **complementary** nucleotides opposite the template strand

Thymine

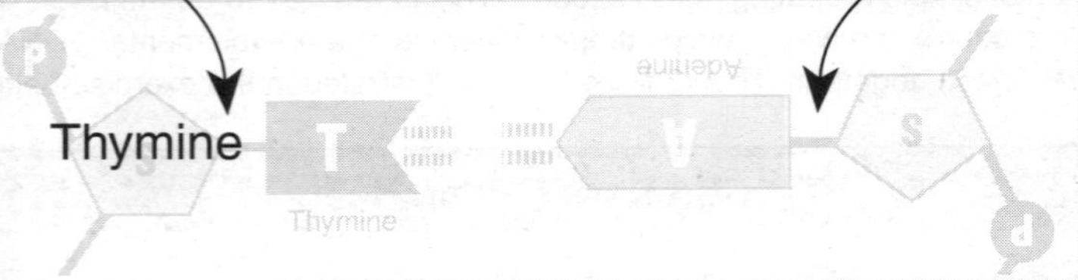

Thymine

Cytosine

Adenine

Adenine

Guanine

Thymine

Thymine

Cytosine

Guanine

Nucleotides

Tear out this page along the perforation and separate each of the 24 nucleotides by cutting along the columns and rows (see arrows indicating the cutting points).

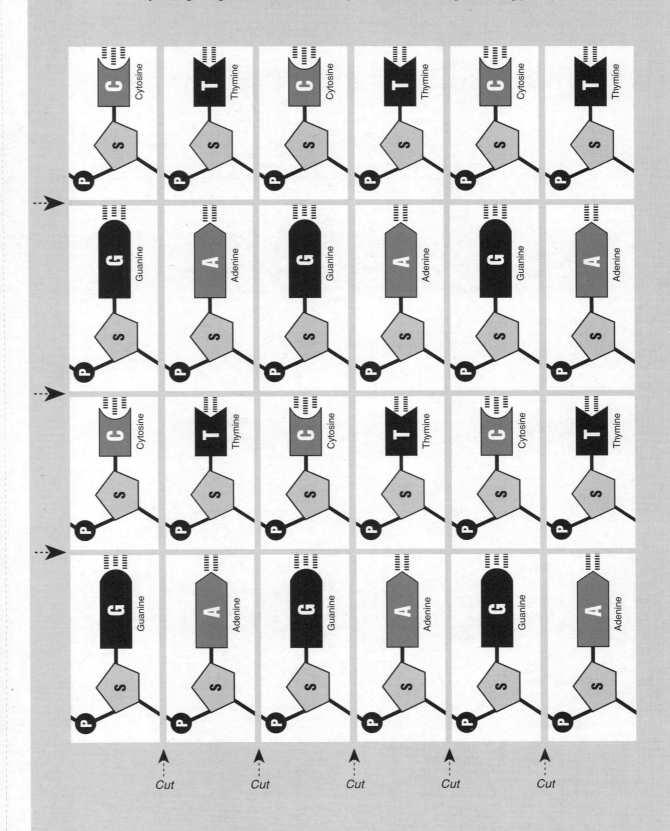

Cut   Cut   Cut   Cut   Cut

DNA Replication

DNA replication is a necessary preliminary step for cell division (both mitosis and meiosis). This process ensures that each resulting cell receives a complete set of genes from the original cell. After DNA replication, each chromosome is made up of two chromatids, joined at the **centromere**. Each **chromatid** contains half original (parent) DNA and half new (daughter) DNA. The two chromatids will become separated during cell division to form two separate chromosomes. During DNA replication, nucleotides are added at a region called the **replication fork**. The position of the replication fork moves along the chromosome as replication progresses. This whole process occurs simultaneously for each chromosome of a cell and the entire process is tightly controlled by enzymes. The diagram below describes essential steps in the process, while that on the next page identifies the role of the enzymes at each stage.

The Genetic Code

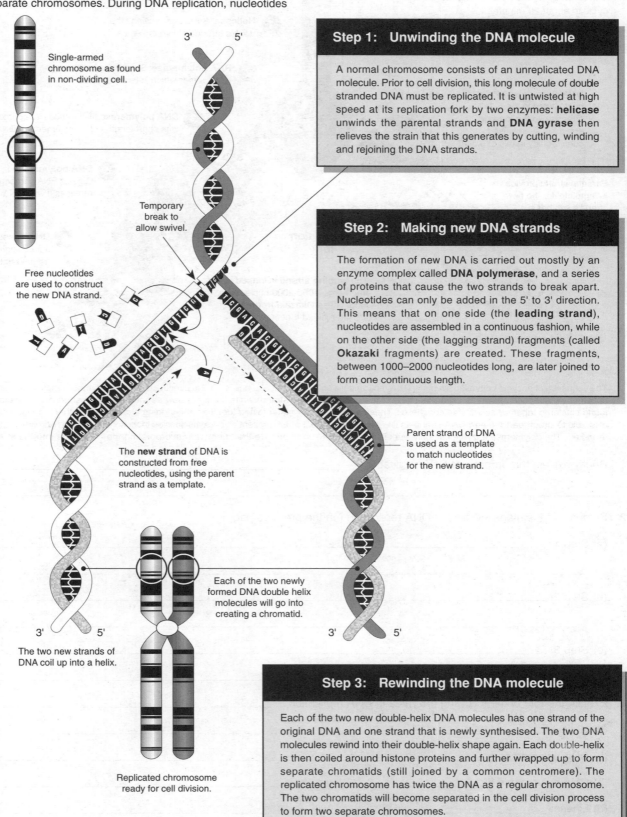

Single-armed chromosome as found in non-dividing cell.

Temporary break to allow swivel.

Free nucleotides are used to construct the new DNA strand.

The **new strand** of DNA is constructed from free nucleotides, using the parent strand as a template.

Parent strand of DNA is used as a template to match nucleotides for the new strand.

Each of the two newly formed DNA double helix molecules will go into creating a chromatid.

The two new strands of DNA coil up into a helix.

Replicated chromosome ready for cell division.

Step 1: Unwinding the DNA molecule

A normal chromosome consists of an unreplicated DNA molecule. Prior to cell division, this long molecule of double stranded DNA must be replicated. It is untwisted at high speed at its replication fork by two enzymes: **helicase** unwinds the parental strands and **DNA gyrase** then relieves the strain that this generates by cutting, winding and rejoining the DNA strands.

Step 2: Making new DNA strands

The formation of new DNA is carried out mostly by an enzyme complex called **DNA polymerase**, and a series of proteins that cause the two strands to break apart. Nucleotides can only be added in the 5' to 3' direction. This means that on one side (the **leading strand**), nucleotides are assembled in a continuous fashion, while on the other side (the lagging strand) fragments (called **Okazaki** fragments) are created. These fragments, between 1000–2000 nucleotides long, are later joined to form one continuous length.

Step 3: Rewinding the DNA molecule

Each of the two new double-helix DNA molecules has one strand of the original DNA and one strand that is newly synthesised. The two DNA molecules rewind into their double-helix shape again. Each double-helix is then coiled around histone proteins and further wrapped up to form separate chromatids (still joined by a common centromere). The replicated chromosome has twice the DNA as a regular chromosome. The two chromatids will become separated in the cell division process to form two separate chromosomes.

Related activities: Mitosis and the Cell Cycle, Review of DNA Replication
Web links: DNA Replication

DA 3

Enzyme Control of DNA Replication

DNA replication occurs during interphase of the cell cycle at an astounding rate. As many as 4000 nucleotides per second are replicated. This explains how under ideal conditions, bacterial cells with as many as 4 million nucleotides, can complete a cell cycle in about 20 minutes.

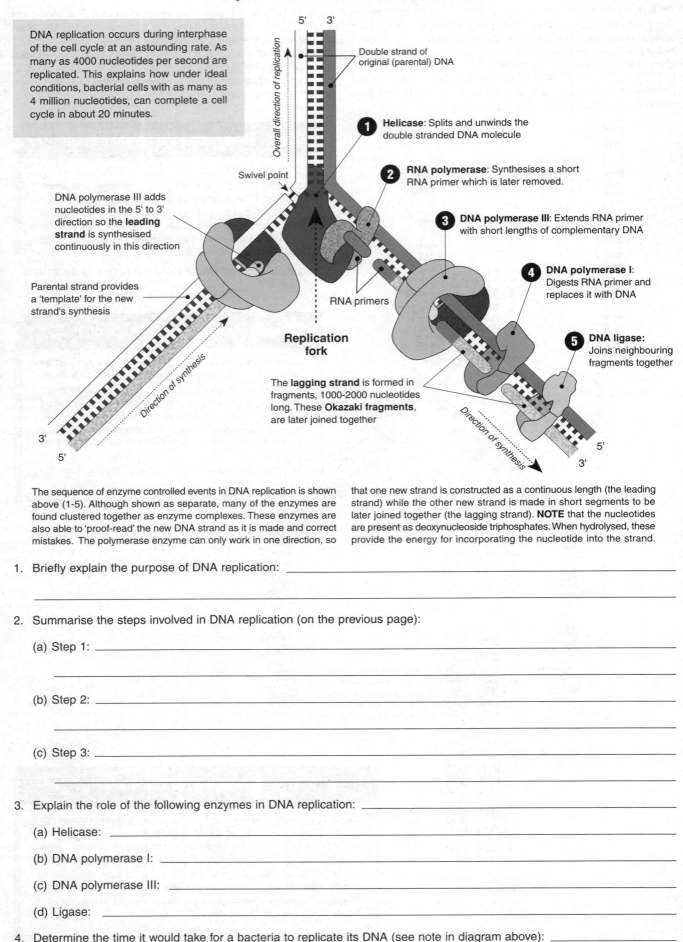

5' 3'

Overall direction of replication

Double strand of original (parental) DNA

1 **Helicase**: Splits and unwinds the double stranded DNA molecule

2 **RNA polymerase**: Synthesises a short RNA primer which is later removed.

3 **DNA polymerase III**: Extends RNA primer with short lengths of complementary DNA

4 **DNA polymerase I**: Digests RNA primer and replaces it with DNA

5 **DNA ligase**: Joins neighbouring fragments together

Swivel point

DNA polymerase III adds nucleotides in the 5' to 3' direction so the **leading strand** is synthesised continuously in this direction

Parental strand provides a 'template' for the new strand's synthesis

Direction of synthesis

RNA primers

Replication fork

The **lagging strand** is formed in fragments, 1000-2000 nucleotides long. These **Okazaki fragments**, are later joined together

Direction of synthesis

3'
5'

5'
3'

The sequence of enzyme controlled events in DNA replication is shown above (1-5). Although shown as separate, many of the enzymes are found clustered together as enzyme complexes. These enzymes are also able to 'proof-read' the new DNA strand as it is made and correct mistakes. The polymerase enzyme can only work in one direction, so that one new strand is constructed as a continuous length (the leading strand) while the other new strand is made in short segments to be later joined together (the lagging strand). **NOTE** that the nucleotides are present as deoxynucleoside triphosphates. When hydrolysed, these provide the energy for incorporating the nucleotide into the strand.

1. Briefly explain the purpose of DNA replication: _____

   _____

2. Summarise the steps involved in DNA replication (on the previous page):

   (a) Step 1: _____

   _____

   (b) Step 2: _____

   _____

   (c) Step 3: _____

   _____

3. Explain the role of the following enzymes in DNA replication: _____

   (a) Helicase: _____

   (b) DNA polymerase I: _____

   (c) DNA polymerase III: _____

   (d) Ligase: _____

4. Determine the time it would take for a bacteria to replicate its DNA (see note in diagram above): _____

Review of DNA Replication

The diagram below summarises the main steps in DNA replication. You should use this activity to test your understanding of the main features of DNA replication, using the knowledge gained in the previous activity to fill in the missing information. You should attempt this from what you have learned, but refer to the previous activity if you require help.

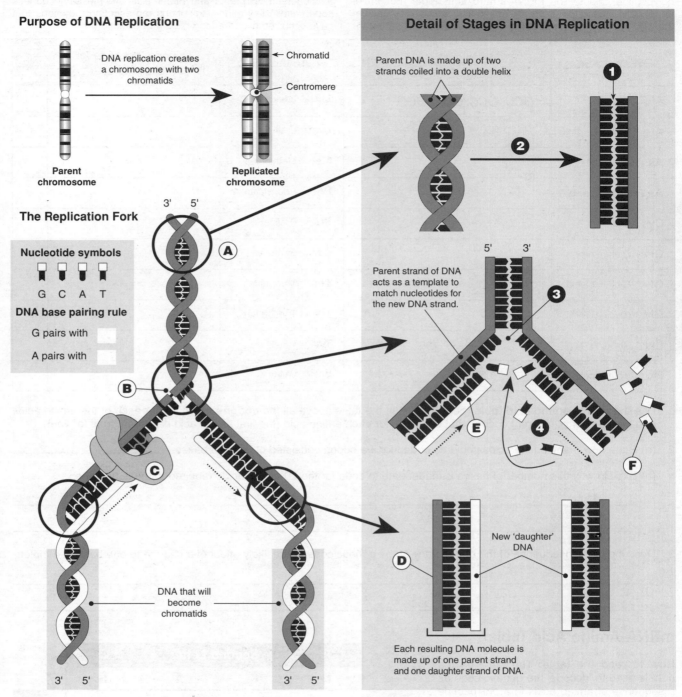

Purpose of DNA Replication

DNA replication creates a chromosome with two chromatids

Parent chromosome

Replicated chromosome

← Chromatid

← Centromere

The Replication Fork

3' 5'

Nucleotide symbols

G C A T

DNA base pairing rule

G pairs with ☐

A pairs with ☐

DNA that will become chromatids

3' 5'   3' 5'

Detail of Stages in DNA Replication

Parent DNA is made up of two strands coiled into a double helix

Parent strand of DNA acts as a template to match nucleotides for the new DNA strand.

5' 3'

New 'daughter' DNA

Each resulting DNA molecule is made up of one parent strand and one daughter strand of DNA.

1. (a) In the white boxes provided in the diagram, state the base pairing rule for making a strand of DNA:

(b) Identify each of the structures marked with a letter. (A-F):

A: _____   C: _____   E: _____

B: _____   D: _____   F: _____

3. Match each of the processes (1-4) to the correct summary of the process provided below:

☐ Unwinding of parent DNA double helix

☐ Free nucleotides occupy spaces alongside exposed bases

☐ Unzipping of parent DNA

☐ DNA strands are joined by base pairing

Related activities: DNA Replication   RA 1

The Genetic Code

The genetic information that codes for the assembly of amino acids is stored as three-letter codes, called **codons**. Each codon represents one of 20 amino acids used in the construction of polypeptide chains. The **mRNA-amino acid table** (bottom of page) can be used to identify the amino acid encoded by each of the mRNA codons. Note that the code is **degenerate** in that for each amino acid, there may be more than one codon. Most of this degeneracy involves the third nucleotide of a codon. The genetic code is **universal**; all living organisms on Earth, from viruses and bacteria, to plants and humans, share the same genetic code (with a few minor exceptions representing mutations that have occurred over the long history of evolution).

Amino acid		Codons that code for this amino acid	No.	Amino acid		Codons that code for this amino acid	No.
Ala	Alanine	GCU, GCC, GCA, GCG	4	**Leu**	Leucine		
Arg	Arginine			**Lys**	Lysine		
Asn	Asparagine			**Met**	Methionine		
Asp	Aspartic acid			**Phe**	Phenylalanine		
Cys	Cysteine			**Pro**	Proline		
Gln	Glutamine			**Ser**	Serine		
Glu	Glutamic acid			**Thr**	Threonine		
Gly	Glycine			**Try**	Tryptophan		
His	Histidine			**Tyr**	Tyrosine		
Iso	Isoleucine			**Val**	Valine		

1. Use the **mRNA-amino acid table** (below) to list in the table above all the **codons** that code for each of the amino acids and the number of different codons that can code for each amino acid (the first amino acid has been done for you).

2. (a) State how many amino acids could be coded for if a codon consisted of just two bases: _____

   (b) Explain why this number of bases is inadequate to code for the 20 amino acids required to make proteins:

   _____

   _____

3. Describe the consequence of the degeneracy of the genetic code to the likely effect of a change to one base in a triplet:

   _____

   _____

mRNA-Amino Acid Table

How to read the table: The table on the right is used to 'decode' the genetic code as a sequence of amino acids in a polypeptide chain, from a given mRNA sequence. To work out which amino acid is coded for by a codon (triplet of bases) look for the first letter of the codon in the row label on the left hand side. Then look for the column that intersects the same row from above that matches the second base. Finally, locate the third base in the codon by looking along the row from the right hand end that matches your codon.

Example: Determine **CAG**

C on the left row, A on the top column, G on the right row
CAG is Gln (**glutamine**)

Read second letter here
Read first letter here
Read third letter here

Second Letter			
U	**C**	**A**	**G**

First Letter **U**

				Third Letter
UUU Phe	UCU Ser	UAU Tyr	UGU Cys	U
UUC Phe	UCC Ser	UAC Tyr	UGC Cys	C
UUA Leu	UCA Ser	UAA STOP	UGA STOP	A
UUG Leu	UCG Ser	UAG STOP	UGG Try	G

First Letter **C**

CUU Leu	CCU Pro	CAU His	CGU Arg	U
CUC Leu	CCC Pro	CAC His	CGC Arg	C
CUA Leu	CCA Pro	CAA Gln	CGA Arg	A
CUG Leu	CCG Pro	CAG Gln	CGG Arg	G

First Letter **A**

AUU Iso	ACU Thr	AAU Asn	AGU Ser	U
AUC Iso	ACC Thr	AAC Asn	AGC Ser	C
AUA Iso	ACA Thr	AAA Lys	AGA Arg	A
AUG Met	ACG Thr	AAG Lys	AGG Arg	G

First Letter **G**

GUU Val	GCU Ala	GAU Asp	GGU Gly	U
GUC Val	GCC Ala	GAC Asp	GGC Gly	C
GUA Val	GCA Ala	GAA Glu	GGA Gly	A
GUG Val	GCG Ala	GAG Glu	GGG Gly	G

Third Letter

Related activities: Amino Acids, The Simplest Case: Genes to Proteins

The Simplest Case: Genes to Proteins

The traditionally held view of genes was as sections of DNA coding only for protein. This view has been revised in recent years with the discovery that much of the nonprotein-coding DNA encodes functional RNAs; it is not all non-coding "junk" DNA as was previously assumed. In fact, our concept of what constitutes a gene is changing rapidly and now encompasses all those segments of DNA that are transcribed (to RNA). This activity considers only the simplest scenario: one in which the gene codes for a functional protein. **Nucleotides**, the basic unit

of genetic information, are read in groups of three (**triplets**). Some triplets have a special controlling function in the making of a polypeptide chain. The equivalent of the triplet on the mRNA molecule is the **codon**. Three codons can signify termination of the amino acid chain (UAG, UAA and UGA in the mRNA code). The codon AUG is found at the beginning of every gene (on mRNA) and marks the starting point for reading the gene. The genes required to form a functional end-product (in this case, a functional protein) are collectively called a **transcription unit**.

Note: This start code is for the **coding strand** of the DNA. The template DNA strand from which the mRNA is made has the sequence: **TAC**.

Three **nucleotides** make up a **triplet**

Nucleotide

In models of nucleic acids, nucleotides are denoted by their base letter. (In this case: **G** is for guanine)

1. Describe the structure in a protein that corresponds to each of the following levels of genetic information:

   (a) Triplet   codes for: _____

   (b) Gene   codes for: _____

   (c) Transcription unit   codes for: _____

2. Describe the basic building blocks for each of the following levels of genetic information:

   (a) **Nucleotide** is made up of: _____

   _____

   (b) **Triplet** is made up of: _____

   _____

   (c) **Gene** is made up of: _____

   _____

   (d) **Transcription unit** is made up of: _____

   _____

3. Describe the steps involved in forming a functional protein: _____

   _____

© Biozone International 2008
Photocopying Prohibited

Related activities: Transcription, Translation

A 2

Analysing a DNA Sample

The nucleotide (base sequence) of a section of DNA can be determined using DNA sequencing techniques. The base sequence determines the amino acid sequence of the resultant protein therefore the DNA tells us what type of protein that gene encodes. This exercise reviews the areas of DNA replication, transcription, and translation using an analysis of a gel electrophoresis column. **Attempt it after you have completed the rest of this topic**. Remember that the gel pattern represents the sequence in the synthesised strand.

1. Determine the amino acid sequence of a protein from the nucleotide sequence of its DNA, with the following steps:

   (a) Determine the sequence of **synthesised DNA** in the gel
   (b) Convert it to the complementary sequence of the **sample DNA**
   (c) Complete the **mRNA** sequence
   (d) Determine the **amino acid** sequence by using the *mRNA - amino acid table* in this workbook.

   NOTE: The nucleotides in the gel are read from bottom to top and the sequence is written in the spaces provided from left to right (the first four have been done for you).

Triplet (×11)

C G T A ...

(DNA sequence read from the gel; comprises radioactive nucleotides that bind to the coding strand DNA in the sample). **Synthesised DNA**

Replication

G C A T ...

(This is the DNA that is being investigated) **DNA sample**

Transcription

C G U A ...

mRNA

Translation

Arginine ... **Amino acids**

Read in this direction

A, T, G, C

T C G A

Part of a polypeptide chain

2. For each single strand DNA sequence below, write the base sequence for the **complementary DNA** strand:

   (a) DNA: T A C   T A G   C C G   C G A   T T T   A C A   A T T

   DNA: _____

   (b) DNA: T A C   G C C   T T A   A A G   G G C   C G A   A T C

   DNA: _____

   (c) Identify the cell process that this exercise represents: _____

3. For each single strand DNA sequence below, write the base sequence for the **mRNA** strand and the **amino acid** that it codes for (refer to the mRNA-amino acid table to determine the amino acid sequence):

   (a) DNA: T A C   T A G   C C G   C G A   T T T   A C A   A T·T

   mRNA: _____

   Amino acids: _____

   (b) DNA: T A C   G C C   T T A   A A G   G G C   C G A   A T C

   mRNA: _____

   Amino acids: _____

   (c) Identify the cell process that this exercise represents: _____

Transcription

Transcription is the process by which the code contained in the DNA molecule is transcribed (rewritten) into a **mRNA** molecule. Transcription is under the control of the cell's metabolic processes which must activate a gene before this process can begin. The enzyme that directly controls the process is RNA polymerase, which makes a strand of mRNA using the single strand of DNA (the **template strand**) as a template (hence the term). The enzyme transcribes only a gene length of DNA at a time and therefore recognises start and stop signals (codes) at the beginning and end of the gene. Only RNA polymerase is involved in mRNA synthesis; it causes the unwinding of the DNA as well. It is common to find several RNA polymerase enzyme molecules on the same gene at any one time, allowing a high rate of mRNA synthesis to occur.

The Genetic Code

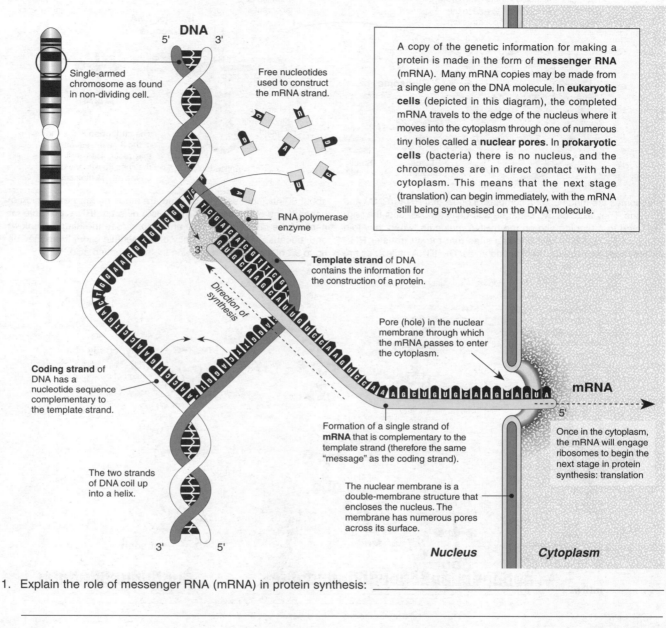

DNA

Single-armed chromosome as found in non-dividing cell.

Free nucleotides used to construct the mRNA strand.

A copy of the genetic information for making a protein is made in the form of **messenger RNA** (mRNA). Many mRNA copies may be made from a single gene on the DNA molecule. In **eukaryotic cells** (depicted in this diagram), the completed mRNA travels to the edge of the nucleus where it moves into the cytoplasm through one of numerous tiny holes called a **nuclear pores**. In **prokaryotic cells** (bacteria) there is no nucleus, and the chromosomes are in direct contact with the cytoplasm. This means that the next stage (translation) can begin immediately, with the mRNA still being synthesised on the DNA molecule.

RNA polymerase enzyme

Direction of synthesis

Template strand of DNA contains the information for the construction of a protein.

Pore (hole) in the nuclear membrane through which the mRNA passes to enter the cytoplasm.

Coding strand of DNA has a nucleotide sequence complementary to the template strand.

mRNA

Formation of a single strand of **mRNA** that is complementary to the template strand (therefore the same "message" as the coding strand).

Once in the cytoplasm, the mRNA will engage ribosomes to begin the next stage in protein synthesis: translation

The two strands of DNA coil up into a helix.

The nuclear membrane is a double-membrane structure that encloses the nucleus. The membrane has numerous pores across its surface.

Nucleus　　*Cytoplasm*

1. Explain the role of messenger RNA (mRNA) in protein synthesis: _____

_____

_____

2. The genetic code contains punctuation codons to mark the starting and finishing points of the code for synthesis of polypeptide chains and proteins. Consult the *mRNA–amino acid table* earlier in this workbook and state the codes for:

(a) Start codon: _____ (b) Stop (termination) codons: _____

3. For the following triplets on the DNA, determine the **codon** sequence for the mRNA that would be synthesised:

(a) Triplets on the DNA:　　T A C　　T A G　　C C G　　C G A　　T T T

Codons on the mRNA: _____

(b) Triplets on the DNA:　　T A C　　A A G　　C C T　　A T A　　A A A

Codons on the mRNA: _____

Related activities: The Genetic Code, Review of Gene Expression
Web links: Transcription in Prokaryotes, Transcription Animation

RA 2

Translation

The diagram below shows the translation phase of protein synthesis. The scene shows how a single mRNA molecule can be 'serviced' by many ribosomes at the same time. The ribosome on the right is in a more advanced stage of constructing a polypeptide chain because it has 'translated' more of the mRNA than the ribosome on the left. The anti-codon at the base of each tRNA must make a perfect complementary match with the codon on the mRNA before the amino acid is released. Once released, the amino acid is added to the growing polypeptide chain by enzymes.

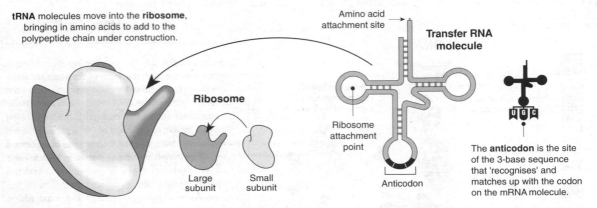

tRNA molecules move into the **ribosome**, bringing in amino acids to add to the polypeptide chain under construction.

Ribosome

Large subunit

Small subunit

Amino acid attachment site

Transfer RNA molecule

Ribosome attachment point

Anticodon

The **anticodon** is the site of the 3-base sequence that 'recognises' and matches up with the codon on the mRNA molecule.

Ribosomes are made up of a complex of ribosomal RNA (rRNA) and proteins. They exist as two separate sub-units (above) until they are attracted to a binding site on the mRNA molecule, when they join together. Ribosomes have binding sites that attract transfer RNA (**tRNA**) molecules loaded with amino acids. The tRNA molecules are about 80 nucleotides in length and are made under the direction of genes in the chromosomes. There is a different tRNA molecule for each of the different possible anticodons (see the diagram below) and, because of the degeneracy of the genetic code, there may be up to six different tRNAs carrying the same amino acid.

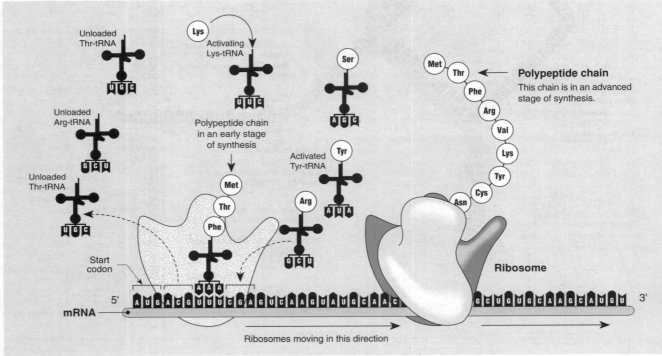

Unloaded Thr-tRNA

Lys Activating Lys-tRNA

Ser

Met Thr Phe Arg Val Lys Tyr Cys Asn

Polypeptide chain
This chain is in an advanced stage of synthesis.

Unloaded Arg-tRNA

Polypeptide chain in an early stage of synthesis

Activated Tyr-tRNA

Tyr

Unloaded Thr-tRNA

Met Thr Phe

Arg

Start codon

5' mRNA

Ribosome

3'

Ribosomes moving in this direction

1. For the following codons on the mRNA, determine the **anticodons** for each tRNA that would deliver the amino acids:

   Codons on the mRNA: U A C   U A G   C C G   C G A   U U U

   Anticodons on the tRNAs: _____

2. There are many different types of tRNA molecules, each with a different anticodon (HINT: see the *mRNA table*).

   (a) State how many different tRNA types there are, each with a unique anticodon: _____

   (b) Explain your answer: _____

   _____

   _____

Related activities: The Genetic Code
Web links: Polyribosomes

Review of Gene Expression

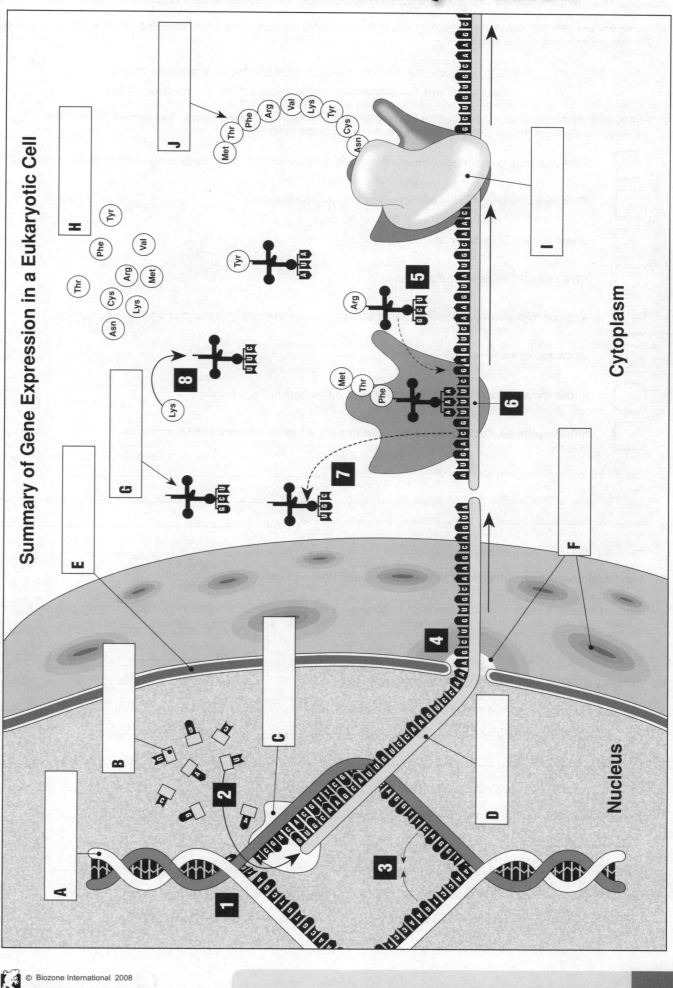

Summary of Gene Expression in a Eukaryotic Cell

Cytoplasm

Nucleus

The diagram on the previous page summarises gene expression (transcription and protein synthesis) in a eukaryotic cell. Important structures are labelled with letters (**A-J**), and major steps in the process are identified with numbers (**1-8**).

1. Using the word list provided below, identify each of the structures marked with a letter. Write the name of that structure in the spaces provided on the diagram.

    DNA, nuclear pore, free nucleotides, tRNA, RNA polymerase enzyme,

    amino acids, mRNA, ribosome, nuclear membrane, polypeptide chain

2. Match each of the processes (identified on the diagram with numbers 1-8) to the correct summary of the process provided below. Write the process number next to the appropriate sentence.

    ☐ tRNA molecule is recharged with another amino acid of the same type, ready to take part in protein synthesis

    ☐ tRNA molecule brings in the correct amino acid to the ribosome

    ☐ Unwinding the DNA molecule

    ☐ DNA rewinds into double helix structure

    ☐ Anti-codon on the tRNA matches with the correct codon on the mRNA and drops off the amino acid

    ☐ tRNA leaves the ribosome

    ☐ mRNA moves through nuclear pore in nuclear membrane to the cytoplasm

    ☐ mRNA synthesis: nucleotides added to the growing strand of messenger RNA molecule

3. Explain the purpose of gene expression: _____

    _____

4. Identify the three different types of RNA involved in expressing the protein product of a gene: _____

    _____

5. Outline three structural or functional differences between RNA and DNA:

    (a) _____

    (b) _____

    (c) _____

6. (a) Name the general process taking place in the **nucleus**: _____

    (b) Name the general process taking place in the **cytoplasm**: _____

7. Describe two factors that would determine whether or not a particular protein is produced in the cell:

    (a) _____

    (b) _____

8. Explain the statement "the synthesis of enzymes is controlled by DNA": _____

    _____

    _____

9. Describe one important way in which gene expression in eukaryotes (pictured) differs from that in prokaryotes:

    _____

    _____

Food and Health

OCR: Unit F212, Module 2: Food and Health

2.2.1: Diet and food production

CIE: CORE SYLLABUS

H: (j): Cardiovascular disease only

Learning Objectives

☐ 1. Compile your own glossary from the **KEY WORDS** displayed in **bold type** in the learning objectives below.

Diet and Its Role in Disease *(pages 193-200)*

☐ 2. Describe the concept of a **balanced diet**, recognising its components in terms of adequate nutrient intake and the functions of **protein, fats, carbohydrates, vitamins,** and **minerals**.

☐ 3. Recognise that the energy and nutrient requirements of people varies depending on their "age and stage" of life. Explain what is meant by a dietary reference value (DRV) and describe how DRVs may be used to help make informed, healthy food choices.

☐ 4. Explain what is meant by **malnutrition**, and describe its causes and consequences, including reference to:
   (a) Energy and protein deficiency
   (b) Deficiency of vitamins A and D
   (c) Deficiency of vitamin C and mineral ions

☐ 5. Explain how malnutrition can result in **obesity**. Discuss the health risks associated with obesity, including its role as a risk factor in cardiovascular disease.

☐ 6. Discuss the possible links between diet and **coronary heart disease**. In particular, discuss the possible effects of high **blood cholesterol** levels on the cardiovascular system (heart and circulation).

☐ 7. Describe the functional differences between high-density lipoproteins (**HDL**) and low-density lipoproteins (**LDL**) and discuss how the **LDL:HDL ratio** can affect cardiovascular health.

☐ 8. Recognise the features and risk factors of some cardiovascular diseases, including **atherosclerosis** and its link to **hypertension,** and heart attack.

☐ 9. Discuss the ways in which **smoking** may increase the risk of developing cardiovascular disease.

Food Production *(pages 192, 201-211)*

☐ 10. Recognise that **plants** are the basis of all food chains, and that as such humans are dependent on them for all food. Understand the role that the **green revolution** has played in increasing global food production rates.

☐ 11. Discuss how **selective breeding** is used to breed high yield **crop plants,** or crops with properties such as increased resistance to disease and pests.

☐ 12. Describe how selective breeding techniques such as **inbreeding, line-breeding,** and **out-crossing** are used to breed highly productive **domestic animals.** Explain how the domestic animals bred for food today have been obtained by selective breeding from their wild ancestors. Appreciate the value in maintaining the biodiversity of these ancient lines (e.g. in the wild and in seed and gene banks).

☐ 13. Discuss how fertilisers, pesticides, and antibiotics can increase **food production.** Include in your discussion the wider implications of these practices.

☐ 14. Describe how **microorganisms** are used in **food technology** industries to make food for humans. Include reference to both the advantages and disadvantages of using such techniques.

☐ 15. Understand that **food preservation** techniques act by reducing the growth of microbial contaminants. Explain how common food preservation techniques prevent the spoilage of food by microorganisms. Include reference to: **salting, adding sugar, pickling, freezing, heat treatment,** and **irradiation**.

See the 'Textbook Reference Grid' on pages 7 for textbook page references relating to material in this topic.

Supplementary Texts
See pages 5 for additional details of these texts:

■ Fullick, A., 1998. **Human Health and Disease** (Heinemann), chpt. 1, 3-6 as required.

Presentation MEDIA to support this topic:

HEALTH & DISEASE:
• **Non-infectious Disease**

See page 6 for details of publishers of periodicals:

■ **Heart Disease and Cholesterol** Biol. Sci. Rev., 13(2) Nov. 2000, pp. 2-5. *The links between dietary fat, cholesterol level, and heart disease.*

■ **Why are we so Fat?** National Geographic, 206(2), August 2004, pp. 46-61. *A comprehensive account of the obesity. Includes a summary of health problems associated with obesity.*

■ **Obesity: Size Matters** Biol. Sci. Rev., 18(4) April 2006, pp. 10-13. *Obesity and health.*

■ **Genetic Manipulation of Plants** Biol. Sci. Rev., 15(1) Sept. 2002, pp. 10-13. *The genetic modification of crop plants to improve tolerance to herbicides, pests and environmental stress.*

■ **The Adaptations of Cereals** Biol. Sci. Rev., 13(3) Jan. 2001, pp. 30-33. *A look at the world's major cereal crops: production and adaptations.*

■ **Feast and Famine** Scientific American, Sept. 2007, (special issue). *A special issue covering the most recent developments in health and nutrition science, including the best diet for good health, the role of exercise in weight management, what controls obesity, and the role of globalisation in the impoverished nutrition of the world's poor.*

See pages 8-9 for details of how to access **Bio Links** from our web site: **www.biozone.co.uk**. From Bio Links, access sites under the topics:

HEALTH & DISEASE: • WHO/OMS: Health topics • NIH: Science education • Smoking and your digestive system ... *and others* > **Human Health Issues:** • British Nutrition Foundation • Eating disorders • Food safety & nutrition info Institute of Crop and Food Research ... *and others*

Global Human Nutrition

Globally, 854 million people are undernourished and, despite advances in agricultural practices and technologies, the number of hungry people in the world continues to rise. The majority of these people live in developing nations, but 9 million live in industrialised countries. Over 6 million people die annually from starvation, while millions of others suffer debilitating diseases as a result of malnutrition. Protein deficiencies (such as kwashiorkor), are common amongst the world's malnourished, because the world's poorest nations consume only a fraction of the world's protein resources, surviving primarily on cereal crops. Political and environmental factors contribute significantly to the world's hunger problem. In some countries, food production is sufficient to meet needs, but inadequate distribution methods cause food shortages in some regions.

Human Nutritional Requirements

A **balanced diet,** taken from the components below, is essential for human growth, development, metabolism, and good health. In many developing countries, deficiency diseases and starvation are prevalent either because of an absolute scarcity of food or because of inadequate nutrition. In many developed Western nations, an oversupply of cheap, nutritionally poor and highly processed food is contributing to an increase of diet-related diseases such as obesity, diabetes, and heart disease. **Malnutrition** (a lack of specific nutrients), once commonly associated with undernutrition, is now rising in developed nations over consuming on poor quality processed foods.

beans
lentils

Proteins (supplied by beans and pulses, and animal products such as meat and fish) are essential to growth and repair of muscle and other tissues. Unlike animal protein, plant protein is incomplete and sources must be chosen to complement one another nutritionally. Deficiencies result in kwashiorkor or marasmus.

Carbohydrates (right) are supplied in breads, starchy vegetables, cereals, and grains. They form the staple of most diets and provide the main energy source for the body.

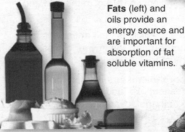

Fats (left) and oils provide an energy source and are important for absorption of fat soluble vitamins.

Minerals (inorganic elements) and **vitamins** (essential organic compounds) are both required for numerous normal body functions. They are abundant in fruit and vegetables (right)

Humans and Agriculture

Via photosynthesis, plants are the ultimate source of food and metabolic energy for nearly all animals. Besides foods (e.g. grains, fruits, and vegetables), plants also provide humans with shelter, clothing, medicines, fuels, and the raw materials from which many other products are made.

Plant tissues provide the energy for almost all heterotrophic life. Low technology, low-input subsistence agriculture can provide enough food to supply a family unit, but the diet may not always be balanced because of limited access to seed and fertilisers and limitations on the crops that can be grown regionally.

Industrialised agriculture produces high yields per unit of land at cheaper prices, but has a large environmental impact because of high inputs of energy, fertilisers, and pesticides. **Wheat production** (left) and animal "factory farming" are examples. Rice production is also an example of intensive agriculture, but remains largely traditional (not mechanised) in many parts of the world.

Plantation agriculture is practised mainly in tropical countries solely to produce a high value cash crop for sale in developed countries. Typical crops include bananas (left), cotton, coffee, sugarcane, tobacco, and cocoa. Cash crops can deprive subsistence farmers of the land they need to grow their own food.

1. Contrast the primary causes of malnutrition in developed and developing countries: _____

_____

_____

_____

_____

2. *One of the likely effects of a global fuel crisis would be food shortage.* Explain this statement: _____

_____

_____

_____

Related activities: Deficiency Diseases, The Green Revolution

A Balanced Diet

Nutrients are required for metabolism, tissue growth and repair, and as an energy source. Good nutrition (provided by a **balanced diet**) is recognised as a key factor in good health. Conversely poor nutrition (malnutrition) may cause ill-health or **deficiency diseases**. A diet refers to the quantity and nature of the food eaten. While not all foods contain all the representative nutrients, we can obtain the required balance of different nutrients by eating a wide variety of foods. In a recent overhaul of previous dietary recommendations, the health benefits of monounsaturated fats (such as olive and canola oils), fish oils, and whole grains have

been recognised, and people are being urged to reduce their consumption of highly processed foods and saturated (rather than total) fat. Those on diets that restrict certain food groups (e.g. vegans) must take care to balance their intake of foods to ensure an adequate supply of protein and other nutrients (e.g. iron and B vitamins). **Reference Nutrient Intakes** (RNIs) (see the next page) provide nutritional guidelines for different sectors of the population in the UK. RNIs help to define the upper and lower limits of adequate nutrient intake for most people, but they are not recommendations for intakes by individuals.

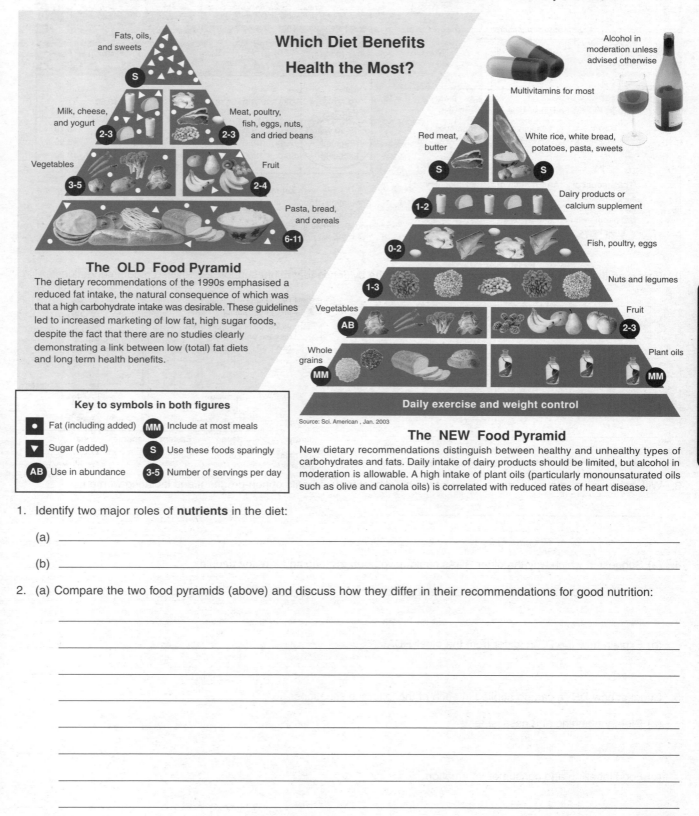

Which Diet Benefits Health the Most?

The OLD Food Pyramid

The dietary recommendations of the 1990s emphasised a reduced fat intake, the natural consequence of which was that a high carbohydrate intake was desirable. These guidelines led to increased marketing of low fat, high sugar foods, despite the fact that there are no studies clearly demonstrating a link between low (total) fat diets and long term health benefits.

Source: Sci. American , Jan. 2003

The NEW Food Pyramid

New dietary recommendations distinguish between healthy and unhealthy types of carbohydrates and fats. Daily intake of dairy products should be limited, but alcohol in moderation is allowable. A high intake of plant oils (particularly monounsaturated oils such as olive and canola oils) is correlated with reduced rates of heart disease.

Key to symbols in both figures

- Fat (including added)
- MM Include at most meals
- Sugar (added)
- S Use these foods sparingly
- AB Use in abundance
- 3-5 Number of servings per day

Food and Health

1. Identify two major roles of **nutrients** in the diet:

   (a) _____

   (b) _____

2. (a) Compare the two food pyramids (above) and discuss how they differ in their recommendations for good nutrition:

   _____

   _____

   _____

   _____

   _____

   _____

   _____

   _____

Nutritional Guidelines in the UK

In the UK, Dietary Reference Values (DRVs) provide guidelines for nutrient and energy intake for particular groups of the population. In a population, it is assumed that the nutritional requirements of the population as a whole are represented by a normal, bell-shaped, curve (below). DRVs collectively encompass RNIs, LRNIs, and EARs, and replace the earlier Recommended Daily Amounts (RDAs), which *recommended* nutrient intakes for particular groups in the population, including those with very high needs.

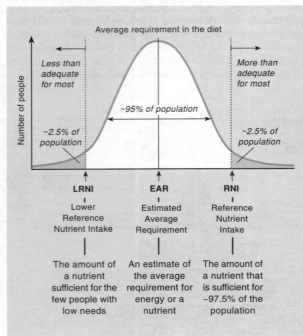

Table 1 (below): Estimated Average Requirements (EAR) for energy, and Reference Nutrient Intakes (RNIs) for selected nutrients, for UK males and females aged 19-50 years (per day).

Source: Dept of Health. Dietary Reference Values for Food Energy and Nutrients for the UK, 1991.

Age range	Reference Nutrient Intakes (RNIs)					EARs	
	Protein (g)	Calcium (mg)	Iron (mg)	Folate (μg)	Vit.C (mg)	EAR (MJ) Males	Females
Males							
19-50 years	55.5	700	8.7	700	40	10.60	
Females							
19-50 years	45.0	700	14.8	600	40		8.10
Pregnant	51.0	1250	14.8	700	50		8.90
Lactating	56.0	1250	14.8	950	70		10.20

DRVs have been set for population groups within the UK, taking into account age and gender. Only a portion of the table is shown here.

RNIs are provided for each constituent of a balanced diet

EARs for energy are based on the present lifestyles and activity levels of the UK population.

(b) Based on the information on the graph (right), state the evidence that might support the revised recommendations:

_____

_____

_____

_____

_____

_____

_____

_____

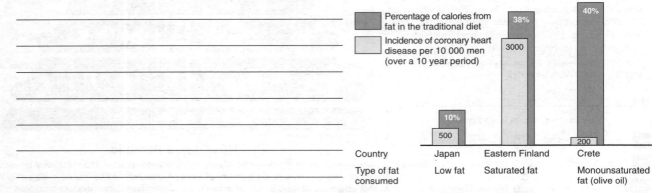

3. With reference to the table above, contrast the nutritional requirements of non-pregnant and lactating women:

_____

_____

4. (a) Suggest in which way the older RDAs could have been misleading for many people: _____

_____

_____

(b) Explain how the DRVs differ from the older RDAs: _____

_____

5. Suggest how **DRVs** can be applied in each of the following situations:

(a) Dietary planning and assessment: _____

_____

(b) Food labelling and consumer information: _____

_____

Deficiency Diseases

Malnutrition is the general term for nutritional disorders resulting from not having enough food (starvation), not enough of the right food (deficiency), or too much food (obesity). Children under 5 are the most at risk from starvation and deficiency diseases because they are growing rapidly and are more susceptible to disease. Malnutrition is a key factor in the deaths of 6 million children each year and, in developing countries, dietary deficiencies are a major problem. In these countries, malnutrition usually presents as **marasmus** or **kwashiorkor** (energy and protein deficiencies).

Specific vitamin and mineral deficiencies (below and following page) in adults are associated with specific disorders, e.g. **beriberi** (vitamin B$_1$), **scurvy** (vitamin C), **rickets** (vitamin D), **pellagra** (niacin), or **anaemia** (iron). Vitamin deficiencies in childhood result in chronic, lifelong disorders. Deficiency diseases are rare in developed countries. People who do suffer from some form of dietary deficiency are either alcoholics, people with intestinal disorders that prevent proper nutrient uptake, or people with very restricted diets (e.g. vegans).

Vitamin D Deficiency
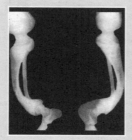
Lack of vitamin D in children produces the disease rickets. In adults a similar disease is called osteomalacia. Suffers typically show skeletal deformities (e.g. bowed legs, left) because inadequate amounts of calcium and phosphorus are incorporated into the bones. Vitamin D is produced by the skin when exposed to sunlight and it is vital for the absorption of calcium from the diet.

Vitamin A Deficiency
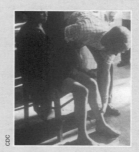
Vitamin A (found in animal livers, eggs, and dairy products) is essential for the production of light-absorbing pigments in the eye and for the formation of cell structures. Symptoms of deficiency include loss of night vision, inflammation of the eye, **keratomalacia** (damage to the cornea), and the appearance of **Bitots spots**, evident as foamy, opaque patches on the white of the eye (refer to photo).

Vitamin C Deficiency
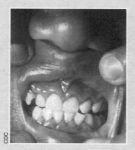
Vitamin C deficiency causes a disease known as scurvy. It is now rare in developed countries because of increased consumption of fresh fruit and vegetables. Inadequate vitamin C intake disturbs the body's normal production of collagen, a protein in connective tissue that holds body structures together. This results in poor wound healing, rupture of small blood vessels (visible bleeding in the skin), swollen gums, and loose teeth.

Vitamin B$_1$ Deficiency

Vitamin B$_1$ (thiamine) is required for respiratory metabolism, and nerve and muscle function. Lack of thiamine causes the metabolic disorder, **beriberi**, which occurs predominantly in underfed populations, or in breast fed babies whose mother is on a restrictive diet. Symptoms of beriberi include nerve degeneration, heart failure, and oedema (swelling caused by fluid accumulation). Without medical treatment, sufferers will die.

Kwashiorkor
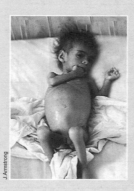
A severe type of protein-energy deficiency in young children (1-3 years old), occurring mainly in poor rural areas in the tropics. Kwashiorkor occurs when a child is suddenly weaned on to a diet that is low in calories, protein, and certain essential micronutrients. The problem is often made worse by a poor appetite due to illnesses such as measles. Children have stunted growth, oedema (accumulation of fluid in the tissues), and are inactive, apathetic and weak. Resistance against infection is lost, which may be fatal.

Marasmus

Marasmus is the most common form of deficiency disease. It is a severe form of protein and energy malnutrition that usually occurs in famine or starvation conditions. Children suffering from marasmus are stunted and extremely emaciated. They have loose folds of skin on the limbs and buttocks, due to the loss of fat and muscle tissue. Unlike kwashiorkor sufferers, marasmus does not cause the bloated and elongated abdomen. However sufferers have no resistance to disease and common infections are typically fatal.

Food and Health

1. Distinguish between **malnutrition** and **starvation**:

2. For each of the following vitamins, identify the natural sources of the vitamin, its function, and effect of deficiency:

(a) Vitamin A:

Function:

Deficiency:

(b) Vitamin B$_1$:

Function:

Deficiency:

Related activities: Dietary Disorders, A Balanced Diet

RA 2

Common Mineral Deficiencies

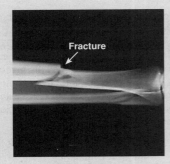

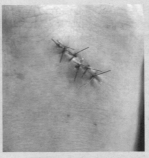

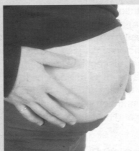

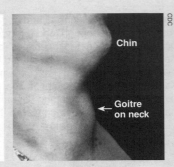

Calcium Deficiency

Calcium is required for enzyme function, formation of bones and teeth, blood clotting, and muscular contraction. Calcium deficiency causes poor bone growth and structure, increasing the tendency of bones to fracture and break. It also results in muscular spasms and poor blood clotting ability.

Zinc Deficiency

Zinc is found in red meat, poultry, fish, whole grain cereals and breads, legumes, and nuts. It is important for enzyme activity, production of insulin, making of sperm, and perception of taste. A deficiency in zinc causes growth retardation, a delay in puberty, muscular weakness, dry skin, and a delay in wound healing.

Iron Deficiency

Anaemia results from lower than normal levels of haemoglobin in red blood cells. Iron from the diet is required to produce haemoglobin. People most at risk include women during **pregnancy** and those with an inadequate dietary intake. Symptoms include fatigue, fainting, breath-lessness, and heart palpitations.

Iodine Deficiency

Iodine is essential for the production of thyroid hormones. These hormones control the rate of metabolism, growth, and development. Shortage of iodine in the diet may lead to **goitre** (thyroid enlargement as shown above). Iodine deficiency is also responsible for some cases of thyroid underactivity (**hypothyroidism**).

(c) Vitamin C: _____

   Function: _____

   Deficiency: _____

(d) Vitamin D: _____

   Function: _____

   Deficiency: _____

3. Suggest why young children, pregnant women, and athletes are among the most susceptible to dietary deficiencies:

_____

_____

_____

4. Explain why a lack of iron leads to the symptoms of anaemia (fatigue and breathlessness): _____

_____

_____

5. Suggest why a zinc deficiency is associated with muscular weakness and a delay in puberty: _____

_____

_____

6. Using the example of **iodine**, explain how artificial dietary supplementation can be achieved and discuss its benefits:

_____

_____

7. Explain why people suffering from nutritional deficiencies have a poor resistance to disease: _____

_____

_____

_____

_____

Malnutrition and Obesity

Malnutrition describes an imbalance between what someone eats and what is required to remain healthy. In economically developed areas of the world, most (but not all) forms of malnutrition are the result of poorly balanced nutrient intakes rather than a lack of food *per se*. Amongst the most common of these is **obesity**, as indicated by BMI values in excess of 30 (below). In Britain 20-30% of all adults are obese. Although some genetic and hormonal causes are known, obesity is commonly the result of excessive energy intake, usually associated with a highly processed diet, high in fat and sugar. Obesity is a risk factor in a number of chronic diseases, including hypertension, cardiovascular disease, type 2 diabetes and insulin resistance, and osteoarthritis. Somewhat paradoxically, obesity in developed countries is more common in poorly educated, lower socio-economic groups than amongst the wealthy, who often have more options in terms of food choices. Worryingly, obesity is also increasing in incidence in developing nations, especially those with emerging economies such as China. Dieting is often ineffective for long-term weight loss because once normal eating is resumed the body responds by storing more fat in fat cells.

Obesity and Malnutrition

In adults, the exact level of obesity is determined by reference to the Body Mass Index (BMI). A score of 30+ on the BMI indicates mild obesity, while those with severe or morbid obesity have BMIs of 40+. Child obesity is based on BMI-for-age, and is assessed in relation to the weight of other children of a similar age and gender. Central or abdominal obesity, now classified as an independent risk factor for some serious diseases, refers to excessive fat around the abdomen. While the simple explanation for excessive body fat is simple (energy in exceeds energy out), a complex of biological and socio-economic factors are implicated in creating the problems of modern obesity.

Possible Root Causes of Obesity

Overconsumption

- Eating too many calories for energy needs
- Increased consumption of calorie-dense foods
- Overconsumption of trans-fatty acids and refined carbohydrates combined with a low fibre intake

These eating patterns are known to interfere with food and energy metabolism, and cause excessive fat storage.

Reduced Energy Expenditure

People who eat more calories need to burn more calories, otherwise their calorie surplus is stored as fat. Incidental physical activity is declining: we drive more, use labour-saving machines, and exercise less.

Contributors to Obesity

Family diet and lifestyle are important contributory causes to modern child obesity, especially at a time of rising affluence. Since obese children and adolescents frequently grow up to become obese adults, family influence extends to adult obesity.

Genes affect a number of weight-related processes in the body, such as metabolic rate, blood glucose metabolism, hormonal levels, and fat-storage. Evidence suggests that a predisposition to obesity can be inherited, but also discounts genetics as a main cause.

Health Effects of Obesity

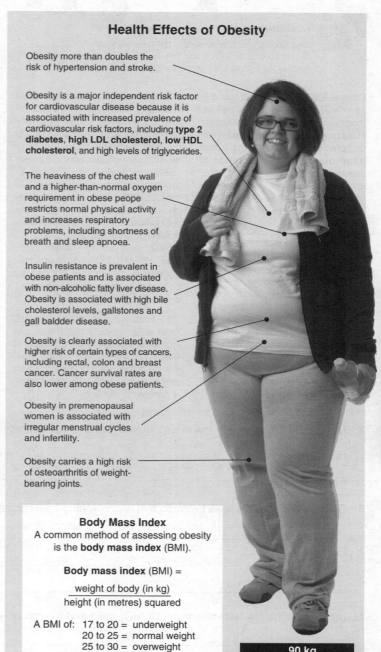

Obesity more than doubles the risk of hypertension and stroke.

Obesity is a major independent risk factor for cardiovascular disease because it is associated with increased prevalence of cardiovascular risk factors, including **type 2 diabetes**, **high LDL cholesterol**, **low HDL cholesterol**, and high levels of triglycerides.

The heaviness of the chest wall and a higher-than-normal oxygen requirement in obese peope restricts normal physical activity and increases respiratory problems, including shortness of breath and sleep apnoea.

Insulin resistance is prevalent in obese patients and is associated with non-alcoholic fatty liver disease. Obesity is associated with high bile cholesterol levels, gallstones and gall baldder disease.

Obesity is clearly associated with higher risk of certain types of cancers, including rectal, colon and breast cancer. Cancer survival rates are also lower among obese patients.

Obesity in premenopausal women is associated with irregular menstrual cycles and infertility.

Obesity carries a high risk of osteoarthritis of weight-bearing joints.

Body Mass Index

A common method of assessing obesity is the **body mass index** (BMI).

Body mass index (BMI) =

$$\frac{\text{weight of body (in kg)}}{\text{height (in metres) squared}}$$

A BMI of: 17 to 20 = underweight
20 to 25 = normal weight
25 to 30 = overweight
over 30 = obesity

$$BMI = \frac{90 \text{ kg}}{(1.68)^2} = 32$$

Food and Health

1. (a) Explain why obesity is regarded as a form of malnutrition: _____

_____

(b) Describe the two basic energy factors that determine how a person's weight will change: _____

_____

Related activities: A Balanced Diet, Cardiovascular Disease

RA 2

Cholesterol and Risk of Cardiovascular Disease

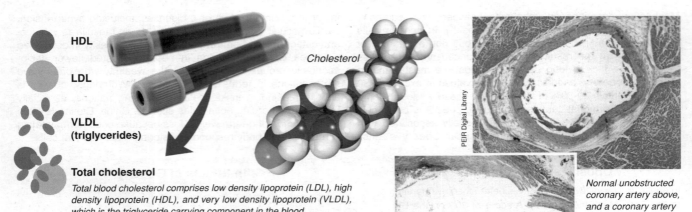

HDL

LDL

VLDL
(triglycerides)

Total cholesterol

Total blood cholesterol comprises low density lipoprotein (LDL), high density lipoprotein (HDL), and very low density lipoprotein (VLDL), which is the triglyceride carrying component in the blood.

Cholesterol

PEIR Digital Library

Normal unobstructed coronary artery above, and a coronary artery (left) showing moderately severe atheroma. Note the formation of the plaque on the inside surface of the artery. Plaques obstruct blood flow through the artery.

Cholesterol is a sterol lipid found in all animal tissues as part of cellular membranes. Cholesterol is not soluble in the blood, so it is transported within complex spherical particles called **lipoproteins**. There are range of various sized lipoproteins in the blood, and the different way in which they behave has implications for how cholesterol is dealt with by the body.

One form of cholesterol-transporting molecule, called **HDL** (or **high density lipoprotein**), forms packets of cholesterol which move easily through the blood. HDL helps remove cholesterol from the bloodstream by transporting it to the liver. Another form of lipoprotein, called **LDL** (**low density lipoprotein**) does not aid in the transportation of cholesterol to the liver, but instead deposits cholesterol onto the walls of blood vessels to form **plaques**.

Abnormally high concentrations of LDL and lower concentrations of functional HDL are strongly associated with cardiovascular disease because these promote development of atheroma in arteries (lower photograph, right). This disease process leads to heart attack. It is the **LDL:HDL ratio**, rather than total cholesterol itself, that provides the best indicator of risk of cardiovascular disease, and the risk profile is different for men and women (tables right). The LDL:HDL ratio is mostly genetically determined but can be changed by body build, diet, and exercise regime.

*LDL is often called "bad cholesterol" (and HDL "good") but these are misnomers because the cholesterol itself is not any different in each case. It is the composition of the lipoprotein that determines how the cholesterol is handled in the body.

Ratio of LDL to HDL		
Risk	Men	Women
Very low (half average)	1.0	1.5
Average risk	3.6	3.2
Moderate risk (2X average risk)	6.3	5.0
High (3X average risk)	8.0	6.1

How to increase HDL (the good cholesterol*)	How to decrease LDL (the bad cholesterol*)
1. Exercise	1. Decrease saturated fat intake
2. Stop smoking	2. Increase dietary fibre
3. Reduce weight	3. Increase aerobic exercise

2. Using the BMI, calculate the minimum and maximum weight at which a 1.85 m tall man would be considered:

(a) Overweight: _____

(c) Obese: _____

(b) Normal weight: _____

(d) Underweight: _____

3. Discuss the possible links between diet and coronary heart disease: _____

_____

_____

_____

4. (a) Explain the link between high LDL:HDL ratio and the risk of cardiovascular disease: _____

_____

_____

_____

(b) Explain why this ratio is more important to medical practitioners than total blood cholesterol *per se*:

_____

(c) Suggest how this ratio could be lowered in at-risk individuals: _____

_____

Cardiovascular Disease

Cardiovascular disease (CVD) is a term describing all diseases involving the heart and blood vessels. It includes coronary heart disease (CHD), atherosclerosis, hypertension (high blood pressure), peripheral vascular disease, stroke, and congenital heart disorders. CVD is responsible for 20% of all deaths worldwide and is the principal cause of deaths in developed countries. In the UK, deaths due to CVD have been declining since the 1970s due to better prevention and treatment. Despite this, CVD is still the leading cause of mortality, and accounted for 37% of all deaths in 2004. The continued prevalence of CVD is of considerable public health concern, particularly as many of the **risk factors** involved, such as cigarette smoking, obesity, and high blood cholesterol, are controllable. Uncontrollable risk factors include advancing age, gender, and heredity.

Cardiovascular Diseases

Atherosclerosis: Atherosclerosis (sometimes called hardening of the arteries or ischaemic heart disease), is a disease of the arteries caused by **atheroma** (deposits of fats and cholesterol) on the inner walls of the arteries. The lining of the arteries degenerates due to the accumulation of fat and plaques. Atheroma eventually restricts blood flow through the arteries and increases the risk of blood clot formation (**thrombosis**). Complications arising as a result of atherosclerosis include heart attack (**infarction**), stroke and gangrene.

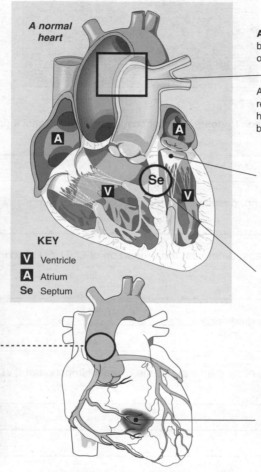

A normal heart

KEY

V Ventricle
A Atrium
Se Septum

Aortic aneurysm: A ballooning and weakening of the wall of the aorta.

Aneurysms usually result from generalised heart disease and high blood pressure.

Valve defects: Unusual heart sounds (murmurs) can result when a valve (often the mitral valve) does not close properly, allowing blood to bubble back into the atria. Valve defects may be congenital (present at birth) but they can also occur as a result of rheumatic fever.

Septal defects: These hole-in-the-heart congenital defects occur where the dividing wall (**septum**) between the left and right sides of the heart is not closed. These defects may occur between the atria or the ventricles, and are sometimes combined with valve problems.

Myocardial infarction (*heart attack*): Occurs when an area of the heart is deprived of blood supply resulting in tissue damage or death. It is the major cause of death in developed countries. Symptoms of infarction include a sudden onset of chest pain, breathlessness, nausea, and cold clammy skin. Damage to the heart may be so severe that it leads to heart failure and even death (myocardial infarction is fatal within 20 days in 40 to 50% of all cases).

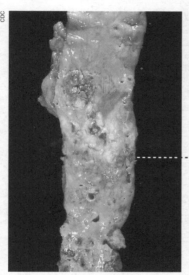

This aorta has been opened lengthwise to reveal the inner surface studded with the lesions of atherosclerosis.

Restricted supply of blood to heart muscle resulting in myocardial infarction

Food and Health

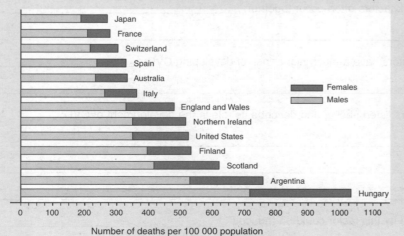

Death rates from CVD for males and females from selected countries (2001)

Japan
France
Switzerland
Spain
Australia
Italy
England and Wales
Northern Ireland
United States
Finland
Scotland
Argentina
Hungary

■ Females
■ Males

0   100   200   300   400   500   600   700   800   900   1000   1100

Number of deaths per 100 000 population

The graph shows the death rate (per 100 000 population) attributable to cardiovascular disease (CVD) in both men and women in selected countries. Data are current to 2001. The rate of CVD is lowest in Japan and France and high in Eastern Europe.

There are many suggested causes for these differences. One study by the World Health Organisation (WHO) stated that variation between countries can be primarily attributed to diet (i.e. saturated fat, salt, vitamin and antioxidant content). The WHO study also found strong north-south gradients in both fruit and vegetable consumption between countries. For example, people in England consumed twice as much fruit and one third more vegetables than those living in Northern Ireland.

Source for data and graph: WHO

Related activities: Malnutrition and Obesity, Diseases Caused By Smoking

RDA 3

Cardiovascular disease is suspected in people who experience breathlessness, chest pain, or palpitations during exercise, particularly if they also fall into a high-risk category (see table, far right).

Diagnosis of *coronary artery disease* and *angina pectoris* can be made from the results of a **cardiac exercise tolerance test**. During the test, the patient (photo, right) is attached to an electrocardiograph (ECG) machine, which records the electrical activity of the heart during exercise on a treadmill. Angina (chest pain caused by insufficient blood supply to the heart) is confirmed when there are specific changes in the ECG wave patterns as the intensity of exercise is increased.

Diagnosing Cardiovascular Disease

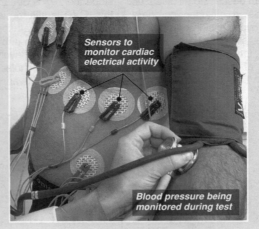

Sensors to monitor cardiac electrical activity

Blood pressure being monitored during test

Risk factors for CVD

- High blood pressure
- Cigarette smoking
- High blood cholesterol
- Obesity
- Type 2 diabetes mellitus
- High achiever personality
- Environmental stress
- Sedentary lifestyle

Controllable risk factors in the development of cardiovascular disease are listed above. The risks associated with any genetic predisposition to CVD are not included in the list.

1. Explain briefly how atherosclerosis leads to death of heart tissue and a heart attack (infarct): _____

_____

_____

2. Mortality attributable to CVD is declining, despite its increasing prevalence. Suggest why: _____

_____

3. (a) From the graph on the previous page, determine the proportion of CVD deaths occurring in females and males in England and Wales:

Females: _____   Males: _____

(b) Suggest a possible reason for this difference: _____

_____

4. Suggest possible alternative reasons, other than diet, for the global distribution of CVD: _____

_____

_____

_____

5. (a) Distinguish between controllable and uncontrollable risk factors in the development of CVD: _____

_____

_____

(b) Suggest why some of the controllable risk factors often occur together: _____

_____

(c) Explain why patients with several risk factors have a much higher risk of developing CVD: _____

_____

6. (a) Choose one of the controllable risk factors listed above, and describe its role in the development of CVD:

_____

_____

_____

(b) Suggest how the risk (of CVD) presented by this factor could be reduced: _____

_____

The Green Revolution

Since the 1950s, most increases in global food production have come from increased yields per unit area of cropland rather than farming more land. The initial **green revolution** increased the intensity and frequency of cropping, using high inputs of fertilisers, pesticides, and water to increase yields in improved varieties. The **second green revolution** began in the 1960s and improved production by further developing high yielding crop varieties. The countries whose crop yields per unit of land area have increased during the two green revolutions are illustrated below. Several

agricultural research centres and **seed** or **gene banks** also play a key role in developing high yielding crop varieties. Most of the world's gene banks store the seeds of the hundred or so plant species that collectively provide approximately 90% of the food consumed by humans. However, some banks are also storing the seeds of species threatened with extinction or a loss of genetic diversity. Producing more food on less land is an important way of protecting biodiversity by saving large areas of natural habitat from being used to grow food.

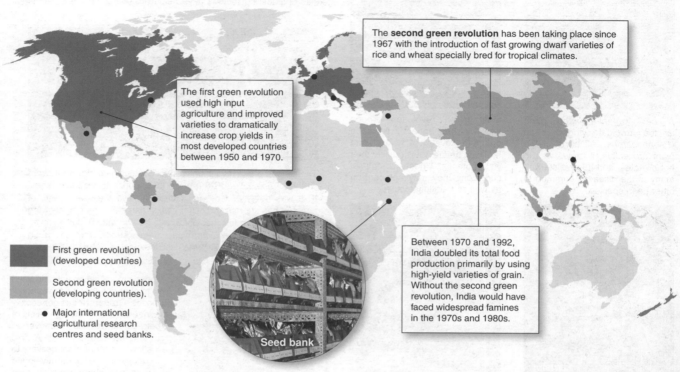

The **second green revolution** has been taking place since 1967 with the introduction of fast growing dwarf varieties of rice and wheat specially bred for tropical climates.

The first green revolution used high input agriculture and improved varieties to dramatically increase crop yields in most developed countries between 1950 and 1970.

Between 1970 and 1992, India doubled its total food production primarily by using high-yield varieties of grain. Without the second green revolution, India would have faced widespread famines in the 1970s and 1980s.

- ■ First green revolution (developed countries)
- ■ Second green revolution (developing countries).
- ● Major international agricultural research centres and seed banks.

Seed bank

Food and Health

High-input, intensive agriculture uses large amounts of fossil fuel energy, water, commercial inorganic fertilisers, and pesticides to produce large quantities of single crops (monocultures) from relatively small areas of land. At some point though, outputs diminish or even decline.

There are approximately 30 000 plant species with parts suitable for human consumption, but just three grain crops (wheat, rice, and corn) provide more than half the calories the world's population consumes. These crops have been the focus of the second green revolution.

Increased yields from industrialised agriculture depend on the extensive use of fossil fuels to run machinery, produce and apply fertilisers and pesticides, and pump water for irrigation. Since 1950, the use of fossil fuels in agriculture has increased four-fold.

1. Describe how the technologies of the first and second green revolutions differ: _____

_____

_____

_____

_____

_____

_____

Related activities: Global Human Nutrition, Selective Breeding in Crop Plants
Web links: Green Revolution, FAO: Crop and Grasslands Service

A 2

The second green revolution (also called the **gene revolution**) is based on further developments in **selective breeding** and **genetic engineering**. It has grown rapidly in scope and importance since it began in 1967. Initially, it involved the development of fast growing, high yielding varieties of rice, corn, and wheat, which were specially bred for tropical and subtropical climates to meet global food demand. More recently, genetically modified seeds have been used to create plants with higher yields and specific tolerances (e.g. pest resistance, herbicide tolerance, or drought tolerance). GM seed is also used to improve the nutritional quality of crops (e.g. by increasing protein or vitamin levels), or to produce plants for edible vaccine delivery.

Recent Crop Developments

Winged bean

Upland rice

A new potential crop plant is the tropical winged bean (*Psophocarpus*). All parts of the plant are edible, it grows well in hot climates, and it is resistant to many of the diseases common to other bean species.

Most green revolution breeds are "high-responders", requiring optimum levels of water and fertiliser before they realise their yield potential. Under sub-optimal conditions they may not perform as well as traditional varieties.

Wheat

Maize

Improvements in crop production have come from the modification of a few, well known species. Future research aims to maintain genetic diversity in high-yielding, disease resistant varieties.

A century ago, yields of maize (corn) in the USA were around 25 bushels per acre. In 1999, yields from hybrid maize were five to ten times this, depending on the growing conditions.

Improving Rice Crops

Rice is the world's second most important cereal crop, providing both a food and an income source to millions of people worldwide. Traditional rice strains lack many of the essential vitamins and minerals required by humans for good health and are susceptible to crop failure and low yields if not tended carefully. Advances in plant breeding, biotechnology, and genetic engineering (below) have helped to overcome these problems.

IR-8 rice

The second green revolution produced a high-yielding, semi-dwarf variety of rice called **IR-8** (above) in response to food shortages. IR-8 was developed by cross breeding two parental strains of rice and has shorter and stiffer stalks than either parent, allowing the plant to support heavier grain heads without falling over. More recently, a new improved variety, '**super rice**' has been developed to replace IR-8. Yields are expected to be 20% higher.

Genetic modification is being used to alter rice for a wide variety of purposes. **Golden rice** is genetically engineered to contain high levels of beta-carotene, which is converted in the body to vitamin A. This allows better nutrient delivery to people in poor underdeveloped countries where rice is the food staple. Other companies are focusing on improving the resistance of rice crops to insects, bacteria, and herbicides, improving yields, or delivering edible hepatitis and cholera vaccines in the rice.

2. Using examples, explain how the technologies of the second green revolution are being used to:

(a) Improve crop yields: _____

_____

_____

(b) Improve the nutritional quality of crops: _____

_____

_____

3. (a) Explain how countries currently suffering from food shortages might benefit from recent crop developments:

_____

_____

_____

(b) Describe the constraints that might exist on developing countries taking advantage of these potential benefits:

_____

_____

Selective Breeding in Crop Plants

Most agricultural plants and animals have undergone **selective breeding** (artificial selection), resulting in an astounding range of phenotypic variation over a relatively short period of time. Selective breeding involves breeding from the individuals with the most desirable phenotypes (e.g. high yield) to alter the average phenotype in the species. Wheat has been cultivated for more than 9000 years and has undergone many changes during the process of its domestication (below). Wheat's evolution involved

two natural hybridisation events, accompanied by **polyploidy**. **Hybrids** are the offspring of genetically dissimilar parents and are important because they recombine the genetic characteristics of parental lines and show increased **heterozygosity**. This is associated with greater adaptability, survival, growth, and fertility in the offspring; a phenomenon known as **hybrid vigour**. Selective breeding is used to increase yield, and to produce disease and pest resistant crops (bottom).

Polyploidy Events in the Evolution of Wheat

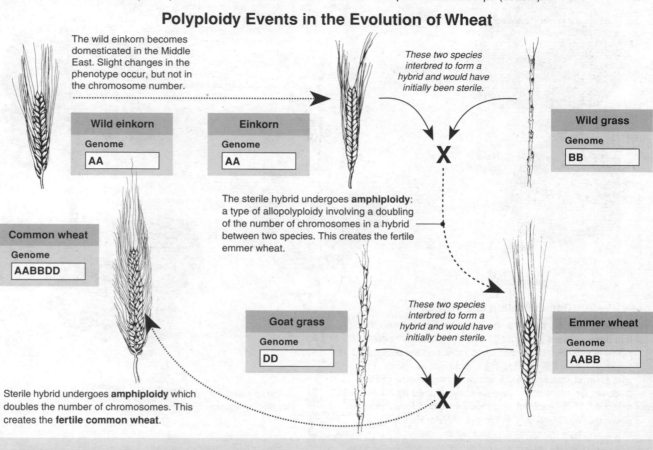

The wild einkorn becomes domesticated in the Middle East. Slight changes in the phenotype occur, but not in the chromosome number.

These two species interbred to form a hybrid and would have initially been sterile.

Wild einkorn
Genome
AA

Einkorn
Genome
AA

Wild grass
Genome
BB

The sterile hybrid undergoes **amphiploidy**: a type of allopolyploidy involving a doubling of the number of chromosomes in a hybrid between two species. This creates the fertile emmer wheat.

Common wheat
Genome
AABBDD

These two species interbred to form a hybrid and would have initially been sterile.

Goat grass
Genome
DD

Emmer wheat
Genome
AABB

Sterile hybrid undergoes **amphiploidy** which doubles the number of chromosomes. This creates the **fertile common wheat**.

Food and Health

Breeding programmes around the world are developing apples resistant to the bacterial disease that causes fireblight (above).

Modern wheat (above) has been selected for its non shattering heads, high yield, and high gluten (protein) content.

Hybrid corn varieties have been bred to minimise harm inflicted by insect pests such as the corn rootworm (above).

1. Explain how a farmer thousands of years ago was able to improve the phenotypic character of a cereal crop:

_____

_____

_____

_____

_____

Related activities: The Green Revolution, Selective Breeding in Animals

RA 2

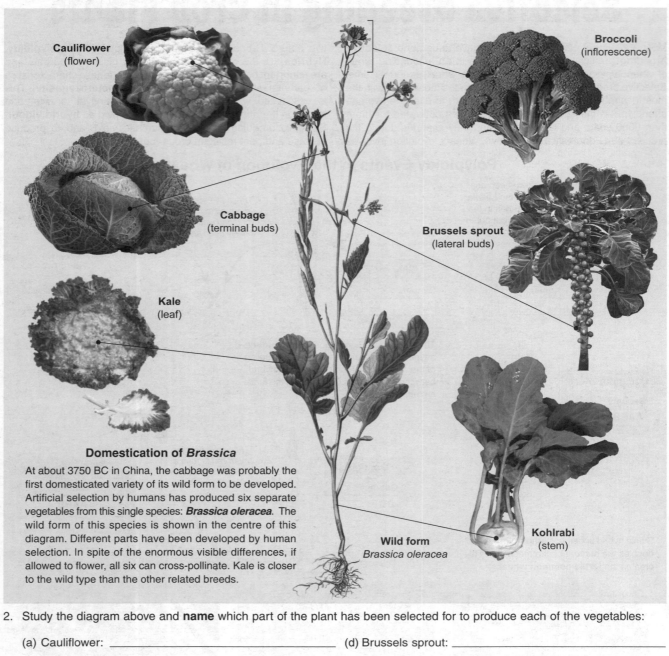

Cauliflower
(flower)

Broccoli
(inflorescence)

Cabbage
(terminal buds)

Brussels sprout
(lateral buds)

Kale
(leaf)

Domestication of *Brassica*

At about 3750 BC in China, the cabbage was probably the first domesticated variety of its wild form to be developed. Artificial selection by humans has produced six separate vegetables from this single species: ***Brassica oleracea***. The wild form of this species is shown in the centre of this diagram. Different parts have been developed by human selection. In spite of the enormous visible differences, if allowed to flower, all six can cross-pollinate. Kale is closer to the wild type than the other related breeds.

Wild form
Brassica oleracea

Kohlrabi
(stem)

2. Study the diagram above and **name** which part of the plant has been selected for to produce each of the vegetables:

(a) Cauliflower: _____   (d) Brussels sprout: _____

(b) Kale: _____   (e) Cabbage: _____

(c) Broccoli: _____   (f) Kohlrabi: _____

3. Describe the feature of these vegetables that suggests they are members of the same species: _____

_____

4. Human selection pressures can also influence the development of characteristics in 'unwanted' species. Suggest how human weed control measures may inadvertently select for weed plants that have a resistance to the measures:

_____

_____

5. Describe two phenotypic characteristics that might be desirable in a cereal crop plant and explain your choice:

(a) _____

_____

(b) _____

_____

Selective Breeding in Animals

The domestication of livestock has a long history dating back at least 8000 years. Today's important stock breeds were all derived from wild ancestors that were domesticated by humans who then used **selective breeding** to produce livestock to meet specific requirements. Selective breeding of domesticated animals involves identifying desirable qualities (e.g. high wool production or meat yield), and breeding together individuals with those qualities so the trait is reliably passed on. Practices such as **inbreeding**, **line-breeding**, and **outcrossing** are used to select and 'fix' desirable traits in varieties. Today, modern breeding techniques often employ reproductive technologies, such as

artificial insemination, so that the desirable characteristics of one male can be passed on to many females. These new technologies refine the selection process and increase the rate at which stock improvements are made. Rates are predicted to accelerate further as new technologies, such as genomic selection, become more widely available and less costly. Producing highly inbred lines of animals with specific traits can have disadvantages however. Homozygosity for a number of desirable traits can cause physiological or physical problems to the animal itself. For example, animals bred specifically for rapid weight gain often grow so fast that they have skeletal and muscular difficulties.

The Origin of Domestic Animals

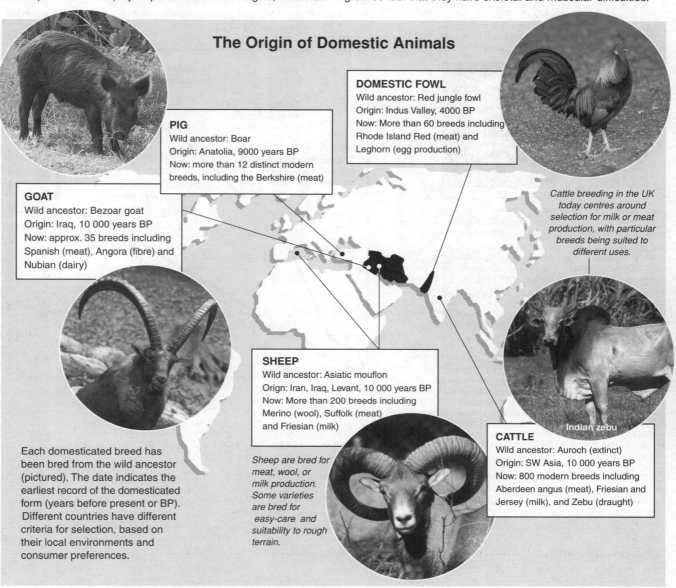

PIG
Wild ancestor: Boar
Origin: Anatolia, 9000 years BP
Now: more than 12 distinct modern breeds, including the Berkshire (meat)

DOMESTIC FOWL
Wild ancestor: Red jungle fowl
Origin: Indus Valley, 4000 BP
Now: More than 60 breeds including Rhode Island Red (meat) and Leghorn (egg production)

GOAT
Wild ancestor: Bezoar goat
Origin: Iraq, 10 000 years BP
Now: approx. 35 breeds including Spanish (meat), Angora (fibre) and Nubian (dairy)

Cattle breeding in the UK today centres around selection for milk or meat production, with particular breeds being suited to different uses.

SHEEP
Wild ancestor: Asiatic mouflon
Origin: Iran, Iraq, Levant, 10 000 years BP
Now: More than 200 breeds including Merino (wool), Suffolk (meat) and Friesian (milk)

Indian zebu

CATTLE
Wild ancestor: Auroch (extinct)
Origin: SW Asia, 10 000 years BP
Now: 800 modern breeds including Aberdeen angus (meat), Friesian and Jersey (milk), and Zebu (draught)

Each domesticated breed has been bred from the wild ancestor (pictured). The date indicates the earliest record of the domesticated form (years before present or BP). Different countries have different criteria for selection, based on their local environments and consumer preferences.

Sheep are bred for meat, wool, or milk production. Some varieties are bred for easy-care and suitability to rough terrain.

Food and Health

1. Distinguish between inbreeding and out-crossing, explaining the significance of each technique in selective breeding:

_____

_____

_____

_____

2. Describe the contribution that new reproductive technologies are making to selective breeding:

_____

_____

Related activities: Selective Breeding in Crop Plants

RA 2

Beef breeds: Simmental, Aberdeen-Angus, Hereford (above), Galloway, Charolais. Consumer demand has led to the shift towards continental breeds such as Charolais because they are large, with a high proportion of lean muscle. **Desirable traits**: high muscle to bone ratio, rapid growth and weight gain, hardy, easy calving, docile temperament.

Dairy breeds: Jersey, Friesian (above), Holstein, Aryshire. **Desirable traits**: high yield of milk with high butterfat, milking speed, docile temperament, and udder characteristics such as teat placement.

Special breeds: Some cattle are bred for their suitability for climate or terrain. Scottish highland cattle (above) are a hardy, long coated breed and produce well where other breeds cannot thrive.

Artificial Selection and Genetic Gain in Cattle

Cattle are selected on the basis of particular desirable traits (e.g. milk fat or muscle mass). Most of the genetic improvement in dairy cattle has relied on selection of high quality progeny from proven stock and extensive use of superior sires through artificial insemination (AI). In beef cattle, AI is useful for introducing new breeds.

Improved breeding techniques accelerate the **genetic gain**, i.e. the gain toward the desirable phenotype of a **breed**. The graph (below) illustrates the predicted gains based on artificial insemination and standard selection techniques (based on criteria such as production or temperament). These are compared with the predicted gains using breeding values and various reproductive technologies such as embryo multiplication and transfer (EMT) of standard and transgenic stock, marker (gene) assisted selection, and sib-selection (selecting bulls on the basis of their sisters performance).

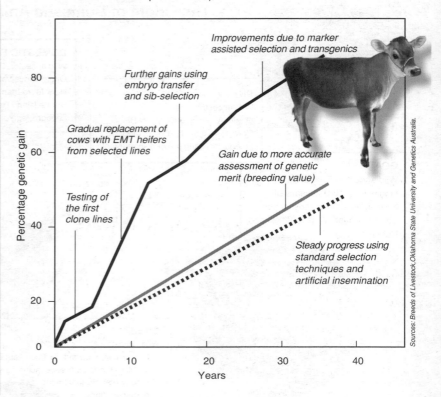

3. Describe some of the positive and negative outcomes of selective breeding in domestic animals: _____

_____

_____

_____

_____

_____

4. Identify the two methods by which most of the genetic progress in dairy cattle has been achieved:

(a) _____ (b) _____

5. Explain what is meant by the term **genetic gain** as it applies to livestock breeding: _____

_____

_____

6. Suggest why mixed breeds, such as Hereford-Friesian crosses, are popular for mixed beef/milk production:

_____

_____

Producing Food With Microorganisms

Bacteria and fungi are used extensively in many aspects of food technology. The microorganisms mainly act as production agents. They are used to turn ingredients into food, or to modify food ingredients, rather than as a raw ingredient itself. Microorganisms have traditionally been used in the production of fermented foods: alcoholic beverages, bread, and fermented dairy products. The control and efficiency of these uses have been greatly refined in recent times. The advent of genetic engineering has increased the range of microbial products available and has provided alternative sources for products that were once available only through expensive or wasteful means (e.g. production of the enzyme chymosin). Some microorganisms, such as the yeast *Saccharomyces cerevisiae*, are used as food additives because they contain several vitamins essential to good health. Future applications include the wider use of genetically engineered microbes in crop improvement.

Microorganisms in the Food Industry

Cheese production uses cultures of lactic acid bacteria (e.g. *Streptococcus* spp.) and genetically engineered microbial rennin, which is added to curd the milk protein. Microbial activity occurs at several stages to produce characteristic flavours and textures.

Yoghurt is produced from milk by the action of lactic acid bacteria particularly *Lactobacillus bulgaricus* and *Streptococcus thermophilus*. These bacteria break down milk proteins into peptides.

Soy sauce (shoyu): Filamentous fungi (*Aspergillus soyae* and *A.oryzeae*) digest soy proteins and solids. The culture is fermented in the presence of lactic acid bacteria (*Lactobacillus* spp.) and acid tolerant yeast (e.g. *Torulopsis*) over a year or more.

Bread (leavened): The sugars in the dough are fermented by the yeast, *Saccharomyces cerevisiae*, producing alcohol and CO_2. The gas causes the dough to rise, while the alcohol is converted to flavour compounds during baking.

Beer and wine: The sugars in fruits (wine) or grains (beers) are fermented by yeast (e.g. *Saccharomyces carlsbergensis*, *S. cerevisiae*) to alcohol. Beer production first requires a malting process to convert starches in the grain to fermentable sugars.

Sauerkraut production involves the fermentation of cabbage. The initial fermentation involves lactic acid bacteria (*Leuconostoc mesenteroides* and *Enterobacter cloacae*), followed by acid production with *Lactobacillus plantarum*.

Vinegar production uses cultures of acetic acid bacteria (e.g. *Acetobacter* and *Gluconobacter*). When you leave wine exposed to oxygen, these bacteria convert the alcoholic brew (ethanol) to ethanoic acid (vinegar).

Vitamins and amino acids are dietary supplements produced as by-products of faulty or altered microbial metabolism. Examples include lysine and vitamin B_{12}. Microbial species used include: *Corynebacterium glutamicum*, *Pseudomonas*, *Propionibacterium*.

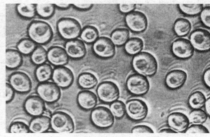

Commercial production of microorganisms: Baker's yeast (*Saccharomyces cerevisiae*, above) is sold for both industrial use and home brewing and baking. *Bacillus thuringiensis* is a widely used biological pest control agent. Nitrogen fixing bacteria (e.g. *Rhizobium*) are used to enhance plant nutrition.

Food and Health

1. Explain what is meant by the term **industrial microbiology**: _____

_____

2. Briefly describe two examples of how microorganisms are used for the production of alcoholic beverages:

_____

_____

_____

_____

Problems with Microorganisms in Food Technology

Many microorganisms used in food production are grown in **biofermenters** (below). There are a number of problems associated with these large scale fermentations, including providing adequate supply of oxygen and nutrients, maintaining a constant temperature and pH, and removing wastes as they build up so growth is not inhibited. Rigorous testing using scale models must be carried out to ensure that the problems associated with scaling up have been eliminated.

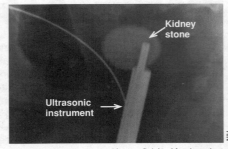

If bacteria are not removed from a finished food product, their high nucleic acid content can cause elevated **uric acid** levels. This can result in a variety of painful diseases such as gout or **kidney stones** (above), which form when uric acid crystallises in the kidney.

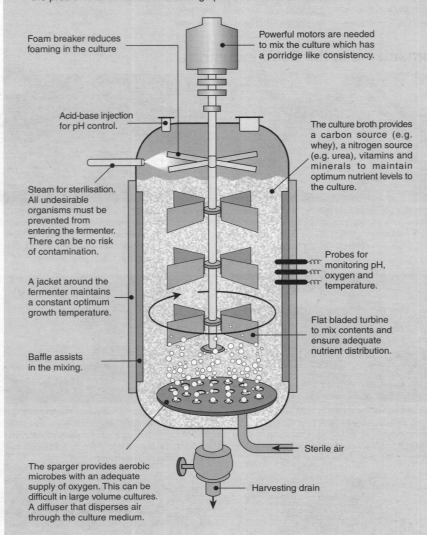

Foam breaker reduces foaming in the culture

Powerful motors are needed to mix the culture which has a porridge like consistency.

Acid-base injection for pH control.

The culture broth provides a carbon source (e.g. whey), a nitrogen source (e.g. urea), vitamins and minerals to maintain optimum nutrient levels to the culture.

Steam for sterilisation. All undesirable organisms must be prevented from entering the fermenter. There can be no risk of contamination.

A jacket around the fermenter maintains a constant optimum growth temperature.

Probes for monitoring pH, oxygen and temperature.

Baffle assists in the mixing.

Flat bladed turbine to mix contents and ensure adequate nutrient distribution.

Sterile air

The sparger provides aerobic microbes with an adequate supply of oxygen. This can be difficult in large volume cultures. A diffuser that disperses air through the culture medium.

Harvesting drain

Many consumers have a negative perception of food produced using microbes, especially GMOs. The safety and ethics of GMO food are often questioned and can sway consumer choice when it comes to purchasing food products. In the EU, food containing GMOs or produced from GM ingredients must be labelled.

Microbial chymosin, used in the cheese making process to coagulate the milk, often produces bitter cheeses. **Genetically engineered chymosin** does not contain all the enzymes found in natural calf rennet, so can require additional enzymes to be added to produce a realistic flavour profile.

3. Historically, cheese-making has used calf rennet (a complex of enzymes from the stomach of unweaned calves) to coagulate the milk. Genetically engineered chymosin (rennin) is now most often used. Bearing this in mind, discuss:

   (a) Some advantages of using genetically modified chymosin: _____

   _____

   _____

   (b) Some disadvantages of using genetically modified chymosin: _____

   _____

   _____

4. Suggest why consumers may be more accepting of foods produced using yeast, rather than those made using bacteria:

   _____

   _____

   _____

   _____

Increasing Food Production

The accelerating demands of the world's population on food resources creates a need to produce more food, more quickly, at minimal cost. For the most part, this has involved intensive, industrialised agricultural systems, where high inputs of energy are used to obtain high yields per unit of land farmed. Such systems apply not just to crop plants, but to animals too, which are raised to slaughter weight at high densities in confined areas (a technique called **factory farming**). Producing food from a limited amount of land presents several challenges: to maximise yield while minimising losses to disease and pests, to ensure sustainability of the practice, and (in the case of animals) to meet certain standards of welfare and safety. Intensive agriculture makes use of chemical pesticides and fertilisers, as well as antibiotics and hormones to achieve these aims, often with deleterious effects on the environment and on crop and animal health. An alternative approach to meeting global food demands is to develop sustainable farming systems based on sound crop and animal management practices. Such systems make use of organic fertilisers and natural pest controls to achieve profitable, efficient food production that is sustainable in the long term.

One View: Intensive Farming Practices

Antibiotics are used in the intensive farming of **poultry** for egg and meat production. Proponents regard antibiotics as an important management tool to prevent, control, and treat disease, allowing farmers to raise healthy animals and produce safe food.

The application of inorganic fertilisers has been a major factor in the increased yields of industrialised agriculture. Excessive application can be detrimental however, leading to enrichment of water bodies and contamination of groundwater.

Fertilisers can be sprayed using aerial topdressing in inaccessible areas.

Clearing land of trees for agriculture can lead to slope instability, soil erosion, and land degradation.

Pesticides and fungicides are used extensively to control crop pests and diseases in industrialised agriculture. Indiscriminate use of these leads to increased resistance to commonly used chemicals and contamination of land and water.

Antibiotics are used to treat diseases such as mastitis in dairy cattle. Milk must be withheld until all antibiotic residues have disappeared.

Feedlots are a type of confined animal feeding operation which is used for rapidly feeding livestock, notably cattle (above left), up to slaughter weight. Diet for stock in feedlots are very dense in energy to encourage rapid growth and deposition of fat in the meat (marbling). As in many forms of factory farming, antibiotics are used to combat disease in the crowded environment.

Food and Health

1. Discuss the use of chemical pesticides and fertilisers to increase crop yields in intensive systems. In your discussion, include reference to the advantages and disadvantages of such applications:

_____

_____

_____

2. Animals raised for food production in intensive systems (e.g. feedlot cattle, and factory farmed pigs and poultry) are often supplied with antibiotics at low doses in the feed:

(a) Explain the benefits of this practice to production: _____

_____

(b) Discuss the environmental, health, and animal welfare issues associated with this practice: _____

_____

_____

_____

_____

Related activities: The Green Revolution
Web links: Factory Farming

A 2

An Alternative View: Sustainability and Diversity

Sustainable agricultural practices are economically viable and environmentally sound. Increasingly, farmers are investigating methods by which they can earn a reasonable living from the land, while remaining less reliant on government subsidies, and petroleum and chemical inputs. As in intensive farming, there are many approaches to sustainable agriculture. That pictured here just one.

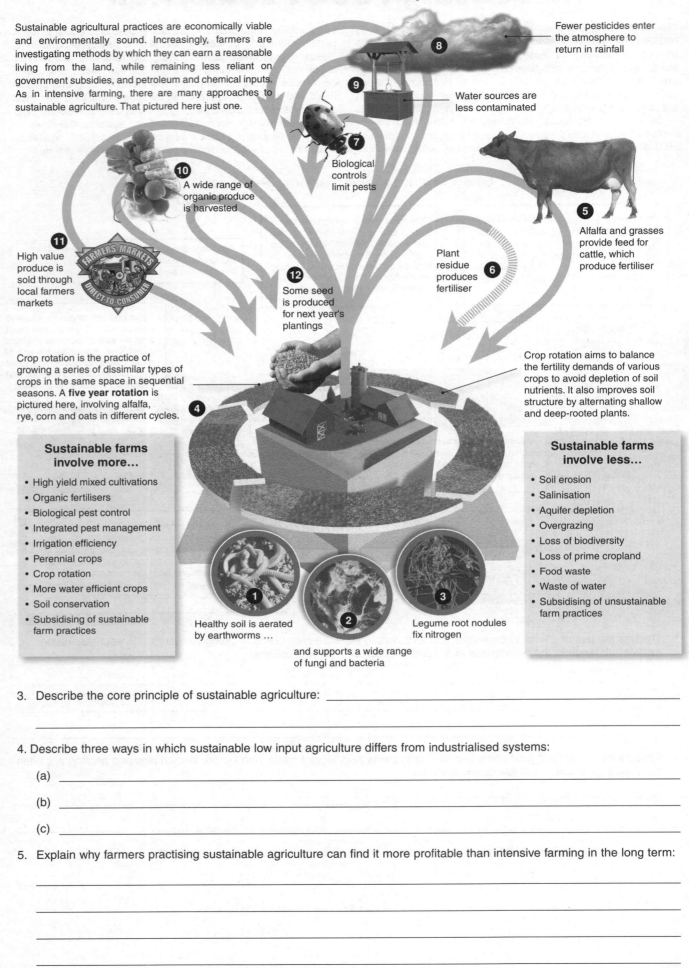

8 Fewer pesticides enter the atmosphere to return in rainfall

9

7 Biological controls limit pests

Water sources are less contaminated

5 Alfalfa and grasses provide feed for cattle, which produce fertiliser

10 A wide range of organic produce is harvested

11 High value produce is sold through local farmers markets

FARMERS MARKETS DIRECT-TO-CONSUMER

6 Plant residue produces fertiliser

12 Some seed is produced for next year's plantings

Crop rotation is the practice of growing a series of dissimilar types of crops in the same space in sequential seasons. A **five year rotation** is pictured here, involving alfalfa, rye, corn and oats in different cycles.

4

Crop rotation aims to balance the fertility demands of various crops to avoid depletion of soil nutrients. It also improves soil structure by alternating shallow and deep-rooted plants.

Sustainable farms involve more...

- High yield mixed cultivations
- Organic fertilisers
- Biological pest control
- Integrated pest management
- Irrigation efficiency
- Perennial crops
- Crop rotation
- More water efficient crops
- Soil conservation
- Subsidising of sustainable farm practices

Sustainable farms involve less...

- Soil erosion
- Salinisation
- Aquifer depletion
- Overgrazing
- Loss of biodiversity
- Loss of prime cropland
- Food waste
- Waste of water
- Subsidising of unsustainable farm practices

1 Healthy soil is aerated by earthworms ...

2 and supports a wide range of fungi and bacteria

3 Legume root nodules fix nitrogen

3. Describe the core principle of sustainable agriculture: _____
_____

4. Describe three ways in which sustainable low input agriculture differs from industrialised systems:

(a) _____

(b) _____

(c) _____

5. Explain why farmers practising sustainable agriculture can find it more profitable than intensive farming in the long term:

_____

_____

_____

_____

Food Preservation

Without intervention, **food spoilage** begins as soon as an item is picked, slaughtered, or manufactured. While many food spoilage factors (bruising, oxidation, humidity) alter the nutritional quality and appearance (texture, colour, flavour) of food, other spoilage factors can have more serious consequences. The consumption of food spoiled by the presence of microbes or their toxins, could cause illness, or even death, from **food poisoning**. For this

reason, it is vital that perishable foods be preserved to prevent microbial growth and extend their shelf life. **Food preservation** describes any process that prevents or slows food spoilage. Basic storage and handling techniques often safeguard the flavour and appearance of food, but more advanced techniques (below) are required to ensure that food stored for a prolonged period remains safe for human consumption.

Preparing Korean kimchi (pickled vegetables)

Pickling preserves food by lowering the pH to below 4.6 and killing the microbes that cannot survive the acidic environment. There are two pickling methods. The first involves **adding salt** and allowing an anaerobic fermentation by the native bacteria (e.g. *Lactobacillus*). This fermentation produces lactic acid, which lowers the pH and inhibits the growth of harmful microbes. The second method involves storing the food in a prepared **acid solution**, often vinegar (acetic acid) to achieve the lower pH.

Preserving food in a **sugar syrup** produces a high osmotic pressure environment. Microbial cells have a lower osmotic pressure than the medium, so water leaves their cells causing cell dehydration and death. Fruits are commonly preserved in this manner.

Why preserve food?
Food may harbour pathogenic organisms such as *Salmonella* and *Campylobacter* (above). Food preservation techniques aim to reduce or destroy the number of harmful microbes, increasing the food's shelf life and lowering the risk of food poisoning on consumption.

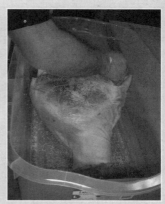

Curing ham by adding salt

Adding **salt** to food draws moisture out from the food by osmosis. The food environment becomes drier, reducing the available water and thereby inhibiting microbial growth. Salt concentrations of up to 20% are required for effective preservation. Meat, such as pork products (above), are often preserved in this way.

HTST equipment for pasteurising

Heat treatments are used with liquid food products such as milk and fruit juice to logarithmically reduce (but not eliminate) the numbers of microorganisms present. High temperature short time (HTST) treatments involve heating the product to 71.7°C for 15-20 seconds. The more extreme ultra-heat treatment (UHT) process, which also kills bacterial spores, requires heating to 135°C for 1-2 seconds before packaging into sterile containers. UHT products have a shelf life of 6-9 months, compared with up to two weeks for a HTST treated product.

Food irradiation uses ionising radiation (electron beams, X-rays, or gamma rays) to destroy microbes on food. Irradiation kills microorganisms by damaging their DNA, but it does not destroy prions or toxins. Irradiation is commonly used to preserve fruit, vegetables, and spices but this must be clearly indicated (above).

Freezing turns the water contained within food into ice, reducing its water activity. With no available water present, microbial growth is inhibited. Freezing is not a method of sterilisation, and does not necessarily kill microbes, but the very low temperature (-18°C) slows down most chemical reactions, prolonging the shelf life of frozen food to several months. Fruit, vegetables (above), meat, fish, and shellfish are commonly frozen.

1. Describe a benefit and a disadvantage of using heat treatments to prolong the shelf life of a food product:

   (a) Benefit: _____

   (b) Disadvantage: _____

2. Explain how high salt and sugar act to prolong the shelf life of perishable foods: _____
_____
_____
_____

Food and Health

Defence and the Immune System

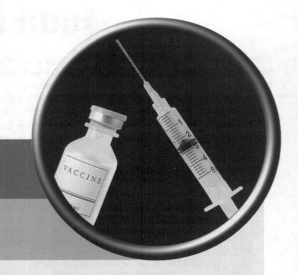

OCR: Unit F212, Module 2: Food and Health

2.2.2 (e)-(o): Defences against disease

CIE: CORE SYLLABUS

J: Immunity

Learning Objectives

□ 1. Compile your own glossary from the **KEY WORDS** displayed in **bold type** in the learning objectives below.

Recognising Self and Non-self *(pages 214-215)*

□ 2. Explain how a body is able to distinguish between self and non-self and comment on the importance of this.

□ 3. Appreciate the role of the **major histocompatibility complex (MHC)** in self-recognition and in determining tissue compatibility in transplant recipients.

□ 4. Explain the basis of the **Rh** and **ABO blood group systems** in humans. Explain what is meant by **agglutination** and how this reaction forms the basis of blood grouping. Explain the consequences of blood type incompatibility in **blood transfusions**.

Defence Mechanisms *(page 216)*

□ 5. Describe the role of **blood clotting** in the resistance of the body to infection by sealing off damage and restricting invasion of the tissues by microorganisms.

Non-specific defences *(pages 217-221)*

□ 6. Explain what is meant by a **non-specific defence mechanism**. Distinguish between first and second lines of defence. Describe the nature and role of each of the following in protecting against pathogens:
   • Skin (including sweat and sebum production)
   • Mucus-secreting and ciliated membranes
   • Body secretions (tears, urine, saliva, gastric juice)
   • Natural anti-bacterial and anti-viral proteins such as **interferon** and **complement**
   • The **inflammatory response**, **fever**, and cell death
   • **Phagocytosis**

□ 7. Recognise the term phagocyte as referring to any of a number of phagocytic leucocytes (e.g. macrophages).

Specific defences *(pages 217, 222, 227)*

□ 8. Describe the role of **specific resistance** in body's resistance to infection. Contrast specific and non-specific defences in terms of time for activation and action towards a pathogen.

□ 9. Explain how the **immune response** involves recognition and response to foreign material. Explain the significance of the immune system having both **specificity** and **memory**. Providing examples, distinguish between **naturally acquired** and **artificially acquired immunity** and between active and passive immunity. Compare the duration of the immunity gained by active and passive means.

□ 10. Recognise the role of the **lymphatic system** in the production and transport of leucocytes.

The Immune System *(pages 223-226)*

□ 11. Distinguish between: **cell-mediated immunity** and **humoral (antibody-mediated) immunity**.

□ 12. Recall that other types of white blood cells are involved in non-specific defence mechanisms.

□ 13. Explain the role of the **thymus** in the immune response. Describe the nature, origin, and role of **macrophages** (a type of phagocyte). Appreciate the role of macrophages in processing and presenting foreign antigens and in stimulating lymphocyte activity.

□ 14. Explain the origin and maturation of **B lymphocytes** (cells) and **T lymphocytes** (cells). Describe and distinguish between the activities of the B and T lymphocytes in the immune response.

□ 15. With reference to **clonal selection theory**, explain how the immune system is able to respond to the large and unpredictable range of antigens in the environment.

□ 16. Appreciate that **self-tolerance** occurs during development as a result of the selective destruction of B cells that react to self-antigens.

Cell-mediated immunity

□ 17. T cells are responsible for **cell-mediated immunity**. Describe how T cells recognise **specific** foreign antigens. Describe the functional roles of named T cells, including the **cytotoxic** (killer) **T cells** (T_C) and the **helper T cells** (T_H). Identify the organisms against which these T cells act.

Humoral immunity

□ 18. Describe how B cells bring about **humoral** (antibody-mediated) **immunity**. Identify the organisms that are the main targets for the humoral response.

□ 19. Describe and contrast the functional roles of **plasma cells** and **memory cells** and explain the basis for **immunological memory**. Discuss the role of cell signalling and immunological memory in long term immunity (ability to respond quickly to previously encountered antigens).

□ 20. Name some common **antigens** (**immunoglobulins**) and explain their role in provoking a specific immune response. Describe the structure of an **antibody**, identifying the constant and variable regions, and the antigen binding site. Relate the structure of antibodies to their function.

□ 21. Describe the methods by which antibodies inactivate antigens and facilitate their destruction.

Vaccines and Immunisation *(pages 227, 229-232)*

□ 22. Appreciate that **immunisation** involves the production of immunity by artificial means and that **vaccination** usually refers to immunisation by inoculation. Know that these terms are frequently used synonymously.

□ 23. Recognise that vaccination provides **artificially acquired immunity**. Recall the difference between **passive** and **active immunity**.

□ 24. Describe what is meant by a **primary** and a **secondary response** to infection. Explain the role of these responses and the immune system memory in the success of vaccines against specific pathogens.

□ 25. Explain the role of **vaccination** programmes in preventing disease. Discuss the role of aggressive vaccination programmes in the eradication (or near-eradication) of some (named) infectious diseases.

□ 26. Explain the biological and sociological reasons why vaccination has been successful in eradicating some diseases (e.g. smallpox) but not other diseases such as measles, malaria, or cholera.

□ 27. Outline the vaccination schedule for the UK, identifying critical times for vaccination against specific diseases. With reference to the concept of **herd immunity**, comment on the role of effective vaccination programmes in public health and the incidence of infectious disease in the UK.

□ 28. Discuss how governments and health organisations respond to changing patterns of infection each year, e.g. the seasonal appearance of new strains of influenza or meningococcal disease.

□ 29. Describe the principles involved in the production of vaccines. Giving examples, explain how vaccines are administered. Distinguish between **subunit** and **whole-agent vaccines** and between **inactivated** (dead) and **live** (attenuated) **vaccines**. Contrast the risks and benefits associated with live and dead vaccines.

□ 30. Evaluate the risks associated with immunisation. Compare these risks with the risks associated with contracting the disease itself.

□ 31. Describe possible new sources of medicines, including those sourced from microorganisms (including fungi) and plants. Discuss the importance of conserving biodiversity as a resource from which potential new therapeutic drugs can be sourced.

See the 'Textbook Reference Grid' on page 7 for textbook page references relating to material in this topic.

Supplementary Texts

See pages 5-6 for additional details of these texts:

■ Clegg, C.J., 1998. **Mammals: Structure and Function** (John Murray), pp. 40-41.

■ Fullick, A., 1998. **Human Health and Disease** (Heinemann), pp. 27-36.

■ Hudson, T. & K. Mannion, 2001. **Microbes and Disease** (Collins), pp. 70-86.

See page 6 for details of publishers of periodicals:

STUDENT'S REFERENCE

■ **Skin, Scabs and Scars** Biol. Sci. Rev., 17(3) Feb. 2005, pp. 2-6. *The many roles of skin, including its importance in wound healing and the processes involved in its repair when damaged.*

■ **Looking Out for Danger: How White Blood Cells Protect Us** Biol. Sci. Rev., 19 (4) April 2007, pp. 34-37. *The various types of lymphocytes (white blood cells) and they work together to protect the body against infection.*

■ **Antibodies** Biol. Sci. Rev., 11(3) Jan. 1999, pp. 34-35. *The structure and function of antibodies: their roles and how they can be used in medicine.*

■ **Monoclonals as Medicines** Biol. Sci. Rev., 18(4) April 2006, pp. 38-40. *The use of monoclonal antibodies in therapeutic and diagnostic medicine.*

■ **Inflammation** Biol. Sci. Rev., 17(1) Sept. 2004, pp. 18-20. *The role of this nonspecific defence response to tissue injury and infection. The processes involved in inflammation are discussed.*

■ **Lymphocytes - The Heart of the Immune System** Biol. Sci. Rev., 12(1) Sept. 1999, pp. 32-35. *An excellent account of the role of the various lymphocytes in the immune response.*

■ **Fanning the Flames** New Scientist, 22 May 2004, pp. 40-43. *Inflammation is one of the first lines of internal defence, but it has been implicated in a host of disparate diseases.*

■ **Fight For Your Life** Biol. Sci. Rev., 18(1) Sept. 2005, pp. 2-6. *Internal defence: pathogen recognition, the immune response, and the nature of adaptive and maladaptive immune reactions.*

■ **Immunotherapy** Biol. Sci. Rev., 15(1), Sept. 2002, pp. 39-41. *Medical research is uncovering ways in which our immune system can be used in developing vaccines for cancer.*

■ **A Jab in Time** Biol. Sci. Rev., 9(4) March 1997, pp. 17-20. *Infection and transmission of disease and the use of vaccination to combat diseases.*

■ **Let Them Eat Dirt** New Scientist, 18 July 1998, pp. 26-31. *It seems that normal immune function requires some early exposure to microorganisms.*

■ **Intestinal Worms - Can They Keep You Healthy?** Biol. Sci. Rev., 19(2) Nov. 2006, pp. 2-6. *Having intestinal worms appears to suppress inappropriate allergic responses.*

■ **Beware! Allergens** New Scientist (Inside Science), 22 January 2000. *The allergic response: sensitisation and the role of the immune system.*

■ **Misery for all Seasons** National Geographic, 209(5) May 2006, pp. 116-135. *The causes, effects, and prevention of common allergies.*

TEACHER'S REFERENCE

■ **Life, Death, and the Immune System** Scientific American, Sept. 1993. *An entire special issue on human infection, immune system, and disease.*

■ **Anaphylactic Shock** Biol. Sci. Rev., 19(2) Nov. 2006, pp. 11-13. *An account of anaphylactic shock, a severe allergic reaction caused by a massive overreaction of the body's immune system.*

■ **Immunity's Early-warning System** Scientific American, Jan. 2005, pp. 24-31. *The immune response is mediated by a family of molecules made by defensive cells. When they detect an invader, they trigger the production of signalling proteins that initiate an immune response.*

■ **Edible Vaccines** Scientific American, Sept. 2000, pp. 48-53. *Vaccines in food may be the way of future immunisation programmes.*

■ **Peacekeepers of the Immune System** Scientific American, Oct. 2006, pp. 34-41. *Regulatory T cells suppress immune activity and combat autoimmunity.*

■ **Disarming Flu Viruses** Scientific American, January 1999, pp. 56-65. *The influenza virus, its life cycle, and vaccine development for its control.*

■ **The Long Arm of the Immune System** Sci. American, Nov. 2002, pp. 34-41. *The role of dendritic cells, a class of leucocytes with a role in activating the immune system (good extension).*

■ **Taming Lupus** Scientific American, March 2005, pp. 58-65. *An account of the autoimmune disorder, lupus: its causes, pathways to disease, triggers for disease onset, and possible treatments.*

■ **Filthy Friends** New Scientist, 16 April 2005, pp. 34-39. *Early contact with a range of harmless microbes is important in reducing the risk of allergy.*

See pages 8-9 for details of how to access **Bio Links** from our web site: **www.biozone.co.uk**. From Bio Links, access sites under the topics:

GENERAL BIOLOGY ONLINE RESOURCES > **General Online Biology Resources**: • AP interactive animation • Biointeractive • ken's BioWeb Resources > **Online Textbooks and Lecture Notes**: • S-Cool! A level biology revision guide • Biology Online.org • Human Biology Help • Welcome to the Biology Web... *and others*

ANIMAL BIOLOGY: • Anatomy and physiology • Human physiology lecture notes ... *and others*

HEALTH & DISEASE > **Defence and the Immune System**: • Blood group antigens • Immune defence against microbial pathogens • Inducible defences against pathogens • Microbiology and immunology • Constitutive defences against pathogens • The immune system: An overview • Understanding the immune system ... *and others*

Presentation MEDIA to support this topic:

Health & Disease CD-ROM: • Defence & Immunity

Defence and the Immune System

Targets for Defence

In order for the body to present an effective defence against pathogens, it must first be able to recognise its own tissues (self) and ignore the body's normal microflora (e.g. the bacteria of the skin and gastrointestinal tract). In addition, the body needs to be able to deal with abnormal cells which, if not eliminated, may become cancerous. Failure of self/non-self recognition can lead to autoimmune disorders, in which the immune system mistakenly attacks its own tissues. The body's ability to recognise its own molecules has implications for procedures such as tissue grafts, organ transplants, and blood transfusions. Incompatible tissues (identified as foreign) are attacked by the body's immune system (**rejected**). Even a healthy pregnancy involves suppression of specific features of the self recognition system, allowing the mother to tolerate a nine month gestation with the foetus.

The Body's Natural Microbiota

After birth, normal and characteristic microbial populations begin to establish themselves on and in the body. A typical human body contains 1×10^{13} body cells, yet harbours 1×10^{14} bacterial cells. These microorganisms establish more or less permanent residence but, under normal conditions, do not cause disease. In fact, this normal microflora can benefit the host by preventing the overgrowth of harmful pathogens. They are not found throughout the entire body, but are located in certain regions.

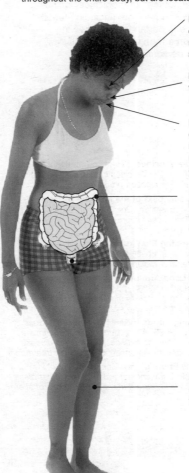

Eyes: The conjuctiva, a continuation of the skin or mucous membrane, contains a similar microbiota to the skin.

Nose and throat: Harbours a variety of microorganisms, e.g. *Staphylococcus spp.*

Mouth: Supports a large and diverse microbiota. It is an ideal microbial environment; high in moisture, warmth, and nutrient availability.

Large intestine: Contains the body's largest resident population of microbes because of its available moisture and nutrients.

Urinary and genital systems: The lower urethra in both sexes has a resident population; the vagina has a particular acid-tolerant population of microbes because of the low pH nature of its secretions.

Skin: Skin secretions prevent most of the microbes on the skin from becoming residents.

Distinguishing Self from Non-Self

The human immune system achieves self-recognition through the **major histocompatibility complex** (MHC). This is a cluster of tightly linked genes on chromosome 6 in humans. These genes code for protein molecules (MHC antigens) that are attached to the surface of body cells. They are used by the immune system to recognise its own or foreign material. **Class I MHC** antigens are located on the surface of virtually all human cells, but **Class II MHC** antigens are restricted to macrophages and the antibody-producing B-lymphocytes.

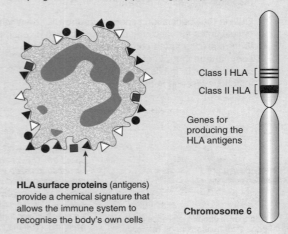

Class I HLA [

Class II HLA [

Genes for producing the HLA antigens

Chromosome 6

HLA surface proteins (antigens) provide a chemical signature that allows the immune system to recognise the body's own cells

Tissue Transplants

The MHC is responsible for the rejection of tissue grafts and organ transplants. Foreign MHC molecules are antigenic, causing the immune system to respond in the following way:

- T cells directly lyse the foreign cells
- Macrophages are activated by T cells and engulf foreign cells
- Antibodies are released that attack the foreign cell
- The complement system injures blood vessels supplying the graft or transplanted organ

To minimise this rejection, attempts are made to match the MHC of the organ donor to that of the recipient as closely as possible.

1. Explain why it is healthy to have a natural population of microbes on and inside the body: _____

_____

2. (a) Explain the nature and purpose of the **major histocompatibility complex** (MHC): _____

_____

_____

_____

(b) Explain the importance of such a self-recognition system: _____

_____

3. Name two situations when the body's recognition of 'self' is undesirable: _____

RA 2   **Related activities**: The Body's Defences, The Immune System

Blood Group Antigens

Blood groups classify blood according to the different marker proteins on the surface of red blood cells (RBCs). These marker proteins act as **antigens** and affect the ability of RBCs to provoke an immune response. The **ABO blood group** is the most important blood typing system in medical practice, because of the presence of anti-A and anti-B antibodies in nearly all people who lack the corresponding red cell antigens (these antibodies are carried in the plasma and are present at birth). If a patient is to receive blood from a blood donor, that blood must be compatible otherwise the red blood cells of the donated blood will clump together (agglutinate), break apart, and block capillaries. There is a small margin of safety in certain blood group combinations, because the volume of donated blood is usually relatively small and the donor's antibodies are quickly diluted in the plasma. In practice, blood is carefully matched, not only for ABO types, but for other types as well. Although human RBCs have more than 500 known antigens, fewer than 30 (in 9 blood groups) are regularly tested for when blood is donated for transfusion. The blood groups involved are: *ABO, Rh, MNS, P, Lewis, Lutheran, Kell, Duffy,* and *Kidd.* The ABO and rhesus (Rh) are the best known. Although blood typing has important applications in medicine, it can also be used to rule out individuals in cases of crime (or paternity) and establish a list of potential suspects (or fathers).

	Blood type A	Blood type B	Blood type AB	Blood type O
Antigens present on the **red blood cells**	antigen *A*	antigen *B*	antigens *A* and *B*	Neither antigen *A* nor *B*
Anti-bodies present in the **plasma**	Contains **anti-B** antibodies; but no antibodies that would attack its own antigen *A*	Contains **anti-A** antibodies; but no antibodies that would attack its own antigen *B*	Contains neither **anti-A** nor **anti-B** antibodies	Contains both **anti-A** and **anti-B** antibodies

Blood type	Frequency in UK Rh⁺	Frequency in UK Rh⁻	Antigen	Antibody	Can donate blood to:	Can receive blood from:
A	36%	7%	A	anti-B	A, AB	A, O
B	8%	1%				
AB	2%	1%				
O	38%	7%				

1. Complete the table above to show the antibodies and antigens in each blood group, and donor/recipient blood types:

2. In a hypothetical murder case, blood from both the victim and the murderer was left at the scene. There were five suspects under investigation:

   (a) Describe what blood typing could establish about the guilt or innocence of the suspects: _____

   _____

   (b) Identify what a blood typing could not establish: _____

   _____

   (c) Suggest how the murderer's identity could be firmly established (assuming that s/he was one of the five suspects): ___

   _____

   (d) Explain why blood typing is not used forensically to any great extent: _____

   _____

3. Explain why the discovery of the ABO system was such a significant medical breakthrough: _____

   _____

Defence and the Immune System

Related activities: Blood
Web links: Blood Typing Game

A 2

Blood Clotting and Defence

Apart from its transport role, **blood** has a role in the body's defence against infection and **haemostasis** (the prevention of bleeding and maintenance of blood volume). The tearing or puncturing of a blood vessel initiates **clotting**. Clotting is normally a rapid process that seals off the tear, preventing blood loss and the invasion of bacteria into the site. Clot formation is triggered by the release of clotting factors from the damaged cells at the site of the tear or puncture. A hardened clot forms a scab, which acts to prevent further blood loss and acts as a mechanical barrier to the entry of pathogens.

Blood Clotting

1 Injury to the lining of a blood vessels exposes collagen fibres to the blood. Platelets stick to the collagen fibres.

3 Platelets clump together. The platelet plug forms an emergency protection against blood loss.

When tissue is wounded, the blood quickly coagulates to prevent further blood loss and maintain the integrity of the circulatory system. For external wounds, clotting also prevents the entry of pathogens. Blood clotting involves a cascade of reactions involving at least twelve clotting factors in the blood. The end result is the formation of an insoluble network of fibres, which traps red blood cells and seals the wound.

4 A fibrin clot reinforces the seal. The clot traps blood cells and the clot eventually dries to form a **scab**.

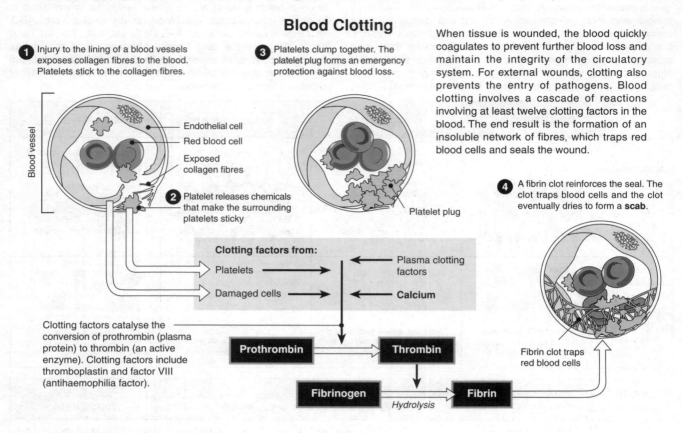

Blood vessel

Endothelial cell
Red blood cell
Exposed collagen fibres

2 Platelet releases chemicals that make the surrounding platelets sticky

Platelet plug

Clotting factors from:
Platelets
Damaged cells

Plasma clotting factors
Calcium

Clotting factors catalyse the conversion of prothrombin (plasma protein) to thrombin (an active enzyme). Clotting factors include thromboplastin and factor VIII (antihaemophilia factor).

Prothrombin → **Thrombin**

Fibrinogen → *Hydrolysis* → **Fibrin**

Fibrin clot traps red blood cells

1. Explain two roles of the blood clotting system in internal defence and haemostasis:

   (a) _____

   (b) _____

2. Explain the role of each of the following in the sequence of events leading to a blood clot:

   (a) Injury: _____

   (b) Release of chemicals from platelets: _____

   _____

   (c) Clumping of platelets at the wound site: _____

   _____

   (d) Formation of a fibrin clot: _____

   _____

3. (a) Explain the role of clotting factors in the blood in formation of the clot: _____

   _____

   (b) Explain why these clotting factors are not normally present in the plasma: _____

   _____

4. (a) Name one inherited disease caused by the absence of a clotting factor: _____

   (b) Name the clotting factor involved: _____

Related activities: Proteins, Enzymes, Blood
Web links: Haemostasis

The Body's Defences

If microorganisms never encountered resistance from our body defences, we would be constantly ill and would eventually die of various diseases. Fortunately, in most cases our defences prevent this from happening. Some of these defences are designed to keep microorganisms from entering the body. Other defences remove the microorganisms if they manage to get inside. Further defences attack the microorganisms if they remain inside the body. The ability to ward off disease through the various defence mechanisms is called **resistance**. The lack of resistance, or vulnerability to disease, is known as **susceptibility**. One form of defence is referred to as **non-specific resistance**, and includes defences that protect us from any invading pathogen. This includes a first line of defence such as the physical barriers to infection (skin and mucous membranes) and a second line of defence (phagocytes, inflammation, fever, and antimicrobial substances). **Specific resistance** is a third line of defence that forms the **immune response** and targets specific pathogens. Specialised cells of the immune system, called lymphocytes, produce specific proteins called antibodies which are produced against specific antigens.

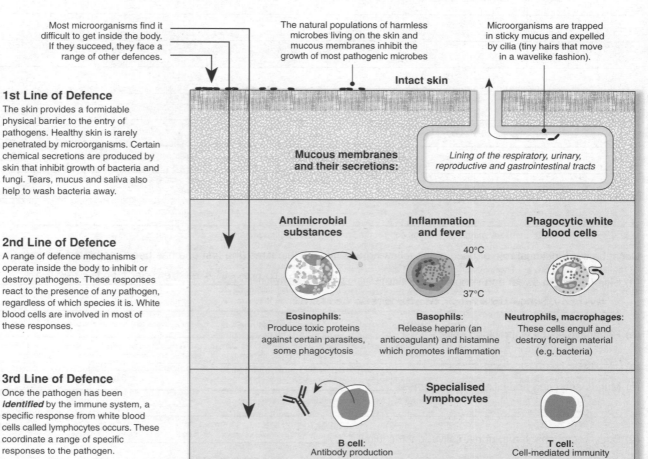

Most microorganisms find it difficult to get inside the body. If they succeed, they face a range of other defences.

The natural populations of harmless microbes living on the skin and mucous membranes inhibit the growth of most pathogenic microbes

Microorganisms are trapped in sticky mucus and expelled by cilia (tiny hairs that move in a wavelike fashion).

Intact skin

Mucous membranes and their secretions:

Lining of the respiratory, urinary, reproductive and gastrointestinal tracts

Antimicrobial substances

Eosinophils:
Produce toxic proteins against certain parasites, some phagocytosis

Inflammation and fever

40°C
37°C

Basophils:
Release heparin (an anticoagulant) and histamine which promotes inflammation

Phagocytic white blood cells

Neutrophils, macrophages:
These cells engulf and destroy foreign material (e.g. bacteria)

Specialised lymphocytes

B cell:
Antibody production

T cell:
Cell-mediated immunity

1st Line of Defence
The skin provides a formidable physical barrier to the entry of pathogens. Healthy skin is rarely penetrated by microorganisms. Certain chemical secretions are produced by skin that inhibit growth of bacteria and fungi. Tears, mucus and saliva also help to wash bacteria away.

2nd Line of Defence
A range of defence mechanisms operate inside the body to inhibit or destroy pathogens. These responses react to the presence of any pathogen, regardless of which species it is. White blood cells are involved in most of these responses.

3rd Line of Defence
Once the pathogen has been *identified* by the immune system, a specific response from white blood cells called lymphocytes occurs. These coordinate a range of specific responses to the pathogen.

1. Compare and contrast the type of response against pathogens carried out by each of the three levels of defence:

_____

_____

_____

_____

_____

_____

_____

_____

_____

_____

_____

_____

Defence and the Immune System

Related activities: The Action of Phagocytes, Inflammation, Fever, The Immune System   **Web links**: Immunoanimations

RA 2

2. Distinguish between specific and non-specific resistance: _____

_____

_____

_____

_____

3. Describe features of the different types of white blood cells and explain how these relate to their role in the second line of defence:

_____

_____

_____

_____

_____

_____

_____

_____

_____

_____

4. Describe the functional role of each of the following defence mechanisms (the first one has been completed for you):

(a) Skin (including sweat and sebum production): _____Skin helps to prevent direct entry of pathogens into the body. Sebum slows growth of bacteria and fungi._____

(b) Phagocytosis by white blood cells: _____

_____

(c) Mucus-secreting and ciliated membranes: _____

_____

(d) Body secretions: tears, urine, saliva, gastric juice: _____

_____

(e) Natural antimicrobial proteins (e.g. interferon): _____

_____

(f) Antibody production: _____

_____

(g) Fever: _____

_____

(h) Cell-mediated immunity: _____

_____

(i) The inflammatory response: _____

_____

5. Infection with HIV results in the progressive destruction of T lymphocytes. Suggest why this leads to an increasing number of opportunistic infections in AIDS sufferers:

_____

The Action of Phagocytes

Human cells that ingest microbes and digest them by the process of **phagocytosis** are called **phagocytes**. All are types of white blood cells. During many kinds of infections, especially bacterial infections, the total number of white blood cells increases by two to four times the normal number. The ratio of various white blood cell types changes during the course of an infection.

How a Phagocyte Destroys Microbes

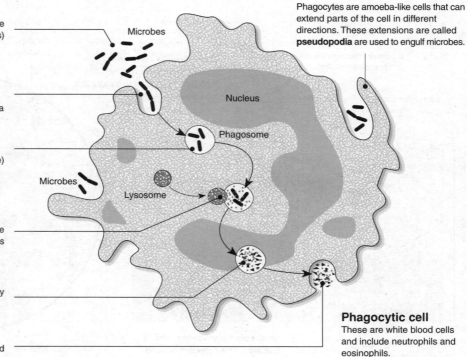

1 **Detection**
Phagocyte detects microbes by the chemicals they give off (chemotaxis) and sticks the microbes to its surface.

2 **Ingestion**
The microbe is engulfed by the phagocyte wrapping pseudopodia around it to form a vesicle.

3 **Phagosome forms**
A phagosome (phagocytic vesicle) is formed, which encloses the microbes in a membrane.

4 **Fusion with lysosome**
Phagosome fuses with a lysosome (which contains powerful enzymes that can digest the microbe).

5 **Digestion**
The microbes are broken down by enzymes into their chemical constituents.

6 **Discharge**
Indigestible material is discharged from the phagocyte cell.

Phagocytes are amoeba-like cells that can extend parts of the cell in different directions. These extensions are called **pseudopodia** are used to engulf microbes.

Labels on figure: Microbes, Nucleus, Phagosome, Microbes, Lysosome

Phagocytic cell
These are white blood cells and include neutrophils and eosinophils.

The Interaction of Microbes and Phagocytes

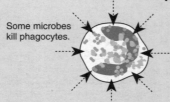

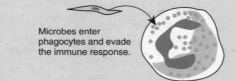

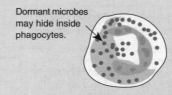

Some microbes kill phagocytes
Some microbes produce toxins that can actually kill phagocytes, e.g. toxin-producing staphylococci and the dental plaque-forming bacteria *Actinobacillus*.

Microbes evade immune system
Some microbes can evade the immune system by entering phagocytes. The microbes prevent fusion of the lysosome with the phagosome and multiply inside the phagocyte, almost filling it. Examples include *Chlamydia*, *Mycobacterium tuberculosis*, *Shigella*, and malarial parasites.

Dormant microbes hide inside
Some microbes can remain dormant inside the phagocyte for months or years at a time. Examples include the microbes that cause brucellosis and tularemia.

1. Identify the white blood cells capable of phagocytosis: _____

_____

2. Describe how a blood sample from a patient may be used to determine whether they have a microbial infection (without looking for the microbes themselves):

_____

_____

3. Explain how some microbes are able to overcome phagocytic cells and use them to their advantage: _____

_____

_____

Related activities: The Body's Defences, Blood

RA 2

Defence and the Immune System

Inflammation

Damage to the body's tissues can be caused by physical agents (e.g. sharp objects, heat, radiant energy, or electricity), microbial infection, or chemical agents (e.g. gases, acids and bases). The damage triggers a defensive response called **inflammation**. It is usually characterised by four symptoms: pain, redness, heat and swelling. The inflammatory response is beneficial and has the following functions: (1) to destroy the cause of the infection and remove it and its products from the body; (2) if this fails, to limit the effects on the body by confining the infection to a small area; (3) replacing or repairing tissue damaged by the infection. The process of inflammation can be divided into three distinct stages. These are described below.

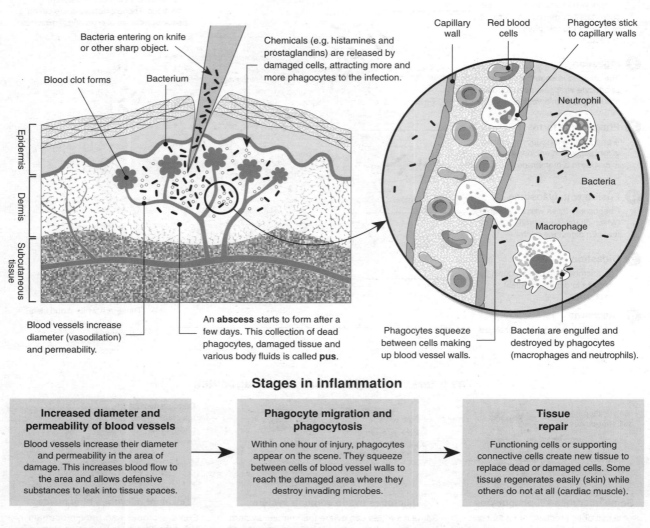

Bacteria entering on knife or other sharp object.

Chemicals (e.g. histamines and prostaglandins) are released by damaged cells, attracting more and more phagocytes to the infection.

Blood clot forms

Bacterium

Epidermis

Dermis

Subcutaneous tissue

Blood vessels increase diameter (vasodilation) and permeability.

An **abscess** starts to form after a few days. This collection of dead phagocytes, damaged tissue and various body fluids is called **pus**.

Capillary wall

Red blood cells

Phagocytes stick to capillary walls

Neutrophil

Bacteria

Macrophage

Phagocytes squeeze between cells making up blood vessel walls.

Bacteria are engulfed and destroyed by phagocytes (macrophages and neutrophils).

Stages in inflammation

Increased diameter and permeability of blood vessels	Phagocyte migration and phagocytosis	Tissue repair
Blood vessels increase their diameter and permeability in the area of damage. This increases blood flow to the area and allows defensive substances to leak into tissue spaces.	Within one hour of injury, phagocytes appear on the scene. They squeeze between cells of blood vessel walls to reach the damaged area where they destroy invading microbes.	Functioning cells or supporting connective cells create new tissue to replace dead or damaged cells. Some tissue regenerates easily (skin) while others do not at all (cardiac muscle).

1. Outline the three stages of inflammation and identify the beneficial role of each stage:

(a) _____

_____

(b) _____

_____

(c) _____

_____

2. Identify two features of phagocytes important in the response to microbial invasion: _____

_____

3. State the role of histamines and prostaglandins in inflammation: _____

4. Explain why pus forms at the site of infection: _____

_____

Related activities: The Body's Defences, The Action of Phagocytes

Fever

Fever describes a condition where the internal body temperature increases to above-normal levels. It arises because of an increase in the body's thermoregulatory set-point so that the previous "normal body temperature" is considered hypothermic. Fever is not a disease, but it is a symptom of infection and, to a point, it is beneficial, because it assists a number of the defence processes. The release of the protein **interleukin-1** helps to reset the thermostat of the body to a higher level, and increases production of **T cells** (lymphocytes). High body temperature also intensifies the effect of **interferon** (an antiviral protein) and may inhibit the growth of some bacteria and viruses. High temperatures also speed up the body's **metabolism**, so promote more rapid tissue repair. Fever also increases heart rate so that white blood cells are delivered to sites of infection more rapidly.

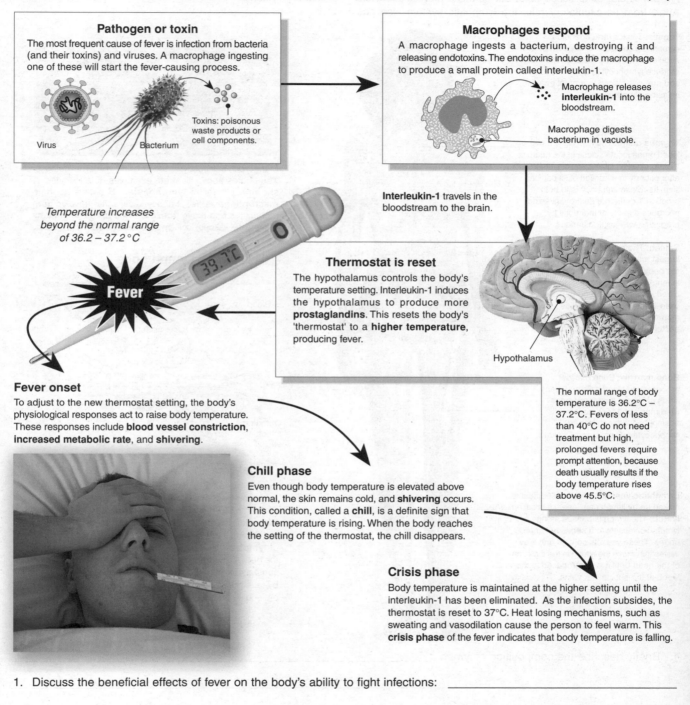

Pathogen or toxin

The most frequent cause of fever is infection from bacteria (and their toxins) and viruses. A macrophage ingesting one of these will start the fever-causing process.

Virus

Bacterium

Toxins: poisonous waste products or cell components.

Macrophages respond

A macrophage ingests a bacterium, destroying it and releasing endotoxins. The endotoxins induce the macrophage to produce a small protein called interleukin-1.

Macrophage releases **interleukin-1** into the bloodstream.

Macrophage digests bacterium in vacuole.

Interleukin-1 travels in the bloodstream to the brain.

Temperature increases beyond the normal range of 36.2 – 37.2 °C

Fever

39.7°C

Thermostat is reset

The hypothalamus controls the body's temperature setting. Interleukin-1 induces the hypothalamus to produce more **prostaglandins**. This resets the body's 'thermostat' to a **higher temperature**, producing fever.

Hypothalamus

Fever onset

To adjust to the new thermostat setting, the body's physiological responses act to raise body temperature. These responses include **blood vessel constriction**, **increased metabolic rate**, and **shivering**.

The normal range of body temperature is 36.2°C – 37.2°C. Fevers of less than 40°C do not need treatment but high, prolonged fevers require prompt attention, because death usually results if the body temperature rises above 45.5°C.

Chill phase

Even though body temperature is elevated above normal, the skin remains cold, and **shivering** occurs. This condition, called a **chill**, is a definite sign that body temperature is rising. When the body reaches the setting of the thermostat, the chill disappears.

Crisis phase

Body temperature is maintained at the higher setting until the interleukin-1 has been eliminated. As the infection subsides, the thermostat is reset to 37°C. Heat losing mechanisms, such as sweating and vasodilation cause the person to feel warm. This **crisis phase** of the fever indicates that body temperature is falling.

1. Discuss the beneficial effects of fever on the body's ability to fight infections: _____

_____

_____

2. Summarise the key steps of how the body's thermostat is set at a higher level by infection: _____

_____

_____

_____

Defence and the Immune System

Related activities: Bacterial Diseases, The Body's Defences, The Action of Phagocytes

A 2

The Lymphatic System

Fluid leaks out from capillaries and forms the tissue fluid, which is similar in composition to plasma but lacks large proteins. This fluid bathes the tissues, supplying them with nutrients and oxygen, and removing wastes. Some of the tissue fluid returns directly into the capillaries, but some drains back into the blood circulation through a network of lymph vessels. This fluid, called **lymph**, is similar to tissue fluid, but contains more leucocytes. Apart from its circulatory role, the lymphatic system also has an important function in the immune response. Lymph nodes are the primary sites where the destruction of pathogens and other foreign substances occurs. A lymph node that is fighting an infection becomes swollen and hard as the lymph cells reproduce rapidly to increase their numbers. The thymus, spleen, and bone marrow also contribute leucocytes to the lymphatic and circulatory systems.

Tonsils: Tonsils (and adenoids) comprise a collection of large lymphatic nodules at the back of the throat. They produce lymphocytes and antibodies and are well-placed to protect against invasion of pathogens.

Thymus gland: The thymus is a two-lobed organ located close to the heart. It is prominent in infants and diminishes after puberty to a fraction of its original size. Its role in immunity is to help produce **T cells** that destroy invading microbes directly or indirectly by producing various substances.

Spleen: The oval spleen is the largest mass of lymphatic tissue in the body, measuring about 12 cm in length. It stores and releases blood in case of demand (e.g. in cases of bleeding), produces mature **B cells**, and destroys bacteria by phagocytosis.

Bone marrow: Bone marrow produces red blood cells and many kinds of leucocytes: monocytes (and macrophages), neutrophils, eosinophils, basophils, and lymphocytes (B cells and T cells).

Lymphatic vessels: When tissue fluid is picked up by lymph capillaries, it is called **lymph**. The lymph is passed along lymphatic vessels to a series of lymph nodes. These vessels contain one-way valves that move the lymph in the direction of the heart until it is reintroduced to the blood at the subclavian veins.

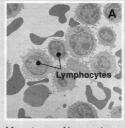

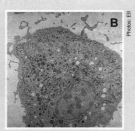

Many types of leucocytes are involved in internal defence. The photos above illustrate examples of leucocytes. **A** shows a cluster of **lymphocytes**. **B** shows a single **macrophage**: large, phagocytic cells that develop from monocytes and move from the blood to reside in many organs and tissues, including the spleen and lymph nodes.

Lymph node

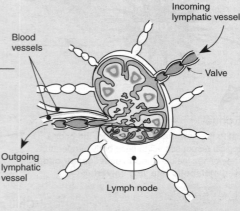

Lymph nodes are oval or bean-shaped structures, scattered throughout the body, usually in groups, along the length of lymphatic vessels. As lymph passes through the nodes, it filters foreign particles (including pathogens) by trapping them in fibres. Lymph nodes are also a "store" of **lymphocytes**, which may circulate to other parts of the body. Once trapped, macrophages destroy the foreign substances by phagocytosis. T cells may destroy them by releasing various products, and/or B cells may release antibodies that destroy them.

1. Briefly describe the composition of lymph: _____

    _____

2. Discuss the various roles of lymph: _____

    _____

    _____

3. Describe one role of each of the following in the lymphatic system:

    (a) Lymph nodes: _____

    (b) Bone marrow: _____

The Immune System

The efficient internal defence provided by the immune system is based on its ability to respond specifically against a foreign substance and its ability to hold a memory of this response. There are two main components of the immune system: the humoral and the cell-mediated responses. They work separately and together to protect us from disease. The **humoral immune response** is associated with the serum (non-cellular part of the blood) and involves the action of **antibodies** secreted by B cell lymphocytes. Antibodies are found in extracellular fluids including lymph, plasma, and mucus secretions. The humoral response protects the body against circulating viruses, and bacteria and their toxins. The **cell-mediated immune response** is associated with the production of specialised lymphocytes called **T cells**. It is most effective against bacteria and viruses located within host cells, as well as against parasitic protozoa, fungi, and worms. This system is also an important defence against cancer, and is responsible for the rejection of transplanted tissue. Both B and T cells develop from stem cells located in the liver of foetuses and the bone marrow of adults. T cells complete their development in the thymus, whilst the B cells mature in the bone marrow.

Lymphocytes and their Functions

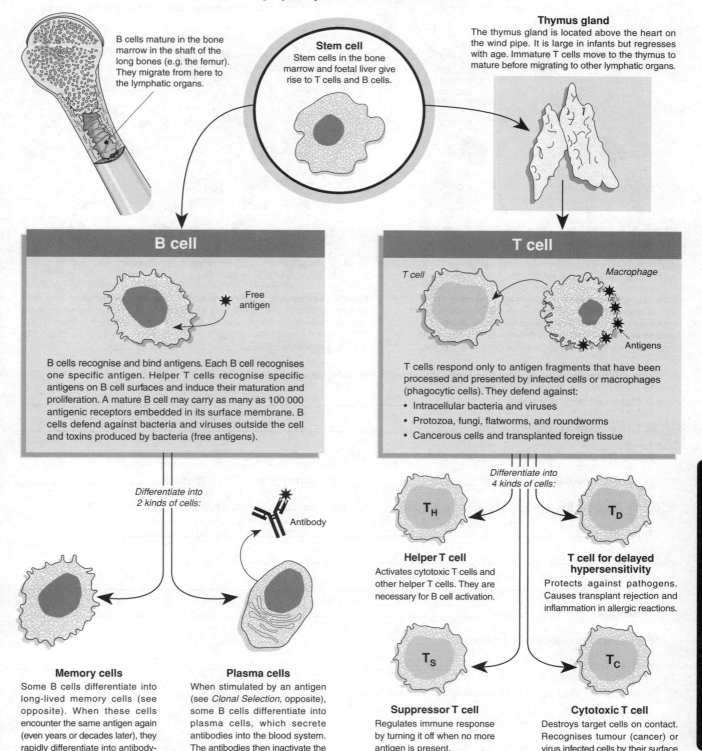

B cells mature in the bone marrow in the shaft of the long bones (e.g. the femur). They migrate from here to the lymphatic organs.

Stem cell
Stem cells in the bone marrow and foetal liver give rise to T cells and B cells.

Thymus gland
The thymus gland is located above the heart on the wind pipe. It is large in infants but regresses with age. Immature T cells move to the thymus to mature before migrating to other lymphatic organs.

B cell

Free antigen

B cells recognise and bind antigens. Each B cell recognises one specific antigen. Helper T cells recognise specific antigens on B cell surfaces and induce their maturation and proliferation. A mature B cell may carry as many as 100 000 antigenic receptors embedded in its surface membrane. B cells defend against bacteria and viruses outside the cell and toxins produced by bacteria (free antigens).

T cell

T cell

Macrophage

Antigens

T cells respond only to antigen fragments that have been processed and presented by infected cells or macrophages (phagocytic cells). They defend against:

• Intracellular bacteria and viruses
• Protozoa, fungi, flatworms, and roundworms
• Cancerous cells and transplanted foreign tissue

Differentiate into 2 kinds of cells:

Antibody

Differentiate into 4 kinds of cells:

T_H

T_D

Helper T cell
Activates cytotoxic T cells and other helper T cells. They are necessary for B cell activation.

T cell for delayed hypersensitivity
Protects against pathogens. Causes transplant rejection and inflammation in allergic reactions.

T_S

T_C

Memory cells
Some B cells differentiate into long-lived memory cells (see opposite). When these cells encounter the same antigen again (even years or decades later), they rapidly differentiate into antibody-producing plasma cells.

Plasma cells
When stimulated by an antigen (see *Clonal Selection*, opposite), some B cells differentiate into plasma cells, which secrete antibodies into the blood system. The antibodies then inactivate the circulating antigens.

Suppressor T cell
Regulates immune response by turning it off when no more antigen is present.

Cytotoxic T cell
Destroys target cells on contact. Recognises tumour (cancer) or virus infected cells by their surface (antigens and MHC markers).

Defence and the Immune System

Related activities: The Lymphatic System, Antibodies
Web links: Introducing...Specific Immunity, The Immune System Overview

A 2

The immune system has the ability to respond to the large and unpredictable range of potential antigens encountered in the environment. The diagram below explains how this ability is based on **clonal selection** after antigen exposure. The example illustrated is for B cell lymphocytes. In the same way, a T cell stimulated by a specific antigen will multiply and develop into different types of T cells. Clonal selection and differentiation of lymphocytes provide the basis for **immunological memory**.

Five (a-e) of the many, randomly generated B cells. Each one can recognise only one specific antigen.

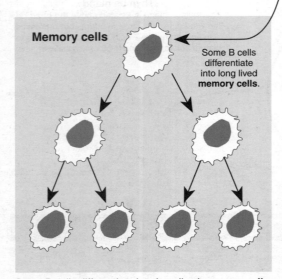

This B cell encounters and binds an antigen. It is then stimulated to proliferate.

Clonal Selection Theory

During development, millions of randomly generated B cells are formed. These are able to recognise many different antigens, including those never before encountered. Each B cell has one specific type of antigenic receptor on its surface whose shape is identical to the antibodies that the cell can make. The receptor will react only to a single antigen. When a B cell encounters its specific antigen, it responds by proliferating into a large clone of cells, all with the same genetic material and the same kind of antibody. This is called **clonal selection** because the antigen selects the B cells that will proliferate.

Memory cells

Some B cells differentiate into long lived **memory cells**.

Plasma cells

Some B cells differentiate into **plasma cells**.

Antibodies inactivate antigens

Some B cells differentiate into long lived **memory cells**. These are retained in the lymph nodes to provide future immunity (**immunological memory**). In the event of a second infection, B-memory cells react more quickly and vigorously than the initial B-cell reaction to the first infection.

Plasma cells secrete antibodies specific to the antigen that stimulated their development. Each plasma cell lives for only a few days, but can produce about 2000 antibody molecules per second. Note that during development, any B cells that react to the body's own antigens are selectively destroyed in a process that leads to **self tolerance** (acceptance of the body's own tissues).

1. State the general action of the two major divisions in the immune system:

   (a) Humoral immune system: _____

   (b) Cell-mediated immune system: _____

2. Identify the origin of B cells and T cells (before maturing): _____

3. (a) Identify where B cells mature: _____ (b) Identify where T cells mature: _____

4. Briefly describe the function of each of the following cells in the immune system response:

   (a) Memory cells: _____

   (b) Plasma cells: _____

   (c) Helper T cells: _____

   (d) Suppressor T cells: _____

   (e) Delayed hypersensitivity T cells: _____

   (f) Cytotoxic T cells: _____

5. Briefly explain the basis of **immunological memory**: _____

   _____

   _____

   _____

Antibodies

Antibodies and antigens play key roles in the response of the immune system. Antigens are foreign molecules that are able to bind to antibodies (or T cell receptors) and provoke a specific immune response. Antigens include potentially damaging microbes and their toxins (see below) as well as substances such as pollen grains, blood cell surface molecules, and the surface proteins on transplanted tissues. **Antibodies** (also called immunoglobulins) are proteins that are made in response to antigens. They are secreted into the plasma where they circulate and can recognise, bind to, and help to destroy antigens. There are five classes of **immunoglobulins**. Each plays a different

role in the immune response (including destroying protozoan parasites, enhancing phagocytosis, protecting mucous surfaces, and neutralising toxins and viruses). The human body can produce an estimated 100 million antibodies, recognising many different antigens, including those it has never encountered. Each type of antibody is highly specific to only one particular antigen. The ability of the immune system to recognise and ignore the antigenic properties of its own tissues occurs early in development and is called **self-tolerance**. Exceptions occur when the immune system malfunctions and the body attacks its own tissues, causing an **autoimmune disorder**.

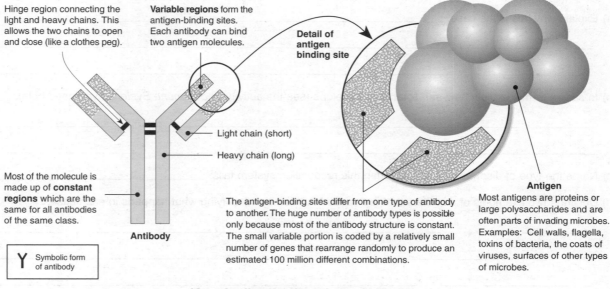

Hinge region connecting the light and heavy chains. This allows the two chains to open and close (like a clothes peg).

Variable regions form the antigen-binding sites. Each antibody can bind two antigen molecules.

Detail of antigen binding site

Light chain (short)

Heavy chain (long)

Most of the molecule is made up of **constant regions** which are the same for all antibodies of the same class.

Antibody

Y Symbolic form of antibody

The antigen-binding sites differ from one type of antibody to another. The huge number of antibody types is possible only because most of the antibody structure is constant. The small variable portion is coded by a relatively small number of genes that rearrange randomly to produce an estimated 100 million different combinations.

Antigen
Most antigens are proteins or large polysaccharides and are often parts of invading microbes. Examples: Cell walls, flagella, toxins of bacteria, the coats of viruses, surfaces of other types of microbes.

How Antibodies Inactivate Antigens

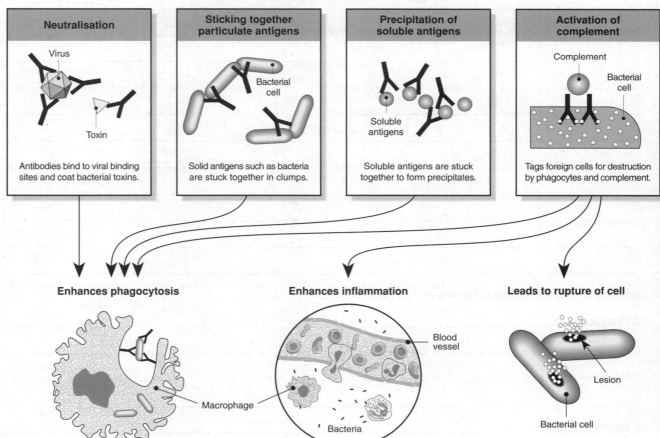

Neutralisation	Sticking together particulate antigens	Precipitation of soluble antigens	Activation of complement
Virus / Toxin	Bacterial cell	Soluble antigens	Complement / Bacterial cell
Antibodies bind to viral binding sites and coat bacterial toxins.	Solid antigens such as bacteria are stuck together in clumps.	Soluble antigens are stuck together to form precipitates.	Tags foreign cells for destruction by phagocytes and complement.

Enhances phagocytosis

Macrophage

Enhances inflammation

Blood vessel

Bacteria

Leads to rupture of cell

Lesion

Bacterial cell

Related activities: Targets for Defence, The Immune System, Acquired Immunity, Vaccination

RA 2

Defence and the Immune System

1. Distinguish between an antibody and an antigen: _____

_____

_____

_____

_____

_____

2. It is necessary for the immune system to clearly distinguish the body's own cells and proteins from foreign ones.

    (a) Explain why this is the case: _____

_____

_____

    (b) In simple terms, explain how **self tolerance** develops (see the activity *The Immune System* if you need help):

_____

_____

    (c) Name the type of disorder that results when this recognition system fails: _____

    (d) Describe two examples of disorders that are caused in this way, identifying what happens in each case:

_____

_____

_____

_____

3. Discuss the ways in which antibodies work to inactivate antigens: _____

_____

_____

_____

_____

_____

_____

_____

_____

_____

4. Explain how antibody activity enhances or leads to:

    (a) Phagocytosis: _____

_____

    (b) Inflammation: _____

_____

    (c) Bacterial cell lysis: _____

_____

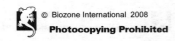

Acquired Immunity

We have natural or **innate resistance** to certain illnesses; examples include most diseases of other animal species. **Acquired immunity** refers to the protection an animal develops against certain types of microbes or foreign substances. Immunity can be acquired either passively or actively and is developed during an individual's lifetime. **Active immunity** develops when a person is exposed to microorganisms or foreign substances and

the immune system responds. **Passive immunity** is acquired when antibodies are transferred from one person to another. Recipients do not make the antibodies themselves and the effect lasts only as long as the antibodies are present, usually several weeks or months. Immunity may also be **naturally acquired**, through natural exposure to microbes, or **artificially acquired** as a result of medical treatment.

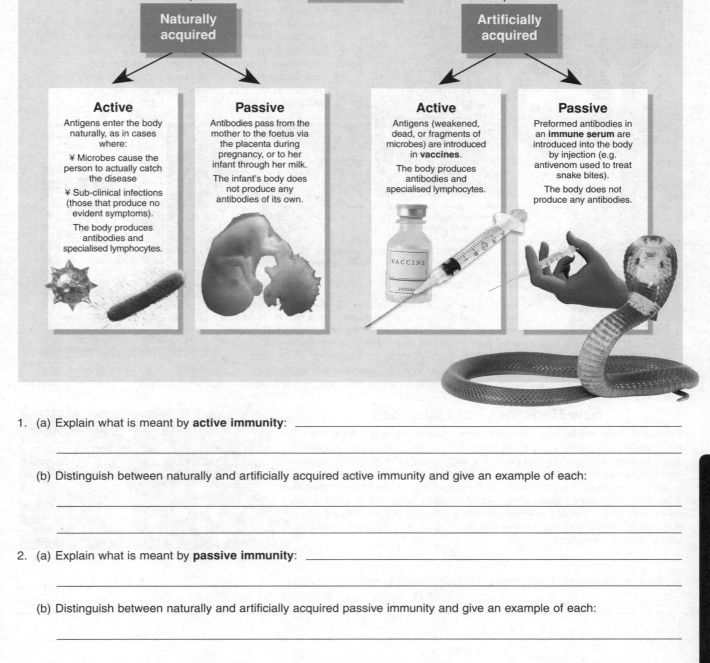

1. (a) Explain what is meant by **active immunity**: _____

_____

(b) Distinguish between naturally and artificially acquired active immunity and give an example of each:

_____

_____

_____

2. (a) Explain what is meant by **passive immunity**: _____

_____

(b) Distinguish between naturally and artificially acquired passive immunity and give an example of each:

_____

_____

3. (a) Explain why a newborn baby needs to have received a supply of maternal antibodies prior to birth: _____

_____

(b) Explain why this supply is supplemented by antibodies provided in breast milk: _____

_____

Defence and the Immune System

Related activities: Vaccination

A 2

New Medicines

One of the concerning issues in modern medicine is the need to discover and develop new treatments for disease, not only infectious diseases, but diseases such as cancers, cardiovascular disease, diabetes, and neurological disorders. Increasingly, researchers are looking towards our natural biological resources for these new medicines. Plants in particular have yielded a vast array of medicinal compounds, yet these have been obtained from relatively few species. The advantages of using plants as starting points for drug development are compelling. There are many species whose properties are yet unknown and it is possible that some of these could be useful medicinally. Much the same scenario applies to microorganisms, whose biodiversity is only just beginning to be discovered. Future medical treatments may depend on our conservation of this biodiversity.

Medicines from Plants

Opium poppy codeine, morphine

Periwinkle plant-anti-cancer

Approximately 120 pure chemical substances extracted from higher plants are used in medicine throughout the world. Some, including **aspirin** (salicylic acid from willow bark) and **digitalin** (from foxglove) have been in medical use since antiquity. Others, including plant alkaloids such as **taxol** (an anticancer drug), are more recent discoveries. Most of the plant-derived medicines are now synthesised in the laboratory, but only about six are produced entirely by synthetic procedures. The rest are still extracted commercially from plants.

The bark and needles of the Pacific yew (left) provide the anti-cancer drug taxol.

White willow bark yields the active ingredient of aspirin, used to treat pain fever, and inflammation.

In recent decades, the search for new medicines has focussed on tropical plants (e.g. the periwinkle and opium). However, the increased sensitivity of the new chemical screening technologies has revealed potential new drugs from plants that were not detected by previous methods. Moreover, plants can be engineered as biofactories to manufacture medicines such as vaccines and antibodies.

Digitalin, derived from foxglove, is used to treat congestive heart disease

New Medicines from Microbes

The use of drugs isolated from microorganisms is a relatively recent phenomenon, which started with the discovery of the antibiotic penicillin in 1928. Now the use of microbes to produce antimicrobial drugs is a huge industry. Some medicines come from unlikely sources. The drug **botox**, derived from the toxin of *Clostridium botulinum*, is used to treat facial neuralgia as well as for cosmetic purposes. New approaches to microbial medicines include using **bacteriophages** (viruses that infect attack bacteria) to control bacterial infections in different tissues. A better understanding of microbial diversity may also provide the means to produce more effective drugs against microbial pathogens.

Left: *Bacteriophages (arrowed) attacking a bacterial cell.*

1. Describe the present and potential value of plants to modern medicine: _____

_____

_____

_____

2. Explain why a loss of tropical biodiversity could reduce the potential options for new drugs discoveries:

_____

_____

_____

Related activities: Types of Vaccines

Vaccination

A vaccine is a suspension of microorganisms (or pieces of them) that protects against disease by stimulating the production of antibodies and inducing **immunity**. **Vaccination** (often used synonymously with **immunisation**) is a procedure that provides **artificially acquired active immunity** in the recipient. A concerted vaccination campaign led to the eradication (in 1977) of **smallpox**, the only disease to have been eradicated in this way. Once eradicated, a pathogen is no longer present in the environment and vaccination is no longer necessary. Features of smallpox made it particularly suitable for complete eradication. It was a very recognisable and visible disease, with no long-term, human carriers and no non-human carriers. In addition, people who had not been vaccinated against the disease were identifiable by the absence of a vaccination scar on the upper arm. Disease control (as opposed to eradication) does not necessarily require that everyone be immune. **Herd immunity**, where most of the population is immune, limits outbreaks to sporadic cases because there are too few susceptible individuals to support an epidemic. Vaccination provides effective control over many common bacterial and viral diseases. Viral diseases in particular are best prevented with vaccination, as they cannot be effectively treated once contracted.

Primary and Secondary Responses to Antigens

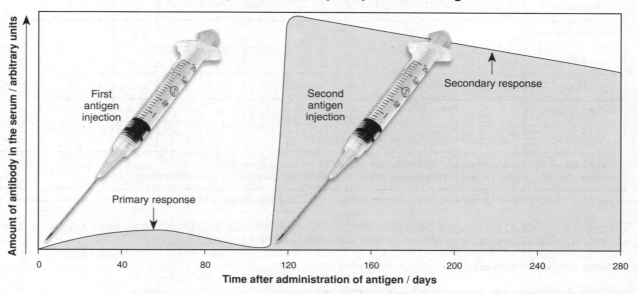

Amount of antibody in the serum / arbitrary units (y-axis)

First antigen injection

Primary response

Second antigen injection

Secondary response

Time after administration of antigen / days (x-axis): 0, 40, 80, 120, 160, 200, 240, 280

Vaccines to protect against common diseases are administered at various stages during childhood according to an immunisation schedule.

While most vaccinations are given in childhood, adults may be vaccinated against specific diseases (e.g. tuberculosis) if they are in a high risk group or if they are travelling to a region in the world where a disease is prevalent.

Selected Vaccines Used To Prevent Diseases In Humans

Disease	Type of vaccine	Recommendation
Diphtheria	Purified diphtheria toxoid	From early childhood and every 10 years for adults
Meningococcal meningitis	Purified polysaccharide of *Neisseria menigitidis*	For people with substantial risk of infection
Whooping cough	Killed cells or fragments of *Bordetella pertussis*	Children prior to school age
Tetanus	Purified tetanus toxoid	14-16 year olds with booster every 10 years
Meningitis caused by *Haemophilus influenzae* b	Polysaccharide from virus conjugated with protein to enhance effectiveness	Early childhood
Influenza	Killed virus (vaccines using genetically engineered antigenic fragments are also being developed)	For chronically ill people, especially with respiratory diseases, or for healthy people over 65 years of age
Measles	Attenuated virus	Early childhood
Mumps	Attenuated virus	Early childhood
Rubella	Attenuated virus	Early childhood; for females of child-bearing age who are not pregnant
Polio	Attenuated or killed virus (enhanced potency type)	Early childhood
Hepatitis B	Antigenic fragments of virus	Early childhood

Defence and the Immune System

Related activities: Acquired Immunity, Types of Vaccine, Viral Diseases, Bacterial Diseases, The Control of Disease

RDA 2

1. The table below provides a list of the vaccines used in the standard vaccination schedule for children and young adults in the United Kingdom. Additional vaccinations are available for those at high risk of contracting certain diseases.

   (a) List the diseases that each vaccine protects against.

   (b) Consult your family doctor, medical centre or other medical authority to determine the ages that each vaccine should be administered. Place a tick (✔) in each age column as appropriate (the last one has been done for you).

Vaccination Schedule Available to Children in the United Kingdom

Vaccine	Diseases protected from	Age in months				Age in years		
		2	3	4	12-15	3-5	10-14	13-18
DTP (Triple antigen)								
Hib vaccine*								
OPV (Sabin vaccine)								
MMR								
BCG								
DT booster								
Td booster	Tetanus, diphtheria (low strength dose)							✔

Vaccination schedules are also available *for high risk groups* for the following diseases: anthrax, hepatitis A, hepatitis B, influenza, pneumococcal disease, typhoid, varicella (chickenpox), and yellow fever.

* Depending on an individual's vaccine tolerance, the Hib vaccine may be conjugated with the DTP vaccine or given as a separate vaccination

2. The graph at the top of the previous page illustrates how a person reacts to the injection of the same antibody on two separate occasions. This represents the initial vaccination followed by a booster shot.

   (a) State over what time period the antigen levels were monitored: _____

   (b) State what happens to the antibody levels after the first injection: _____

   _____

   (c) State what happens to the antibody levels after the booster shot: _____

   _____

   (d) Explain why the second injection has a markedly different effect: _____

   _____

3. The whole question of whether young children should be vaccinated has been a point of hot debate with some parents. The parents that do not want their children vaccinated have strongly held reasons for doing so. In a balanced way, explore the arguments for and against childhood vaccination:

   (a) State clearly the benefits from childhood vaccination: _____

   _____

   _____

   (b) Explain why some parents are concerned about vaccinating their children: _____

   _____

   _____

   _____

4. Consult your family doctor or medical centre and list three vaccinations that are recommended for travellers to overseas destinations with high risk of infectious disease:

   (a) Country/region: _____   Vaccine required: _____

   (b) Country/region: _____   Vaccine required: _____

   (c) Country/region: _____   Vaccine required: _____

Types of Vaccine

There are two basic types of vaccine: subunit vaccines and whole-agent vaccines. **Whole-agent vaccines** contain complete nonvirulent microbes, either **inactivated** (killed), or alive but **attenuated** (weakened). Attenuated viruses make very effective vaccines and often provide life-long immunity without the need for booster immunisations. Killed viruses are less effective and many vaccines of this sort have now been replaced by newer subunit vaccines. **Subunit vaccines** contain only the parts of the pathogen that induce the immune response. They are safer than attenuated vaccines because they cannot reproduce in the recipient, and they produce fewer adverse effects because they contain little or no extra material. Subunit vaccines can be made

using a variety of methods, including cell fragmentation (*acellular vaccines*), inactivation of toxins (*toxoids*), genetic engineering (*recombinant vaccines*), and combination with antigenic proteins (*conjugated vaccines*). In all cases, the subunit vaccine loses its ability to cause disease but retains its antigenic properties so that it is still effective in inducing an immune response. Some of the most promising types of vaccine under development are the DNA vaccines, consisting of naked DNA which is injected into the body and produces an antigenic protein. The safety of DNA vaccines is uncertain but they show promise for use against rapidly mutating viruses such as influenza and HIV.

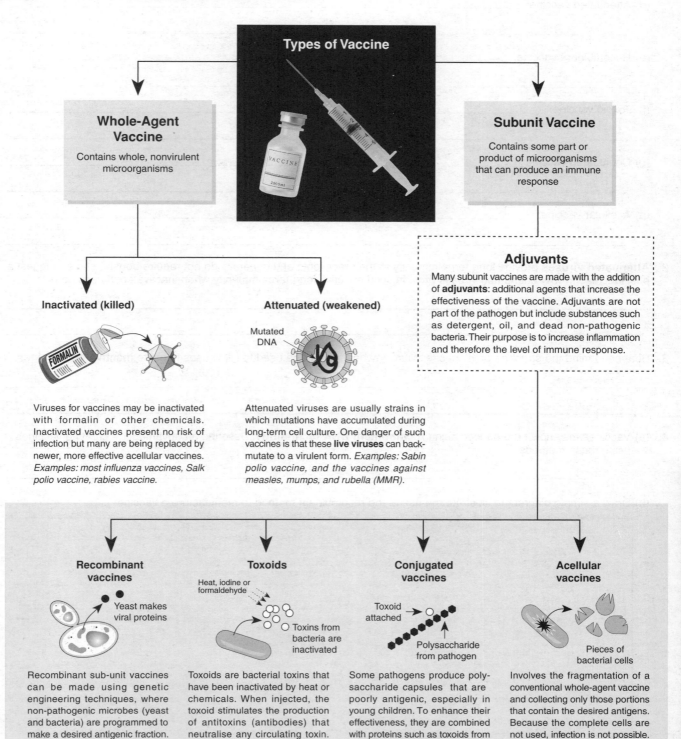

Types of Vaccine

Whole-Agent Vaccine

Contains whole, nonvirulent microorganisms

Subunit Vaccine

Contains some part or product of microorganisms that can produce an immune response

Adjuvants

Many subunit vaccines are made with the addition of **adjuvants**: additional agents that increase the effectiveness of the vaccine. Adjuvants are not part of the pathogen but include substances such as detergent, oil, and dead non-pathogenic bacteria. Their purpose is to increase inflammation and therefore the level of immune response.

Inactivated (killed)

Viruses for vaccines may be inactivated with formalin or other chemicals. Inactivated vaccines present no risk of infection but many are being replaced by newer, more effective acellular vaccines. *Examples: most influenza vaccines, Salk polio vaccine, rabies vaccine.*

Attenuated (weakened)

Mutated DNA

Attenuated viruses are usually strains in which mutations have accumulated during long-term cell culture. One danger of such vaccines is that these **live viruses** can back-mutate to a virulent form. *Examples: Sabin polio vaccine, and the vaccines against measles, mumps, and rubella (MMR).*

Recombinant vaccines

Yeast makes viral proteins

Recombinant sub-unit vaccines can be made using genetic engineering techniques, where non-pathogenic microbes (yeast and bacteria) are programmed to make a desired antigenic fraction. *Example: hepatitis B vaccine.*

Toxoids

Heat, iodine or formaldehyde

Toxins from bacteria are inactivated

Toxoids are bacterial toxins that have been inactivated by heat or chemicals. When injected, the toxoid stimulates the production of antitoxins (antibodies) that neutralise any circulating toxin. *Examples: diphtheria vaccine, tetanus vaccine.*

Conjugated vaccines

Toxoid attached

Polysaccharide from pathogen

Some pathogens produce poly-saccharide capsules that are poorly antigenic, especially in young children. To enhance their effectiveness, they are combined with proteins such as toxoids from other pathogens. *Example: vaccine against Haemophilus influenzae b.*

Acellular vaccines

Pieces of bacterial cells

Involves the fragmentation of a conventional whole-agent vaccine and collecting only those portions that contain the desired antigens. Because the complete cells are not used, infection is not possible. *Examples: newer whooping cough and typhoid vaccines.*

Defence and the Immune System

1. Describe briefly how each of the following types of vaccine are made and name an example of each:

(a) Whole-agent vaccine: _____

_____

(b) Subunit vaccine: _____

_____

(c) Inactivated vaccine: _____

_____

(d) Attenuated vaccine: _____

_____

(e) Recombinant vaccine: _____

_____

(f) Toxoid vaccine: _____

_____

(g) Conjugated vaccine: _____

_____

(h) Acellular vaccine: _____

_____

2. **Attenuated viruses** provide long term immunity to their recipients and generally do not require booster shots. Suggest a possible reason why attenuated viruses provide such effective long-term immunity when inactivated viruses do not:

_____

_____

3. Bearing in mind the structure of viruses, explain why heat cannot be used to kill viruses to make **inactivated vaccines**:

_____

_____

4. (a) Vaccines may now be produced using **recombinant DNA technology**. Describe an advantage of creating vaccines using these methods:

_____

(b) Draw a simple diagram to illustrate the use of the recombinant method to manufacture a vaccine:

Human Disease

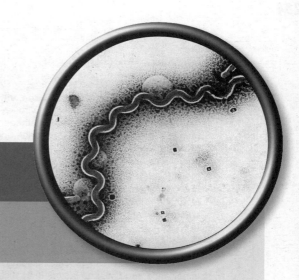

OCR: Unit F212, Module 2: Food and Health
2.2.2 (a)-(d): Infectious disease

CIE: CORE SYLLABUS
I: Infectious disease

Learning Objectives

☐ 1. Compile your own glossary from the **KEY WORDS** displayed in **bold type** in the learning objectives below.

The Nature of Disease *(pages 235-237)*

☐ 2. Discuss what is meant by **health** and **disease**, and distinguish between **infectious** and **non-infectious** disease. If required, recognise different categories of non-infectious disease, including **inherited** (genetic), **degenerative**, and **social diseases**. Appreciate that the distinction between infectious and non-infectious disease is becoming less clear as we accumulate knowledge about the nature of pathogens and their possible role in diseases such as cancer.

☐ 3. Define the terms **pathogen** and **parasite**, and discuss the meanings and use of these terms. Identify pathogens in different taxa including the bacteria, viruses, fungi, and protoctists.

☐ 4. Describe modes of **transmission** for some named infectious diseases. Identify the role of better hygiene and sanitation in controlling some infectious diseases.

☐ 5. Appreciate the significance of drug resistance to the effective control of infectious disease. With reference to a particular example (malaria, tuberculosis, or HIV) describe causes of drug resistance in pathogens and suggest how the problem might feasibly be tackled.

Bacterial Diseases *(pages 238-241, 255-258)*

☐ 6. Recognise that bacteria are widespread and only a small proportion ever cause disease. Describe how pathogenic bacteria cause disease. Explain how new strains of pathogenic bacteria can arise.

☐ 7. Giving examples, explain the ways in which bacterial diseases are transmitted. Relate the type and incidence of bacterial disease to the prevailing social conditions.

☐ 8. Describe factors affecting bacterial **pathogenicity**, including: features of the cell wall and capsule, **toxin** production, **infectivity**, and **invasiveness**.

☐ 9. Recognise different types of bacterial toxins and their actions: **endotoxins** (e.g. *Salmonella*) and **exotoxins** (e.g. *Staphylococcus*). Recognise **enterotoxins** as exotoxins that affect the gastrointestinal tract.

☐ 10. With reference to **disinfectants**, **antiseptics**, and **antibiotics**, explain how bacterial diseases are controlled and treated. Describe the role of antibiotics in medicine and identify problems with their use.

Case study: tuberculosis (TB)

☐ 11. Describe the causes and modes of transmission of tuberculosis (TB). Recognise TB as a **reemerging disease**. Assess the global importance of TB and understand its history in the human population, including reference to its prevalence, and its decline and subsequent reemergence.

☐ 12. Discuss the factors important in the prevalence of TB in a population. Explain what is meant by the term **carrier** and explain the role of carriers in the spread of TB.

☐ 13. Explain the role of **antibiotics** in the treatment of TB. Discuss the difficulties associated with the treatment of TB (including the importance of bacterial resistance to antibiotics). Describe the roles of social, economic, and biological factors in the control and prevention of TB.

Contamination of food and water

☐ 14. Describe the involvement of inadequate provision of clean drinking water, poor sanitation, and/or poor food hygiene in the transmission of food and water borne pathogens. Examples spread by the **faecal-oral route** include: *Salmonella*, *Vibrio cholerae*, and *E. coli*.

☐ 15. Recognise the role of **faecal coliforms** as indicators for the faecal contamination of water supplies.

Case study: cholera

☐ 16. Describe the agent involved and modes of transmission of **cholera**. Assess the past and current global importance of cholera and relate its distribution to factors such as levels of sanitation and general poverty.

☐ 17. Describe the roles of social, economic, and biological factors in the control and prevention of cholera.

☐ 18. Describe the treatment for cholera (both mild and severe cases) and comment on the importance of prompt and adequate provision of this treatment.

Case study: bacterial food poisoning

☐ 19. Describe the cause and transmission of **salmonellosis** or **staphylococcal food poisoning**. Identify factors governing their occurrence and severity.

Protozoan Diseases *(pages 242-244)*

☐ 20. Describe examples of diseases caused by protozoans. Understand that many pathogenic protozoans are highly specialised parasites with part of their life cycle occurring within a human.

Case study: malaria

☐ 21. Describe the agent involved and modes of transmission of **malaria**. Evaluate the global importance of malaria and describe factors in its distribution.

☐ 22. Describe the roles of social, economic, and biological factors in the treatment, control, and prevention of malaria. Comment on the adequacy of these methods with reference to the difficulties associated with developing drugs against protozoans.

Viral Diseases (pages 229-230, 245-258)

☐ 23. Define the terms **viral disease**, **virus**, **viroid**, and **retrovirus**. Identify the features of viruses that make them such effective host-specific pathogens. Using a named example or examples, describe how viral diseases are transmitted, and how they infect a host and cause disease.

☐ 24. Identify some viral diseases of global importance today and the causative agent in each case. Using examples, identify the role of **vaccination** in the past and present control of viral diseases.

Case study: HIV/AIDS

☐ 25. Describe the agent involved and modes of transmission of **HIV/AIDS**. Assess its global (including economic) importance and describe factors in its distribution.

☐ 26. Identify stages in the development of an HIV infection, including the effect of HIV on the immune system. Explain why AIDS is termed a **syndrome**.

☐ 27. Describe social, economic, and biological factors in the treatment, control, and prevention of HIV/AIDS.

Diseases Caused by Smoking (pages 259-260)

☐ 28. Explain the role of tobacco as a cause of preventable disease. Evaluate the epidemiological and experimental evidence linking cigarette smoking to the incidence of disease and early death.

☐ 29. Describe the effects of cigarette smoking on the mammalian gas exchange and cardiovascular systems, as shown in humans. Include reference to:

(a) The effects of the **tars** and **carcinogens** in tobacco smoke on the respiratory and cardiovascular systems and the addictive component of tobacco.

(b) The symptoms of some diseases directly or indirectly associated with tobacco smoking, including **chronic bronchitis**, **emphysema**, **lung cancer**, and **cardiovascular disease**.

(c) The effects of **nicotine** and **carbon monoxide** (components of tobacco smoke) on the cardiovascular system, including reference to the development of **atherosclerosis**, **coronary heart disease**, and **stroke**.

See the 'Textbook Reference Grid' on pages 8-9 for textbook page references relating to material in this topic.

Supplementary Texts

See pages 5-6 for additional details of these texts:

■ Clegg, C.J., 2002. **Microbes in Action**, (John Murray), chpt 1-5, and chpt 10.

■ Fullick, A., 1998. **Human Health and Disease** (Heinemann), chpt. 2.

■ Hudson, T. & K. Mannion, 2001. **Microbes and Disease** (Collins), pp. 48-69.

See page 7 for details of publishers of periodicals:

STUDENT'S REFERENCE

■ **War on Disease** National Geographic, 201(2) February 2002, pp. 4-31. *An excellent account on the global importance of a range of infectious diseases. A great overview for students & teachers.*

■ **Rules of Contagion** New Scientist, 28 Oct. 2006, pp. 44-47. *The different levels of virulence of infectious diseases and which are the most deadly.*

■ **Deadly Contact** National Geographic 212 (4) Oct. 2007, pp. 78-105. *An account of how disease and pathogens are exchanged between species.*

■ **Chasing the Superbugs** Biol. Sci. Rev., 18(4) April 2006, pp. 21-27. *Gene transfer and its implications to multi-drug resistance in bacteria.*

■ **March of the Superbugs** New Scientist (Inside Science),19 July 2003. *It now seems widespread resistance is making antibiotics worthless. This account describes how resistance arises and how it spreads through bacterial populations.*

■ **Finding and Improving Antibiotics** Biol. Sci. Rev. 12(1) Sept. 1999, pp. 36-38. *Antibiotics, their production & testing, and the search for new drugs.*

Viral Disease

■ **Are Viruses Alive?** Scientific American, Dec. 2004, pp. 77-81. *This account covers the nature of viruses, including viral replication and an evaluation of the status of viruses in the world.*

■ **AIDS** Biol. Sci. Rev., 20(1) Sept. 2007, pp. 30-12. *The HIV virus can evade the immune system and acquire drug resistance. This has prevented effective cures from being developed.*

■ **Opportunistic Infections and AIDS** Biol. Sci. Rev., 14 (4) April 2002, pp. 21-24. *An account of the suite of infections characterising AIDS (good).*

■ **Search for a Cure** National Geographic, 201(2) February 2002, pp. 32-43. *An account of the status of the AIDS epidemic and the measures to stop it.*

Bacterial Disease

■ **The White Plague** New Scientist (Inside Science), 9 Nov. 2002. *The causes and nature of TB, its global incidence, and a discussion of the implications of drug resistance to TB treatment.*

■ **Tuberculosis** Biol. Sci. Rev., 14(1) Sept. 2001, pp. 30-33. *Despite vaccination, TB has become more common recently. Why has it returned?*

Malaria

■ **Mosquitoes** Biol. Sci. Rev., 20(1) Sept. 2007, pp 34-37. *Life cycle of mosquitoes, and the disease they carry including malaria an dengue fever.*

■ **Malaria** Biol. Sci. Rev., 15(1) Sept. 2002, pp. 29-33. *An account of the world's most important parasitic infection of humans. The parasite's life cycle, disease symptoms, control and prevention, and future treatment options are all discussed.*

■ **Beating the Bloodsuckers** Biol. Sci. Rev., 16(3) Feb. 2004, pp. 31-35. *The global distribution of malaria, the current state of malaria research, and an account of the biology of the Plasmodium parasite and the body's immune response to it.*

■ **Will there ever be a Malaria Vaccine?** Biol. Sci. Rev., 19(1), Sept. 2006, pp. 24-28. *An outline of the categories of malarial vaccine development.*

TEACHER'S REFERENCE

■ **Viral Plagues** Biol. Sci. Rev., 17(3) Feb. 2005, pp. 37-41. *The nature of viruses and viral transmission, how viral infections are diagnosed, and what we can do to combat them.*

■ **Tracking the Next Killer Flu** National Geographic, 208(4) Oct. 2005, pp. 4-31. *Discussion on flu viruses and how they spread.*

■ **Preparing for a Pandemic** Scientific American, Nov. 2005, pp. 22-31. *A predicted global epidemic caused by some newly evolved strain of influenza may be temporarily contained with antiviral drugs.*

■ **Capturing a Killer Flu Virus** Scientific American, Jan. 2005, pp. 48-57. *The origin of the killer flu virus remains unsolved even after the virus's genes have been analysed.*

■ **HIV: Vaccines out of Africa** Biologist, 48(2) April 2002. *Vaccination programmes have been successful in wiping out some viral diseases, but they are often difficult to construct. AIDS is proving the famous case to illustrate this difficulty.*

■ **Superbugs Bite Back** New Scientist, 29 Sept. 2007, pp. 37-39. *The difficulties of drug resistant bacteria such as MRSA in hospitals.*

■ **New Medicines for the Developing World** Biol. Sci. Rev. 14 (1) Sept. 2001, pp. 22-26. *The politics of treating disease in the developing world: why is there little incentive to develop programmes to prevent and treat some diseases?*

See pages 10-11 for details of how to access **Bio Links** from our web site: **www.biozone.co.uk**. From Bio Links, access sites under the topics:

GENERAL BIOLOGY ONLINE RESOURCES
• Biology I interactive animations • Instructional multimedia, University of Alberta ... *and others* > **Online Textbooks and Lecture Notes:** • S-Cool! A level biology revision guide Learn.co.uk ... *and others* > **Glossaries:** • Health glossary

HEALTH & DISEASE: • CDC disease links • WHO/OMS: health topics > **Infectious Diseases:** • Centers for Disease Control and Prevention (CDC) • Cholera and epidemic dysentery • Disease-causing bacteria • Emerging infectious diseases • HIV Insite • Koch's postulates • Public Health Laboratory Service: Disease facts • The bad bug book • The science of HIV • Insect vectors of human pathogens ... *and others* > **Prevention and Treatment:** • Antimicrobial agents ... *and others*

Presentation MEDIA to support this topic:

HEALTH & DISEASE:
• Infectious Disease

Health vs Disease

Disease is more difficult to define than **health**, which is described as a state of complete physical, mental, and social well-being. A disease is usually associated with particular **symptoms** that help to define and diagnose it. The term **disease** is used to describe a condition whereby part or all of an organism's normal physiological function is upset. All diseases, with the exception of some mental diseases, can be classified as **physical diseases** (i.e. diseases that cause permanent or temporary damage to the body). Physical diseases can be subdivided into two major groups: **infectious diseases** caused by an infectious agent (**pathogen**) and **non-infectious diseases** (most of which are better described as disorders). Non-infectious diseases are often not clearly the result of any single factor, but they can be further categorised into major subgroups according to their principal cause (outlined below). However, many diseases fall into more than one category, e.g. Alzheimer's disease and some cancers.

The Nature of Disease

Infectious Diseases

Infectious diseases are diseases that are caused by pathogens and which can be transmitted from one person to another. Most, although not all, pathogens are microorganisms, and they fall into five main categories: viruses, bacteria, fungi, protozoans, and multicellular parasites.

Mental Disorders

The term mental disorder encompasses a range of diseases that affect a person's thoughts, memory, emotions, and personal behaviour. Examples include Alzheimer's, schizophrenia, and depression.

Deficiency Diseases

Deficiency diseases are non-infectious diseases caused by an inadequate or unbalanced diet, or by over eating. Examples include obesity, rickets, scurvy, marasmus, and kwashiorkor.

Degenerative Diseases

Degenerative diseases are non-infectious diseases caused by ageing and the inability of the body to carry out effective repairs and regeneration. Examples include osteoarthritis, Alzheimer's disease, and many cancers.

Social Diseases

Social diseases include a wide range of disorders that are influenced by living conditions and personal behaviour. They may or may not be caused by an infectious agent. Examples include obesity, sexually transmitted diseases, and lung cancer and emphysema due to smoking.

Inherited Diseases

Some diseases result from inherited malfunctions in a body system and have no external cause. Defective genes may cause the failure of a body system throughout a person's life, or the onset of disease may occur later in life. Examples include cystic fibrosis, multiple sclerosis, Alzheimer's, and Huntington's disease.

Down syndrome is a congenital disease caused by having three copies of chromosome 21.

Smoking is a common social behaviour that causes lung cancer, chronic bronchitis, and emphysema.

Mental diseases encompass a range of often unrelated disorders involving disturbances to personality.

Asthma is a common, non-infectious respiratory disease with a number of underlying causes.

1. Discuss the differences between health and disease: _____

_____

_____

_____

2. Using illustrative examples, suggest why many diseases fall into more than one disease category:

_____

_____

Related activities: Infection and Disease

A 2

Infection and Disease

The term disease often refers to **infectious disease**; disease caused by an infectious agent or **pathogen**. Many pathogens are also **parasites**, in that they obtain their nutrition from the host and cause disease in doing so. In 1861, **Louis Pasteur** demonstrated experimentally that microorganisms can be present in non-living matter and can contaminate seemingly sterile solutions. He also showed conclusively that microbes can be destroyed by heat; a discovery that formed the basis of modern-day **aseptic technique**. The development of the germ theory of disease followed Pasteur's discoveries and, in 1876-1877, **Robert Koch** established a sequence of experimental steps (now known as **Koch's postulates**) for directly relating a specific microbe to a specific disease. During the past 100 years, the postulates have been invaluable in determining the agents of many diseases.

Infectious Disease

Pathogens and Parasites

Pathogens are organisms that cause disease. Some pathogens are also (intra- or extracellular) **parasites** and derive their nutrition from the host's tissues. The invasion of the body by pathogens is called **infection**. Pathogens can be classified as microorganisms (bacteria, fungi, and viruses) or macroorganisms (i.e. organisms that are visible to the naked eye, such as worms, ticks, and mites). Macroorganisms can cause disease as a direct result of their activity, or they can serve as **vectors** for the transmission of other infectious agents.

Robert Koch

In 1876-1877, the German physician Robert Koch demonstrated that a specific infectious disease (anthrax) was caused by a specific micro-organism (*Bacillus anthracis*). From his work he devised what are now known as **Koch's postulates**.

Koch's postulates

1. The same pathogen must be present in every case of the disease.

2. The pathogen must be isolated from the diseased host and grown in pure culture.

3. The pathogen from the pure culture must cause the disease when it is introduced by inoculation into a healthy, but susceptible organism (usually animal).

4. The pathogen must be isolated from the inoculated animal and be shown to be the original organism.

Exceptions to Koch's Postulates

- Some bacteria and viruses cannot be grown on artificial media (they multiply only within cells).

- Some pathogens cause several disease conditions (e.g. *Mycobacterium tuberculosis*, *Streptococcus pyogenes*).

Types of Pathogens

Bacteria: All bacteria are prokaryotes, but they are diverse in both their structure and metabolism. Bacteria are categorised according to the properties of their cell walls and characteristics such as cell shape and arrangements, oxygen requirement, and motility. Many bacteria are useful, but the relatively few species that are pathogenic are responsible for enormous social and economic cost.

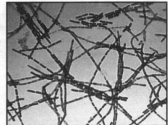

Bacillus anthracis: the rod-shaped bacterial pathogen that causes anthrax

Eukaryotic pathogens: Eukaryotic pathogens (fungi, algae, protozoa, and parasitic worms) include the pathogens responsible for malaria and schistosomiasis. Many are highly specialised parasites with a number of hosts. Serious fungal diseases are also more prevalent now than in the past, affecting those with compromised immune systems, such as AIDS patients.

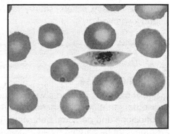

The malarial parasite, *Plasmodium*, seen in a red blood cell smear.

Viral pathogens: Viruses are responsible for many of the everyday diseases with which we are familiar (e.g. the common cold), as well as rather more alarming and dangerous diseases, such as Ebola. Viruses were first distinguished from other pathogens because of their small size and because they are obligate intracellular parasites and need living host cells in order to multiply.

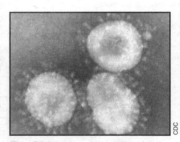

The *Coronavirus* responsible for the 2003 global epidemic of SARS.

1. (a) Using an example, explain clearly what is meant by a **pathogen**: _____

    _____

    (b) Identify a parasite that is also a pathogen, explaining the reasons for your choice: _____

    _____

    _____

2. Describe the contribution of Robert Koch to the **aetiology** of disease: _____

    _____

3. Suggest why diseases caused by **intracellular protozoan parasites** can be particularly difficult to control and treat:

    _____

    _____

Transmission of Disease

The human body, like that of other large animals, is under constant attack by a wide range of potential parasites and pathogens. Once inside us, these organisms seek to reproduce and exploit us for food. Pathogens may be transferred from one individual to another by a number of methods (below). The transmission of infectious diseases can be virtually eliminated by observing appropriate personal hygiene procedures, and by chlorinating drinking water and providing adequate sanitation.

Human Disease

Portals of Entry

The Body Under Assault

Modes of Transmission

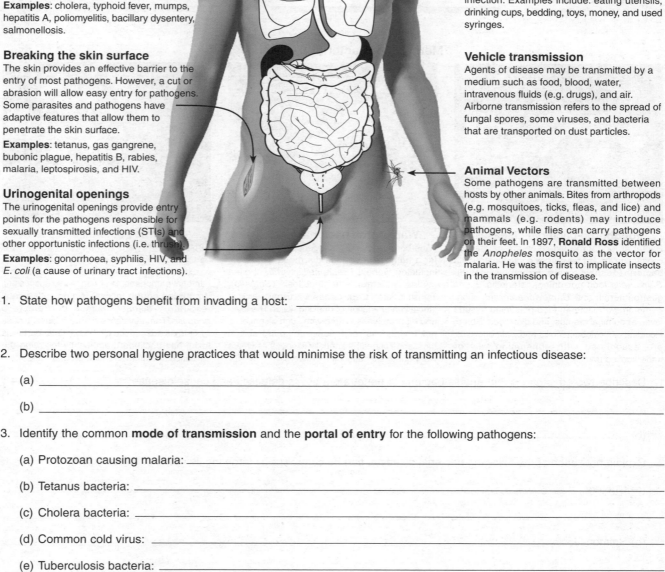

Respiratory tract

The mouth and nose are major entry points for pathogens, particularly airborne viruses, which are inhaled from other people's expelled mucus.

Examples: diphtheria, meningococcal meningitis, tuberculosis, whooping cough, influenza, measles, German measles (rubella), chickenpox.

Gastrointestinal tract

The mouth is one of the few openings where we deliberately place foreign substances into our body. Food is often contaminated with microorganisms, but most of these are destroyed in the stomach.

Examples: cholera, typhoid fever, mumps, hepatitis A, poliomyelitis, bacillary dysentery, salmonellosis.

Breaking the skin surface

The skin provides an effective barrier to the entry of most pathogens. However, a cut or abrasion will allow easy entry for pathogens. Some parasites and pathogens have adaptive features that allow them to penetrate the skin surface.

Examples: tetanus, gas gangrene, bubonic plague, hepatitis B, rabies, malaria, leptospirosis, and HIV.

Urinogenital openings

The urinogenital openings provide entry points for the pathogens responsible for sexually transmitted infections (STIs) and other opportunistic infections (i.e. thrush).

Examples: gonorrhoea, syphilis, HIV, and *E. coli* (a cause of urinary tract infections).

Contact transmission

The agent of disease may occur by contact with other infected humans or animals:

Droplet transmission: Mucus droplets are discharged into the air by coughing, sneezing, laughing, or talking within a radius of 1 m.

Direct contact: Direct transmission of an agent by physical contact between its source and a potential host. Includes touching, kissing, and sexual intercourse. May be person to person, or between humans and other animals.

Indirect contact: Includes touching objects that have been in contact with the source of infection. Examples include: eating utensils, drinking cups, bedding, toys, money, and used syringes.

Vehicle transmission

Agents of disease may be transmitted by a medium such as food, blood, water, intravenous fluids (e.g. drugs), and air. Airborne transmission refers to the spread of fungal spores, some viruses, and bacteria that are transported on dust particles.

Animal Vectors

Some pathogens are transmitted between hosts by other animals. Bites from arthropods (e.g. mosquitoes, ticks, fleas, and lice) and mammals (e.g. rodents) may introduce pathogens, while flies can carry pathogens on their feet. In 1897, **Ronald Ross** identified the *Anopheles* mosquito as the vector for malaria. He was the first to implicate insects in the transmission of disease.

1. State how pathogens benefit from invading a host: _____

_____

2. Describe two personal hygiene practices that would minimise the risk of transmitting an infectious disease:

(a) _____

(b) _____

3. Identify the common **mode of transmission** and the **portal of entry** for the following pathogens:

(a) Protozoan causing malaria: _____

(b) Tetanus bacteria: _____

(c) Cholera bacteria: _____

(d) Common cold virus: _____

(e) Tuberculosis bacteria: _____

(f) HIV (AIDS) virus: _____

(g) Gonorrhoea bacteria: _____

Bacterial Diseases

Relatively few of the world's bacterial species cause disease. Those that do, the so-called pathogenic bacteria, have and range of adaptations that enable them to penetrate the defences of a host and cause an infection (diagram below). Bacterial diseases are commonly transmitted through food, water, air, or by direct contact. The natural reservoir (source of infection) of a disease varies from species to species, ranging from humans and other organisms, to sewage or contaminated water. Much of our control of bacterial disease is achieved through identifying reservoirs of infection and limiting the routes of transmission.

How Bacteria Invade a Host's Tissues

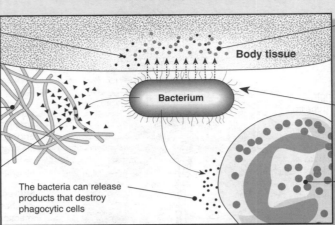

Toxins: Bacterial toxins can act locally to promote bacterial invasion (e.g. the enzymes that degrade collagen), or they may have cytotoxic activity and destroy cells directly.

Fibrin: Fibrous threads of protein are deposited when blood clots. This action by the host effectively limits the movement of pathogens in infected areas.

Enzymes are released that break down fibrin, allowing the bacteria greater freedom of movement.

The bacteria can release products that destroy phagocytic cells

Body tissue

Bacterium

The bacterium releases enzymes that degrade the connective tissue of the host, allowing the spread of infection.

Fimbriae: Fine, threadlike extensions from the bacterial cell, called fimbriae, enable the bacteria to attach to the mucous membranes and directly attack the nearby host tissues.

Phagocyte: These white blood cells are very effective in identifying and destroying foreign cells such as pathogens.

Methods of Bacterial Transmission

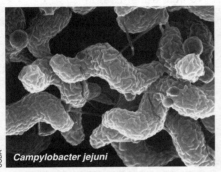

Campylobacter jejuni

Salmonella typhi

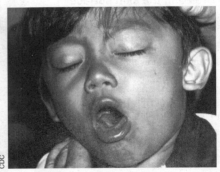

Foodborne bacterial diseases

Bacterial foodborne illnesses are caused by consuming food or beverages contaminated with bacteria or their toxins. Examples include *Salmonella* food poisoning, listeriosis, *E.coli* gastroenteritis and *Campylobacter* infection. Symptoms of bacterial food poisoning include fever, abdominal cramps, and diarrhoea. Some, including campylobacteriosis and salmonellosis, are associated with consuming raw or undercooked poultry.

Waterborne bacterial diseases

Waterborne bacterial pathogens are responsible for a number of serious diarrhoeal illnesses, including typhoid (*Salmonella typhi*), cholera (*Vibrio cholerae*), and shigellosis (*Shigella*). Transmission of these diseases is usually through faecal contamination of drinking water. The fever and diarrhoea associated with such diseases is not trivial; it is responsible for hundreds of thousands of deaths annually in countries where inadequate sanitation is a problem.

Airborne bacterial diseases

Airborne pathogens are transmitted on dust particles or droplets when people cough, sneeze, or exhale. Vaccination against certain airborne bacterial pathogens has been highly successful. **Whooping cough** (above) is a potentially fatal respiratory disease caused by *Bordetella pertussis*. The prevalence of this disease, whose symptoms are caused by the bacterial pertussis toxin, has declined dramatically following the introduction of immunisation programmes.

1. Describe two adaptations that enable bacteria to penetrate a host's defences and cause disease:

   (a) _____

   (b) _____

2. Explain how each of the following bacterial diseases can be controlled by targeting its mode of transmission:

   (a) Cholera: _____

   _____

   (b) Salmonellosis: _____

   _____

3. Explain why immunisation is often a good option for controlling airborne bacterial diseases: _____

   _____

Related activities: TB, Foodborne Disease, Cholera, Antimicrobial Drugs
Web links: Microbiology in Motion

Tuberculosis

Tuberculosis (TB) is a contagious disease caused by the *Mycobacterium tuberculosis* bacterium (**MTB**). The breakdown in health services in some countries, the spread of HIV/AIDS, and the emergence of **multidrug-resistant TB** are contributing to the increasingly harmful impact of this disease. In 1993, the World Health Organisation (WHO) responded to the growing pandemic and declared TB a global emergency. By 1998, the WHO estimated that about a third of the world's population were already infected with MTB. They estimate that 8 million new cases are added annually and that TB causes about 2 million deaths each year (note that in the figures below, only **notified cases** are reported). If controls are not strengthened, it is anticipated that between 2002 and 2020, approximately 1000 million people will be newly infected, over 150 million people will get sick, and 36 million will die from TB.

Infection and Transmission

TB is a contagious disease, and is spread through the air when infectious people cough, sneeze, talk, or spit. A person needs only to inhale a small number of MTB to be infected.

Left untreated, each person with active TB will infect on average between 10 and 15 people every year. People infected with MTB will not necessarily get sick with the disease; the immune system 'walls off' the MTB which can lie dormant for years, protected by a thick waxy coat. When the immune system is weakened, the chance of getting sick (showing symptoms) is greater.

Symptoms

TB usually affects the lungs, but it can also affect other parts of the body, such as the brain, the kidneys, and the spine.

The general symptoms of TB disease include weakness and nausea, weight loss, fever, and night sweats. The symptoms of TB of the lungs include coughing, chest pain, and coughing up blood. The bacteria can spread from the bronchioles to other body systems, where the symptoms depend on the part of the body that is affected.

Treatment

TB is treated with an aggressive antibiotic regime. Since the early 1990s, the WHO has recommended the DOTS (Directly Observed Therapy, Short-course) strategy to control TB worldwide. This programme improves the proportion of patients successfully completing therapy (taking their full course of antibiotics). Proper completion of treatment is the most effective way in which to combat increasing drug resistance.

The Pathogenesis of Tuberculosis

The series below illustrates stages in MTB infection.

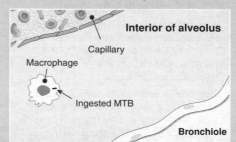

MTB enter the lung and are ingested by macrophages (phagocytic white blood cells).

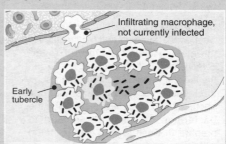

The multiplying bacteria cause the macrophages to swell and rupture. The newly released bacilli infect other macrophages. At this stage a tubercle may form and the disease may lie dormant.

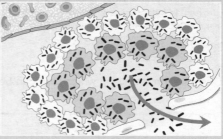

Eventually the tubercle ruptures, allowing bacilli to spill into the bronchiole. The bacilli can now be transmitted when the infected person coughs.

Estimated TB Incidence Rates in 2006 (cases per 100 000)

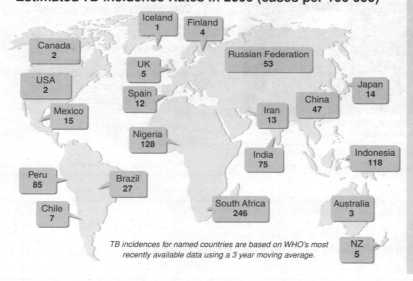

TB incidences for named countries are based on WHO's most recently available data using a 3 year moving average.

1. Identify the pathogen that causes tuberculosis (TB): _____

2. Explain how MTB may exist in a dormant state in a person for many years without causing disease symptoms:

_____
_____

3. State how TB is transmitted between people: _____

_____

4. Suggest how some strains of MTB have acquired **multi-drug resistance**: _____

_____
_____

Related activities: Bacteria Cells, The Human Respiratory System, Bacterial Disease, Emerging Diseases   **Web links**: Microbiology in Motion

RA 2

Foodborne Disease

Foodborne disease is caused by consuming contaminated foods or beverages. More than 250 food and waterborne diseases have been identified. The symptoms and severity of these vary according to the infectious agent, although diarrhoea and vomiting are two universal symptoms. Food poisoning is a term used for any gastrointestinal illness with sudden onset, usually accompanied by stomach pain, diarrhoea, and vomiting, and caused by eating **contaminated food**. It is a common cause of **gastroenteritis** (inflammation of the stomach and intestines). In 2005, there were an estimated 79 000 foodborne illnesses in the UK alone, although about 20% of these were acquired abroad. Such illnesses usually result from food contaminated with viruses, or bacteria or their toxins. They may also result from contamination of food or water by chemicals such as nitrates.

Common Sources of Bacterial Food Poisoning

Salmonella Infections

Most serotypes of *Salmonella* bacteria are pathogenic. **Endotoxins** released from dead bacteria are a likely (but not proven) cause of the symptoms associated with infection.

Salmonella enteritidis can spread to humans via a variety of foods of animal origin (especially poultry products) and is the cause of **salmonellosis** (*Salmonella* food poisoning). Typical symptoms include fever, accompanied by diarrhoea and abdominal cramps.

Salmonella typhi is a highly pathogenic *Salmonella* serotype and causes the life threatening disease, **typhoid fever**. *S. typhi* lives in humans and is shed in the faeces. Transmission occurs through the ingestion of food or drink that has been handled by a person shedding the bacterium, or when water used to prepare of wash food is contaminated with sewage containing the pathogen. Recovered patients can become carriers and continue to shed the bacteria and spread infection. Typhoid fever is common in most regions of the world except in industrialised nations such as the USA, Canada, and western Europe.

Faecal contamination of the hands at meal times is a common cause of gastroenteritis.

Sharing food and utensils may transmit foodborne pathogens between individuals.

Inadequate supply of clean drinking water is a major problem in many parts of the world.

E. coli Gastroenteritis

Escherichia coli is the most common form of infantile and travellers' diarrhoea in developing countries. *E. coli* is the most abundant microbe in the intestinal tract and is normally harmless. However, certain strains are pathogenic and have specialised fimbriae allowing them to bind to the intestinal epithelial cells. They also release **exotoxins** which cause the production of copious watery diarrhoea and symptoms similar to mild cholera. *E. coli* infection is caused by poor sanitation and can be very difficult to avoid in developing countries.

Staphylococcus aureus

S. aureus is a normal inhabitant of human nasal passages. From here, it can contaminate the hands, where it may cause skin lesions and/or contaminate food. Contaminated food held at room temperature will rapidly produce a population of about 1 million bacteria per gram of food and enough **exotoxin** to cause illness. Unusually, the toxin is heat stable and can survive up to 30 minutes of boiling. Reheating the contaminated food may destroy the bacteria but not the toxin itself.

1. Describe three ways in which food can become contaminated by *E. coli*: _____

_____

_____

2. Describe why food poisoning is more prevalent in developing countries than in developed countries: _____

_____

_____

3. Outline the basic precautions that should be taken with drinking water when travelling to developing countries: _____

_____

_____

4. (a) Describe the symptoms of salmonellosis: _____

_____

(b) Identify the method of transmission of this disease: _____

5. Explain why reheating food will still cause food poisoning if the food is contaminated with *Staphylococcus aureus*:

_____

Related activities: The Control of Disease

Cholera

Cholera is an acute intestinal infection caused by the bacterium *Vibrio cholerae*. The disease has a short incubation period, from one to five days. The bacterium produces an enterotoxin that causes a copious, painless, watery diarrhoea that can quickly lead to severe dehydration and death if treatment is not promptly given. Most people infected with *V. cholerae* do not become ill, although the bacterium is present in their faeces for 7-14 days. When cholera appears in a community it is essential to take measures against its spread. These include: **hygienic disposal of human faeces**, provision of an adequate supply of **safe drinking water**, **safe food handling and preparation** (e.g. preventing contamination of food and cooking food thoroughly), and **effective general hygiene** (e.g. hand washing with soap). Cholera has reemerged as a global health threat after virtually disappearing from the Americas and most of Africa and Europe for more than a century. Originally restricted to the Indian subcontinent, cholera spread to Europe in 1817 in the first of seven pandemics. The current pandemic (below) shows signs of slowly abating, although under-reporting is a problem.

Symptoms

More than 90% of cases are of mild or moderate severity and are difficult to distinguish from other types of acute diarrhoea. Less than 10% of ill people develop typical cholera with signs of moderate or severe dehydration.

Treatment

Most cases of diarrhoea can be treated by giving a solution of oral rehydration salts. During an epidemic, 80-90% of diarrhoea patients can be treated by oral rehydration alone, but patients who become severely dehydrated must be given intravenous fluids. In severe cases, antibiotics can reduce the volume and duration of diarrhoea and reduce the presence of *V. cholerae* in the faeces.

Transmission

Cholera is spread by contaminated water and food. Sudden large outbreaks are usually caused by a contaminated water supply. *Vibrio cholerae* is often found in the aquatic environment and is part of the normal flora of brackish water and estuaries. Human beings are also one of the reservoirs of the pathogenic form of *Vibrio cholerae*.

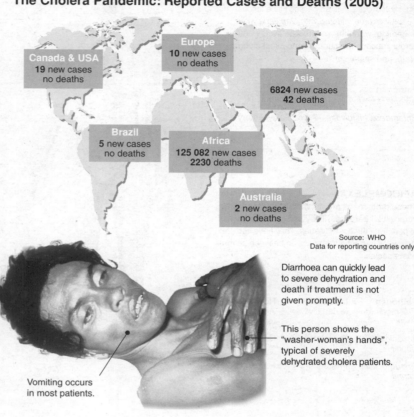

The Cholera Pandemic: Reported Cases and Deaths (2005)

Europe
10 new cases
no deaths

Canada & USA
19 new cases
no deaths

Asia
6824 new cases
42 deaths

Brazil
5 new cases
no deaths

Africa
125 082 new cases
2230 deaths

Australia
2 new cases
no deaths

Source: WHO
Data for reporting countries only

Diarrhoea can quickly lead to severe dehydration and death if treatment is not given promptly.

This person shows the "washer-woman's hands", typical of severely dehydrated cholera patients.

Vomiting occurs in most patients.

1. Identify the pathogen that causes cholera: _____

2. Describe the symptoms of cholera and explain why these symptoms are so dangerous if not treated quickly:

_____

_____

_____

3. State how cholera is transmitted between people: _____

_____

4. Describe the effective treatment of cholera at the following stages in the progression of the disease:

   (a) Mild onset of dehydration: _____

   (b) Severe symptoms: _____

5. Identify the risk factors associated with the incidence of cholera and relate these to social and economic conditions:

_____

_____

_____

Related activities: The Control of Disease

A 2

Protozoan Diseases

Protozoa are one-celled, eukaryotic organisms that belong to the Kingdom Protoctista. Among the protozoans, there are many variations on cell structure. While most inhabit water and soil habitats, some are part of the natural microbiota of animals (i.e. they are microorganisms that live on or in animals). Relatively few of the nearly 20 000 species of protozoans cause disease; those that do are often highly specialised, intracellular parasites with complex life cycles involving one or more hosts. Under certain adverse conditions, some protozoans produce a protective capsule called a **cyst**. A cyst allows the protozoan to survive conditions unsuitable for survival. For specialised parasitic species, this includes survival for periods outside a host.

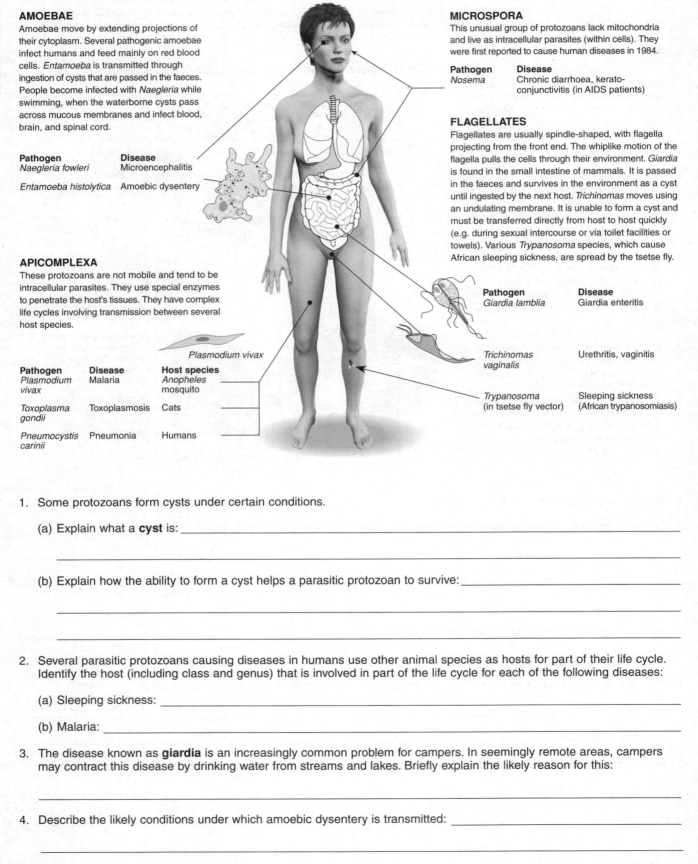

AMOEBAE

Amoebae move by extending projections of their cytoplasm. Several pathogenic amoebae infect humans and feed mainly on red blood cells. *Entamoeba* is transmitted through ingestion of cysts that are passed in the faeces. People become infected with *Naegleria* while swimming, when the waterborne cysts pass across mucous membranes and infect blood, brain, and spinal cord.

Pathogen	Disease
Naegleria fowleri	Microencephalitis
Entamoeba histolytica	Amoebic dysentery

APICOMPLEXA

These protozoans are not mobile and tend to be intracellular parasites. They use special enzymes to penetrate the host's tissues. They have complex life cycles involving transmission between several host species.

Plasmodium vivax

Pathogen	Disease	Host species
Plasmodium vivax	Malaria	*Anopheles* mosquito
Toxoplasma gondii	Toxoplasmosis	Cats
Pneumocystis carinii	Pneumonia	Humans

MICROSPORA

This unusual group of protozoans lack mitochondria and live as intracellular parasites (within cells). They were first reported to cause human diseases in 1984.

Pathogen	Disease
Nosema	Chronic diarrhoea, kerato-conjunctivitis (in AIDS patients)

FLAGELLATES

Flagellates are usually spindle-shaped, with flagella projecting from the front end. The whiplike motion of the flagella pulls the cells through their environment. *Giardia* is found in the small intestine of mammals. It is passed in the faeces and survives in the environment as a cyst until ingested by the next host. *Trichinomas* moves using an undulating membrane. It is unable to form a cyst and must be transferred directly from host to host quickly (e.g. during sexual intercourse or via toilet facilities or towels). Various *Trypanosoma* species, which cause African sleeping sickness, are spread by the tsetse fly.

Pathogen	Disease
Giardia lamblia	Giardia enteritis
Trichinomas vaginalis	Urethritis, vaginitis
Trypanosoma (in tsetse fly vector)	Sleeping sickness (African trypanosomiasis)

1. Some protozoans form cysts under certain conditions.

   (a) Explain what a **cyst** is: _____

   _____

   (b) Explain how the ability to form a cyst helps a parasitic protozoan to survive: _____

   _____

   _____

2. Several parasitic protozoans causing diseases in humans use other animal species as hosts for part of their life cycle. Identify the host (including class and genus) that is involved in part of the life cycle for each of the following diseases:

   (a) Sleeping sickness: _____

   (b) Malaria: _____

3. The disease known as **giardia** is an increasingly common problem for campers. In seemingly remote areas, campers may contract this disease by drinking water from streams and lakes. Briefly explain the likely reason for this:

   _____

4. Describe the likely conditions under which amoebic dysentery is transmitted: _____

   _____

Related activities: Malaria
Web links: Animations for Parasitism

Malaria

Malaria is a serious parasitic disease, spread by bites of **Anopheles mosquitoes**, affecting up to 300 million people in the tropics each year. The parasites responsible for malaria are protozoa known as **plasmodia**. Four species can cause the disease in humans. Each spends part of its life cycle in humans and part in *Anopheles* mosquitoes. Even people who take antimalarial drugs and precautions against being bitten may contract malaria. Malaria, especially *falciparum* malaria, is often a medical emergency that requires hospitalisation. Treatment involves the use of antimalarial drugs and, in severe cases, blood transfusions may be necessary. Symptoms, which appear one to two weeks after being bitten, include headache, shaking, chills, and fever. *Falciparum* malaria is more severe, with high fever, coma, and convulsions, and it can be fatal within a few days of the first symptoms. These more severe symptoms result from this plasmodium's ability to infect all ages of red blood cells (whereas other species attack only young or old cells). Destruction of a greater proportion of blood cells results in *haemolytic anaemia*. The infected blood cells become sticky and block blood vessels to vital organs such as the kidneys and the brain.

Malaria

Malaria occurs in over 100 countries and territories. More than 40% of the people in the world are at risk. Large areas of Central and South America, Hispaniola (Haiti and the Dominican Republic), Africa, the Indian subcontinent, Southeast Asia, the Middle East, and Oceania are considered malaria-risk areas (an area of the world that has malaria).

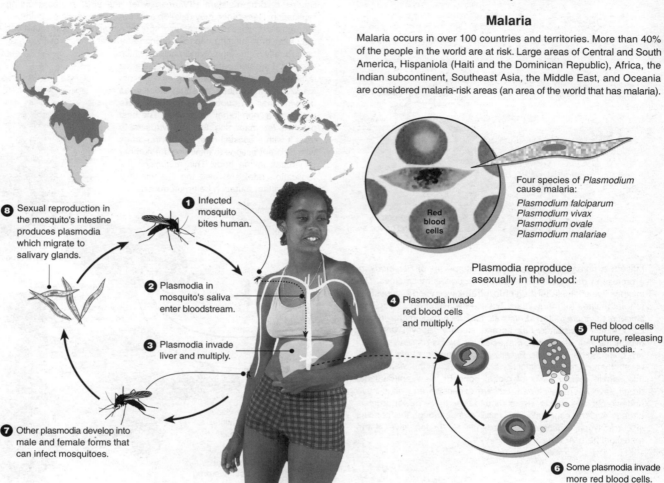

Four species of *Plasmodium* cause malaria:

Plasmodium falciparum
Plasmodium vivax
Plasmodium ovale
Plasmodium malariae

Red blood cells

Plasmodia reproduce asexually in the blood:

8 Sexual reproduction in the mosquito's intestine produces plasmodia which migrate to salivary glands.

1 Infected mosquito bites human.

2 Plasmodia in mosquito's saliva enter bloodstream.

3 Plasmodia invade liver and multiply.

4 Plasmodia invade red blood cells and multiply.

5 Red blood cells rupture, releasing plasmodia.

6 Some plasmodia invade more red blood cells.

7 Other plasmodia develop into male and female forms that can infect mosquitoes.

1. Explain how a plasmodium parasite enters the body: _____

_____

2. Suggest a way in which villagers could reduce the occurrence of malaria carrying mosquitoes in their immediate area:

_____

3. (a) Describe the symptoms of a malaria attack: _____

_____

(b) Explain why the symptoms of *falciparum* malaria are more severe than other forms of malaria: _____

_____

_____

4. Global warming is expected to increase the geographical area of malaria infection. Explain why this is expected:

_____

_____

Resistance in Pathogens

Many pathogens are effectively controlled by the use of drugs and vaccines, but the emergence of drug resistant pathogens is increasingly undermining the ability to treat and control killer diseases such as HIV/AIDS, tuberculosis, and malaria. High mutation rates and short generation times in viral, bacterial, and protozoan pathogens have contributed to the rapid spread of drug resistance through populations. This is well documented for malaria (below), TB, and HIV/AIDS. Rapid evolution in pathogens is exacerbated too by the strong selection pressure created by the wide use and misuse of antimicrobial drugs, the poor quality of available drugs, and poor patient compliance. The most successful treatment for several diseases, including HIV/AIDS and TB appears to be a multi-pronged attack using a cocktail of drugs to target the pathogen at many stages.

Global Spread of Chloroquine Resistance

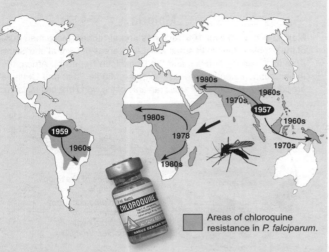

Areas of chloroquine resistance in *P. falciparum*.

Malaria in humans is caused by various species of *Plasmodium*, a protozoan parasite transmitted by *Anopheles* mosquitoes. The inexpensive antimalarial drug **chloroquine** was used successfully to treat malaria for many years, but its effectiveness has declined since resistance to the drug was first recorded in the 1960s. Chloroquine resistance has spread steadily (above) and now two of the four *Plasmodium* species, *P. falciparum* and *P. vivax* are chloroquine-resistant. *P. falciparum* alone accounts for 80% of all human malarial infections and 90% of the deaths, so this rise in resistance is of global concern. New anti-malarial drugs have been developed, but are expensive and often have undesirable side effects. Resistance to even these newer drugs is already evident, especially in *P. falciparum*, although this species is currently still susceptible to artemisinin, a derivative of the medicinal herb *Artemisia annua*.

Drug Resistance in HIV

Strains of drug-resistant HIV arise when the virus mutates during replication. Resistance may develop as a result of a single mutation, or through a step-wise accumulation of specific mutations. These mutations may alter drug binding capacity or increase viral fitness, or they may be naturally occurring polymorphisms (which occur in untreated patients). Drug resistance is likely to develop in patients who do not follow their treatment schedule closely, as the virus has an opportunity to adapt more readily to a "non-lethal" drug dose. The best practice for managing the HIV virus is to treat it with a cocktail of anti-retroviral drugs with different actions to minimise the number of viruses in the body. This minimises the replication rate, and also the chance of a drug resistant mutation being produced.

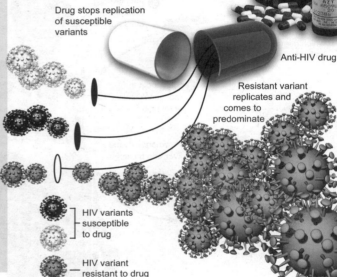

Anti-HIV drug

Drug stops replication of susceptible variants

Resistant variant replicates and comes to predominate

HIV variants susceptible to drug

HIV variant resistant to drug

1. Describe factors contributing to the rapid spread of drug resistance in pathogens: _____

_____

_____

2. With reference to a specific example, explain how drug resistance arises in a pathogen population:

_____

_____

_____

_____

3. Suggest how health authorities could target multiple drug resistance in common pathogens: _____

_____

_____

_____

Viral Diseases

Some crop and livestock diseases, and many diseases of humans are caused by viruses (see below and the next page). Most viruses are able to infect specific types of cells of only one host species. The particular **host range** is determined by the virus's requirements for its specific attachment to the host cell and the availability, within the host, of the cellular factors needed for viral multiplication. For animal viruses, the receptor sites are on the plasma membranes of the host cells. Antiviral drugs are difficult to design because they must kill the virus without killing the host cells. Moreover, viruses cannot be attacked when in an inert state.

Antiviral drugs work by preventing entry of the virus into the host cell or by interfering with their replication. There are only a few antiviral drugs currently in use (e.g. ribavirin to combat influenza, acyclovir to combat herpes, AZT and protease inhibitors to combat HIV/AIDS). Immunisation is still regarded as the most effective way in which to control viral disease. However immunisation against viruses does not necessarily provide lifelong immunity. New viral strains develop as preexisting strains acquire mutations. These mutations allow the viruses to change their surface proteins and thus evade detection by the host's immune system.

Types of Viruses Affecting Humans

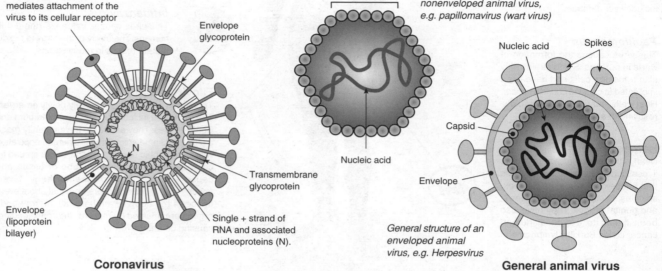

Spike glycoprotein has a receptor binding region that mediates attachment of the virus to its cellular receptor

Envelope glycoprotein

Transmembrane glycoprotein

Single + strand of RNA and associated nucleoproteins (N).

Envelope (lipoprotein bilayer)

Coronavirus

Protein capsid

General structure of a nonenveloped animal virus, e.g. papillomavirus (wart virus)

Nucleic acid

Nucleic acid

Spikes

Capsid

Envelope

General structure of an enveloped animal virus, e.g. Herpesvirus

General animal virus

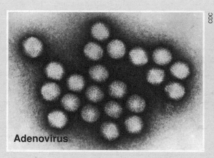

Adenovirus

Adenoviruses are medium-sized (90-100 nm), nonenveloped viruses containing double-stranded DNA. They most commonly cause respiratory illness and are unusually stable to chemical or physical agents, allowing for prolonged survival outside of the body.

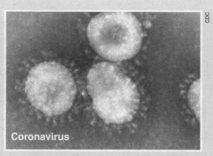

Coronavirus

Coronaviruses primarily infect the upper respiratory and gastrointestinal tracts of birds and mammals, including humans. Their name derives from the crown or corona of spikes and they have the largest genome of any of the single stranded RNA viruses.

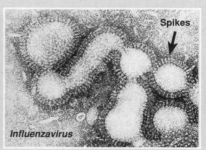

Influenzavirus

Spikes

In some viruses, the capsid is covered by an **envelope**, which protects the virus from the host's nuclease enzymes. Spikes on the envelope provide a binding site for attachment to the host. *Influenzavirus* is an enveloped virus with many glycoprotein spikes.

---

1. Summarise important features of each of the following viral pathogens. For disease symptoms, consult a textbook, the internet, a good dictionary, or an encyclopedia:

(a) HIV causes the disease: _____

Natural reservoir: _____ Symptoms: _____

_____

_____

(b) Coronaviruses cause: _____

Natural reservoir: _____ Symptoms: _____

Related activities: HIV and AIDS, Replication in Animal Viruses
Web links: Viral Infection

RA 2

Human Viral Pathogens

HIV (*Lentivirus*)

The human immunodeficiency virus (HIV) causes AIDS. AIDS is a complex assortment of secondary infections that result after HIV has severely weakened the body's immune system.

Hepatitis viruses

The viruses responsible for hepatitis A, B, and C are not related and are from different viral families. Symptoms include liver damage.

Papillomavirus

This virus causes the formation of warts in humans. Some strains may also transform cells and have been implicated in causing cervical cancer. Host cells may reproduce rapidly, resulting in a tumour.

Herpesviruses

Nearly 100 herpesviruses are known. Types found in humans include those that cause cold sores, chickenpox, shingles, infectious mononucleosis, and genital herpes. They have also been linked to a type of human cancer called Burkitt's lymphoma.

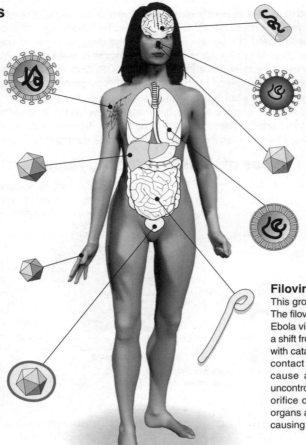

Lyssavirus

This bullet-shaped virus causes rabies and is usually contracted from a bite by a rabid dog or fox.

Coronaviruses

Associated with upper respiratory infections and responsible for 15-20% of colds. A coronavirus is responsible for the disease SARS.

Rhinoviruses

More than 100 rhinoviruses exist and are the most common cause of colds.

Influenzavirus

This virus causes influenza (the flu) in humans. The ability of this virus to rapidly mutate results in many strains.

Filoviruses

This group of viruses is relatively newly emerged. The filoviruses include the dangerous Marburg and Ebola viruses. They appear to have recently made a shift from some animal into the human population with catastrophic results. Filoviruses are spread by contact with contaminated blood or tissue and cause a severe form of haemorrhagic fever; uncontrolled bleeding occurs from just about every orifice of the body. Eventually, all internal body organs are affected by massive internal bleeding, causing death.

(c) *Influenzavirus* causes the disease: _____

Natural reservoir: _____ Symptoms: _____

_____

(d) Filoviruses cause: _____

Natural reservoir: _____ Symptoms: _____

_____

2. Describe the basis of viral host specificity and explain why viruses generally show a very narrow host range:

_____

_____

3. In view of your answer above, explain why it is not uncommon for viruses to cross the species barrier to infect another host type. Provide an example to illustrate your answer:

_____

_____

_____

4. Giving an example, explain why it is difficult to develop suitable long term vaccines against some viruses:

_____

_____

_____

HIV and AIDS

AIDS (acquired immune deficiency syndrome) first appeared in the news in 1981, with cases being reported in Los Angeles, in the United States. By 1983, the pathogen causing the disease had been identified as a retrovirus that selectively infects **helper T cells**. The disease causes a massive deficiency in the immune system due to infection with **HIV** (human immunodeficiency virus). HIV is a retrovirus (RNA, not DNA) and is able to splice its genes into the host cell's chromosome. As yet, there is no cure or vaccine, and

the disease has taken the form of a **pandemic**, spreading to all parts of the globe and killing more than a million people each year. It has now been established that HIV arose by the recombination of two simian viruses. It has probably been endemic in some central African regions for decades, as HIV has been found in blood samples from several African nations from as early as 1959. HIV's mode of infection is described on the next page and its origin and prevalence are covered in the next activity.

Capsid
Protein coat that protects the nucleic acids (RNA) within.

Viral envelope
A piece of the cell membrane budded off from the last human host cell.

Nucleic acid
Two identical strands of RNA contain the genetic blueprint for making more HIV viruses.

Reverse transcriptase
Two copies of this important enzyme convert the RNA into DNA once inside a host cell.

Surface proteins
These spikes allow HIV to attach to receptors on the host cells (T cells and macrophages).

The structure of HIV

HIV/AIDS

Individuals affected by the human immunodeficiency virus (HIV) may have no symptoms, while medical examination may detect swollen lymph glands. Others may experience a short-lived illness when they first become infected (resembling infectious mononucleosis). The range of symptoms resulting from HIV infection is huge, and is not the result of the HIV infection directly. The symptoms arise from an onslaught of secondary infections that gain a foothold in the body due to the suppressed immune system (due to the few helper T cells). These infections are from normally rare fungal, viral, and bacterial sources. Full blown AIDS can also feature some rare forms of cancer. Some symptoms are listed below:

Fever, lymphoma (cancer) and toxoplasmosis of the brain, dementia.

Eye infections (*Cytomegalovirus*).

Skin inflammation (dermatitis) particularly affecting the face.

Oral thrush (*Candida albicans*) of the oesophagus, bronchi, and lungs.

A variety of opportunistic infections, including: chronic or persistent *Herpes simplex*, tuberculosis (TB), pneumocystis pneumonia, shingles, shigellosis and salmonellosis.

Diarrhoea caused by *Isospora* or *Cryptosporidium*.

Marked weight loss.
A number of autoimmune diseases, especially destruction of platelets.

Kaposi's sarcoma: a highly aggressive malignant skin tumour consisting of blue-red nodules, usually start at the feet and ankles, spreading to the rest of the body later, including respiratory and gastrointestinal tracts.

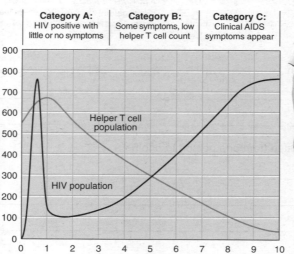

Category A: HIV positive with little or no symptoms	Category B: Some symptoms, low helper T cell count	Category C: Clinical AIDS symptoms appear

Helper T cell concentration in blood / cells mm^{-3}

Helper T cell population

HIV population

Years

The stages of an HIV infection

AIDS is actually only the end stage of an HIV infection. Shortly after the initial infection, HIV antibodies appear within the blood. The progress of infection has three clinical categories shown on the graph above.

1. Explain why the HIV virus has such a devastating effect on the human body's ability to fight disease:

_____

_____

_____

2. Consult the graph above showing the stages of HIV infection (remember, HIV infects and destroys helper T cells).

   (a) Describe how the virus population changes with the progression of the disease: _____

   _____

   _____

Related activities: AIDS Epidemiology, Replication in Animal Viruses
Web links: HIV Interactive Animation

Transmission, Diagnosis, Treatment, and Prevention of HIV

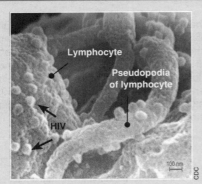

A SEM shows spherical HIV-1 virions on the surface of a human lymphocyte.

Modes of Transmission

1. HIV is transmitted in blood, vaginal secretions, semen, breast milk, and across the placenta.

2. In developed countries, blood transfusions are no longer a likely source of infection because blood is tested for HIV antibodies.

3. Historically, transmission of HIV in developed countries has been primarily through intravenous drug use and homosexual activity, but heterosexual transmission is increasing.

4. Transmission via heterosexual activity is important in Asia and Africa.

Treatment and Prevention

HIV's ability to destroy, evade, and hide inside cells of the human immune system make it difficult to treat. Research into conventional and extremely unconventional approaches to vaccination and chemotherapy is taking place. The first chemotherapy drug to show promise was AZT, which is a nucleotide analogue that inhibits reverse transcriptase. Protease inhibitors (Saquinavir, Ritonavir, Indinavir) are drugs that work by blocking the HIV protease. Once this is blocked, HIV makes copies of itself that cannot infect other cells. These drugs seem to be less toxic and to have less severe side effects than other anti-AIDS drugs. Subunit vaccines are being tested that use HIV glycoproteins inserted into other viruses.

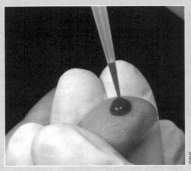

Diagnosis of HIV is possible using a simple antibody-based test on a blood sample.

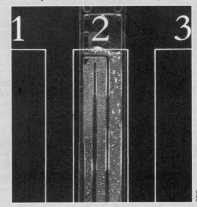

A positive HIV rapid test result shows clumping (aggregation) where HIV antibodies have reacted with HIV protein-coated latex beads.

HIV is easily transmitted between intravenous drug users who share needles.

(b) Describe how the helper T cells respond to the infection: _____

_____

_____

3. Describe three common ways in which HIV can be transmitted from one person to another: _____

_____

_____

4. Explain what is meant by the term **HIV positive**: _____

_____

5. In the years immediately following the discovery of the HIV pathogen, there was a sudden appearance of AIDS cases amongst **haemophiliacs** (people with an inherited blood disorder). State why this group was being infected with HIV:

_____

_____

6. Explain why it has been so difficult to develop a **vaccine** for HIV: _____

_____

_____

7. In a rare number of cases, people who have been HIV positive for many years still have no apparent symptoms. Explain the significance of this observation and its likely potential in the search for a cure for AIDS:

_____

_____

_____

Epidemiology of AIDS

In many urban centres of sub-Saharan Africa, Latin America, and the Caribbean, AIDS has already become the leading cause of death for both men and women aged 15 to 49 years. AIDS kills people in their most productive years and ranks as the leading cause of potential healthy life-years lost in sub-Saharan Africa. Within the next decade, crude death rates in some countries will more than double, and infant and child mortality rates will increase markedly. Perhaps the most significant impact will be seen in projected life expectancies due to the increased mortality of young adults. The AIDS pandemic has lowered the estimated world population level for the year 2050 from 9.4 billion to 8.9 billion, mostly caused by the massive toll of AIDS in Africa.

Human Disease

Regional HIV Statistics and Figures, 2007

North America
People living with HIV / AIDS¶:	1.3 million
Adult prevalence rate*:	0.6%
People newly infected with HIV:	46 000
Deaths of people from AIDS:	21 000
Main modes of transmission**:	MSM, IDU, Hetero

Western & Central Europe
People living with HIV / AIDS¶:	740 000
Adult prevalence rate*:	0.3%
People newly infected with HIV:	31 000
Deaths of people from AIDS:	12 000
Main modes of transmission**:	Hetero, MSM, IDU

Eastern Europe & Central Asia
People living with HIV / AIDS¶:	1.6 million
Adult prevalence rate*:	0.9%
People newly infected with HIV:	150 000
Deaths of people from AIDS:	55 000
Main modes of transmission**:	IDU, Hetero

Caribbean
People living with HIV / AIDS¶:	230 000
Adult prevalence rate*:	1.0%
People newly infected with HIV:	17 000
Deaths of people from AIDS:	11 000
Main modes of transmission**:	Hetero, MSM, IDU

Latin America
People living with HIV / AIDS¶:	1.6 million
Adult prevalence rate*:	0.5%
People newly infected with HIV:	100 000
Deaths of people from AIDS:	58 000
Main modes of transmission**:	Hetero, MSM, IDU

North Africa and Middle East
People living with HIV / AIDS¶:	380 000
Adult prevalence rate*:	0.3%
People newly infected with HIV:	35 000
Deaths of people from AIDS:	25 000
Main modes of transmission**:	Hetero, IDU, MSM

Sub-Saharan Africa
People living with HIV / AIDS¶:	22.5 million
Adult prevalence rate*:	5.0%
People newly infected with HIV:	1.7 million
Deaths of people from AIDS:	1.6 million
Main modes of transmission**:	Hetero

Oceania
People living with HIV / AIDS¶:	75 000
Adult prevalence rate*:	0.4%
People newly infected with HIV:	14 000
Deaths of people from AIDS:	1200
Main modes of transmission**:	MSM, Hetero, IDU

South & South East Asia
People living with HIV / AIDS¶:	4.0 million
Adult prevalence rate*:	0.3%
People newly infected with HIV:	340 000
Deaths of people from AIDS:	270 000
Main modes of transmission**:	Hetero, IDU

East Asia
People living with HIV / AIDS¶:	800 000
Adult prevalence rate*:	0.1%
People newly infected with HIV:	92 000
Deaths of people from AIDS:	32 000
Main modes of transmission**:	IDU, Hetero, MSM

Estimated percentage of adults (15-49) living with HIV/AIDS
- >15%
- 5 – 15%
- 0 – 5%

Source: UNAIDS, WHO

* The proportion of adults (15 to 49 years of age) living with HIV/AIDS in 2007   ¶ People includes adults & children
** Modes of transmission: **Hetero**: heterosexual sex; **IDU**: injecting drug use; **MSM**: sex between men

The origins of HIV

AIDS researchers have confirmed that the two strains of HIV each originated from cross-species transmission (**zoonosis**) from other primates. HIV-1, responsible for the global pandemic, arose as a result of recombination between two separate strains of simian immunodeficiency virus (SIV) in infected **common chimpanzees** in west-central Africa. HIV-2 is less virulent than HIV-1 and, until recently, was restricted to West Africa. It originated from a strain of SIV found in **sooty mangabey** monkeys in that region. The killing of primates as "bushmeat" for human consumption allows the virus to transmit to human hunters when they handle infected carcasses with cuts or other open wounds on their hands. Such cross-species transmissions could be happening every day.

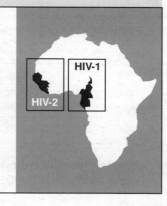

Factors in the spread of HIV

Epidemiologists cannot predict with certainty how rapidly a given epidemic will expand or when it will peak, although short term predictions can be made on the basis of trends in HIV spread and information on risk behaviour. Fortunately, there is strong evidence showing that countries will ultimately reduce their new infections if they carry out effective prevention programmes encouraging abstinence, or fidelity and safer sex. A crucial factor is promoting the acceptance and use of condoms, both the traditional kind and the female condom. Condoms are protective irrespective of age, the scope of sexual networks, or the presence of other sexually transmitted infections. There is evidence from around the world that many factors play a role in starting a sexually transmitted HIV epidemic or driving it to higher levels. Some of these risk factors are listed below.

In many African communities, men travel from rural settlements into the cities in search of work. These men often develop sexual networks while they are away and bring HIV with them when they return.

Social and behavioural risk factors
- Little or no condom use.
- Large proportion of the adult population with multiple partners.
- Overlapping (as opposed to serial) sexual partnerships. Individuals are highly infectious when they first acquire HIV and are more likely to infect any concurrent partners.
- Large sexual networks which are often seen in individuals who move back and forth between home and a far off work place.
- Women's economic dependence on marriage or prostitution, robbing them of control over the circumstances or safety of sex.

Biological risk factors
- High rates of sexually transmitted infections, especially those causing genital ulcers.
- Low rates of male circumcision (for poorly understood reasons, circumcised males have a reduced risk of contracting HIV).
- High viral load (HIV levels in the blood is typically highest when a person is first infected and again in the late stages of illness).

1. Comment on the social, economic, and biological factors involved in the prevalence of HIV in many of the **rural** communities of sub-Saharan Africa:

   _____

   _____

   _____

   _____

2. Describe the effects of AIDS on the countries of sub-Saharan Africa with respect to the following:

   (a) Age structure of their populations: _____

   _____

   (b) Their local economies: _____

   _____

3. Effective antiviral therapies have reduced deaths from HIV/AIDS in developed countries. Suggest why a similar reduction has not occurred in the countries of sub-Saharan Africa:

   _____

   _____

4. Briefly state the origin of the two main strains of HIV:

   HIV-1: _____

   _____

   HIV-2 _____

   _____

5. Using the information provided on the previous page and your own graph paper, plot a column graph of the number of people living with HIV/AIDS for each region. Staple the completed graph into this workbook.

Replication in Animal Viruses

Animal viruses are more complex and varied in structure than the viruses that infect bacteria. Likewise, animal host cells are more diverse in structure and metabolism than bacterial cells. Consequently, animal viruses exhibit a number of different mechanisms for **replicating**, i.e. entering a host cell and producing and releasing new virions. Enveloped viruses bud out from the host cell, whereas those without an envelope are released by rupture of the cell membrane. Three processes (attachment, penetration, and uncoating) are shared by both DNA- and RNA containing animal viruses but the methods

of biosynthesis vary between these two major groups. Generally, DNA viruses replicate their DNA in the nucleus of the host cell using viral enzymes, and synthesise their capsid and other proteins in the cytoplasm using the host cell's enzymes. This is outlined below for a typical enveloped DNA virus. RNA viruses are more variable in their methods of biosynthesis. The example on the next page describes replication in the retrovirus HIV, where the virus uses its own reverse transcriptase to synthesise viral DNA and produce **latent proviruses** or active, mature retroviruses.

Entry of an Enveloped Virus into a Cell

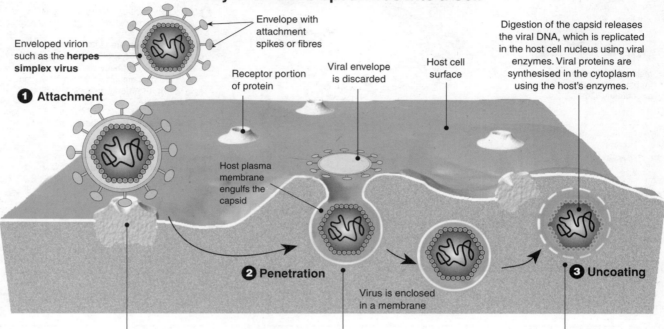

Enveloped virion such as the **herpes simplex virus**

Envelope with attachment spikes or fibres

Receptor portion of protein

Viral envelope is discarded

Host cell surface

Digestion of the capsid releases the viral DNA, which is replicated in the host cell nucleus using viral enzymes. Viral proteins are synthesised in the cytoplasm using the host's enzymes.

❶ **Attachment**

Host plasma membrane engulfs the capsid

❷ **Penetration**

Virus is enclosed in a membrane

❸ **Uncoating**

When a viral particle encounters the cell surface, it attaches to the **receptor sites** of proteins on the cell's plasma membrane.

Once the viral particle is attached, the host cell begins to engulf the virus by **endocytosis**. This is the cell's usual response to foreign particles.

The nucleic acid core is uncoated and the **biosynthesis** of new viruses begins. Mature virions are released by budding from the host cell.

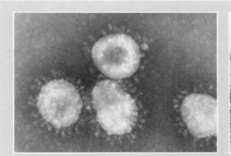

Coronaviruses are irregularly shaped viruses associated with upper respiratory infections and SARS. The envelope bears distinctive projections.

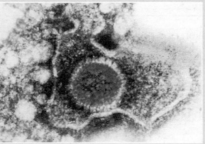

Herpesviruses are medium-sized enveloped viruses that cause various diseases including fever blisters, chickenpox, shingles, and herpes.

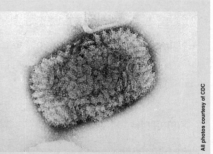

This *Vaccinia* virus belongs to the family of pox viruses; large (200-350 nm), enveloped DNA viruses that cause diseases such as smallpox.

All photos courtesy of CDC

1. Describe the purpose of the glycoprotein spikes found on some enveloped viruses: _____

_____

2. (a) Explain the significance of endocytosis to the entry of an enveloped virus into an animal cell: _____

_____

_____

(b) State where an enveloped virus replicates its viral DNA: _____

(c) State where an enveloped virus synthesises its proteins: _____

Related activities: Viral Diseases, HIV and AIDS

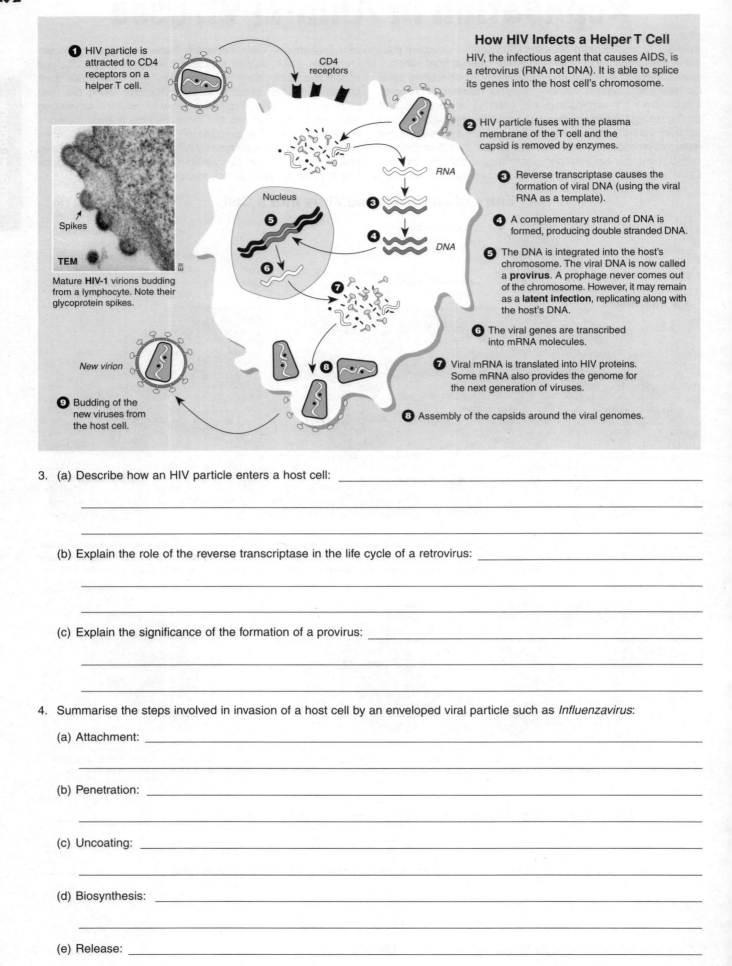

1 HIV particle is attracted to CD4 receptors on a helper T cell.

CD4 receptors

Spikes

TEM

Mature **HIV-1** virions budding from a lymphocyte. Note their glycoprotein spikes.

RNA

Nucleus

5

6

DNA

7

New virion

8

9 Budding of the new viruses from the host cell.

How HIV Infects a Helper T Cell

HIV, the infectious agent that causes AIDS, is a retrovirus (RNA not DNA). It is able to splice its genes into the host cell's chromosome.

2 HIV particle fuses with the plasma membrane of the T cell and the capsid is removed by enzymes.

3 Reverse transcriptase causes the formation of viral DNA (using the viral RNA as a template).

4 A complementary strand of DNA is formed, producing double stranded DNA.

5 The DNA is integrated into the host's chromosome. The viral DNA is now called a **provirus**. A prophage never comes out of the chromosome. However, it may remain as a **latent infection**, replicating along with the host's DNA.

6 The viral genes are transcribed into mRNA molecules.

7 Viral mRNA is translated into HIV proteins. Some mRNA also provides the genome for the next generation of viruses.

8 Assembly of the capsids around the viral genomes.

3. (a) Describe how an HIV particle enters a host cell: _____

_____

_____

(b) Explain the role of the reverse transcriptase in the life cycle of a retrovirus: _____

_____

_____

(c) Explain the significance of the formation of a provirus: _____

_____

_____

4. Summarise the steps involved in invasion of a host cell by an enveloped viral particle such as *Influenzavirus*:

(a) Attachment: _____

_____

(b) Penetration: _____

_____

(c) Uncoating: _____

_____

(d) Biosynthesis: _____

_____

(e) Release: _____

_____

Emerging Diseases

Emerging diseases are so named because they are diseases with no previous history in the human population. Often, as with HIV/AIDS and avian influenza (H5N1), they are **zoonoses** (animal diseases that cross to humans). Zoonoses are capable of causing highly lethal **pandemics** (world-wide epidemics) amongst an unprepared population. The increasing incidence of **multiple drug resistance** in pathogens (including those that cause tuberculosis, malaria, pneumonia, gonorrhoea, and cholera) has lead to the **re-emergence** of diseases that were previously thought to be largely under control. Food-borne diseases, such as *Campylobacter*, are also on the rise, despite improvements in hygiene. Even diseases once thought to be non-infectious (e.g. stomach ulcers and cervical cancer) are now known to be linked to infectious agents. In the 1940s, many common and lethal diseases (e.g. scarlet fever and diphtheria) were conquered using antibiotics. It is now evident that antibiotics are not only losing their power, they are encouraging the emergence of deadly and untreatable infections.

E. coli 0157:H7

A highly pathogenic strain of *Escherichia coli*, **E.coli** O157:H7 (below), causes bloody diarrhoea, sweating, vomiting, and sometimes death. Past sources of contamination include meats (Scotland) and apple juice (western US). In the US, contaminated spinach caused an E.coli outbreak in 26 states in 2006. Of the 199 people infected, 102 were hospitalized, and three died. The numbers in the name refer to specific markers on the surface which distinguish the strains.

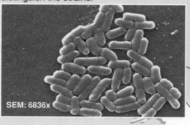

SEM: 6836x

BSE and CJD

Investigation into the appearance of a new form of **Creutzfeldt-Jakob Disease** (vCJD) in Britain in 1994-1995 established a link with **Mad Cow Disease** or BSE (**bovine spongiform encephalopathy**). This **prion** disease is spread through the consumption of contaminated beef.

Avian influenza A (H5N1)

In January 2004, a new strain of 'bird flu' (H5N1) spread rapidly through 8 Asian countries. Outbreaks occurred again in 2005, each time with high human mortality. It is now continuing its spread through Africa and Europe. Avian flu mutates rapidly and crosses species barriers with apparently little difficulty. These features make it a serious public health threat. The **H5N1 virus** is pictured right. At this magnification, the stippled appearance of the protein coat encasing the virion can easily be seen.

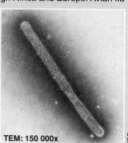

TEM: 150 000x

Resistant Tuberculosis

The reappearance of TB as a virulent disease is the result of an increasing multi-drug resistance to antibiotics and fewer people being immunised.

Hantavirus

An outbreak in Argentina of *hantavirus pulmonary syndrome* in 1996 caused 9 deaths from 17 cases. The source of infection was contact with rodent feces. A recent outbreak in Panama caused 3 deaths.

Severe Acute Respiratory Syndrome

The first case of this respiratory illness was reported 16 November 2002, in China. Initially, epidemiologists thought that people were contracting SARS from infected masked palm civet and racoon-dogs. It is now known that the reservoir for this **coronavirus** is a bat, which passes the infection to other mammals. Once in the human population, SARS spread rapidly through close contact. SARS had a mortality of about 10%, with 50% for people aged 60+.

West Nile Virus

A sometimes fatal encephalitis caused by a flaviviral infection. Most of those infected have no symptoms, but 20% will have some symptoms and a small proportion (less than 1%) will develop severe infection. Symptoms of severe infection include high fever, coma, convulsions, and paralysis. In 2002, there were 277 deaths from West Nile fever in the US, with infection rates concentrated in certain states. The disease is transmitted to humans via **mosquitoes** (below), which are infected with the virus when feeding on bird **reservoir hosts**. Over 110 bird species are known to have been infected with West Nile virus, and bird deaths are closely monitored in the US as indicators of West Nile outbreaks.

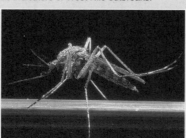

Hemorrhagic Fevers: Ebola & Marburg

Viral hemorrhagic fevers are a group of diseases from four distinct families of viruses. The two best known examples are the filoviruses **Ebola** (below) and **Marburg**. Outbreaks of Ebola have occurred sporadically: in 1976 and 1979, and again in 1995-1996 and 2001-2007. Marburg virus erupted in Angola early in 2005, and more recently in Uganda in 2007. In Angola, the mortality rate was high at 88%. Of the 374 cases reported, 329 were fatal.

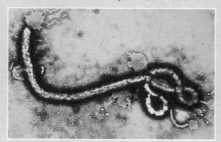

HIV and AIDS

The AIDS pandemic is set to have a lasting effect on the world population. At least two strains are recognized: the deadly **HIV-1 virus** is more widespread than the slightly more benign **HIV-2 strain**. **HIV viruses** (arrowed) are shown below emerging from a human T cell. HIV is responsible for the massive AIDS pandemic that some claim to be species threatening.

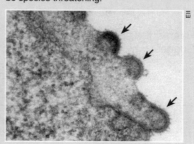

1. Describe the biological and social factors important in the emergence and spread of a named **emerging disease**:

_____

_____

_____

_____

_____

_____

2. Explain the role of **zoonoses** in the emergence of new diseases: _____

_____

_____

3. Using an example, explain what a **re-emerging disease** is: _____

_____

_____

4. Explain how drug resistance in pathogens has led to an increase in the number of re-emerging diseases:

_____

_____

_____

5. Describe the biological and social factors involved when diseases spread rapidly through hospitals:

_____

_____

_____

6. The Spanish influenza pandemic of 1917-18 was made worse by the return of troops from World War I to their home countries. More than 20 million people died in the pandemic, which had a death rate of about 3%. Explain how this pandemic differed from that of SARS in 2003, in terms of its **global spread** and **death rate**:

_____

_____

_____

7. The next pandemic may well be avian flu. Discuss why this disease poses such a public health threat and describe the precautions necessary in preventing its global spread:

_____

_____

_____

_____

8. Haemorrhagic fevers are frightening diseases because of their sudden onset, distressing symptoms, and high fatality. Suggest why, although virulent, they pose less risk of a pandemic than influenza:

_____

_____

_____

The Control of Disease

Many factors can influence the spread of disease, including the social climate, diet, general health, and access to medical care. Human intervention and modification of behaviour can reduce the transmission rate of some diseases and inhibit their spread. Examples include the use of personal physical barriers, such as condoms, to prevent sexually transmitted infections (STIs), and the use of **quarantine** to ensure that potential carriers of disease are isolated until incubation periods have elapsed. Cleaning up the environment also lowers the incidence of disease by reducing the likelihood that pathogens or their vectors will survive. The effective control of infectious disease depends on knowing the origin of the outbreak (its natural reservoir), its mode of transmission within the population, and the methods that can be feasibly employed to contain it. Diseases are often classified according to how they behave in a given population. Any disease that spreads from one host to another, either directly or indirectly, is said to be a **communicable disease**. Those that are easily spread from one person to another, such as chicken pox or measles, are said to be **contagious**. Such diseases are a threat to **public health** and many must be notified to health authorities. **Noncommunicable diseases** are not spread from one host to another and pose less of a threat to public health. A disease that occurs only occasionally and is usually restricted in its spread is called a **sporadic disease**.

Methods for controlling the spread of disease

Transmission of disease can be prevented or reduced by adopting 'safe' behaviours. Examples include using condoms to reduce the spread of STIs, isolation of people with a specific illness (such as SARS), or establishing quarantine procedures for people who may be infected, but are not yet ill.

The development of effective sanitation, sewage treatment, and treatment of drinking water has virtually eliminated dangerous waterborne diseases from developed countries. These practices disrupt the normal infection cycle of pathogens such as cholera and giardia.

Appropriate personal hygiene practices reduce the risk of infection and transmission. Soap may not destroy the pathogens but washing will dilute and remove them from the skin. Although popular, antibacterial soaps encourage development of strains resistant to antimicrobial agents.

The environment can be made less suitable for the growth and transmission of pathogens. For example, spraying drainage ditches and draining swamps eliminates breeding habitats for mosquitoes carrying diseases such as malaria and dengue fever.

Immunisation schedules form part of public health programmes. If most of the population is immune, 'herd immunity' limits outbreaks to sporadic cases. In such populations there are too few susceptible individuals to support the spread of an epidemic.

Disinfectants and sterilisation techniques, such as autoclaving, destroy pathogenic microbes before they have the opportunity to infect. The use of these techniques in medicine has significantly reduced post operative infections and associated deaths.

1. Distinguish between contagious and non-communicable diseases, providing an example of each:

_____

_____

2. (a) Explain the difference between **isolation** and **quarantine**: _____

_____

_____

_____

Related activities: Patterns of Disease, Immunisation, Antimicrobial Drugs

RA 2

(b) Using the recent example of SARS, explain how isolation and quarantine operate to prevent the spread of disease:

_____

_____

3. Explain how the use of condoms reduces the spread of the human immunodeficiency virus (HIV) that causes AIDS:

_____

_____

4. Explain how the drainage of stagnant water in tropical regions may reduce the incidence of malaria in those countries:

_____

_____

5. Describe how each of the following methods is used to control the **growth** of disease-causing microbes:

(a) Disinfectants: _____

_____

(b) Antiseptics: _____

_____

(c) Heat: _____

_____

(d) Ionising radiation (gamma rays): _____

_____

(e) Desiccation: _____

_____

(f) Cold: _____

_____

6. The **Human Genome Project** (HGP) was launched in 1990 and completed in 2003, two years ahead of schedule. Its achieved aim was to sequence the entire human genome, but much of the research since has focussed on determining the various roles of the (expressed) gene products. It is hoped that a more complete understanding the human genome will revolutionise the treatment and prevention of disease. Briefly discuss how the HGP will facilitate:

(a) Diagnosis of disease: _____

_____

_____

(b) Treatment of disease: _____

_____

_____

7. The first measles vaccine was introduced to Britain in 1964. However, in 1993 there were 9000 cases of measles notified to the health authorities in England and Wales.

(a) Suggest why measles has not been eliminated in Britain: _____

_____

(b) Explain how vaccination interrupts the transmission of measles within a population: _____

_____

_____

Antimicrobial Drugs

Human Disease

Antimicrobial drugs include synthetic (manufactured) **drugs** as well as drugs produced by bacteria and fungi, called **antibiotics**. Antibiotics are produced naturally by these microorganisms as a means of inhibiting competing microbes around them (a form of antibiosis, hence the name antibiotic). The first antibiotic, called penicillin, was discovered in 1928 by Alexander Fleming. Since then, similar inhibitory reactions between colonies growing on solid media have been commonly observed. Antibiotics are actually rather easy to discover, but few of them are of medical or commercial value. Many antibiotics are toxic to humans or lack any advantage over those already in use. More than half of our antibiotics are produced by species of filamentous bacteria that commonly inhabit the soil, called *Streptomyces*. A few antibiotics are produced by bacteria of the genus *Bacillus*. Others are produced by moulds, mostly of the genera *Cephalosporium* and *Penicillium*. Antimicrobial drugs are used in **chemotherapy** programmes to treat infectious diseases. Like disinfectants, these chemicals interfere with the growth of microorganisms (see diagram below). They may either kill microbes directly (**bactericidal**) or prevent them from growing (**bacteriostatic**). To be effective, they must often act inside the host, so their effect on the host's cells and tissues is important. The ideal antimicrobial drug has **selective toxicity**, killing the pathogen without damaging the host. Some antimicrobial drugs have a narrow **spectrum of activity**, and affect only a limited number of microbial types. Others are **broad-spectrum drugs** and affect a large number of microbial species (see the table below). When the identity of a pathogen is not known, a broad-spectrum drug may be prescribed in order to save valuable time. There is a disadvantage with this, because broad spectrum drugs target not just the pathogen, but much of the host's normal microflora also. The normal microbial community usually controls the growth of pathogens and other microbes by competing with them. By selectively removing them with drugs, certain microbes in the community that do not normally cause problems, may flourish and become **opportunistic pathogens**.

How Antimicrobial Drugs Work

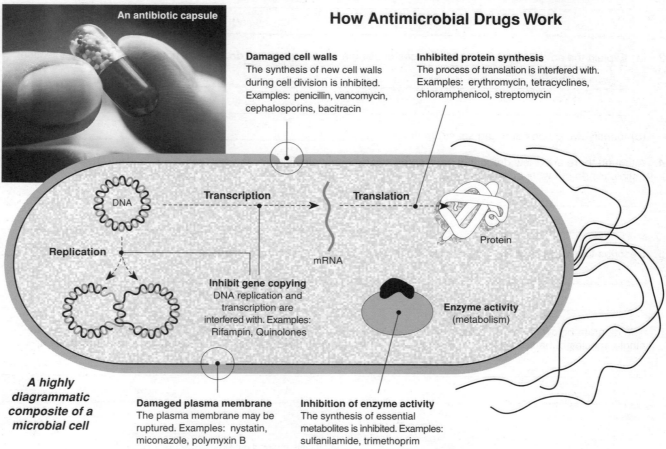

An antibiotic capsule

Damaged cell walls
The synthesis of new cell walls during cell division is inhibited. Examples: penicillin, vancomycin, cephalosporins, bacitracin

Inhibited protein synthesis
The process of translation is interfered with. Examples: erythromycin, tetracyclines, chloramphenicol, streptomycin

Transcription

Translation

DNA

mRNA

Protein

Replication

Inhibit gene copying
DNA replication and transcription are interfered with. Examples: Rifampin, Quinolones

Enzyme activity
(metabolism)

A highly diagrammatic composite of a microbial cell

Damaged plasma membrane
The plasma membrane may be ruptured. Examples: nystatin, miconazole, polymyxin B

Inhibition of enzyme activity
The synthesis of essential metabolites is inhibited. Examples: sulfanilamide, trimethoprim

Spectrum of antimicrobial activity of a number of chemotherapeutic drugs

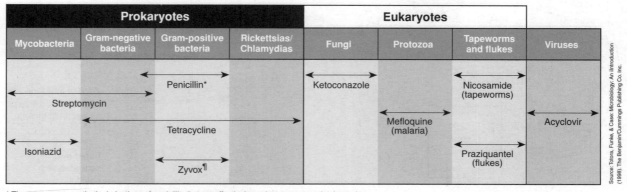

Prokaryotes				Eukaryotes			
Mycobacteria	Gram-negative bacteria	Gram-positive bacteria	Rickettsias/ Chlamydias	Fungi	Protozoa	Tapeworms and flukes	Viruses
		Penicillin*		Ketoconazole		Nicosamide (tapeworms)	
Streptomycin							
	Tetracycline				Mefloquine (malaria)		Acyclovir
Isoniazid						Praziquantel (flukes)	
		Zyvox¶					

Source: Totora, Funke, & Case: Microbiology: An Introduction (1998), The Benjamin/Cummings Publishing Co. Inc.

* There are some synthetic derivatives of penicillin that act effectively against gram-negative bacteria.
¶ The first new class of antibiotics to be used in 35 years.

Related activities: Resistance in Pathogens, Antibiotic resistance, The Control of Disease

A 2

258

1. Discuss the requirements of an "ideal" anti-microbial drug, and explain in what way antibiotics satisfy these requirements:

_____

_____

_____

_____

2. Some bacteria have ways of tolerating treatment by antibiotics, and are termed 'superbugs'.

   (a) Explain what is meant by **antibiotic resistance** in bacteria: _____

   _____

   _____

   (b) Explain why a course of antibiotics should be finished completely, even when the symptoms of infection have gone:

   _____

   _____

3. (a) Explain the advantages and disadvantages of using a **broad-spectrum drug** on an unidentified bacterial infection:

   _____

   _____

   (b) Identify two groups of broad spectrum drugs: _____

4. Although there are a few drugs that have some success in controlling viruses, antibiotics are ineffective. Explain why antibiotics do not work against viruses:

   _____

   _____

5. Describe four ways in which antimicrobial drugs kill or inhibit the growth of microbes: _____

   _____

   _____

6. The diagram below shows an experiment investigating the effectiveness of different antibiotics on a pure culture of a single species of bacteria. Giving a reason, state which antibiotic (A-D) is most effective in controlling the bacteria:

   _____

   _____

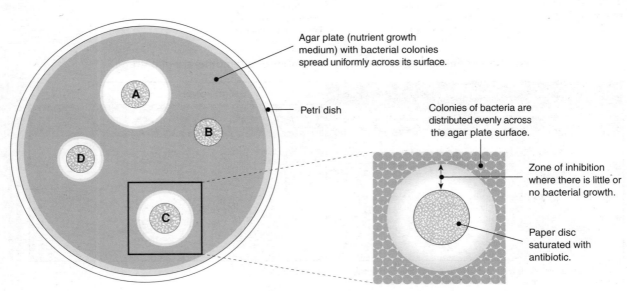

Agar plate (nutrient growth medium) with bacterial colonies spread uniformly across its surface.

Petri dish

Colonies of bacteria are distributed evenly across the agar plate surface.

Zone of inhibition where there is little or no bacterial growth.

Paper disc saturated with antibiotic.

Diseases Caused by Smoking

Tobacco smoking has only recently been accepted as a major health hazard, despite its practice in developed countries for more than 400 years, and much longer elsewhere. Cigarettes became popular at the end of World War I because they were cheap, convenient, and easier to smoke than pipes and cigars. They remain popular for the further reason that they are more addictive than other forms of tobacco. The milder smoke can be more readily inhaled, allowing **nicotine** (a powerful addictive poison) to be quickly absorbed into the bloodstream. **Lung cancer** is the most widely known and most harmful effect of smoking. Tobacco smoking is also directly associated with coronary artery disease, emphysema, chronic bronchitis, peripheral vascular disease, and stroke. Despite recent indications that mortality due to smoking may be declining in the UK, one third of all deaths from cancer, including around 80% of lung cancer deaths, are linked to this cause. The damaging components of cigarette smoke include tar, carbon monoxide, nitrogen dioxide, and nitric oxide. Many of these harmful chemicals occur in greater concentrations in sidestream smoke (**passive smoking**) than in mainstream smoke (inhaled) due to the presence of a filter in the cigarette.

Long term effects of tobacco smoking

Smoking damages the arteries of the brain and may result in a **stroke**.

All forms of tobacco-smoking increase the risk of **mouth cancer**, **lip cancer**, and **cancer of the throat** (pharynx).

Lung cancer is the best known harmful effect of smoking.

In a young man who smokes 20 cigarettes a day, the risk of **coronary artery disease** is increased by about three times over that of a nonsmoker.

Smoking leads to severe constriction of the arteries supplying blood to the extremities and leads to **peripheral vascular disease**.

Short term effects of tobacco smoking

- Reduction in capacity of the lungs.
- Increase in muscle tension and a decrease in steadiness of the hands.
- Raised blood pressure (10-30 points).
- Very sharp rise in carbon monoxide levels in the lungs contributing to breathlessness.
- Increase in pulse rate by up to 20 beats per minute.
- Surface blood vessel constriction drops skin temperature by up to 5°C.
- Dulling of appetite as well as the sense of smell and taste.

How smoking damages the lungs

Non-smoker

Normal alveoli arrangement

Cilia

Thin layer of mucus

Cells lining airways

Smoker

Coalesced alveoli

Smoke particles

Extra mucus produced

Cancerous cell

Smoke particles indirectly destroy the walls of the lung's alveoli.

Cavities lined by heavy black tar deposits.

cm SPECIMEN A-73-309 DATE CDC

Gross pathology of lung tissue from a patient with emphysema. Tobacco tar deposits can be seen. Tar contains at least 17 known carcinogens.

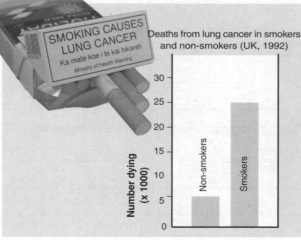

SMOKING CAUSES LUNG CANCER
Ka mate koe i te kai hikareti
Ministry of Health Warning

Deaths from lung cancer in smokers and non-smokers (UK, 1992)

Number dying (× 1000)

Non-smokers — Smokers

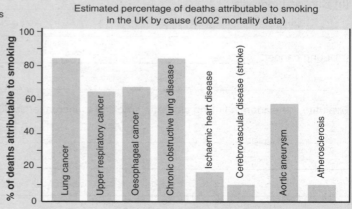

Estimated percentage of deaths attributable to smoking in the UK by cause (2002 mortality data)

% of deaths attributable to smoking

Lung cancer · Upper respiratory cancer · Oesophageal cancer · Chronic obstructive lung disease · Ischaemic heart disease · Cerebrovascular disease (stroke) · Aortic aneurysm · Atherosclerosis

Related activities: Cardiovascular Disease

RDA 2

Components of Cigarette Smoke

Particulate Phase

Nicotine: a highly addictive alkaloid

Tar: composed of many chemicals

Benzene: carcinogenic hydrocarbon

Gas Phase

Carbon monoxide: a poisonous gas

Ammonia: a pungent, colourless gas

Formaldehyde: a carcinogen

Hydrogen cyanide: a highly poisonous gas

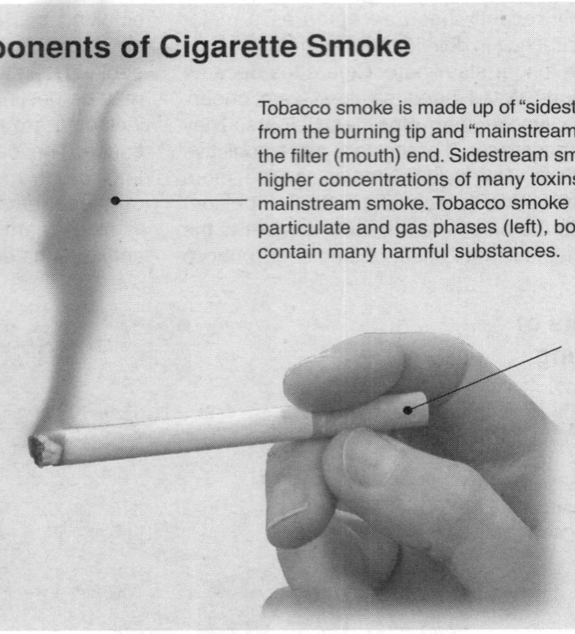

Tobacco smoke is made up of "sidestream smoke" from the burning tip and "mainstream smoke" from the filter (mouth) end. Sidestream smoke contains higher concentrations of many toxins than mainstream smoke. Tobacco smoke includes both particulate and gas phases (left), both of which contain many harmful substances.

Filter
Cellulose acetate filters trap some of the tar and smoke particles. They cool the smoke slightly, making it easier to inhale.

1. Discuss the physical changes to the lung that result from long-term smoking:

_____

_____

_____

_____

2. Determine the physiological effect of each of the following constituents of tobacco smoke when inhaled:

(a) Tar: _____

_____

(b) Nicotine: _____

_____

(c) Carbon monoxide: _____

_____

3. Describe the symptoms of the following diseases associated with long-term smoking:

(a) Emphysema: _____

_____

(b) Chronic bronchitis: _____

_____

(c) Lung cancer: _____

_____

4. Evaluate the evidence linking cigarette smoking to increased incidence of respiratory and cardiovascular diseases:

_____

_____

_____

_____

Classification

OCR: Unit F212, Module 3: Biodiversity and Evolution

2.3.2: Classification

CIE: APPLICATIONS OF BIOLOGY

Q (a): Classification of organisms

Learning Objectives

☐ 1. Compile your own glossary from the **KEY WORDS** displayed in **bold type** in the learning objectives below.

Biodiversity *(page 286)*

☐ 2. Explain the importance of classification in recognising, appreciating, and conserving the **biodiversity** on Earth. Understand the concept of a **species** in terms of their reproductive isolation and potential for breeding.

Classification Systems

The five kingdoms *(pages 262, 264-281)*

☐ 3. Describe the principles and importance of scientific classification. Recognise **taxonomy** as the study of the theory and practice of classification.

☐ 4. Describe the **distinguishing features** of each kingdom in the **five kingdom classification system**:
- **Prokaryotae** (Monera): bacteria and cyanobacteria.
- **Protoctista**: includes the algae and protozoans.
- **Fungi**: includes yeasts, moulds, and mushrooms.
- **Plantae**: includes mosses, liverworts, tracheophytes.
- **Animalia**: all invertebrate phyla and the chordates.

Note that the **six kingdom classification system separates out the Prokaryotae** into two separate kingdoms, i.e. **Archaebacteria**: the archaebacteria and **Eubacteria**: the "true" bacteria.

☐ 5. Recognise at least seven major **taxonomic categories**: **kingdom, phylum, class, order, family, genus,** and **species**. Distinguish taxonomic categories from **taxa**, which are groups of organisms: "genus" is a taxonomic category, whereas the genus *Drosophila* is a taxon.

☐ 6. Understand the basis for assigning organisms to different taxonomic categories. Recall what is meant by a **distinguishing feature**. Appreciate that species are classified on the basis of **shared derived characters** rather than primitive (ancestral) characters. *For example, within the vertebrates, the presence of a backbone is a derived, therefore a distinguishing, feature. Within the mammals, the backbone is an ancestral feature and is not distinguishing, whereas mammary glands (a distinguishing feature) are derived.*

☐ 7. Explain how **binomial nomenclature** is used to classify organisms. Appreciate the problems associated with using **common names** to describe organisms.

☐ 8. Explain the relationship between classification and phylogeny. Appreciate that newer classification schemes attempt to better reflect the **phylogeny** of organisms.

New classification schemes *(pages 262-263)*

☐ 9. Recognise recent reclassifications of organisms, e.g. into six kingdoms or into three **domains** (**Archaea, Eubacteria,** and **Eukarya**). Explain the basis and rationale for these classifications.

☐ 10. Appreciate that **cladistics** provides a method of classification based on relatedness, and emphasises the presence of **shared derived characters**. Discuss the benefits and disadvantages of cladistic schemes.

Classification keys *(pages 282-284)*

☐ 11. Explain what a **classification key** is and what it is used for. Describe the essential features of a classification key. Use a simple taxonomic key to recognise and classify some common organisms.

See the 'Textbook Reference Grid' on pages 8-9 for textbook page references relating to material in this topic.

See page 7 for details of publishers of periodicals:

STUDENT'S REFERENCE

■ **A Passion for Order** National Geographic, 211(6) June 2007, pp. 73-87. *The history of Carl Linnaeus and the classification of plant species.*

■ **How Many Mammals in Britain?** Biol. Sci. Rev., 12(4) March 2000, pp. 18-22. *The nature of species and abundance of mammals in Britain.*

■ **The Species Enigma** New Scientist, 13 June 1998 (Inside Science). *An account of the nature of species, ring species, and the status of hybrids.*

■ **Taxonomy: The Naming Game Revisited** Biol. Sci. Rev., 9(5) May 1997, pp. 31-35. *New tools for taxonomy and how they are used (includes the exemplar of the reclassification of the kingdoms).*

TEACHER'S REFERENCE

■ **What's in a Name?** Scientific American, Nov. 2004, pp. 20-21. *A proposed classification system called phyloclode, based solely on phylogeny.*

■ **Family Feuds** New Scientist, 24 January 1998, pp. 36-40. *Molecular and morphological analysis used for determining species inter-relatedness.*

■ **The Loves of the Plants** Scientific American, Feb. 1996, pp. 98-103. *The classification of plants and the development of keys to plant identification.*

■ **The Problematic Red Wolf** Sci. American, July 1995, pp. 26-31. *Is the red wolf a species or a long-established hybrid? Correctly naming and recognising species can affect conservation efforts.*

■ **Crumbling Foundations** SSR, Dec. 2005, pp. 65-74. *The current diminution of taxonomic expertise is nothing short of a disaster.*

See pages 10-11 for details of how to access **Bio Links** from our web site: **www.biozone.co.uk**. From Bio Links, access sites under the topics:
BIODIVERSITY > **Taxonomy and Classification**:
• Birds and DNA • Taxonomy: Classifying life • The phylogeny of life... *and others*
MICROBIOLOGY > **General Microbiology**: • British Mycological Society • Major groups of prokaryotes • The microbial world ... *and others*
PLANT BIOLOGY > **Classification and Diversity**: • Flowering plant diversity ... *and others*

Presentation MEDIA to support this topic:
ECOLOGY:
Biodiversity & Conservation

The New Tree of Life

With the advent of more efficient genetic (DNA) sequencing technology, the genomes of many bacteria began to be sequenced. In 1996, the results of a scientific collaboration examining DNA evidence confirmed the proposal that life comprises three major evolutionary lineages (domains) and not two as was the convention.

The recognised lineages were the **Eubacteria**, the **Eukarya** and the **Archaea** (formerly the Archaebacteria). The new classification reflects the fact that there are very large differences between the archaea and the eubacteria. All three domains probably had a distant common ancestor.

A Five (or Six) Kingdom World (right)

The diagram (right) represents the **five kingdom system** of classification commonly represented in many biology texts. It recognises two basic cell types: prokaryote and eukaryote. The domain Prokaryota includes all bacteria and cyanobacteria. Domain Eukaryota includes protoctists, fungi, plants, and animals. More recently, based on 16S ribosomal RNA sequence comparisons, Carl Woese divided the prokaryotes into two kingdoms, the Eubacteria and Archaebacteria. Such **six-kingdom systems** are also commonly recognised in texts.

A New View of the World (below)

In 1996, scientists deciphered the full DNA sequence of an unusual bacterium called *Methanococcus jannaschii*. An **extremophile**, this methane-producing archaebacterium lives at 85°C; a temperature lethal for most bacteria as well as eukaryotes. The DNA sequence confirmed that life consists of three major evolutionary lineages, not the two that have been routinely described. Only 44% of this archaebacterium's genes resemble those in bacteria or eukaryotes, or both.

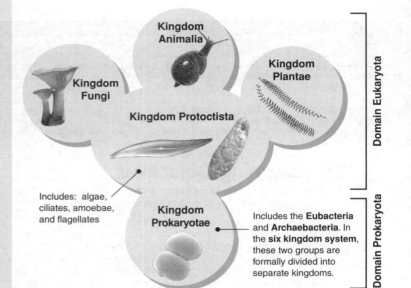

Kingdom Animalia

Kingdom Plantae

Kingdom Fungi

Kingdom Protoctista

Domain Eukaryota

Includes: algae, ciliates, amoebae, and flagellates

Kingdom Prokaryotae

Includes the **Eubacteria** and **Archaebacteria**. In the **six kingdom system**, these two groups are formally divided into separate kingdoms.

Domain Prokaryota

Domain Eubacteria

Lack a distinct nucleus and cell organelles. Generally prefer less extreme environments than Archaea. Includes well-known pathogens, many harmless and beneficial species, and the cyanobacteria (photosynthetic bacteria containing the pigments chlorophyll *a* and phycocyanin).

Domain Archaea

Closely resemble eubacteria in many ways but cell wall composition and aspects of metabolism are very different. Live in extreme environments similar to those on primeval Earth. They may utilise sulfur, methane, or halogens (chlorine, fluorine), and many tolerate extremes of temperature, salinity, or pH.

Domain Eukarya

Complex cell structure with organelles and nucleus. This group contains four of the kingdoms classified under the more traditional system. Note that Kingdom Protoctista is separated into distinct groups: e.g. amoebae, ciliates, flagellates.

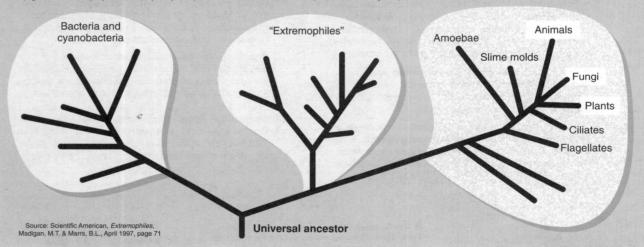

Bacteria and cyanobacteria

"Extremophiles"

Amoebae

Slime molds

Animals

Fungi

Plants

Ciliates

Flagellates

Source: Scientific American, *Extremophiles*, Madigan, M.T. & Marrs, B.L., April 1997, page 71

Universal ancestor

1. Explain why some scientists have recommended that the conventional classification of life be revised so that the Archaea, Eubacteria and Eukarya are three separate domains:

_____

_____

2. Describe one feature of the three domain system that is very different from the five kingdom classification:

_____

_____

3. Describe one way in which the three domain system and the six kingdom classification are alike: _____

_____

Related activities: New Classification Schemes, Features of Taxonomic Groups
Web links: Types of Microbes, Introduction to the Archaea

New Classification Schemes

Taxonomy is the study of classification. Ever since Darwin, the aim of classification has been to organise species, and to reflect their evolutionary history (**phylogeny**). Each successive group in the taxonomic hierarchy should represent finer and finer branching from a common ancestor. In order to reconstruct evolutionary history, phylogenetic trees must be based on features that are due to shared ancestry (homologies). Traditional taxonomy has relied mainly on **morphological characters** to do this. Modern technology has assisted taxonomy by providing **biochemical evidence** (from proteins and DNA) for the relatedness of species. The most familiar approach to classifying organisms is to use **classical evolutionary taxonomy**. It considers branching sequences and overall likeness. A more recent approach has been to use **cladistics**: a technique which emphasises phylogeny or relatedness, usually based on biochemical evidence (and largely ignoring morphology or appearance). Each branch on the tree marks the point where a new species has arisen by evolution. Traditional and cladistic schemes do not necessarily conflict, but there have been reclassifications of some taxa (notably the primates, but also the reptiles, dinosaurs, and birds). Traditional taxonomists criticise cladistic schemes because they do not recognise the amount of visible change in morphology that occurs in species after their divergence from a common ancestor. Popular classifications will probably continue to reflect similarities and differences in appearance, rather than a strict evolutionary history. In this respect, they are a compromise between phylogeny and the need for a convenient filing system for species diversity.

Classification

A Classical Taxonomic View

On the basis of overall anatomical similarity (e.g. bones and limb length, teeth, musculature), apes are grouped into a family (Pongidae) that is separate from humans and their immediate ancestors (Hominidae). The family Pongidae (the great apes) is not monophyletic (of one phylogeny), because it stems from an ancestor that also gave rise to a species in another family (i.e. humans). This traditional classification scheme is now at odds with schemes derived after considering genetic evidence.

A Cladistic View

Based on the evidence of genetic differences (% values above), chimpanzees and gorillas are more closely related to humans than to orangutans, and chimpanzees are more closely related to humans than they are to gorillas. Under this scheme there is no true family of great apes. The family Hominidae includes two subfamilies: Ponginae and Homininae (humans, chimpanzees, and gorillas). This classification is monophyletic: the Hominidae includes all the species that arise from a common ancestor.

1. Briefly explain the benefits of classification schemes based on:

    (a) Morphological characters: _____

    _____

    _____

    (b) Relatedness in time (from biochemical evidence): _____

    _____

    _____

2. Describe the contribution of biochemical evidence to taxonomy: _____

    _____

3. Based on the diagram above, state the family to which the chimpanzees belong under:

    (a) A traditional scheme: _____ (b) A cladistic scheme: _____

Features of Taxonomic Groups

In order to distinguish organisms, it is desirable to classify and name them (a science known as **taxonomy**). An effective classification system requires features that are distinctive to a particular group of organisms. The distinguishing features of some major taxonomic groups are provided in the following pages by means of diagrams and brief summaries. Revised classification systems, recognising three domains (rather than five kingdoms) are now recognised as better representations of the true diversity of life. However, for the purposes of describing the groups with which we are most familiar, the five kingdom system (used here) is still appropriate. Note that most animals show **bilateral symmetry** (body divisible into two halves that are mirror images). **Radial symmetry** (body divisible into equal halves through various planes) is a characteristic of cnidarians and ctenophores. Definitions of specific terms relating to features of structure or function can be found in any general biology text.

Kingdom: PROKARYOTAE (Bacteria)

- Also known as monerans or prokaryotes.
- Two major bacterial lineages are recognised: the primitive **Archaebacteria** and the more advanced **Eubacteria**.
- All have a prokaryotic cell structure: they lack the nuclei and chromosomes of eukaryotic cells, and have smaller (70S) ribosomes.
- Have a tendency to spread genetic elements across species barriers by sexual conjugation, viral transduction and other processes.
- Can reproduce rapidly by binary fission in the absence of sex.

- Have evolved a wider variety of metabolism types than eukaryotes.
- Bacteria grow and divide or aggregate into filaments or colonies of various shapes.
- They are taxonomically identified by their appearance (form) and through biochemical differences.

Species diversity: 10 000 + Bacteria are rather difficult to classify to the species level because of their relatively rampant genetic exchange, and because their reproduction is usually asexual.

Eubacteria

- Also known as 'true bacteria', they probably evolved from the more ancient Archaebacteria.
- Distinguished from Archaebacteria by differences in cell wall composition, nucleotide structure, and ribosome shape.
- Very diverse group comprises most bacteria.
- The **gram stain** provides the basis for distinguishing two broad groups of bacteria. It relies on the presence of peptidoglycan (unique to bacteria) in the cell wall. The stain is easily washed from the thin peptidoglycan layer of gram negative walls but is retained by the thick peptidoglycan layer of gram positive cells, staining them a dark violet colour.

Gram-Positive Bacteria

The walls of gram positive bacteria consist of many layers of peptidoglycan forming a thick, single-layered structure that holds the gram stain.

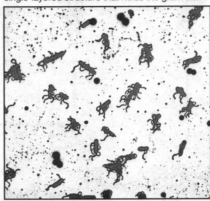

Bacillus alvei: a gram positive, flagellated bacterium. Note how the cells appear dark.

Gram-Negative Bacteria

The cell walls of gram negative bacteria contain only a small proportion of peptidoglycan, so the dark violet stain is not retained by the organisms.

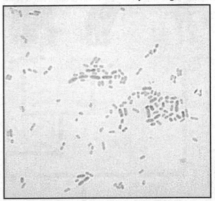

Photos: CDC

Alcaligenes odorans: a gram negative bacterium. Note how the cells appear pale.

Kingdom: FUNGI

- Heterotrophic.
- Rigid cell wall made of chitin.
- Vary from single celled to large multicellular organisms.
- Mostly saprotrophic (i.e. feeding on dead or decaying material).
- Terrestrial and immobile.

Examples:
Mushrooms/toadstools, yeasts, truffles, morels, moulds, and lichens.

Species diversity: 80 000 +

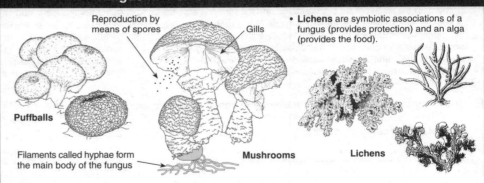

Reproduction by means of spores

Gills

- **Lichens** are symbiotic associations of a fungus (provides protection) and an alga (provides the food).

Puffballs

Filaments called hyphae form the main body of the fungus

Mushrooms

Lichens

Kingdom: PROTOCTISTA

- A diverse group of organisms that do not fit easily into other taxonomic groups.
- Unicellular or simple multicellular.
- Widespread in moist or aquatic environments.

Examples of algae: green, brown, and red algae, dinoflagellates, diatoms.

Examples of protozoa: amoebas, foraminiferans, radiolarians, ciliates.

Species diversity: 55 000 +

Algae 'plant-like' protuctists

- Autotrophic (photosynthesis)
- Characterised by the type of chlorophyll present

Cell walls of cellulose, sometimes with silica

Diatom

Protozoa 'animal-like' protuctists

- Heterotrophic nutrition and feed via ingestion
- Most are microscopic (5 μm–250 μm)

Lack cell walls

Move via projections called pseudopodia

Amoeba

Kingdom: PLANTAE

- Multicellular organisms (the majority are photosynthetic and contain chlorophyll).
- Cell walls made of cellulose; Food is stored as starch.
- Subdivided into two major divisions based on tissue structure: **Bryophytes** (non-vascular) and **Tracheophytes** (vascular) plants.

Non-Vascular Plants:

- Non vascular, lacking transport tissues (no xylem or phloem).
- They are small and restricted to moist, terrestrial environments.
- Do not possess 'true' roots, stems or leaves.

Phylum Bryophyta: Mosses, liverworts, and hornworts.

Species diversity: 18 600 +

Phylum: Bryophyta

Sexual reproductive structures

Flattened thallus (leaf like structure)

Sporophyte: reproduce by spores

Rhizoids anchor the plant into the ground

Liverworts

Mosses

Vascular Plants:

- Vascular: possess transport tissues.
- Possess true roots, stems, and leaves, as well as stomata.
- Reproduce via spores, not seeds.
- Clearly defined *alternation of sporophyte and gametophyte generations*.

Seedless Plants:

Spore producing plants, includes:

Phylum Filicinophyta: Ferns

Phylum Sphenophyta: Horsetails

Phylum Lycophyta: Club mosses

Species diversity: 13 000 +

Phylum: Lycophyta

Leaves

Club moss

Phylum: Sphenophyta

Leaves

Horsetail

Phylum: Filicinophyta

Reproduce via spores on the underside of leaf

Large dividing leaves called fronds

Rhizome

Adventitious roots

Fern

Seed Plants:

Also called Spermatophyta. Produce seeds housing an embryo. Includes:

Gymnosperms

- Lack enclosed chambers in which seeds develop.
- Produce seeds in cones which are exposed to the environment.

Phylum Cycadophyta: Cycads

Phylum Ginkgophyta: Ginkgoes

Phylum Coniferophyta: Conifers

Species diversity: 730 +

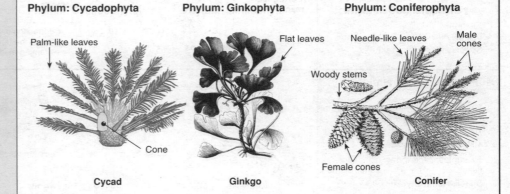

Phylum: Cycadophyta

Palm-like leaves

Cone

Cycad

Phylum: Ginkophyta

Flat leaves

Ginkgo

Phylum: Coniferophyta

Needle-like leaves

Male cones

Woody stems

Female cones

Conifer

Angiosperms

Phylum: Angiospermophyta

- Seeds in specialised reproductive structures called flowers.
- Female reproductive ovary develops into a fruit.
- Pollination usually via wind or animals.

Species diversity: 260 000 +

The phylum Angiospermophyta may be subdivided into two classes:

Class *Monocotyledoneae* (Monocots)

Class *Dicotyledoneae* (Dicots)

Angiosperms: **Monocotyledons**

Flower parts occur in multiples of 3

Leaves have parallel veins

- Only have one cotyledon (food storage organ)
- Normally herbaceous (non-woody) with no secondary growth

Lily

Examples: cereals, lilies, daffodils, palms, grasses.

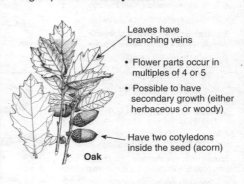

Angiosperms: **Dicotyledons**

Leaves have branching veins

- Flower parts occur in multiples of 4 or 5
- Possible to have secondary growth (either herbaceous or woody)
- Have two cotyledons inside the seed (acorn)

Oak

Examples: many annual plants, trees and shrubs.

Kingdom: ANIMALIA

- Over 800 000 species described in 33 existing phyla.
- Multicellular, heterotrophic organisms.
- Animal cells lack cell walls.

- Further subdivided into various major phyla on the basis of body symmetry, type of body cavity, and external and internal structures.

Phylum: Rotifera

- A diverse group of small organisms with sessile, colonial, and planktonic forms.
- Most freshwater, a few marine.
- Typically reproduce via cyclic parthenogenesis.
- Characterised by a wheel of cilia on the head used for feeding and locomotion, a large muscular pharynx (mastax) with jaw like trophi, and a foot with sticky toes.

Species diversity: 1500 +

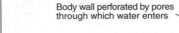

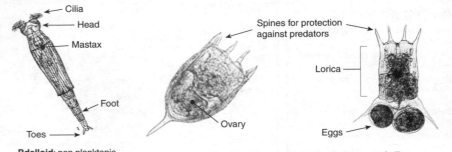

Cilia
Head
Mastax
Foot
Toes

Bdelloid: non planktonic, creeping rotifer

Spines for protection against predators
Lorica
Ovary
Eggs

Planktonic forms swim using their crown of cilia

Phylum: Porifera

- Lack organs.
- All are aquatic (mostly marine).
- Asexual reproduction by budding.
- Lack a nervous system.

Examples: sponges.

Species diversity: 8000 +

Body wall perforated by pores through which water enters

Water leaves by a larger opening - the osculum

Sponge

- Capable of regeneration (the replacement of lost parts)
- Possess spicules (needle-like internal structures) for support and protection

Tube sponge

Sessile (attach to ocean floor)

Phylum: Cnidaria

- Two basic body forms:

  Medusa: umbrella shaped and free swimming by pulsating bell.

  Polyp: cylindrical, some are sedentary, others can glide, or somersault or use tentacles as legs.
- Some species have a life cycle that alternates between a polyp stage and a medusa stage.
- All are aquatic (most are marine).

Examples: Jellyfish, sea anemones, hydras, and corals.

Species diversity: 11 000 +

Some have air-filled floats

Single opening acts as mouth and anus

Polyps may aggregate in colonies

Nematocysts (stinging cells)

Jellyfish (Portuguese man-o-war)

Brain coral

Polyps stick to seabed

Sea anemone

Colonial polyps

Contraction of the bell propels the free swimming medusa

Phylum: Platyhelminthes

- Unsegmented body.
- Flattened body shape.
- Mouth, but no anus.
- Many are parasitic.

Examples: Tapeworms, planarians, flukes.

Species diversity: 20 000 +

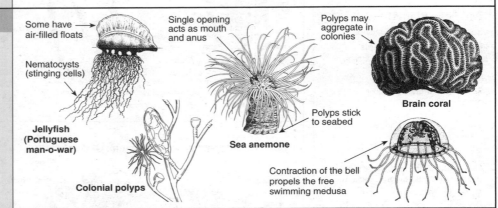

Hooks

Detail of head (scolex)

Liver fluke

Tapeworm

Planarian

Phylum: Nematoda

- Tiny, unsegmented roundworms.
- Many are plant/animal parasites

Examples: Hookworms, stomach worms, lung worms, filarial worms

Species diversity: 80 000 - 1 million

Muscular pharynx
Ovary
Anus

A roundworm parasite

Mouth
Intestine

A general nematode body plan

Phylum: Annelida

- Cylindrical, segmented body with chaetae (bristles).
- Move using hydrostatic skeleton and/or parapodia (appendages).

Examples: Earthworms, leeches, polychaetes (including tubeworms).

Species diversity: 15 000 +

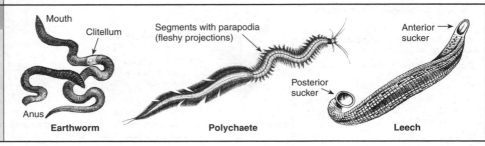

Mouth
Clitellum

Segments with parapodia (fleshy projections)

Anterior sucker

Posterior sucker

Anus

Earthworm

Polychaete

Leech

Kingdom: ANIMALIA *(continued)*

Phylum: Mollusca

- Soft bodied and unsegmented.
- Body comprises head, muscular foot, and visceral mass (organs).
- Most have radula (rasping tongue).
- Aquatic and terrestrial species.
- Aquatic species possess gills.

Examples: Snails, mussels, squid.

Species diversity: 110 000 +

Class: Bivalvia

Radula lost in bivalves

Mantle secretes shell

Two shells hinged together

Scallop

Class: Gastropoda

Mantle secretes shell

Muscular foot for locomotion

Head

Land snail

Class: Cephalopoda

Well developed eyes

Tentacles with eyes

Squid

Foot divided into tentacles

Phylum: Arthropoda

- Exoskeleton made of chitin.
- Grow in stages after moulting.
- Jointed appendages.
- Segmented bodies.
- Heart found on dorsal side of body.
- Open circulation system.
- Most have compound eyes.

Species diversity: 1 million +
Make up 75% of all living animals.

Arthropods are subdivided into the following classes:

Class: Crustacea (crustaceans)
- Mainly marine.
- Exoskeleton impregnated with mineral salts.
- Gills often present.
- Includes: Lobsters, crabs, barnacles, prawns, shrimps, isopods, amphipods
- **Species diversity:** 35 000 +

Class: Arachnida (chelicerates)
- Almost all are terrestrial.
- 2 body parts: cephalothorax and abdomen (except horseshoe crabs).
- Includes: spiders, scorpions, ticks, mites, horseshoe crabs.
- **Species diversity:** 57 000 +

Class: Insecta (insects)
- Mostly terrestrial.
- Most are capable of flight.
- 3 body parts: head, thorax, abdomen.
- Include: Locusts, dragonflies, cockroaches, butterflies, bees, ants, beetles, bugs, flies, and more
- **Species diversity:** 800 000 +

Myriapods (=many legs)
Class Diplopoda (millipedes)
- Terrestrial.
- Have a rounded body.
- Eat dead or living plants.
- **Species diversity:** 2000 +

Class Chilopoda (centipedes)
- Terrestrial.
- Have a flattened body.
- Poison claws for catching prey.
- Feed on insects, worms, and snails.
- **Species diversity:** 7000 +

Class: Crustacea

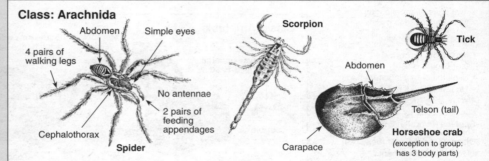

2 pairs of antennae

Cephalothorax (fusion of head and thorax)

Abdomen

3 pairs of mouthparts

Cheliped (first leg)

Shrimp

Walking legs

Swimmerets

Crab

Amphipod

Class: Arachnida

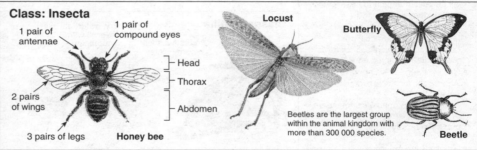

Abdomen

Simple eyes

4 pairs of walking legs

Cephalothorax

2 pairs of feeding appendages

No antennae

Spider

Scorpion

Tick

Abdomen

Telson (tail)

Carapace

Horseshoe crab
(exception to group: has 3 body parts)

Class: Insecta

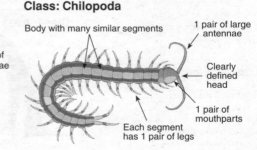

1 pair of antennae

1 pair of compound eyes

2 pairs of wings

Head

Thorax

Abdomen

3 pairs of legs   **Honey bee**

Locust

Butterfly

Beetles are the largest group within the animal kingdom with more than 300 000 species.

Beetle

Class: Diplopoda

Body with many similar segments

Clearly defined head

1 pair of antennae

Each segment has 2 pairs of legs

1 pair of mouthparts

Class: Chilopoda

Body with many similar segments

1 pair of large antennae

Clearly defined head

1 pair of mouthparts

Each segment has 1 pair of legs

Phylum: Echinodermata

- Rigid body wall, internal skeleton made of calcareous plates.
- Many possess spines.
- Ventral mouth, dorsal anus.
- External fertilisation.
- Unsegmented, marine organisms.
- Tube feet for locomotion.
- Water vascular system.

Examples: Starfish, brittlestars, feather stars, sea urchins, sea lilies.

Species diversity: 6000 +

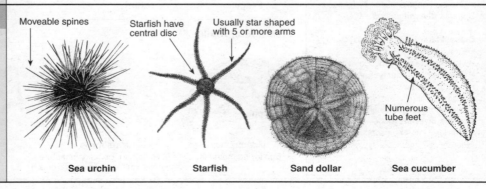

Moveable spines

Starfish have central disc

Usually star shaped with 5 or more arms

Numerous tube feet

Sea urchin

Starfish

Sand dollar

Sea cucumber

Kingdom: ANIMALIA *(continued)*

Phylum: Chordata

- Dorsal notochord (flexible, supporting rod) present at some stage in the life history.
- Post-anal tail present at some stage in their development.
- Dorsal, tubular nerve cord.
- Pharyngeal slits present.
- Circulation system closed in most.
- Heart positioned on ventral side.

Species diversity: 48 000 +

- A very diverse group with several sub-phyla:
  - Urochordata (sea squirts, salps)
  - Cephalochordata (lancelet)
  - Craniata (vertebrates)

Sub-Phylum Craniata (vertebrates)
- Internal skeleton of cartilage or bone.
- Well developed nervous system.
- Vertebral column replaces notochord.
- Two pairs of appendages (fins or limbs) attached to girdles.

Further subdivided into:

Class: Chondrichthyes (cartilaginous fish)
- Skeleton of cartilage (not bone).
- No swim bladder.
- All aquatic (mostly marine).
- Include: Sharks, rays, and skates.

Species diversity: 850 +

Class: Osteichthyes (bony fish)
- Swim bladder present.
- All aquatic (marine and fresh water).

Species diversity: 21 000 +

Class: Amphibia (amphibians)
- Lungs in adult, juveniles may have gills (retained in some adults).
- Gas exchange also through skin.
- Aquatic and terrestrial (limited to damp environments).
- Include: Frogs, toads, salamanders, and newts.

Species diversity: 3900 +

Class Reptilia (reptiles)
- Ectotherms with no larval stages.
- Teeth are all the same type.
- Eggs with soft leathery shell.
- Mostly terrestrial.
- Include: Snakes, lizards, crocodiles, turtles, and tortoises.

Species diversity: 7000 +

Class: Aves (birds)
- Terrestrial endotherms.
- Eggs with hard, calcareous shell.
- Strong, light skeleton.
- High metabolic rate.
- Gas exchange assisted by air sacs.

Species diversity: 8600 +

Class: Mammalia (mammals)
- Endotherms with hair or fur.
- Mammary glands produce milk.
- Glandular skin with hair or fur.
- External ear present.
- Teeth are of different types.
- Diaphragm between thorax/abdomen.

Species diversity: 4500 +
Subdivided into three subclasses:
Monotremes, marsupials, placentals.

Class: Chondrichthyes (cartilaginous fish)

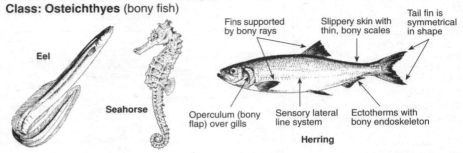

Ectotherms with endoskeleton made of cartilage

Lateral line sense organ

Asymmetrical tail fin provides lift

Skin with toothlike scales

Pelvic fin

Pectoral fin

No operculum (bony flap) over gills

Hammerhead shark

Stingray

Class: Osteichthyes (bony fish)

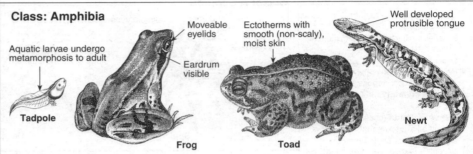

Fins supported by bony rays

Slippery skin with thin, bony scales

Tail fin is symmetrical in shape

Eel

Seahorse

Operculum (bony flap) over gills

Sensory lateral line system

Ectotherms with bony endoskeleton

Herring

Class: Amphibia

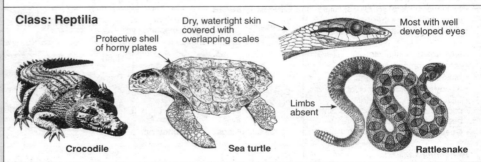

Aquatic larvae undergo metamorphosis to adult

Moveable eyelids

Ectotherms with smooth (non-scaly), moist skin

Well developed protrusible tongue

Eardrum visible

Tadpole

Frog

Toad

Newt

Class: Reptilia

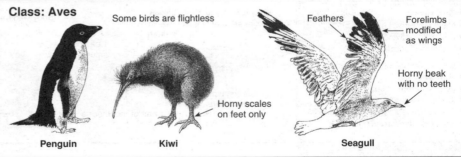

Protective shell of horny plates

Dry, watertight skin covered with overlapping scales

Most with well developed eyes

Limbs absent

Crocodile

Sea turtle

Rattlesnake

Class: Aves

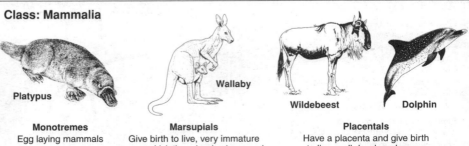

Some birds are flightless

Feathers

Forelimbs modified as wings

Horny scales on feet only

Horny beak with no teeth

Penguin

Kiwi

Seagull

Class: Mammalia

Platypus

Wallaby

Wildebeest

Dolphin

Monotremes
Egg laying mammals

Marsupials
Give birth to live, very immature young which then develop in a pouch

Placentals
Have a placenta and give birth to live, well developed young

Classification System

The classification of organisms is designed to reflect how they are related to each other. The fundamental unit of classification of living things is the **species**. Its members are so alike genetically that they can interbreed. This genetic similarity also means that they are almost identical in their physical and other characteristics. Species are classified further into larger, more comprehensive categories (higher taxa). It must be emphasised that all such higher classifications are human inventions to suit a particular purpose.

1. The table below shows part of the classification for humans using the seven major levels of classification. For this question, use the example of the classification of the European hedgehog, on the next page, as a guide.

   (a) Complete the list of the classification levels on the left hand side of the table below:

	Classification level	Human classification
1.	_____	_____
2.	_____	_____
3.	_____	_____ ,
4.	_____	_____
5.	Family	Hominidae
6.	_____	_____
7.	_____	_____

   (b) The name of the Family that humans belong to has already been entered into the space provided. Complete the classification for humans (*Homo sapiens*) on the table above.

2. Describe the two-part scientific naming system (called the **binomial system**) that is used to name organisms:

   _____

   _____

3. Give two reasons why the classification of organisms is important:

   (a) _____

   _____

   (b) _____

   _____

4. Traditionally, the classification of organisms has been based largely on similarities in physical appearance. More recently, new methods involving biochemical comparisons have been used to provide new insights into how species are related. Describe an example of a biochemical method for comparing how species are related:

   _____

   _____

   _____

5. As an example of physical features being used to classify organisms, mammals have been divided into three major sub-classes: monotremes, marsupials, and placentals. Describe the main physical feature distinguishing each of these taxa:

   (a) Monotreme: _____

   _____

   (b) Marsupial: _____

   _____

   (c) Placental: _____

   _____

Related activities: New Classification Schemes, Classification Keys, Features of Taxonomic Groups

RA 2

Classification of the European Hedgehog

Below is the classification for the **European hedgehog**. Only one of each group is subdivided in this chart showing the levels that can be used in classifying an organism. Not all possible subdivisions have been shown here. For example, it is possible to indicate such categories as **super-class** and **sub-family**. The only natural category is the **species**, often separated into geographical **races**, or **sub-species**, which generally differ in appearance.

Kingdom:
Animalia
Animals: one of five kingdoms

Phylum:
Chordata
Animals with a notochord (supporting rod of cells along the upper surface).
tunicates, salps, lancelets, and vertebrates

23 other phyla

Sub-phylum:
Vertebrata
Animals with backbones.
fish, amphibians, reptiles, birds, mammals

Class:
Mammalia
Animals that suckle their young on milk from mammary glands.
placentals, marsupials, monotremes

Sub-class:
Eutheria
Mammals whose young develop for some time in the female's reproductive tract gaining nourishment from a placenta.
placentals

Order:
Insectivora
Insect eating mammals.
An order of over 300 species of primitive, small mammals that feed mainly on insects and other small invertebrates.

17 other orders

Sub-order:
Erinaceomorpha
The hedgehog-type insectivores. One of the three suborders of insectivores. The other suborders include the tenrec-like insectivores (*tenrecs and golden moles*) and the shrew-like insectivores (*shrews, moles, desmans, and solenodons*).

Family:
Erinaceidae
The only family within this suborder. Comprises two subfamilies: the true or spiny hedgehogs and the moonrats (gymnures). Representatives in the family include the desert hedgehog, long-eared hedgehog, and the greater and lesser moonrats.

Genus:
Erinaceus
One of eight genera in this family. The genus *Erinaceus* includes four Eurasian species and another three in Africa.

7 other genera

Species:
europaeus
The European hedgehog. Among the largest of the spiny hedgehogs. Characterised by a dense covering of spines on the back, the presence of a big toe (hallux) and 36 teeth.

6 other species

The order *Insectivora* was first introduced to group together shrews, moles, and hedgehogs. It was later extended to include tenrecs, golden moles, desmans, tree shrews, and elephant shrews, and the taxonomy of the group became very confused. Recent reclassification of the elephant shrews and tree shrews into their own separate orders has made the Insectivora a more cohesive group taxonomically.

European hedgehog
Erinaceus europaeus

Features of the Five Kingdoms

The classification of organisms into taxonomic groups is based on how biologists believe they are related in an evolutionary sense. Organisms in a taxonomic group share features which set them apart from other groups. By identifying these features, it is possible to develop an understanding of the evolutionary history of the group. The focus of this activity is to summarise the **distinguishing features** of each of the five kingdoms in the five kingdom classification system.

1. Distinguishing features of Kingdom **Prokaryotae**:

_____

_____

_____

_____

2. Distinguishing features of Kingdom **Protoctista**:

_____

_____

_____

_____

_____

3. Distinguishing features of Kingdom **Fungi**:

_____

_____

_____

_____

_____

4. Distinguishing features of Kingdom **Plantae**:

_____

_____

_____

_____

_____

5. Distinguishing features of Kingdom **Animalia**:

_____

_____

_____

_____

_____

Staphylococcus dividing

Helicobacter pylori

Red blood cell

Trypanosoma parasite

Amoeba

Mushrooms

Yeast cells in solution

Maple seeds

Pea plants

Cicada moulting

Gibbon

Classification

Related activities: The New Tree of Life, Features of Taxonomic Groups

RA 1

Features of Microbial Groups

A microorganism (or microbe) is literally a microscopic organism. The term is usually reserved for the organisms studied in microbiology: bacteria, fungi, microscopic protoctistans, and viruses. Most of these taxa also have macroscopic representatives. This is especially the case within the fungi. The distinction between a macrofungus and a microfungus is an artificial but convenient one. Unlike microfungi, which are made conspicuous by the diseases or decay they cause, macrofungi are the ones most likely to be observed with the naked eye. Examples of microfungi, which include yeasts and pathogenic species, are illustrated in this activity. Macrofungi, which include mushrooms, toadstools, and lichens, are illustrated in *Features of Macrofungi and Plants*.

1. Distinguishing features of Kingdom **Prokaryotae**:

_____

_____

_____

_____

_____

_____

_____

_____

_____

2. Distinguishing features of Kingdom **Protoctista**:

_____

_____

_____

_____

_____

_____

_____

_____

_____

3. Distinguishing features of Kingdom **Fungi** (microfungi):

_____

_____

_____

_____

_____

_____

_____

_____

_____

_____

Spirillum bacteria

Staphylococcus

Anabaena cyanobacterium

Foraminiferan

Spirogyra algae

Diatoms: *Pleurosigma*

Curvularia sp. conidiophore

Yeast cells in solution

Microsporum distortum (a pathogenic fungus)

Features of Animal Taxa

The animal kingdom is classified into about 35 major **phyla**. Representatives of the more familiar taxa are illustrated below: **cnidarians** (includes jellyfish, sea anemones, and corals), **annelids** (segmented worms), **arthropods** (insects, crustaceans, spiders, scorpions, centipedes and millipedes), **molluscs** (snails, bivalve shellfish, squid and octopus), **echinoderms** (starfish and sea urchins), **vertebrates** from the phylum **chordates** (fish, amphibians, reptiles, birds, and mammals). The **arthropods** and the **vertebrates** have been represented in more detail, giving the **classes** for each of these **phyla**. This activity asks you to describe the **distinguishing features** of each of the taxa represented below.

Classification

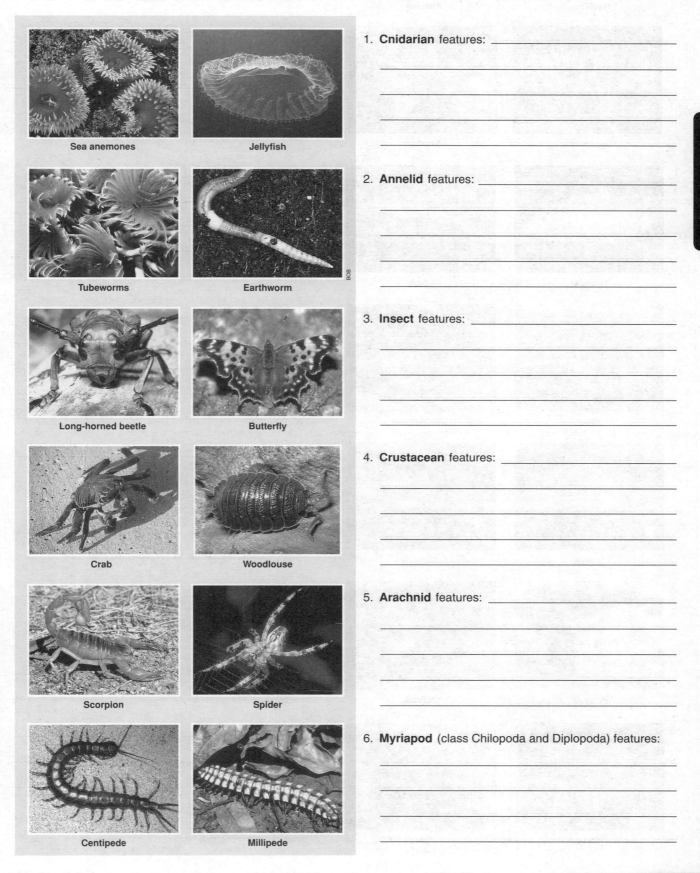

Sea anemones

Jellyfish

Tubeworms

Earthworm

Long-horned beetle

Butterfly

Crab

Woodlouse

Scorpion

Spider

Centipede

Millipede

1. **Cnidarian** features: _____

_____

_____

_____

_____

2. **Annelid** features: _____

_____

_____

_____

_____

3. **Insect** features: _____

_____

_____

_____

_____

4. **Crustacean** features: _____

_____

_____

_____

_____

5. **Arachnid** features: _____

_____

_____

_____

6. **Myriapod** (class Chilopoda and Diplopoda) features:

_____

_____

_____

_____

Related activities: The New Tree of Life, Features of Taxonomic Groups

ER 1

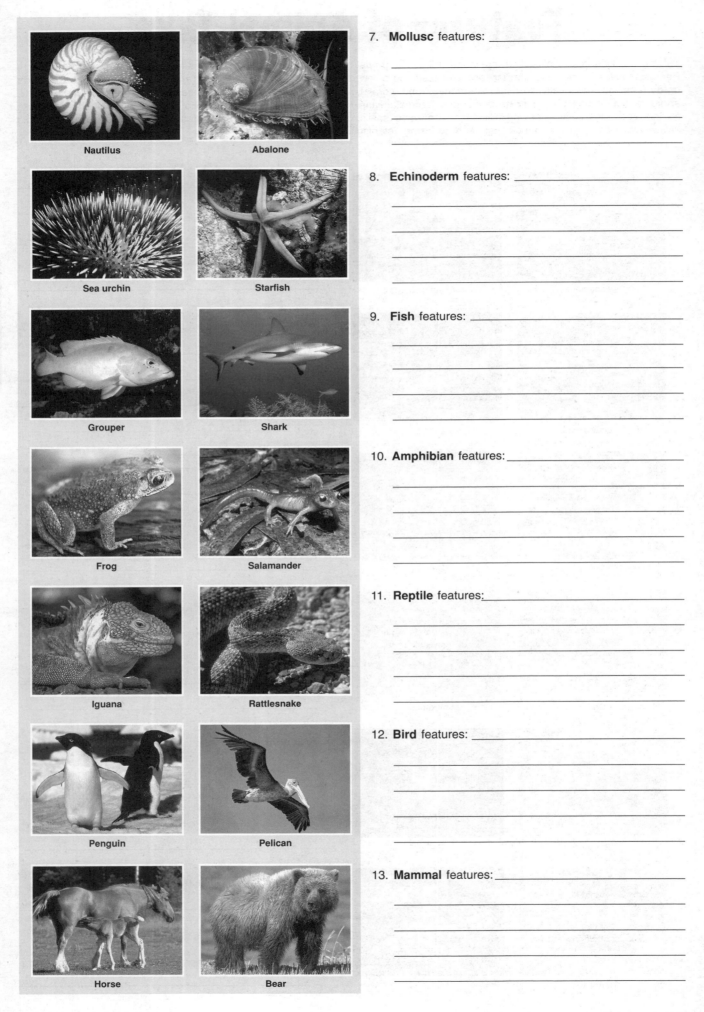

274

7. **Mollusc** features: _____

_____

_____

_____

_____

_____

8. **Echinoderm** features: _____

_____

_____

_____

_____

_____

9. **Fish** features: _____

_____

_____

_____

_____

_____

_____

10. **Amphibian** features: _____

_____

_____

_____

_____

_____

11. **Reptile** features: _____

_____

_____

_____

_____

_____

_____

12. **Bird** features: _____

_____

_____

_____

_____

_____

_____

13. **Mammal** features: _____

_____

_____

_____

_____

_____

Features of Macrofungi and Plants

Although plants and fungi are some of the most familiar organisms in our environment, their classification has not always been straightforward. We know now that the plant kingdom is monophyletic, meaning that it is derived from a common ancestor. The variety we see in plant taxa today is a result of their enormous diversification from the first plants. Although the fungi were once grouped together with the plants, they are unique organisms that differ from other eukaryotes in their mode of nutrition, structural organisation, growth, and reproduction. The focus of this activity is to summarise the features of the fungal kingdom, the major divisions of the plant kingdom, and the two classes of flowering plants (angiosperms).

Lichen

Bracket fungus

Liverwort

Moss

Fern frond

Ground fern

Pine tree cone

Cycad

Coconut palms

Wheat plants

Deciduous tree

Flowering plant

1. **Macrofungi** features:

_____
_____
_____
_____

2. **Moss and liverwort** features:

_____
_____
_____
_____

3. **Fern** features:

_____
_____
_____
_____

4. **Gymnosperm** features:

_____
_____
_____
_____

5. **Monocot angiosperm** features:

_____
_____
_____
_____

6. **Dicot angiosperm** features:

_____
_____
_____
_____

Classification

Related activities: The New Tree of Life, Features of Taxonomic Groups

R 1

The Classification of Life

For this activity, cut away the two pages of diagrams that follow from your book. The five kingdoms that all living things are grouped into, are listed on this page and the following page.

1. Cut out all of the images of different living organisms (cut around each shape closely, taking care to include their names).

2. Sort them into their classification groups by placing them into the spaces provided on this and the following page.

3. To fix the images in place, first use a temporary method, so that you can easily reposition them if you need to. Make a permanent fixture when you are completely satisfied with your placements on the page.

Kingdom Prokaryotae (Monera)

Kingdom Protoctista

Kingdom Fungi

Kingdom Plantae

Phylum Bryophyta

Phylum Filicinophyta

Phylum Angiospermophyta

Class Monocotyledoneae   Class Dicotyledoneae

Phylum Cycadophyta

Phylum Coniferophyta

Related activities: Features of Taxonomic Groups, Classification Keys

Cut out the organisms on this page and paste them into the spaces provided at the start of this activity. Organisms are not to scale.

Marine jellyfish

Liverwort

Earthworm

Blowfly

Seahorse

Centipede

Parrot

Sea star

Tube sponge

Tapeworm

Peccary

Echidna

Staphylococcus bacteria

Freshwater eel

Stingray

Scorpion

Frog

Garden snail

Euglena

Tortoise

Cycad

Kangaroo

Amoeba

African violets

Classification

Remove this page by tearing along the perforation

This page has been deliberately left blank

Cut out the images
on the other side of this page

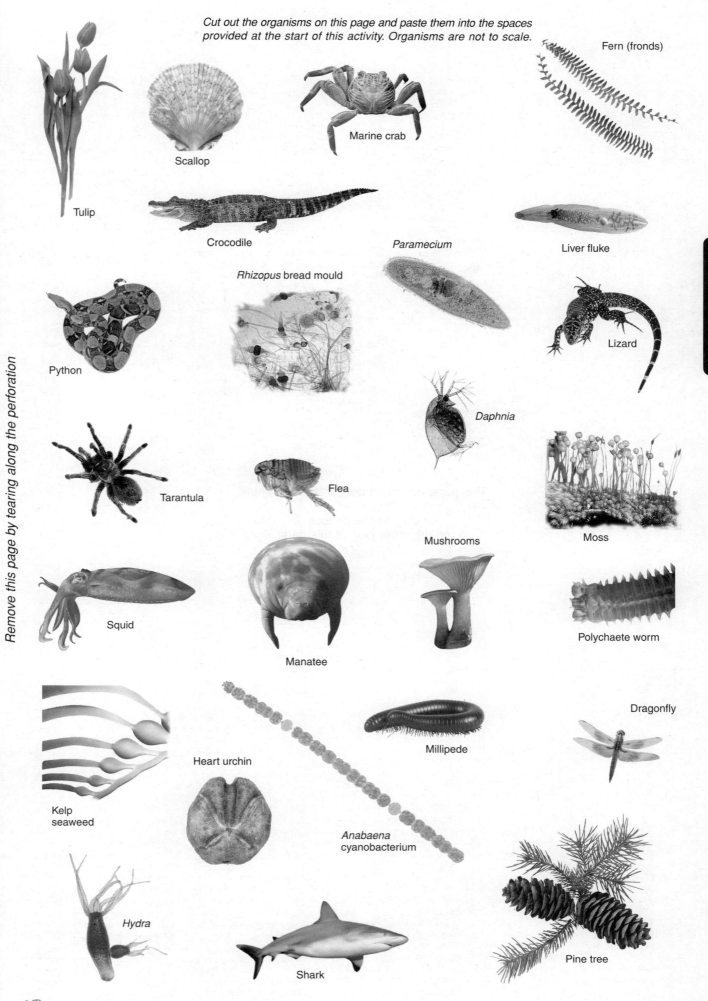

Cut out the organisms on this page and paste them into the spaces provided at the start of this activity. Organisms are not to scale.

Fern (fronds)

Tulip

Scallop

Marine crab

Crocodile

Paramecium

Liver fluke

Classification

Rhizopus bread mould

Python

Lizard

Daphnia

Tarantula

Flea

Moss

Mushrooms

Squid

Manatee

Polychaete worm

Kelp seaweed

Heart urchin

Anabaena cyanobacterium

Millipede

Dragonfly

Hydra

Shark

Pine tree

Remove this page by tearing along the perforation

© Biozone International 2008

Photocopying Prohibited

280

This page has been deliberately left blank

Cut out the images
on the other side of this page

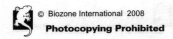

Kingdom Animalia			
Phylum Porifera	**Phylum Cnidaria**	**Phylum Platyhelminthes**	**Phylum Annelida**

Phylum Mollusca

Class Gastropoda   Class Bivalvia   Class Cephalopoda

Phylum Echinodermata

Phylum Arthropoda
Superclass Crustacea   Classes Chilopoda/Diplopoda   Class Arachnida   Class Insecta

Class Chondrichthyes   **Phylum Chordata**   Class Osteichthyes   Class Amphibia

Class Reptilia
Order Squamata   Order Crocodilia   Order Chelonia   Class Aves

Class Mammalia
Subclass Prototheria   Subclass Metatheria   Subclass Eutheria

Classification

Classification Keys

Classification systems provide biologists with a way in which to identify species. They also indicate how closely related, in an evolutionary sense, each species is to others. An organism's classification should include a clear, unambiguous **description**, an accurate **diagram**, and its unique name, denoted by the **genus** and **species**. Classification keys are used to identify an organism and assign it to the correct species (assuming that the organism has already been formally classified and is included in the key). Typically, keys are **dichotomous** and involve a series of linked steps. At each step, a choice is made between two features; each alternative leads to another question until an identification is made. If the organism cannot be identified, it may be a new species or the key may need revision. Two examples of **dichotomous keys** are provided here. The first (below) describes features for identifying the larvae of various genera within the order Trichoptera (caddisflies). From this key you should be able to assign a generic name to each of the caddisfly larvae pictured. The key on the next page identifies aquatic insect orders.

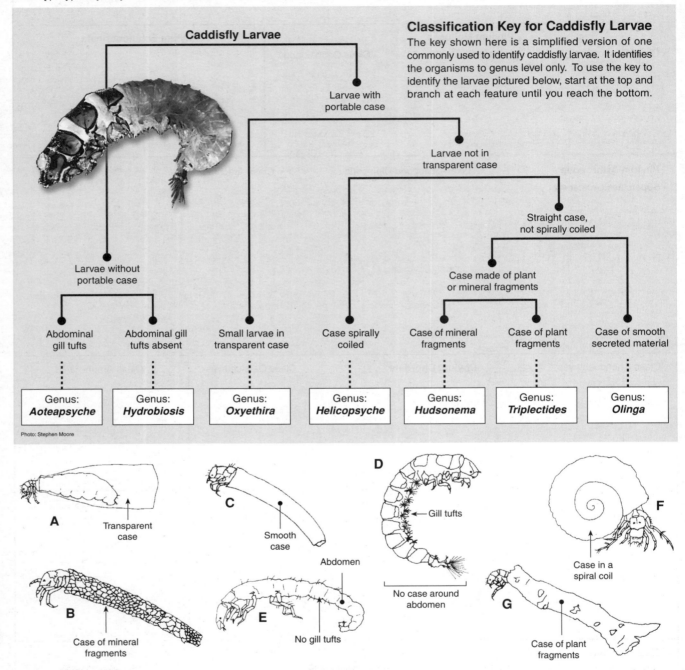

Classification Key for Caddisfly Larvae

The key shown here is a simplified version of one commonly used to identify caddisfly larvae. It identifies the organisms to genus level only. To use the key to identify the larvae pictured below, start at the top and branch at each feature until you reach the bottom.

Caddisfly Larvae

Larvae with portable case

Larvae not in transparent case

Straight case, not spirally coiled

Case made of plant or mineral fragments

Larvae without portable case

| Abdominal gill tufts | Abdominal gill tufts absent | Small larvae in transparent case | Case spirally coiled | Case of mineral fragments | Case of plant fragments | Case of smooth secreted material |

| Genus: *Aoteapsyche* | Genus: *Hydrobiosis* | Genus: *Oxyethira* | Genus: *Helicopsyche* | Genus: *Hudsonema* | Genus: *Triplectides* | Genus: *Olinga* |

Photo: Stephen Moore

A — Transparent case

B — Case of mineral fragments

C — Smooth case

D — Gill tufts / No case around abdomen

E — Abdomen / No gill tufts

F — Case in a spiral coil

G — Case of plant fragments

1. Describe the main feature used to distinguish the genera in the key above: _____

   _____

2. Use the key above to assign each of the caddisfly larvae (**A-G**) to its correct genus:

   A: _____   D: _____   G: _____

   B: _____   E: _____

   C: _____   F: _____

Related activities: Keying Out Plant Species
Web links: What is the Key to Classification?

© Biozone International 2008
Photocopying Prohibited

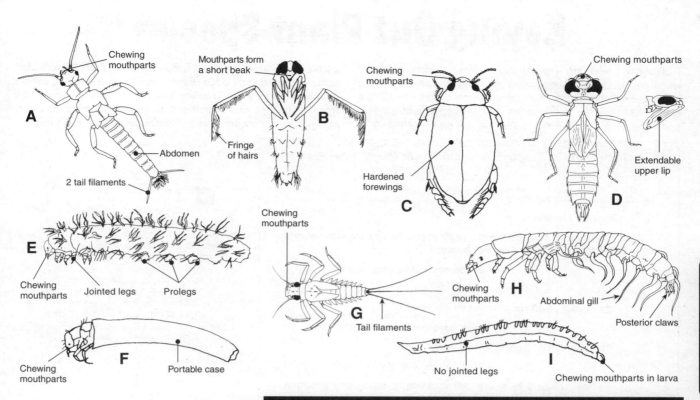

A — Chewing mouthparts; Abdomen; 2 tail filaments

B — Mouthparts form a short beak; Fringe of hairs

C — Chewing mouthparts; Hardened forewings

D — Chewing mouthparts; Extendable upper lip

E — Chewing mouthparts; Jointed legs; Prolegs

F — Chewing mouthparts; Portable case

G — Chewing mouthparts; Tail filaments

H — Chewing mouthparts; Abdominal gill; Posterior claws

I — No jointed legs; Chewing mouthparts in larva

3. Use the simplified key to identify each of the orders (by order or common name) of aquatic insects (**A-I**) pictured above:

(a) Order of insect A:

_____

(b) Order of insect B:

_____

(c) Order of insect C:

_____

(d) Order of insect D:

_____

(e) Order of insect E:

_____

(f) Order of insect F:

_____

(g) Order of insect G:

_____

(h) Order of insect H:

_____

(i) Order of insect I:

_____

Key to Orders of Aquatic Insects

1	Insects with chewing mouthparts; forewings are hardened and meet along the midline of the body when at rest (they may cover the entire abdomen or be reduced in length).	**Coleoptera** (beetles)
	Mouthparts piercing or sucking and form a pointed cone	*Go to 2*
	With chewing mouthparts, but without hardened forewings	*Go to 3*
2	Mouthparts form a short, pointed beak; legs fringed for swimming or long and spaced for suspension on water.	**Hemiptera** (bugs)
	Mouthparts do not form a beak; legs (if present) not fringed or long, or spaced apart.	*Go to 3*
3	Prominent upper lip (labium) extendable, forming a food capturing structure longer than the head.	**Odonata** (dragonflies & damselflies)
	Without a prominent, extendable labium	*Go to 4*
4	Abdomen terminating in three tail filaments which may be long and thin, or with fringes of hairs.	**Ephemeroptera** (mayflies)
	Without three tail filaments	*Go to 5*
5	Abdomen terminating in two tail filaments	**Plecoptera** (stoneflies)
	Without long tail filaments	*Go to 6*
6	With three pairs of jointed legs on thorax	*Go to 7*
	Without jointed, thoracic legs (although non-segmented prolegs or false legs may be present).	**Diptera** (true flies)
7	Abdomen with pairs of non-segmented prolegs bearing rows of fine hooks.	**Lepidoptera** (moths and butterflies)
	Without pairs of abdominal prolegs	*Go to 8*
8	With eight pairs of finger-like abdominal gills; abdomen with two pairs of posterior claws.	**Megaloptera** (dobsonflies)
	Either, without paired, abdominal gills, or, if such gills are present, without posterior claws.	*Go to 9*
9	Abdomen with a pair of posterior prolegs bearing claws with subsidiary hooks; sometimes a portable case.	**Trichoptera** (caddisflies)

Keying Out Plant Species

Dichotomous keys are a useful tool in biology and can enable identification to the species level provided the characteristics chosen are appropriate for separating species. Keys are extensively used by botanists as they are quick and easy to use in the field, although they sometime rely on the presence of particular plant parts such as fruits or flowers. Some also require some specialist knowledge of plant biology. The following simple activity requires you to identify five species of the genus *Acer* from illustrations of the leaves. It provides valuable practice in using characteristic features to identify plants to species level.

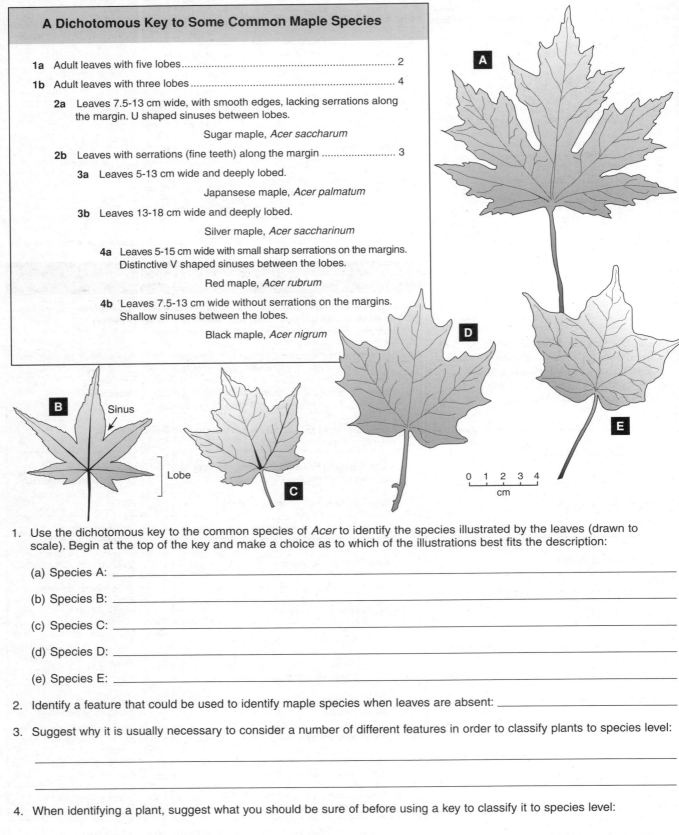

A Dichotomous Key to Some Common Maple Species

1a Adult leaves with five lobes...2

1b Adult leaves with three lobes 4

    2a Leaves 7.5-13 cm wide, with smooth edges, lacking serrations along the margin. U shaped sinuses between lobes.

               Sugar maple, *Acer saccharum*

    2b Leaves with serrations (fine teeth) along the margin 3

        3a Leaves 5-13 cm wide and deeply lobed.

               Japansese maple, *Acer palmatum*

        3b Leaves 13-18 cm wide and deeply lobed.

               Silver maple, *Acer saccharinum*

        4a Leaves 5-15 cm wide with small sharp serrations on the margins. Distinctive V shaped sinuses between the lobes.

               Red maple, *Acer rubrum*

        4b Leaves 7.5-13 cm wide without serrations on the margins. Shallow sinuses between the lobes.

               Black maple, *Acer nigrum*

1. Use the dichotomous key to the common species of *Acer* to identify the species illustrated by the leaves (drawn to scale). Begin at the top of the key and make a choice as to which of the illustrations best fits the description:

    (a) Species A: _____

    (b) Species B: _____

    (c) Species C: _____

    (d) Species D: _____

    (e) Species E: _____

2. Identify a feature that could be used to identify maple species when leaves are absent: _____

3. Suggest why it is usually necessary to consider a number of different features in order to classify plants to species level:

    _____

    _____

4. When identifying a plant, suggest what you should be sure of before using a key to classify it to species level:

    _____

    _____

Related activities: Classification Keys
Web links: Tree ID

Biodiversity and Conservation

OCR: Unit F212, Module 3: Biodiversity and Evolution
2.3.1: Biodiversity and 2.3.4: Maintaining biodiversity

CIE: APPLICATIONS OF BIOLOGY
Q (b)-(f): Conservation issues

Learning Objectives

☐ 1. Compile your own glossary from the **KEY WORDS** displayed in **bold type** in the learning objectives below.

Biodiversity *(pages 286-289, 299-300)*

☐ 2. Recognise the different components of **biodiversity**: **species**, **habitat**, and **genetic diversity** and explain how biodiversity can be studied at each of these levels.

☐ 3. Explain the role of sampling in measuring the biodiversity of a region. Explain the importance of random sampling in studies of biodiversity.

☐ 4. Explain what is meant by **species richness** and **species evenness** in a habitat. Appreciate the role of appropriate sampling methods in fairly investigating these properties.

☐ 4. Explain the use of **diversity indices** in community ecology. Use a **diversity index**, such as the **Simpson's Index of Diversity**, to analyse and compare two local communities. Outline the significance of both high and low values of this diversity index. If required, describe the use of **biotic indices** (including **indicator species**) in monitoring change in the environment.

☐ 5. Discuss current estimates of global biodiversity. Identify regions of naturally-occurring high **biodiversity** (biodiversity hotspots) and describe the importance of these regions to global ecology.

Maintaining Biodiversity *(pages 289-301)*

☐ 6. Recognise that areas of high biodiversity are under increasing pressure as human populations expand.

☐ 7. Using an example (e.g. rainforest destruction), discuss the ethical, ecological, economic, and aesthetic reasons for the conservation of biodiversity. Recognise the relationship between **diversity** and ecosystem **stability** and **resilience**. Appreciate the role of **keystone species** in ecosystem function and the possible consequences of removing these species.

☐ 8. Discuss the consequences of global climate change on the Earth's biodiversity. Include in your discussion reference to changing patterns of agriculture and changes in the patterns and incidence of disease.

☐ 9. Discuss the benefits to agriculture in following farming practices that maintain or enhance biodiversity. Use a local example to explain your argument, e.g. the conservation of hedgerows in Britain.

☐ 10. Discuss the *in-situ* (e.g. pest control) and *ex-situ* (e.g. captive breeding) conservation of endangered plant and animal species. Include reference to advantages and disadvantages of each approach.

☐ 11. Using examples, discuss the role of botanic gardens and **seed banks** in the *ex-situ* conservation of plant species that are rare or extinct in the wild.

☐ 12. Discuss the role of international cooperation in the management of endangered species and the conservation of biodiversity. Include reference to **CITES** and the **Rio Convention of Biodiversity**.

☐ 12. Recognise the impact that local developments can have on biodiversity. Discuss the importance of **environmental impact assessments** (including estimates of biodiversity) when planning decisions are made by local authorities.

See the 'Textbook Reference Grid' on page 7 for textbook page references relating to material in this topic.

STUDENT'S REFERENCE

See page 6 for details of publishers of periodicals:

■ **Global Warming** Time, special issue, 2007. *A special issue on global warming: the causes, perils, solutions, and actions. Comprehensive, well illustrated, engaging, and up-to-date.*

■ **Biodiversity and Ecosystems** Biol. Sci. Rev., 11(4) March 1999, pp. 18-21. *The importance of biodiversity to ecosystem stability and sustainability.*

■ **The Big Thaw** National Geographic, Sept. 2004, pp. 12-75. *Part of a special issue providing an up-to-date, readable account of the state of global warming and climate change.*

■ **Hot Spots** New Scientist, 4 April 1998, pp. 32-36. *An examination of the reasons for the very high biodiversity observed in the tropics.*

■ **Biodiversity: Taking Stock of Life** National Geographic, 195(2) Feb. 1999 (entire issue). *A special issue exploring the Earth's biodiversity and what we can do to preserve it.*

■ **Last of the Amazon** National Geographic, 211(1) Jan. 2007, pp. 40-71. *The current state of the Amazon forest, one of the world's most biologically diverse regions.*

TEACHER'S REFERENCE

■ **Conservation for the People** Scientific American, Oct. 2007, pp. 26-33. *Preserving biodiversity in ecological hotspots is not working as a conservation strategy. We need to protect ecosystems vital to ecosystem and human health.*

■ **The Last Menageries** New Scientist, 19 Jan. 2002, pp. 40-43. *The role of zoos today in conservation, education, and research.*

See pages 8-9 for details of how to access **Bio Links** from our web site: **www.biozone.co.uk** From Bio Links, access sites under the topics:

BIODIVERSITY > Biodiversity: • Convention on biological diversity • Ecology and biodiversity • World atlas of biodiversity … *and others*

CONSERVATION: > **Endangered Species:** • African elephant DB homepage • Endangered species > **Habitat loss:** • Causes of habitat loss and species endangerment • We need our forests > **Conservation Issues:** • CITES • WWF

Presentation MEDIA to support this topic:
ECOLOGY: Biodiversity & Conservation

Global Biodiversity

The species is the basic unit by which we measure biological diversity or **biodiversity**. Biodiversity is not distributed evenly on Earth, being consistently richer in the tropics and concentrated more in some areas than in others. The simplest definition of biodiversity is as the sum of all biotic variation from the level of genes to ecosystems, but often the components of total biodiversity are distinguished. **Species diversity** describes the number of different species in an area (**species richness**), **genetic diversity** is the diversity of genes within a species, and **ecosystem diversity** refers to the diversity at

the higher ecosystem level of organisation. **Habitat diversity** is also sometimes described and is essentially a subset of ecosystem diversity expressed per given unit area. Total biological diversity is often threatened because of the loss of just one of these components. Conservation International recognises 25 **biodiversity hotspots**. These are biologically diverse and ecologically distinct regions under the greatest threat of destruction. They are identified on the basis of the number of species present, the amount of **endemism**, and the extent to which the species are threatened.

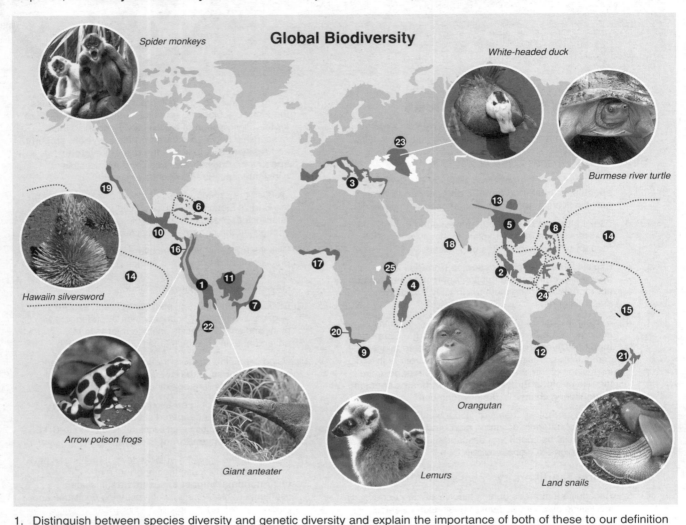

Global Biodiversity

Spider monkeys · White-headed duck · Burmese river turtle · Hawaiin silversword · Arrow poison frogs · Giant anteater · Lemurs · Orangutan · Land snails

1. Distinguish between species diversity and genetic diversity and explain the importance of both of these to our definition of total biological diversity:

_____

_____

_____

_____

2. Explain the importance of considering ecosystem (habitat) diversity when targeting regions for conservation purposes:

_____

_____

_____

3. Use your research tools (e.g. textbook, internet, or encyclopaedia) to identify each of the 25 biodiversity hotspots illustrated in the diagram above. For each region, summarise the characteristics that have resulted in it being identified as a biodiversity hotspot. Present your summary as a short report and attach it to this page of your workbook.

Britain's Biodiversity

The species is the basic unit by which we measure biodiversity. For some taxa, e.g. bacteria, the true extent of species diversity remains unidentified. Some data on species richness for the UK are shown below (note the bias towards large, conspicuous organisms). The biodiversity of the British Isles today is the result of a legacy of past climatic changes and a long history of human influence. Some of the most interesting, species-rich ecosystems, such as hedgerows, downland turf, and woodland, are maintained as a result of human activity. Many of the species characteristic of Britain's biodiversity are also found more widely in Europe. Other species (e.g. the Scottish crossbill), or species associations (e.g. bluebell woodlands) are uniquely British. With increasing pressure on natural areas from urbanisation, roading, and other human encroachment, maintaining species diversity is paramount and should concern us all today.

Peregrine falcon · Acorn barnacle · Bluebell woodland · Hedgehog · Hermit crab · Nuthatch · European otter · Red elf cup fungus · Red fox · Duke of Burgundy fritillary · Woodmouse · European badger · Oak (with gall) · Puffin · Common toad · Field vole

PHOTO CREDITS - see the front of the manual

Biodiversity and Conservation

Left: Fig. 1: British biodiversity, as numbers of terrestrial and freshwater species, compared with recent global estimates of described species in major taxonomic groups.

Major taxonomic group	Estimated no. of British species	Estimated no. of world species
Bacteria	unknown	> 4 000
Viruses	unknown	> 5 000
Protozoa	> 20 000	> 40 000
Algae	> 20 000	> 40 000
Fungi	> 15 000	> 70 000
Ferns and bryophytes	1 080	> 26 000
Lichens	1 500	> 17 000
Flowering plants	1 400	> 250 000
Invertebrate animals	> 28 500	> 1.28 million
Insects	22 500	> 1 million
Non-insect arthropods	> 3 000	> 190 000
All other invertebrates	> 3 000	> 90 000
Vertebrate animals	308	> 33 208
Fish (freshwater)	38	> 8 500
Amphibians	6	> 4 000
Reptiles	6	> 6 500
Birds (breeding residents)	210	9 881
Mammals	48	4 327

Source: Biodiversity: The UK Action Plan, 1994. HMSO

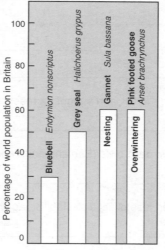

Bluebell *Endymion nonscriptus* · Grey seal *Halichoerus grypus* · Gannet *Sula bassana* (Nesting) · Pink footed goose *Anser brachrynchus* (Overwintering)

Percentage of world population in Britain

Fig. 2: Bar graph illustrating the percentage of world populations of various species permanently or temporarily resident in Britain.

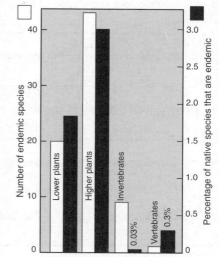

Lower plants · Higher plants · Invertebrates 0.03% · Vertebrates 0.3%

Number of endemic species — Percentage of native species that are endemic

Fig 3: Bar graph illustrating the degree of endemism in Britain. Right axis indicates % endemism in relation to the number of described British native species.

Related activities: Ecosystem Stability, Endangered Species, The Impact of Alien Species
Web links: Space for Species

RA 3

Barn owls are predators of small mammals, birds, insects, and frogs. They are higher order consumers and, as such, have been badly affected by the bioaccumulation of pesticides in recent times. They require suitable nesting and bathing sites, and reliable sources of small prey.

Conservation of the barn owl *(Tyto alba)*

Status: The barn owl is one of the best known and widely distributed owl species in the world. It was once very common in Britain but has experienced severe declines in the last 50 years as a result of the combined impacts of habitat loss, changed farming practices, and increased sources of mortality.

Reasons for decline: Primarily, declines have been the result of changed farm management practices (e.g. increased land clearance and mechanisation) which have resulted in reduced prey abundance and fewer suitable breeding sites. Contributing factors include increases in road deaths as traffic speed and volume rises, and poorer breeding success and reduced chick survival as a result of pesticide bioaccumulation. In addition, more birds are drowned when attempting to bathe in the steep sided troughs which have increasingly replaced the more traditional shallow farm ponds.

Conservation management: A return to the population densities of 50 years ago is very unlikely, but current conservation measures have at least stabilised numbers. These involve habitat enhancement (e.g. provision of nest sites), reduction in pesticide use, and rearing of orphaned young followed by monitored release into suitable habitats.

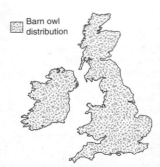

Barn owl distribution

Barn owls are widely distributed in Ireland and the UK, but numbers are not high.

Period of survey (England & Wales)	Breeding pairs (estimates)
1935	12 000
1968 – 1972	6000 – 9000
1983 – 1985	3800

1. Produce a pie graph below to show the proportions of British species in each taxonomic group (ignoring bacteria and viruses). Calculate the percentages from Fig. 1 (opposite) and tabulate the data (one has been completed for you). The chart has been marked in 5° divisions and each % point is equal to 3.6° on the pie chart. Provide a colour key in the space next to the tabulated figures. For the purposes of this exercise, use the values provided, ignoring the > sign:

Proportion of British species in different taxonomic groups

	Percentage of species in each taxon	Segment size	Key
Protozoa			
Algae			
Fungi			
Ferns and bryophytes			
Lichens			
Flowering plants			
Invertebrates	28 500 ÷ 87 788 X 100 = 32.5%	117°	
Vertebrates			

2. Comment on the proportion of biodiversity within each taxonomic group: _____

_____

3. (a) Contrast our knowledge of the biodiversity of bacteria and invertebrates with that of vertebrates:

_____

(b) Suggest a reason for the difference: _____

_____

4. Comment on the level of endemism in the UK and suggest a reason for it: _____

_____

5. (a) Calculate the percentage decline in barn owls (England and Wales) over the 50 year period 1935 – 1985:

_____

(b) Suggest why this species has been less difficult to stabilise against decline than other (more endangered) species:

_____

_____

_____

Loss of Biodiversity

More than a third of the planet's known terrestrial plant and animal species are found within the biodiversity hotspot regions which cover only 1.4% of the Earth's land area. Unfortunately, biodiversity hotspots often occur near areas of dense human habitation and rapid human population growth. Most are located in the tropics and most are forests. Background (natural) extinction rates for all organisms (including bacteria and fungi) are estimated to be 10-100 species a year. The actual extinction rate is estimated to be 100-1000 times higher, mainly due to the effects of human activity. Over 41 000 species are now on the International Union for Conservation's (IUCN) red list, and 16 000 are threatened with extinction. Loss of biodiversity reduces the stability and resilience of natural ecosystems and decreases the ability of their communities to adapt to changing environmental conditions. Humans rely heavily on the biodiversity in nature and a loss of species richness has a deleterious effect on us all.

Insects make up 80% of all known animal species. There are an estimated 6-10 million insect species on Earth, but only 900,000 have been identified. Some 44 000 species may have become extinct over the last 600 years. The Duke of Burgundy butterfly (*Hamearis lucina*), right, is an endangered British species.

Just over 5% of the 8225 reptile species are at risk. These include the two tuatara species (right) from New Zealand, which are the only living members of the order Sphenodontia, and the critically endangered blue iguana. Only about 200 blue iguanas remain, all in the Grand Caymans.

	Total number of species*	Number of IUCN listed species
Plants	310 000 - 422,000	8474
Insects	6 -10 million	622
Fish	28 000	126
Amphibians	5743	1809
Reptiles	8225	423
Birds	10 000	1133
Mammals	5400	1027

* Estimated numbers

The giant panda (above), is one of many critically endangered terrestrial mammals, with fewer than 2000 surviving in the wild. Amongst the 120 species of marine mammals, approximately 25% (including the humpback whale and Hector's dolphin) are on the ICUN's red list.

Prior to the impact of human activity on the environment, one bird species became extinct every 100 years. Today, the rate is one every year, and may increase to 10 species every year by the end of the century. Some at risk birds, such as the Hawaiian crow (right), are now found only in captivity.

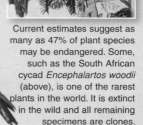

Current estimates suggest as many as 47% of plant species may be endangered. Some, such as the South African cycad *Encephalartos woodii* (above), is one of the rarest plants in the world. It is extinct in the wild and all remaining specimens are clones.

Threats to Biodiversity

Rainforests in some of the most species-rich regions of the world are being destroyed at an alarming rate as world demand for tropical hardwoods increases and land is cleared for the establishment of agriculture.

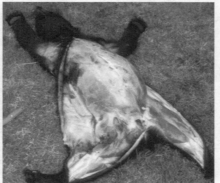

Illegal trade in species (for food, body parts, or for the exotic pet trade) is pushing some species to the brink of extinction. Despite international bans on trade, illegal trade in primates, parrots, reptiles, and big cats (among others) continues.

Pollution and the pressure of human populations on natural habitats threatens biodiversity in many regions. Environmental pollutants may accumulate through food chains or cause harm directly, as with this bird trapped in oil.

1. Discuss, in general terms, the effects of loss of biodiversity on an ecosystem: _____

_____

_____

_____

_____

_____

Related activities: Biodiversity Hotspots

RA 2

Biodiversity and Conservation

Tropical Deforestation

Tropical rainforests prevail in places where the climate is very moist throughout the year (200 to 450 cm of rainfall per year). Almost half of the world's rainforests are in just three countries: **Indonesia** in Southeast Asia, **Brazil** in South America, and **Zaire** in Africa. Much of the world's biodiversity resides in rainforests. Destruction of the forests will contribute towards global warming through a large reduction in photosynthesis. In the Amazon, 75% of deforestation has occurred within 50 km of Brazil's roads. Many potential drugs could still be discovered in rainforest plants, and loss of species through deforestation may mean they will never be found. Rainforests can provide economically sustainable crops (rubber, coffee, nuts, fruits, and oils) for local people.

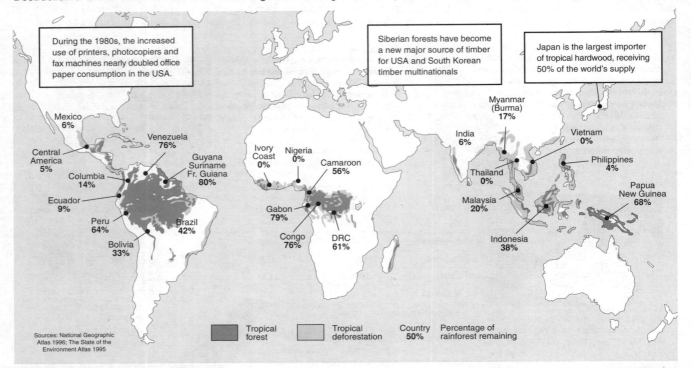

During the 1980s, the increased use of printers, photocopiers and fax machines nearly doubled office paper consumption in the USA.

Siberian forests have become a new major source of timber for USA and South Korean timber multinationals

Japan is the largest importer of tropical hardwood, receiving 50% of the world's supply

Mexico 6%
Central America 5%
Columbia 14%
Ecuador 9%
Peru 64%
Bolivia 33%
Venezuela 76%
Guyana Suriname Fr. Guiana 80%
Brazil 42%

Ivory Coast 0%
Nigeria 0%
Camaroon 56%
Gabon 79%
Congo 76%
DRC 61%

India 6%
Myanmar (Burma) 17%
Vietnam 0%
Thailand 0%
Malaysia 20%
Philippines 4%
Papua New Guinea 68%
Indonesia 38%

Sources: National Geographic Atlas 1996; The State of the Environment Atlas 1995

Tropical forest | Tropical deforestation | Country 50% | Percentage of rainforest remaining

The felling of rainforest trees is taking place at an alarming rate as world demand for tropical hardwoods increases and land is cleared for the establishment of agriculture. The resulting farms and plantations often have shortlived productivity.

Huge forest fires have devastated large amounts of tropical rainforest in Indonesia and Brazil in 1997/98. The fires in Indonesia were started by people attempting to clear the forest areas for farming in a year of particularly low rainfall.

The building of new road networks into regions with tropical rainforests causes considerable environmental damage. In areas with very high rainfall there is an increased risk of erosion and loss of topsoil.

1. Describe three reasons why tropical rainforests should be conserved:

    (a) _____

    (b) _____

    (c) _____

2. Explain why the world's regions of tropical rainforest coincide with hotspots of biodiversity:

    _____

    _____

    _____

Related activities: Global Biodiversity Loss of Biodiversity

Biodiversity and Global Warming

Climate warming is not only an environmental issue; its consequences are interconnected globally and it has implications for economic growth, food security, and world health. A rise in average global temperatures puts greater pressure on species already at risk to adapt, and rates of species loss will accelerate. At least 40% of the world's economy and 80% of the needs of the poor are derived from biological resources, yet the capacity of the current systems to adapt to climate changes puts these resources at risk. The effect on climate change on agriculture and food security depends on a combination of a many factors. Higher temperatures can stress plants but will also prolong growing seasons and allow a wider range of crops to be grown. Higher levels of CO_2 speed plant growth and increase resilience to water stress, but warmer temperatures will also extend the range of pests and diseases. Overall, changes in rainfall, increased frequency of severe climatic events, and more soil erosion will influence patterns of agriculture and disease incidence. Humans will have to prepare appropriately for these changes.

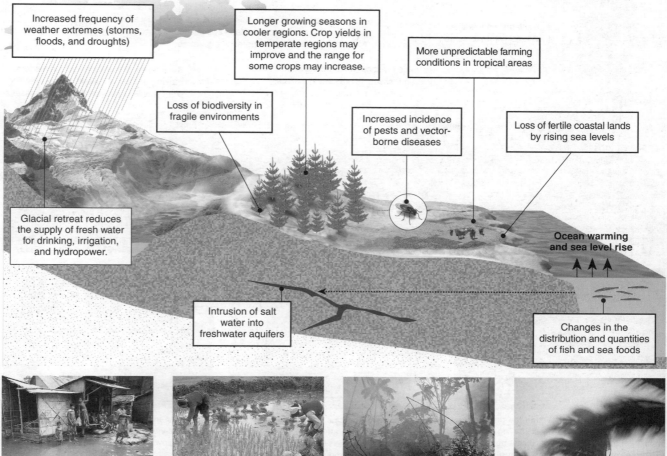

Increased frequency of weather extremes (storms, floods, and droughts)

Longer growing seasons in cooler regions. Crop yields in temperate regions may improve and the range for some crops may increase.

More unpredictable farming conditions in tropical areas

Loss of biodiversity in fragile environments

Increased incidence of pests and vector-borne diseases

Loss of fertile coastal lands by rising sea levels

Glacial retreat reduces the supply of fresh water for drinking, irrigation, and hydropower.

Ocean warming and sea level rise

Intrusion of salt water into freshwater aquifers

Changes in the distribution and quantities of fish and sea foods

Biodiversity and Conservation

Sea levels are expected to rise by 50 cm by the year 2100. This is the result of the thermal expansion of ocean water and melting of glaciers and ice shelves. Warming may also expand the habitat for many pests, e.g. mosquitoes, shifting the range of infectious diseases.

Agriculture: Climate change may threaten the viability of important crop-growing regions. Paradoxically, climate change can cause both too much and too little rain. Changes in precipitation and increased evaporation will affect water availability for irrigation, industry, drinking, and electricity generation.

Forests: Higher temperatures and precipitation changes could increase forest susceptibility to fire, disease, and insect damage. Forest fires release more carbon into the atmosphere and reduce the size of carbon sinks. A richer CO_2 atmosphere will reduce transpiration in plants.

Weather patterns: Global warming may cause regional changes in weather patterns such as El Niño and La Nina, as well as affecting the intensity and frequency of storms. Driven by higher ocean surface temperatures, high intensity hurricanes now occur more frequently.

1. Climate warming is predicted to alter patterns of disease incidence. Describe two of the predicted changes:

   (a) _____

   (b) _____

2. The extent of arable land in temperate regions could increase with a warming climate. Predict the likely impact of this on the biodiversity already found there:

   _____

   _____

   _____

3. Produce a short account (150 words) discussing the predicted effects of climate warming on agriculture (including food security), biodiversity, and incidence of disease. Staple your discussion into the workbook:

Grassland Management

Grasslands are diverse and productive ecosystems. Ancient meadows may have contained 80-100 plant species, in contrast to currently cultivated grasslands, which may contain as few as three species. Unfortunately, many of the management practices that promote grassland species diversity conflict with modern farming methods. For example, the extensive use of fertilisers and selective herbicides on pastures will increase the growth rate of all plants, but those (such as nettles and docks) which grow vigorously under these conditions will outcompete ecologically important species such as orchids and cowslips. Appropriate management (below) can help to conserve grassland ecosystems while maintaining their viability for agriculture.

Managing Grassland Ecosystems

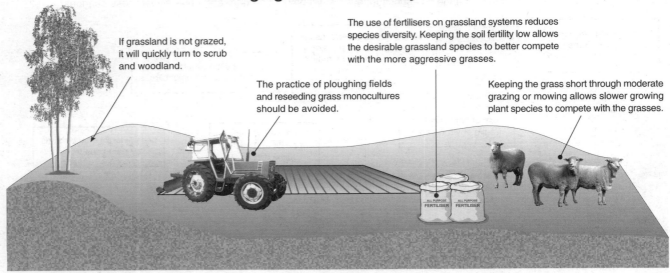

If grassland is not grazed, it will quickly turn to scrub and woodland.

The practice of ploughing fields and reseeding grass monocultures should be avoided.

The use of fertilisers on grassland systems reduces species diversity. Keeping the soil fertility low allows the desirable grassland species to better compete with the more aggressive grasses.

Keeping the grass short through moderate grazing or mowing allows slower growing plant species to compete with the grasses.

An increase in urban sprawl and the pressure on farmers to increase productivity are having a dramatic impact on the once common flowering plants of Britain's grasslands. Only through careful management and conservation of existing ecosystems will the diversity be maintained.

Conservation of grasslands is not only important for maintaining plant diversity Many birds, reptiles, invertebrates, and mammals rely on these ecosystems for food and shelter. A reduction in the diversity of grassland plant species translates to a reduction in the diversity of other species.

Grasslands and moorlands are often maintained by burning. As the desirable plants in these ecosystems age, their growth rate slows, allowing unwanted plants to outcompete them. Burning allows new growth from old stem bases and may encourage the germination of seeds.

1. Explain how the following management practices assist in the conservation of grasslands or moorlands:

   (a) Mowing: _____

   _____

   (b) Burning: _____

   _____

   (c) Maintaining low soil fertility: _____

   _____

2. One solution to the conflicting needs of conservation and productivity is to intensively farm designated areas, leaving other areas for conservation. From the farmer's perspective, outline two advantages of this approach:

   (a) _____

   (b) _____

3. Describe a disadvantage of this management approach: _____

   _____

Related activities: Britain's Biodiversity
Web links: Conservation Grazing

The Impact of Farming

The English countryside has been shaped by many hundreds of years of agriculture. The landscape has changed as farming practices evolved through critical stages. Farming has always had an impact on Britain's rich biodiversity (generally in a negative manner). Modern farming practices, such as increasing mechanisation and the move away from mixed farming operations, have greatly accelerated this decline. In recent years active steps to conserve the countryside, such as **hedgerow legislation**, policies to increase woodland cover, and schemes to promote environmentally sensitive farming practices are slowly meeting their objectives. Since 1990, expenditure on agri-environmental measures has increased, the area of land in organic farming has increased, and the overall volume of inorganic fertilisers and pesticides has decreased. The challenge facing farmers, and those concerned about the countryside, is to achieve a balance between the goals of production and conservation.

Intensive Farming

Intensive farming techniques flourished after World War II. Using **high-yielding hybrid cultivars** and large inputs of **inorganic fertilisers**, **chemical pesticides**, and **farm machinery**, crop yields increased to 3 or 4 times those produced using the more extensive (low-input) methods of 5 decades ago. Large areas planted in monocultures (single crops) are typical. Irrigation and fertiliser programmes are often extensive to allow for the planting of several crops per season. Given adequate irrigation and continued fertiliser inputs, yields from intensive farming are high. Over time, these yields decline as soils are eroded or cannot recover from repeated cropping.

Intensive agriculture relies on the heavy use of irrigation, inorganic fertilisers (produced using fossil fuels), pesticides, and farm machinery. Such farms may specialise in a single crop for many years.

Impact on the environment

- Pesticide use is escalating yet pesticide effectiveness is decreasing. This causes a reduction in species diversity, particularly among the invertebrates.

- Mammals and birds may be affected by **bioaccumulation** of pesticides in the food chain and loss of food sources as invertebrate species diminish.

- Fertiliser use is increasing, resulting in a continued decline in soil and water quality.

- More fertiliser leaches from the soil and enters groundwater as a pollutant, relative to organic farming practices.

- Large fields lacking hedgerows create an impoverished habitat and cause the isolation of remaining wooded areas.

- A monoculture regime leads to reduced biodiversity.

Sustainable Agricultural Practices

Organic farming is a sustainable form of agriculture based on the avoidance of chemicals and applied *inorganic* fertilisers. It relies on mixed (crop and livestock) farming and crop management, combined with the use of environmentally friendly pest controls (e.g., biological controls and flaming), and livestock and green manures. Organic farming uses **crop rotation** and **intercropping**, in which two or more crops are grown at the same time on the same plot, often maturing at different times. If well cultivated, these plots can provide food, fuel, and natural pest control and fertilisers on a sustainable basis. Yields are typically lower than on intensive farms, but the produce can fetch high prices, and pest control and fertiliser costs are reduced.

Some traditional farms in the UK use low-input agricultural practices similar to those used in modern organic farming. However, many small farming units find it difficult to remain economically viable.

Impact on the environment

- Pesticides do not persist in the environment nor accumulate in the food chain.

- Produce is pesticide free and produced in a sustainable way.

- Alternative pest control measures, such as using natural predators and pheromone traps, reduce the dependence on pesticides.

- The retention of hedgerows increases habitat diversity and produces corridors for animal movement between forested areas.

- Crop rotation (alternation of various crops, including legumes) prevents pests and disease species building up to high levels.

- Conservation tillage (ploughing crop residues into the topsoil) as part of the crop rotation cycle improves soil structure.

1. Discuss the conflict of interest between the need for high agricultural production and the need for habitat conservation:

_____

_____

_____

_____

Biodiversity and Conservation

Related activities: Grasslands Management
Web links: Defra: Hedgerows, NatureNet: Hedgerows

RA 2

The Hedgerow Issue

A particularly significant factor of landscape change in recent years has been the amalgamation of fields and the removal of traditional hedgerows. Many traditional, mixed farms (right), which required hedgerows to contain livestock, have been converted to arable farms, and fields have become larger to accommodate modern machinery. In Britain, this conversion has resulted in the loss of thousands of kilometres of hedgerows each year.

Hedgerows are ecologically important because they increase the diversity of wildlife by:

- Providing food and habitats for birds and other animals.
- Acting as corridors, along which animals can move.
- Providing habitat for predators of pest species.

2. From an environmental perspective, outline two advantages of using hedgerows as a form of farm fencing:

(a) _____

(b) _____

3. From the perspective of the farmer, outline two disadvantages of using hedgerows:

(a) _____

(b) _____

4. Populations of wild farmland bird species, because of their wide distribution and position near the top of the food chain, provide good indicators of the state of other wildlife species and of environmental health in general. Over the last 25 years, there has been a marked net decline in the diversity of farmland bird populations. However, since 1986, diversity has ceased to decline further and, in recent years, has actually showed an increase.

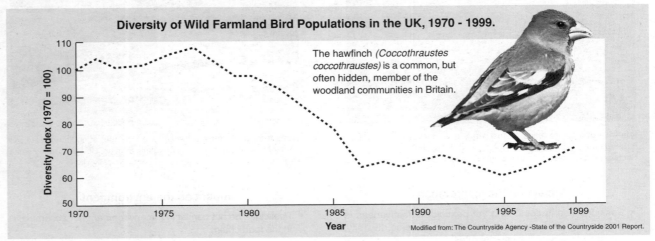

Diversity of Wild Farmland Bird Populations in the UK, 1970 - 1999.

The hawfinch (*Coccothraustes coccothraustes*) is a common, but often hidden, member of the woodland communities in Britain.

Modified from: The Countryside Agency -State of the Countryside 2001 Report.

Suggest two possible reasons for this decline in the diversity of farmland birds:

(a) _____

(b) _____

5. (a) Describe three initiatives local and national government have implemented in an attempt to reverse this decline:

_____

_____

_____

(b) Discuss the role of environmental impact assessments and biodiversity estimates when planning such initiatives

_____

_____

_____

_____

Biodiversity and Conservation

One of the concerns facing conservationists today is the rapidly accelerating rate at which species are being lost. In 1992, the **Convention on Biological Diversity** was adopted in Rio de Janeiro. It is an international treaty and its aims are to conserve biodiversity, use biodiversity in a sustainable way, and ensure that the benefits of genetic resources are shared equitably. Various strategies are available to protect species already at risk, and help threatened species to return to sustainable population sizes. *Ex-situ* methods operate away from the natural environment and are particularly useful where species are critically endangered. *In-situ* methods use ecosystem management and legislation to protect and preserve diversity within the natural environment.

Ex-Situ Conservation Methods

Captive Breeding and Relocation
Individuals are captured and bred under protected conditions. If breeding programs are successful and there is suitable habitat available, captive individuals may be relocated to the wild where they can establish natural populations. Zoos now have an active role in captive breeding. *Photo left: A puppet 'mother' feeds a takahe chick.*

The Role of Zoos
Many zoos specialise in captive breeding programmes and have a major role in public education. Modern zoos tend to concentrate on particular species and are part of global programmes that work together to help retain genetic diversity in captive bred animals. *Photo right: Okapi a rare forest antelope.*

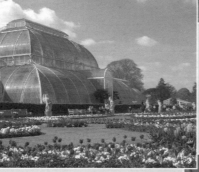

The Role of Botanic Gardens
Botanic gardens have years of collective expertise and resources and play a critical role in plant conservation. They maintain seed banks, nuture rare species, maintain a living collection of plants, and help to conserve indigenous plant knowledge. They also have an important role in both research and education. *Photo left: The palm house at Kew Botanic Gardens.*

Seed and Gene Banks
Seed and **gene banks** around the world have a role in preserving the genetic diversity of species. A seed bank (right) stores seeds as a source for future planting in case seed reserves elsewhere are lost. The seeds may be from rare species whose genetic diversity is at risk, or they may be the seeds of crop plants, in some cases of ancient varieties no longer used in commercial production.

In-Situ Conservation Methods

Woodland-pond restoration (UK)

Habitat Protection and Restoration
Most countries have a system of parks and reserves focussed on **whole ecosystem conservation**. These areas aim to preserve habitats with special importance and they may be intensively managed through pest and weed control programs, revegetation, and reintroduction of threatened species. A *"research by management"* approach is associated with careful population monitoring and management to return threatened species to viable levels.

Orangutan (endangered species)

Ban on Trade in Endangered Species
The Convention on International Trade in Endangered Species (CITES) is an international agreement between governments which aims to ensure that international trade in species of wild animals and plants does not threaten their survival. Unfortunately, even under CITES, species are not guaranteed safety from illegal trade.

In-Situ Conservation: Ecosystem Management

Stoat pest

Ecosystem management involves intensive management of a well defined area with a goal of ecosystem restoration and recovery of one or more at-risk species. In New Zealand, this strategy has been used successfully to restore populations of the endangered wattled crow, kokako (above).

An ecosystem management approach involves careful population monitoring and intensive pest control programmes. Areas must be large enough to sustain a viable population of the at-risk species, yet small enough to implement management strategies such as replanting and pest control.

In New Zealand, kokako (above) are at risk through forest clearance and predation by introduced mammals. Ecosystem management and intensive pest control has seen a reversal in the species decline. In seven years of management, the population of birds doubled. *Above: kokako chick.*

Related activities: Loss of Biodiversity, Biodiversity and Global Warming

RA 2

Biodiversity and Conservation

1. Distinguish between vulnerable, endangered, and extinct: _____

    _____

    _____

    _____

2. Describe two good reasons why any species should be preserved from extinction:

    (a) _____

    _____

    _____

    (b) _____

    _____

    _____

3. Explain the role of the following in preserving species diversity:

    (a) CITES: _____

    _____

    _____

    (b) Gene banks: _____

    _____

    _____

    (c) Habitat restoration: _____

    _____

    _____

    (d) Habitat protection: _____

    _____

    _____

    (e) Captive breeding and release programmes: _____

    _____

    _____

4. Compare and contrast *in-situ* and *ex-situ* methods of conservation, including reference to the advantages and
    disadvantages of each approach:

    _____

    _____

    _____

    _____

    _____

    _____

    _____

    _____

National Conservation

The UK has a highly modified natural environment that has resulted from a legacy of human exploitation reaching far back into prehistory. Few areas have escaped modification. The conservation problems faced by the UK are typical of many other developed nations: loss of biodiversity, natural habitat loss, pollution, waste disposal, and inadequate recycling. The main government agencies for conservation in the UK are **English Nature** (in England), **Scottish Nature Heritage** (Scotland), and **The Countryside Council for Wales** (Wales). These agencies are supported in their roles by a number of voluntary organisations that provide an additional source of expertise, labour, and finance for assisting conservation work. Conservation involves not just preservation of habitats in their existing state but also the restoration of damaged areas that previously had high conservation value.

Protected Habitats in the United Kingdom

National Parks: There are currently 7 National Parks in England and 3 in Wales. While Scotland and Northern Ireland do not have National Parks, they do have essentially equivalent areas in the form of Regional Parks (Scotland) and Areas of Outstanding Beauty (Northern Ireland). Legislation permits some farming, forestry and quarrying within these parks.

Sites of Special Scientific Interest (SSSIs): These are notified by the government agency because of their plants, animals, or geological or physiographical features. In England, about 40% are owned or managed by public bodies or by the Crown (e.g. Ministry of Defence).

Environmentally Sensitive Areas (ESAs): These are areas in the UK whose environmental significance is a result of particular farming practices. If these methods change, then the ecological value of the area will decline. To preserve these areas, restrictions are imposed on the practices allowed.

National Nature Reserves (NNRs): These are sites which have been assigned as reserves under government legislation. They are either owned or controlled by government agencies or held by approved non-governmental organisations.

Marine Nature Reserves (MNRs): In England, these are declared by the Secretary of State for the Environment. At present there two: one in England and one in Wales.

Condition of SSSIs (March 2002)

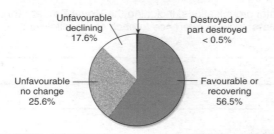

Unfavourable declining 17.6%
Destroyed or part destroyed < 0.5%
Unfavourable no change 25.6%
Favourable or recovering 56.5%

National Parks in the United Kingdom

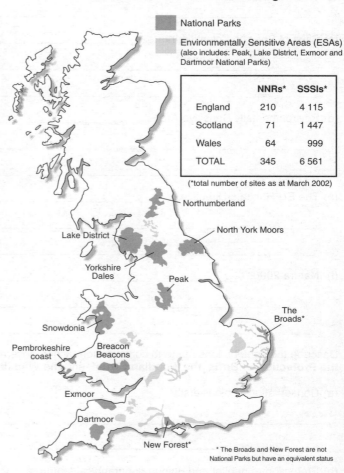

National Parks

Environmentally Sensitive Areas (ESAs) (also includes: Peak, Lake District, Exmoor and Dartmoor National Parks)

	NNRs*	SSSIs*
England	210	4 115
Scotland	71	1 447
Wales	64	999
TOTAL	345	6 561

(*total number of sites as at March 2002)

Northumberland
North York Moors
Lake District
Yorkshire Dales
Peak
The Broads*
Snowdonia
Pembrokeshire coast
Breacon Beacons
Exmoor
Dartmoor
New Forest*

* The Broads and New Forest are not National Parks but have an equivalent status

Biodiversity and Conservation

The European Union Habitats Directive

In 1992, the Council of the European Communities adopted a directive for the conservation of natural habitats and wild flora and fauna, known as the **Habitats Directive**. The global objective of the Habitats Directive is "to contribute towards ensuring biodiversity through the conservation of natural habitats and of wild fauna and flora in the European territory of the Member States to which the Treaty applies". Within the Habitats Directive, is the ecological network of special areas of conservation called **Natura 2000**. Natura 2000 areas aim to conserve natural habitats and species of plants and animals that are rare, endangered, or vulnerable in the European Community. The Natura 2000 network will include two types of areas:

Special Areas of Conservation (SAC): areas with rare, endangered, or vulnerable natural habitats, and plant or animal species (other than birds).

Special Protection Areas (SPAs): areas with significant numbers of wild birds and their habitats.

Areas of very great importance on land and sea may become both SAC and SPA sites.

Environmental cleanup (pond, Glasgow)
High value habitat: woodland and lakes
Paper recycling
Recovery of birds affected by oil spills

Any conservation or restoration programme must be multifaceted: preserving or restoring valuable habitat, repairing damage and aiding species recovery, and educating people to consider environmentally friendly options (e.g. recycling and reuse) in their general lives.

1. Explain the purpose of the following areas in the conservation of habitats and species diversity in the UK:

(a) National Parks: _____

_____

_____

(b) National Nature Reserves: _____

_____

_____

(c) Sites of Specific Scientific Interest: _____

_____

_____

(d) Environmentally Sensitive Areas: _____

_____

_____

(e) The EU Habitats Directive: _____

_____

_____

(f) Natura 2000: _____

_____

_____

2. Describe the contributions made to conservation by non governmental organisations, including the **Royal Society for the Protection of Birds**, **the Woodland Trust**, and **the Wildlife Trusts**. Include reference to each of the following:

(a) Conservation of biodiversity: _____

_____

_____

(b) Protection of habitat and unique geographical features: _____

_____

_____

(c) Environmental restoration: _____

_____

_____

(d) Education and promotion of conservation aims: _____

_____

_____

3. Find out about the EU **set-aside scheme**, and answer the following:

(a) Describe what the set-aside scheme offers to farmers: _____

_____

(b) Describe the benefits of the scheme to farmers: _____

_____

Measuring Diversity in Ecosystems

Measurements of biodiversity have essentially two components: **species richness**, which describes the number of species, and **species evenness**, which quantifies how equally the community composition is distributed. Both are important, especially when rarity is a reflection of how threatened a species is in an environment. Information about the biodiversity of ecosystems is obtained through **sampling** the ecosystem in a manner that provides a fair (unbiased) representation of the organisms present and their distribution. This is usually achieved through

random sampling, a technique in which every possible sample of a given size has the same chance of selection. Measures of biodiversity are commonly used as the basis for making conservation decisions and different measures of biodiversity may support different solutions. Often indicator species and species diversity indices are used as a way of quantifying biodiversity. Such indicators can be particularly useful when monitoring ecosystem change and looking for causative factors in species loss.

Quantifying the Diversity of Ecosystems

Reef community:
high density, clumped distribution

Measurements of biodiversity must be appropriate to the community being investigated. Communities in which the populations are at low density and have a random or clumped distribution will require a different sampling strategy to those where the populations are uniformly distributed and at higher density. There are many sampling options (below), each with advantages and drawbacks for particular communities. How would you estimate the biodiversity of this reef community?

Random point sampling | Point sampling: systematic grid | Line and belt transects | Random quadrats

Marine ecologists use quadrat sampling to estimate biodiversity prior to works such as dredging.

Line transects are appropriate to estimate biodiversity along an environmental gradient.

Keystone Species in Ecosystems

The stability of an ecosystem refers to its apparently unchanging nature over time, something that depends partly on its ability to resist and recover from disturbance. Ecosystem stability is closely linked to biodiversity, and more biodiverse systems tend to be more stable, partly because the many species interactions that sustain them act as a buffer against change. Some species are more influential than others in the stability of an ecosystem because of their pivotal role in some ecosystem function such as nutrient recycling or productivity. Such species are called **keystone species** because of their disproportionate effect on ecosystem function.

The **European beaver**, *Castor fiber*, was originally distributed throughout most of Europe and northern Asia but populations have been decimated as a result of both hunting and habitat loss. The beaver is a keystone species; where they occur, beavers are critical to ecosystem function and a number of species depend partly or entirely on beaver ponds for survival. Their tree-felling activity is akin to a natural coppicing process and promotes vigorous regrowth, while historically they helped the spread of alder (a water-loving species) in Britain.

1. (a) Distinguish between the two measures of biodiversity: species richness and species evenness:

(b) Explain why it is important to consider both these measures when considering species conservation:

Calculation and Use of Diversity Indices

One of the best ways to determine the health of an ecosystem is to measure the variety (rather than the absolute number) of organisms living in it. Certain species, called **indicator species**, are typical of ecosystems in a particular state (e.g. polluted or pristine). An objective evaluation of an ecosystem's biodiversity can provide valuable insight into its status, particularly if the species assemblages have changed as a result of disturbance.

Diversity can be quantified using a **diversity index (DI)**. Diversity indices attempt to quantify the degree of diversity and identify indicators for environmental stress or degradation. Most indices of diversity are easy to use and they are widely used in ecological work, particularly for monitoring ecosystem change or pollution. One example, which is a derivation of **Simpson's index**, is described below. Other indices produce values ranging between 0 and almost 1. These are more easily interpreted because of the more limited range of values, but no single index offers the "best" measure of diversity: they are chosen on their suitability to different situations.

Simpson's Index for finite populations

This diversity index (DI) is a commonly used inversion of Simpson's index, suitable for finite populations.

$$DI = \frac{N(N-1)}{\Sigma n(n-1)}$$

After Smith and Smith as per IOB.

Where:

DI = Diversity index
N = Total number of individuals (of all species) in the sample
n = Number of individuals of each species in the sample

This index ranges between 1 (low diversity) and infinity. The higher the value, the greater the variety of living organisms. It can be difficult to evaluate objectively without reference to some standard ecosystem measure because the values calculated can, in theory, go to infinity.

Example of species diversity in a stream

The example describes the results from a survey of stream invertebrates. The species have been identified, but this is not necessary in order to calculate diversity as long as the different species can be distinguished. Calculation of the DI using Simpson's index for finite populations is:

Species	No. of individuals
A (Common backswimmer)	12
B (Stonefly larva)	7
C (Silver water beetle)	2
D (Caddis fly larva)	6
E (Water spider)	5
Total number of individuals = 32	

$$DI = \frac{32 \times 31}{(12 \times 11) + (7 \times 6) + (2 \times 1) + (6 \times 5) + (5 \times 4)} = \frac{992}{226} = 4.39$$

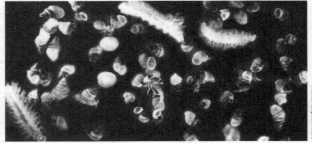

A stream community with a high macroinvertebrate diversity (above) in contrast to a low diversity stream community (below).

Photos: Stephen Moore

---

2. Describe two necessary considerations in attempting to make an unbiased measurement of biodiversity:

_____

_____

3. Explain why high biodiversity is generally associated with greater ecosystem stability: _____

_____

_____

4. Explain why the loss of a keystone species could be particularly disturbing for ecosystem diversity:

_____

_____

5. Describe a situation where a species diversity index may provide useful information: _____

_____

6. An area of forest floor was sampled and six invertebrate species were recorded, with counts of 7, 10, 11, 2, 4, and 3 individuals. Using Simpson's index for finite populations, calculate DI for this community:

(a) DI= _____   DI = _____

(b) Comment on the diversity of this community: _____

_____

CITES and Conservation

Both African and Asian elephant species are under threat of extinction. The International Union for the Conservation of Nature (**IUCN**) has rated the Asian elephant as endangered and the African elephant as vulnerable. In India, the human pressure on wild habitat has increased by 40% in the last 20 years. Where elephants live in close proximity to agricultural areas they raid crops and come into conflict with humans. The ivory trade represents the greatest threat to the African elephant. Elephant tusks have been sought after for centuries as a material for jewellery and artworks. In Africa, elephant numbers declined from 1.3 million to 600 000 during the 1980s. At this time, as many as 2000 elephants were killed for their tusks every week. By the late 1980s, elephant populations continued to fall in many countries, despite the investment of large amounts of money in fighting poaching. From 1975 to 1989 the ivory trade was regulated under CITES, and permits were required for international trading. Additional protection came in 1989, when the African elephant was placed on *Appendix I* of CITES, which imposed a ban on trade in elephant produce. In 1997 Botswana, Namibia, and Zimbabwe, together with South Africa in 2000, were allowed to transfer their elephant populations from Appendix I to Appendix II, allowing limited commercial trade in raw ivory. In 2002, CITES then approved the sale, to Japan, of legally stockpiled ivory by Namibia, South Africa, and Botswana. African countries have welcomed this decision, although there is still great concern that such a move may trigger the reemergence of a fashion for ivory goods and illegal trade.

Two subspecies of African elephant *Loxodonta africana* are currently recognised: the **savannah elephant** (*L. a. africana*) and the less common **forest elephant** (*L. a. cyclotis*). Recent evidence from mitochondrial DNA indicates that they may, in fact, be two distinct species.

In 1989 the Kenyan government publicly burned 12 tonnes of confiscated ivory. With the increased awareness, the United States and several European countries banned ivory imports. The photo above shows game wardens weighing confiscated ivory tusks and rhinoceros horns.

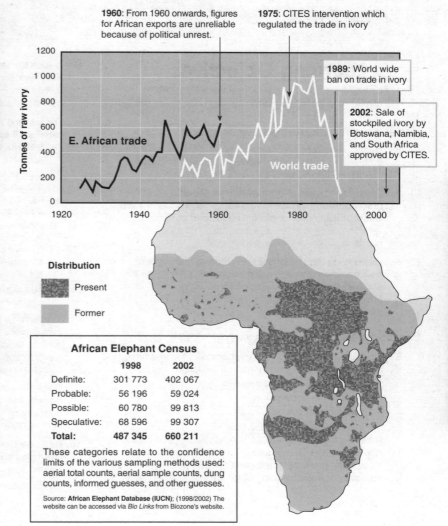

1960: From 1960 onwards, figures for African exports are unreliable because of political unrest.

1975: CITES intervention which regulated the trade in ivory

1989: World wide ban on trade in ivory

2002: Sale of stockpiled ivory by Botswana, Namibia, and South Africa approved by CITES.

E. African trade

World trade

Distribution

Present

Former

African Elephant Census

	1998	2002
Definite:	301 773	402 067
Probable:	56 196	59 024
Possible:	60 780	99 813
Speculative:	68 596	99 307
Total:	**487 345**	**660 211**

These categories relate to the confidence limits of the various sampling methods used: aerial total counts, aerial sample counts, dung counts, informed guesses, and other guesses.

Source: **African Elephant Database (IUCN)**; (1998/2002) The website can be accessed via *Bio Links* from Biozone's website.

Biodiversity and Conservation

1. Outline the action taken in 1989 to try and stop the decline of the elephant populations in Africa: _____

_____

_____

2. In early 1999, Zimbabwe, Botswana and Namibia were allowed a one-off, CITES-approved, experimental sale of ivory to Japan. This involved the sale of 5446 tusks (50 tonnes) and earned the governments approximately US$5 million.

   (a) Suggest why these countries are keen to resume ivory exports: _____

   _____

   (b) Suggest two reasons why the legal trade in ivory is thought by some to put the remaining elephants at risk:

   _____

   _____

Evolution

OCR: Unit F212, Module 3: Biodiversity and Evolution
2.3.3: Evolution (variation, adaptation, selection)

CIE: CORE SYLLABUS
P (a)-(d): Selection and evolution

Learning Objectives

☐ 1. Compile your own glossary from the **KEY WORDS** displayed in **bold type** in the learning objectives below.

Variation and Adaptation *(pages 303-308)*

☐ 2. Define **variation**, and describe how variation occurs both with in and between **species**. Explain both the genetic and environmental causes of variation.

☐ 3. Distinguish between **continuous variation** and **discontinuous variation** and explain the basis of each. Describe examples of discontinuous and continuous variation in a the characteristics (traits) of a variety of plants, animals, and microorganisms.

☐ 4. Understand the use of the term **fitness** and explain how evolution, through **adaptation**, equips species for survival. Describe examples of behavioural, physiological, and structural (anatomical or morphological) adaptation.

Selection and Evolution *(pages 309-326)*

☐ 5. Describe Darwin's four observations on which he based his *"Theory of evolution by natural selection"*:
 – overproduction by populations
 – variation in populations
 – natural selection
 – variation is inherited
Describe the consequences of these four observations. Appreciate how Darwin's original theory how it has since been modified in **the new synthesis** to take into account our understanding of genetics and inheritance.

☐ 6. Define the terms **speciation** and **evolution**, explaining how evolution is a feature of **populations** and not of individuals. Explain how **variation**, **adaptation**, and **selection** are major components of evolution.

☐ 7. Discuss the evidence in support of evolutionary theory:
 (a) **Fossil evidence**, including the significance of **transitional fossils** and the development of accurate dating methods for fossil material.
 (b) **Molecular evidence** from DNA, amino acids, and protein structures for the common ancestry of living organisms. Examples include comparisons of DNA, amino acid sequences, or immunological proteins.
 (c) Evidence provided by homologous anatomical structures, including the vertebrate pentadactyl limb. Using examples, distinguish between **homologous structures** and **analogous structures** arising as a result of convergent evolution.
 (d) The significance of **vestigial organs** as indicators of evolutionary trends in some groups.

☐ 8. Explain how **natural selection** is responsible for most evolutionary change by selectively reducing or changing genetic variation through differential survival and reproduction. Interpret data to explain how natural selection produces change within a population.

☐ 9. Recognise three types of natural selection: **stabilising**, **directional**, and **disruptive selection**. Describe the outcome of each type in a population exhibiting a normal curve in phenotypic variation.

☐ 10. Describe examples of evolution by **natural selection**. Examples should include:
 (a) Evolution of **drug resistance** in microorganisms.
 (b) Evolution of **pesticide resistance** in insects.

 See the 'Textbook Reference Grid' on page 7 for textbook page references relating to material in this topic.

Supplementary Texts

See page 6 for additional details of these texts:
■ Clegg, C.J., 1999. **Genetics and Evolution** (John Murray), pp. 60-65.

Presentation MEDIA to support this topic:

EVOLUTION
• Evolution

See page 6 for details of publishers of periodicals:

STUDENT'S REFERENCE

■ **Species and Species Formation** Biol. Sci. Rev., 20(3), Feb. 2008, pp. 36-39. *A summary feature covering the definition of species and how new species come into being through speciation.*

■ **Was Darwin Wrong?** National Geographic, 206(5) Nov. 2004, pp. 2-35. *An excellent account of the overwhelming scientific evidence for evolution. A good starting point for reminding students that the scientific debate around evolutionary theory is associated with the mechanisms by which evolution occurs, not the fact of evolution itself.*

■ **Speciation** Biol. Sci. Rev., 16(2) Nov. 2003, pp. 24-28. *Speciation: the nature of species, reproductive isolation, and the divergence of separated populations.*

■ **Skin Deep** Scientific American, Oct. 2002, pp. 50-57. *This article presents powerful evidence for skin colour ("race") being the end result of opposing selection forces. Clearly written and of high interest, this is a perfect vehicle for student discussion and for examining natural selection.*

See pages 8-9 for details of how to access **Bio Links** from our web site: **www.biozone.co.uk**. From Bio Links, access sites under the topics:

EVOLUTION: • Evolution on the web for biology students > **Charles Darwin**: • Darwin and evolution overview ... *and others* > **Evolution Theory and Evidence:** • Introduction to evolutionary biology • Transitional vertebrate fossils FAQ ... *and others* > **The Fossil Record**:
• Geological time scale ...*and others*

The Modern Theory of Evolution

Although **Charles Darwin** is credited with the development of the theory of evolution by natural selection, there were many people that contributed ideas upon which he built his own. Since Darwin first proposed his theory, aspects that were problematic (such as the mechanism of inheritance) have now been explained. The development of the modern theory of evolution has a history going back at least two centuries. The diagram below illustrates the way in which some of the major contributors helped to form the currently accepted model, or **new synthesis**. Understanding of evolutionary processes continued to grow through the 1980s and 1990s as comparative molecular sequence data were amassed and understanding of the molecular basis of developmental mechanisms improved. Most recently, in the exciting new area of evolutionary developmental biology (**evo-devo**), biologists have been exploring how developmental gene expression patterns explain how groups of organisms evolved.

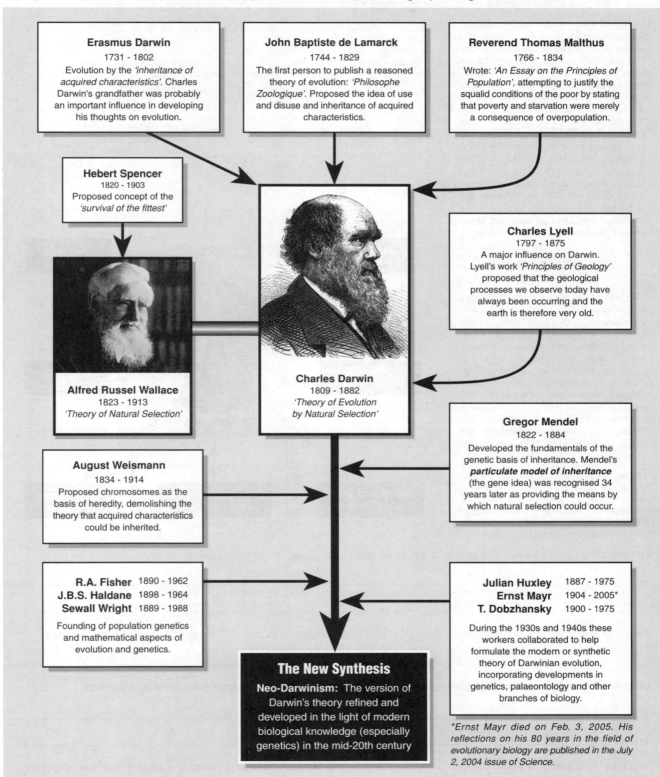

Erasmus Darwin
1731 - 1802
Evolution by the *'inheritance of acquired characteristics'*. Charles Darwin's grandfather was probably an important influence in developing his thoughts on evolution.

John Baptiste de Lamarck
1744 - 1829
The first person to publish a reasoned theory of evolution: *'Philosophe Zoologique'*. Proposed the idea of use and disuse and inheritance of acquired characteristics.

Reverend Thomas Malthus
1766 - 1834
Wrote: *'An Essay on the Principles of Population'*, attempting to justify the squalid conditions of the poor by stating that poverty and starvation were merely a consequence of overpopulation.

Hebert Spencer
1820 - 1903
Proposed concept of the *'survival of the fittest'*

Charles Lyell
1797 - 1875
A major influence on Darwin. Lyell's work *'Principles of Geology'* proposed that the geological processes we observe today have always been occurring and the earth is therefore very old.

Alfred Russel Wallace
1823 - 1913
'Theory of Natural Selection'

Charles Darwin
1809 - 1882
'Theory of Evolution by Natural Selection'

Gregor Mendel
1822 - 1884
Developed the fundamentals of the genetic basis of inheritance. Mendel's **particulate model of inheritance** (the gene idea) was recognised 34 years later as providing the means by which natural selection could occur.

August Weismann
1834 - 1914
Proposed chromosomes as the basis of heredity, demolishing the theory that acquired characteristics could be inherited.

R.A. Fisher 1890 - 1962
J.B.S. Haldane 1898 - 1964
Sewall Wright 1889 - 1988
Founding of population genetics and mathematical aspects of evolution and genetics.

Julian Huxley 1887 - 1975
Ernst Mayr 1904 - 2005*
T. Dobzhansky 1900 - 1975
During the 1930s and 1940s these workers collaborated to help formulate the modern or synthetic theory of Darwinian evolution, incorporating developments in genetics, palaeontology and other branches of biology.

The New Synthesis
Neo-Darwinism: The version of Darwin's theory refined and developed in the light of modern biological knowledge (especially genetics) in the mid-20th century

*Ernst Mayr died on Feb. 3, 2005. His reflections on his 80 years in the field of evolutionary biology are published in the July 2, 2004 issue of Science.

Evolution

1. From the diagram above, choose one of the contributors to the development of evolutionary theory (excluding Charles Darwin himself), and write a few paragraphs discussing their role in contributing to Darwin's ideas. You may need to consult an encyclopaedia or other reference to assist you.

The Species Concept

The concept of a species is not as simple as it may first appear. Interbreeding between closely related species, such as the dog family below and 'ring species' on the next page, suggest that the boundaries of a species gene pool can be somewhat unclear. One of the best recognised definitions for a species has been proposed by the renowned evolutionary biologist Ernst Mayr: "*A species is a group of actually or potentially interbreeding natural populations that is reproductively isolated from other such groups*". Each species is provided with a unique classification name to assist with future identification.

Geographical distribution of selected *Canis* species

The global distribution of most of the species belonging to the genus *Canis* (dogs and wolves) is shown on the map to the right. The **grey wolf** (timber wolf) inhabits the cold, damp forests of North America, northern Europe and Siberia. The range of the three species of **jackal** overlap in the dry, hot, open savannah of Eastern Africa. The now-rare **red wolf** is found only in Texas, while the **coyote** is found inhabiting the open grasslands of the prairies. The **dingo** is found widely distributed throughout the Australian continent inhabiting a variety of habitats. As a result of the spread of human culture, distribution of the domesticated **dog** is global. The dog has been able to interbreed with all other members of the genus listed here, to form fertile hybrids.

Interbreeding between *Canis* species

Members of the genus to which all dogs and wolves belong present problems with the species concept. The domesticated dog is able to breed with numerous other members of the same genus to produce fertile hybrids. The coyote and red wolf in North America have ranges that overlap. They are also able to produce fertile hybrids, although these are rare. By contrast, the ranges of the three distinct species of jackal overlap in the Serengeti of Eastern Africa. These animals are highly territorial, but simply ignore members of the other jackal species and no interbreeding takes place.

For an excellent discussion of species definition among dogs see the article "The Problematic Red Wolf" in Scientific American, July 1995, pp. 26-31. This discusses whether or not the red wolf is a species or a long established hybrid of the grey wolf and coyote.

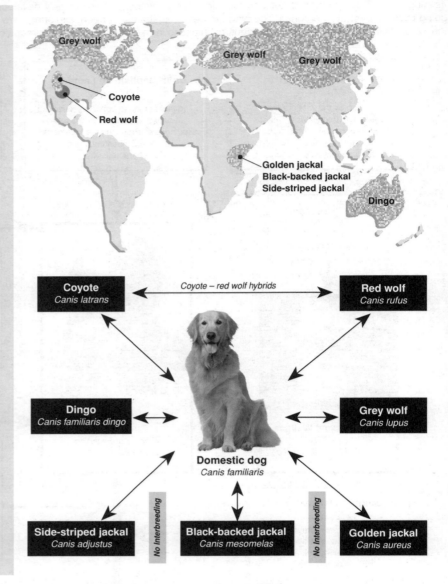

1. Describe the type of barrier that prevents the three species of jackal from interbreeding:

   _____

   _____

2. Describe the factor that has prevented the dingo from interbreeding with other *Canis* species (apart from the dog):

   _____

3. Describe a possible contributing factor to the occurrence of interbreeding between the coyote and red wolf:

   _____

   _____

4. The grey wolf is a widely distributed species. Explain why the North American population is considered to be part of the same species as the northern European and Siberian populations:

   _____

   _____

Related activities: Variation, Classification System

Variation

Variation is a characteristic of all living organisms; we see it not only between species but between individuals of the same species. The genetic variability within species is due mostly to a **shuffling** of the existing genetic material into new combinations as genetic information is passed from generation to generation. In addition to this, **mutation** creates new alleles in individuals. While most mutations are harmful, some are 'silent' (without visible effect on the phenotype), and some may even be beneficial. Depending on the nature of the inheritance pattern,

variation in a population can be continuous or discontinuous. Traits determined by a single gene (e.g. ABO blood groups) show **discontinuous variation**, with a very limited number of variants present in the population. In contrast, traits determined by a large number of genes (e.g. skin colour) show **continuous variation**, and the number of phenotypic variations is exceedingly large. Environmental influences (differences in diet for example) also contribute to the observable variation in a population, helping or hindering the expression of an individual's full genetic potential.

Albinism (above) is the result of the inheritance of recessive alleles for melanin production. Those with the albino phenotype lack melanin pigment in the eyes, skin, and hair.

Comb shape in poultry is a **qualitative trait** and birds have one of four phenotypes depending on which combination of four alleles they inherit. The dash (missing allele) indicates that the allele may be recessive or dominant.

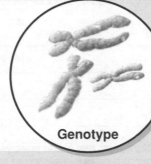

Quantitative traits are characterised by **continuous variation**, with individuals falling somewhere on a normal distribution curve of the phenotypic range. Typical examples include skin colour and height in humans (left), grain yield in corn (above), growth in pigs (above, left), and milk production in cattle (far left). Quantititative traits are determined by genes at many loci (polygenic) but most are also influenced by environmental factors.

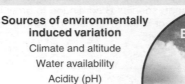

Single comb **rrpp**   Walnut comb **R_P_**   Pea comb **rrP_**   Rose comb **R_pp**

Flower colour in snapdragons (right) is also a **qualitative trait** determined by two alleles. (red and white) The alleles show incomplete dominance and the heterozygote (C^RC^W) exhibits an intermediate phenotype between the two homozygotes.

C^RC^R
C^WC^W

Sources of Variation in Organisms

Sources of genetic variation
Dominant alleles
Recessive alleles
Mutations
Crossing over
Independent assortment
Gene interactions

Genotype

Provides inheritable variation

Phenotype

Combine in their effects

Sources of environmentally induced variation
Climate and altitude
Water availability
Acidity (pH)
Soil type
Light
Predation
Competition

Environment

Provides non-inheritable variation

The phenotype is the product of the genotype and the environment

Evolution

RA 2

The Effects of Environment on Phenotype

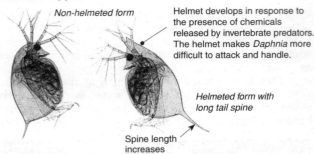

Altitude and achievement of genetic potential in plants
Increasing altitude can stunt the phenotype of plants with the same genotype. In some conifers, e.g. **Engelmann spruce**, plants at low altitude grow to their full genetic potential, but become progressively more stunted as elevation increases, forming gnarled growth forms (krummholz) at the highest elevations. Continuous gradation in a phenotypic character within a species, associated with a change in an environmental variable, is called a **cline**.

Phenotypic response to predation in zooplankton
Some organisms respond to the presence of other, potentially harmful, organisms by changing their morphology or body shape. Invertebrates such as *Daphnia* will grow a large helmet when a predatory midge larva (*Chaoborus*) is present. Such responses are usually mediated through the action of chemicals produced by the predator (or competitor), and are common in plants as well as animals.

1. Describe the differences between **continuous** and **discontinuous** variation, giving examples to illustrate your answer:

    _____

    _____

    _____

    _____

    _____

2. Identify each of the following phenotypic traits as continuous (quantitative) or discontinuous (qualitative):

    (a) Wool production in sheep: _____   (d) Albinism in mammals: _____

    (b) Kernel colour in maize: _____   (e) Body weight in mice: _____

    (c) Blood groups in humans: _____   (f) Flower colour in snapdragons: _____

3. In the examples above, identify those in which an environmental influence on phenotype could be expected:

    _____

4. From a sample of no less than 30 adults, collect data (by request or measurement) for one continuous variable (e.g. height, weight, shoe size, or hand span). On a separate sheet, record your results, produce a tally chart, and then plot a frequency histogram of the data, Staple the sheet into your workbook:

    (a) Describe the pattern of the distribution: _____

    (b) Explain the basis of this distribution: _____

    _____

    _____

5. On a windswept portion of a coast, two different species of plant (species A and species B) were found growing together. Both had a low growing (prostrate) phenotype. One of each plant type was transferred to a greenhouse where "ideal" conditions were provided to allow maximum growth. In this controlled environment, species B continued to grow in its original prostrate form, but species A changed its growing pattern and became erect in form. Identify the **cause** of the prostrate phenotype in each of the coastal grown plant species and explain your answer:

    (a) Plant species A: _____

    _____

    Plant species B: _____

    _____

    (b) Identify which of these species (A or B) would be most likely to exhibit clinal variation: _____

Adaptations and Fitness

An **adaptation**, is any heritable trait that suits an organism to its natural function in the environment (its niche). These traits may be structural, physiological, or behavioural. The idea is important for evolutionary theory because adaptive features promote fitness. **Fitness** is a measure of an organism's ability to maximise the numbers of offspring surviving to reproductive age. Adaptations are distinct from properties which, although they may be striking, cannot be described as adaptive unless they are shown to be functional in the organism's natural habitat. Genetic adaptation must not be confused with **physiological adjustment** (acclimatisation), which refers to an organism's ability to adapt during its lifetime to changing environmental conditions (e.g. a person's acclimatisation to altitude). Examples of adaptive features arising through evolution are illustrated below.

Ear Length in Rabbits and Hares

The external ears of many mammals are used as important organs to assist in thermoregulation (controlling loss and gain of body heat). The ears of rabbits and hares native to hot, dry climates, such as the jack rabbit of south-western USA and northern Mexico, are relatively very large. The Arctic hare lives in the tundra zone of Alaska, northern Canada and Greenland, and has ears that are relatively short. This reduction in the size of the extremities (ears, limbs, and noses) is typical of cold adapted species.

Arctic hare: *Lepus arcticus*

Black-tail jackrabbit: *Lepus californicus*

Body Size in Relation to Climate

Regulation of body temperature requires a large amount of energy and mammals exhibit a variety of structural and physiological adaptations to increase the effectiveness of this process. Heat production in any endotherm depends on body volume (heat generating metabolism), whereas the rate of heat loss depends on surface area. Increasing body size minimises heat loss to the environment by reducing the surface area to volume ratio. Animals in colder regions therefore tend to be larger overall than those living in hot climates. This relationship is know as **Bergman's rule** and it is well documented in many mammalian species. Cold adapted species also tend to have more compact bodies and shorter extremities than related species in hot climates.

Fennec fox

Arctic fox

The **fennec fox** of the Sahara illustrates the adaptations typical of mammals living in hot climates: a small body size and lightweight fur, and long ears, legs, and nose. These features facilitate heat dissipation and reduce heat gain.

The **Arctic fox** shows the physical characteristics typical of cold-adapted mammals: a stocky, compact body shape with small ears, short legs and nose, and dense fur. These features reduce heat loss to the environment.

Number of Horns in Rhinoceroses

Not all differences between species can be convincingly interpreted as adaptations to particular environments. Rhinoceroses charge rival males and predators, and the horn(s), when combined with the head-down posture, add effectiveness to this behaviour. Horns are obviously adaptive, but it is not clear that the possession of one (Indian rhino) or two (black rhino) horns is necessarily related directly to the environment in which those animals live.

Great Indian rhino

African black rhino

Evolution

1. Distinguish between adaptive features (genetic) and acclimatisation: _____

2. Explain the nature of the relationship between the length of extremities (such as limbs and ears) and climate: _____

3. Explain the adaptive value of a larger body size at high latitude: _____

Related activities: Darwin's Finches

A 2

Snow Bunting
(Plectrophenax nivalis)

The snow bunting is a small ground feeding bird that lives and breeds in the Arctic and sub-Arctic islands. Although migratory, snow buntings do not move to traditional winter homes but prefer winter habitats that resemble their Arctic breeding grounds, such as bleak shores or open fields of northern Britain and the eastern United States. Snow buntings have the unique ability to molt very rapidly after breeding. During the warmer months, the buntings are a brown color, changing to white in winter (right). They must complete this color change quickly, so that they have a new set of feathers before the onset of winter and before migration. In order to achieve this, snow buntings lose as many as four or five of their main flight wing feathers at once, as opposed to most birds, which lose only one or two.

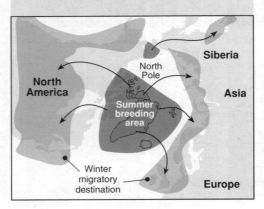

Very few small birds breed in the Arctic, because most small birds lose more heat than larger ones. In addition, birds that breed in the brief Arctic summer must migrate before the onset of winter, often traveling over large expanses of water. Large, long winged birds are better able to do this. However, the snow bunting is superbly adapted to survive in the extreme cold of the Arctic region.

White feathers are hollow and filled with air, which acts as an insulator. In the dark colored feathers the internal spaces are filled with pigmented cells.

Less heat is lost from white plumage compared to dark plumage.

Snow buntings, on average, lay one or two more eggs than equivalent species further south. They are able to rear more young because the continuous daylight and the abundance of insects at high latitudes enables them to feed their chicks around the clock.

During snow storms or periods of high wind, snow buntings will burrow into snowdrifts for shelter.

Habitat and ecology: Widespread throughout Arctic and sub-Arctic Islands. Active throughout the day and night, resting for only 2-3 hours in any 24 hour period. Snow buntings may migrate up to 6000 km but are always found at high latitudes. **Reproduction and behavior**: The nest, which is concealed amongst stones, is made from dead grass, moss, and lichen. The male bird feeds his mate during the incubation period and helps to feed the young.

4. Describe a structural, physiological, and behavioral adaptation of the **snow bunting**, explaining how each adaptation assists survival:

   (a) Structural adaptation: _____

   _____

   _____

   (b) Physiological adaptation: _____

   _____

   _____

   _____

   (c) Behavioral adaptation: _____

   _____

   _____

5. Examples of adaptations are listed below. Identify them as predominantly structural, physiological, and/or behavioral:

   (a) Relationship of body size and shape to latitude (tropical or Arctic): _____

   (b) The production of concentrated urine in desert dwelling mammals: _____

   (c) The summer and winter migratory patterns in birds and mammals: _____

   (d) The C4 photosynthetic pathway and CAM metabolism of plants: _____

   (e) The thick leaves and sunken stomata of desert plants: _____

   (f) Hibernation or torpor in small mammals over winter: _____

   (g) Basking in lizards and snakes: _____

Darwin's Theory

In 1859, Darwin and Wallace jointly proposed that new species could develop by a process of natural selection. Natural selection is the term given to the mechanism by which better adapted organisms survive to produce a greater number of viable offspring. This has the effect of increasing their proportion in the population so that they become more common. It is Darwin who is best remembered for the theory of evolution by natural selection through his famous book: '**On the origin of species by means of natural selection**', written 23 years after returning from his voyage on the Beagle, from which much of the evidence for his theory was accumulated. Although Darwin could not explain the origin of variation nor the mechanism of its transmission (this was provided later by Mendel's work), his basic theory of evolution by natural selection (outlined below) is widely accepted today. The study of population genetics has greatly improved our understanding of evolutionary processes, which are now seen largely as a (frequently gradual) change in allele frequencies within a population. Students should be aware that scientific debate on the subject of evolution centres around the relative merits of various alternative hypotheses about the nature of evolutionary processes. The debate is not about the existence of the phenomenon of evolution itself.

Darwin's Theory of Evolution by Natural Selection

Overproduction
Populations produce too many young: many must die

Populations tend to produce more offspring than are needed to replace the parents. Natural populations normally maintain constant numbers. There must therefore be a certain number dying.

Variation
Individuals show variation: some are more favourable than others

Individuals in a population vary in their phenotype and therefore, their genotype. Some variants are better suited to the current conditions than others and find it easier to survive and reproduce.

Natural Selection
Natural selection favours the best suited at the time

The struggle for survival amongst overcrowded individuals will favour those variations which have the best advantage. This does not necessarily mean that those struggling die, but they will be in a poorer condition.

Inherited
Variations are Inherited. The best suited variants leave more offspring.

The variations (both favourable and unfavourable) are passed on to offspring. Each new generation will contain proportionally more descendents from individuals with favourable characters than those with unfavourable.

1. In your own words, describe how Darwin's theory of evolution by natural selection provides an explanation for the change in the appearance of a species over time:

_____

_____

_____

_____

Related activities: The Modern Theory of Evolution, Darwin's Finches

Evolution

A 2

Natural Selection

Natural selection operates on the phenotypes of individuals, produced by their particular combinations of alleles. In natural populations, the allele combinations of some individuals are perpetuated at the expense of other genotypes. This differential survival of some genotypes over others is called **natural selection**. The effect of natural selection can vary; it can act to maintain the genotype of a species or to change it.

Stabilising selection maintains the established favourable characteristics and is associated with stable environments. In contrast, **directional selection** favours phenotypes at one extreme of the phenotypic range and is associated with gradually changing environments. **Disruptive selection** is a much rarer form of selection favouring two phenotypic extremes, and is a feature of fluctuating environments.

Stabilising Selection

Extreme variations are culled from the population (there is selection against them). Those with the established (middle range) adaptive phenotype are retained in greater numbers. This reduces the variation for the phenotypic character. In the example right, light and dark snails are eliminated, leaving medium coloured snails. Stabilising selection can be seen in the selection pressures on human birth weights.

Directional Selection

Directional selection is associated with gradually changing conditions, where the adaptive phenotype is shifted in one direction and one aspect of a trait becomes emphasised (e.g. colouration). In the example right, light coloured snails are eliminated and the population becomes darker. Directional selection was observed in peppered moths in England during the Industrial Revolution. They responded to the air pollution of industrialisation by increasing the frequency of darker, melanic forms.

Disruptive or Diversifying Selection

Disruptive selection favours two extremes of a trait at the expense of intermediate forms. It is associated with a fluctuating environment and gives rise to **balanced polymorphism** in the population. In the example right, there is selection against medium coloured snails, which are eliminated. There is considerable evidence that predators, such as insectivorous birds, are more likely to find and eat common morphs and ignore rare morphs. This enables the rarer forms to persist in the population.

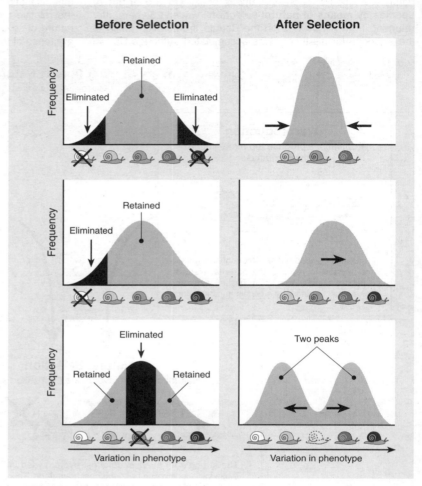

1. (a) Distinguish between directional selection and disruptive selection, identifying when each is likely to operate:

_____

_____

_____

(b) Identify which of the three types of selection described above will lead to evolution, and explain why:

_____

_____

2. Explain how a change in environment may result in selection becoming directional rather than stabilising:

_____

_____

3. Explain how, in a population of snails, through natural selection, shell colour could change from light to dark over time:

_____

_____

_____

_____

Related activities: Selection for Human Birth Weight
Web links: Natural Selection in Populations, Changes in a Gene Pool

Selection for Human Birth Weight

Selection pressures operate on populations in such a way as to reduce mortality. For humans, giving birth is a special, but often traumatic, event. In a study of human birth weights it is possible to observe the effect of selection pressures operating to constrain human birth weight within certain limits. This is a good example of **stabilising selection**. This activity explores the selection pressures acting on the birth weight of human babies. Carry out the steps below:

Step 1: Collect the birth weights from 100 birth notices from your local newspaper (or 50 if you are having difficulty getting enough; this should involve looking back through the last 2-3 weeks of birth notices). If you cannot obtain birth weights in your local newspaper, a set of 100 sample birth weights is provided in the Model Answers booklet.

Step 2: Group the weights into each of the 12 weight classes (of 0.5 kg increments). Determine what percentage (of the total sample) fall into each weight class (e.g. 17 babies weigh 2.5-3.0 kg out of the 100 sampled = 17%)

Step 3: Graph these in the form of a histogram for the 12 weight classes (use the graphing grid provided right). Be sure to use the scale provided on the left vertical (y) axis.

Step 4: Create a second graph by plotting percentage mortality of newborn babies in relation to their birth weight. Use the scale on the right y axis and data provided (below).

Step 5: Draw a line of 'best fit' through these points.

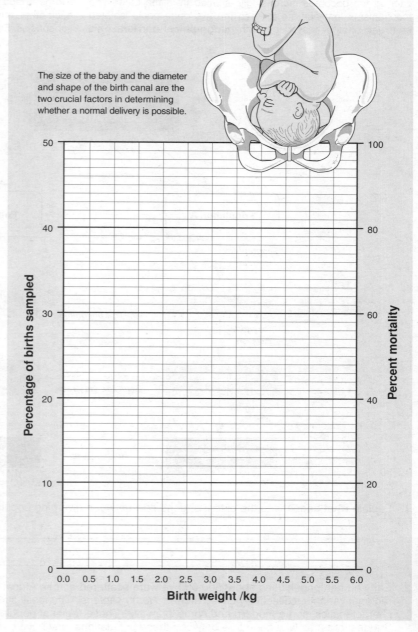

The size of the baby and the diameter and shape of the birth canal are the two crucial factors in determining whether a normal delivery is possible.

Mortality of newborn babies related to birth weight

Weight /kg	Mortality /%
1.0	80
1.5	30
2.0	12
2.5	4
3.0	3
3.5	2
4.0	3
4.5	7
5.0	15

Source: Biology: The Unity & Diversity of Life (4th ed), by Starr and Taggart

Evolution

1. Describe the shape of the histogram for birth weights: _____

2. State the optimum birth weight in terms of the lowest newborn mortality: _____

3. Describe the relationship between newborn mortality and birth weight: _____
_____

4. Describe the selection pressures that are operating to control the range of birth weight: _____
_____
_____

5. Describe how medical intervention methods during pregnancy and childbirth may have altered these selection pressures: _____
_____
_____

Related activities: Natural Selection

PDA 2

Stages in Species Development

The diagram below represents a possible sequence of genetic events involved in the origin of two new species from an ancestral population. As time progresses (from top to bottom of the diagram) the amount of genetic variation increases and each group becomes increasingly isolated from the other. The mechanisms that operate to keep the two gene pools isolated from one another may begin with **geographical barriers**. This may be followed by **prezygotic** mechanisms which protect the gene pool from unwanted dilution by genes from other pools. A longer period of isolation may lead to **postzygotic** mechanisms (see the page on reproductive isolating mechanisms). As the two gene pools become increasingly isolated and different from each other, they are progressively labelled: population, race, and subspecies. Finally they attain the status of separate species.

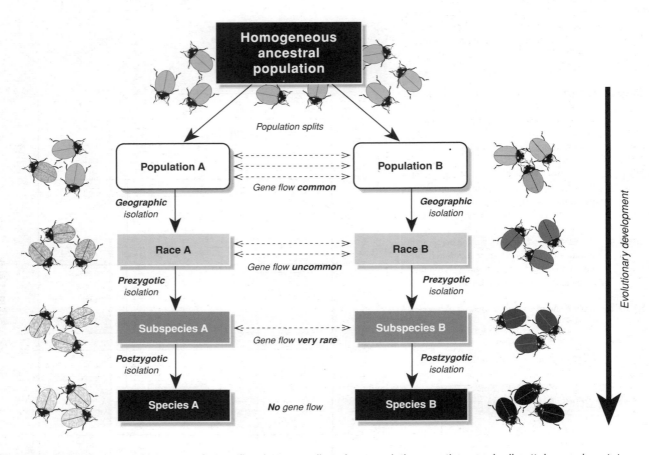

1. Explain what happens to the extent of gene flow between diverging populations as they gradually attain species status:

2. Early human populations about 500 000 ya were scattered across Africa, Europe, and Asia. This was a time of many regional variants, collectively called archaic *Homo sapiens*. The fossil skulls from different regions showed mixtures of characteristics, some modern and some 'primitive'. These regional populations are generally given subspecies status. Suggest reasons why gene flow between these populations may have been rare, but still occasionally occurred:

3. In the southern hemisphere, the native grey duck and the introduced mallard duck (from the Northern hemisphere) are undergoing 'species breakdown'. These two closely related species can interbreed to form hybrids.

   (a) Describe the factor preventing the two species interbreeding before the introduction of the mallards:

   (b) Describe the factor that may be deterring some of the ducks from interbreeding with the other species:

Related activities: The Species Concept
Web links: Mechanisms of Speciation

© Biozone International 2008
Photocopying Prohibited

Fossil Formation

Fossils are the remains of long-dead organisms that have escaped decay and have, after many years, become part of the Earth's crust. A fossil may be the preserved remains of the organism itself, the impression of it in the sediment (moulds), or marks made by it during its lifetime (called trace fossils). For fossilisation to occur, rapid burial of the organism is required (usually in water-borne sediment). This is followed by chemical alteration, where minerals are added or removed. Fossilisation requires the normal processes of decay to be permanently arrested. This can occur if the remains are isolated from the air or water and decomposing microbes are prevented from breaking them down. Fossils provide a record of the appearance and extinction of organisms, from species to whole taxonomic groups. Once this record is calibrated against a time scale (by using a broad range of dating techniques), it is possible to build up a picture of the evolutionary changes that have taken place.

Modes of Preservation

Silicification: Silica from weathered volcanic ash is gradually incorporated into partly decayed wood (also called petrification).

Phosphatisation: Bones and teeth are preserved in phosphate deposits.

Pyritisation: Iron pyrite replaces hard remains of the dead organism.

Tar pit: Animals fall into and are trapped in mixture of tar and sand.

Trapped in amber: Gum from conifers traps insects and then hardens.

Limestone: Calcium carbonate from the remains of marine plankton is deposited as a sediment that traps the remains of other sea creatures.

Brachiopod (lamp shell), Jurassic (New Zealand)

Mould: This impression of a lamp shell is all that is left after the original shell material was dissolved after fossilisation.

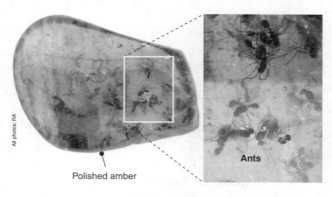

All photos: RA

Ants

Polished amber

Insects in amber: The fossilised resin or gum produced by some ancient conifers trapped these insects (including the ants visible in the enlargement) about 25 million years ago (Madagascar).

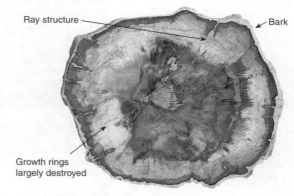

Ray structure — Bark

Growth rings largely destroyed

Petrified wood: A cross-section of a limb from a coniferous tree (Madagascar).

Rock phosphate matrix

Shell

Stone interior

Sand and tar matrix

Wing bones

Shark tooth: The tooth of a shark *Lamna obliqua* from phosphate beds, Eocene (Khouribga, Morocco).

Ammonite: This ammonite still has a layer of the original shell covering the stone interior, Jurassic (Madagascar).

Bird bones: Fossilised bones of a bird that lived about 5 million years ago and became stuck in the tar pits at la Brea, Los Angeles, USA.

Evolution

Shell and chambers replaced by iron pyrite

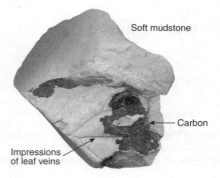

Soft mudstone

Carbon

Impressions of leaf veins

Cast: This ammonite has been preserved by a process called pyritisation, late Cretaceous (Charmouth, England).

Fossil fern: This compression fossil of a fern frond shows traces of carbon and wax from the original plant, Carboniferous (USA).

Sub-fossil: Leaf impression in soft mudstone (can be broken easily with fingers) with some of the remains of the leaf still intact (a few thousand years old, New Zealand).

Related activities: The Fossil Record
Web links: Getting Into the Fossil Record

A 1

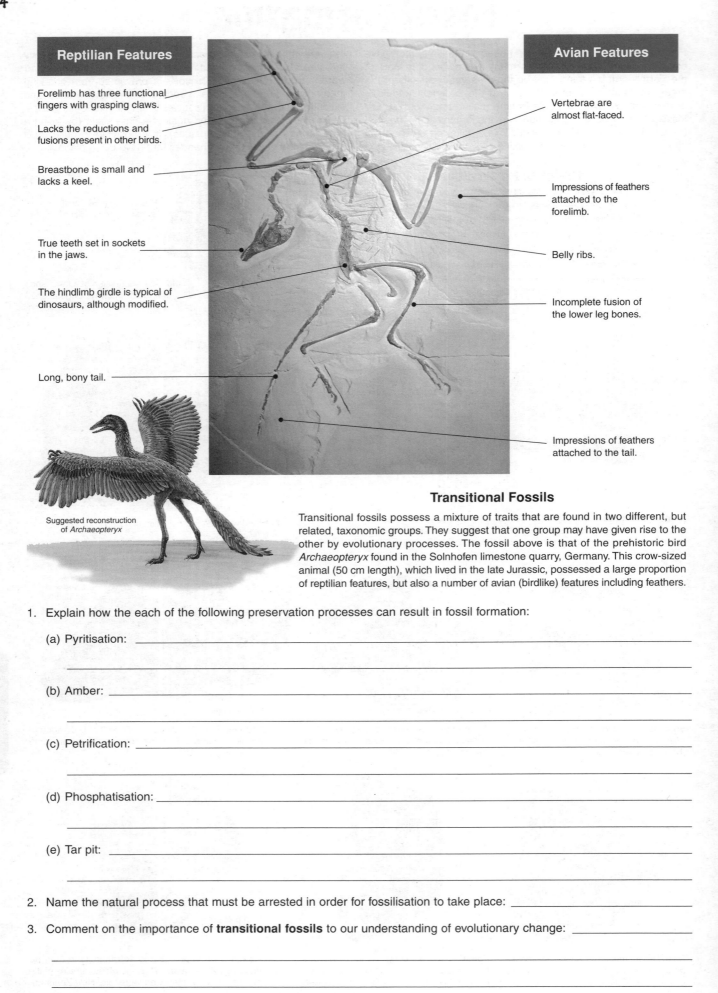

Reptilian Features

Forelimb has three functional fingers with grasping claws.

Lacks the reductions and fusions present in other birds.

Breastbone is small and lacks a keel.

True teeth set in sockets in the jaws.

The hindlimb girdle is typical of dinosaurs, although modified.

Long, bony tail.

Suggested reconstruction of *Archaeopteryx*

Avian Features

Vertebrae are almost flat-faced.

Impressions of feathers attached to the forelimb.

Belly ribs.

Incomplete fusion of the lower leg bones.

Impressions of feathers attached to the tail.

Transitional Fossils

Transitional fossils possess a mixture of traits that are found in two different, but related, taxonomic groups. They suggest that one group may have given rise to the other by evolutionary processes. The fossil above is that of the prehistoric bird *Archaeopteryx* found in the Solnhofen limestone quarry, Germany. This crow-sized animal (50 cm length), which lived in the late Jurassic, possessed a large proportion of reptilian features, but also a number of avian (birdlike) features including feathers.

1. Explain how the each of the following preservation processes can result in fossil formation:

   (a) Pyritisation: _____

   _____

   (b) Amber: _____

   _____

   (c) Petrification: _____

   _____

   (d) Phosphatisation: _____

   _____

   (e) Tar pit: _____

   _____

2. Name the natural process that must be arrested in order for fossilisation to take place: _____

3. Comment on the importance of **transitional fossils** to our understanding of evolutionary change: _____

   _____

   _____

The Fossil Record

The diagram below represents a cutting into the earth revealing the layers of rock. Some of these layers may have been laid down by water (sedimentary rocks) or by volcanic activity (volcanic rocks). Fossils are the actual remains or impressions of plants or animals that become trapped in the sediments after their death. Layers of sedimentary rock are arranged in the order that they were deposited, with the most recent layers near the surface (unless they have been disturbed).

Profile with Sedimentary Rocks Containing Fossils

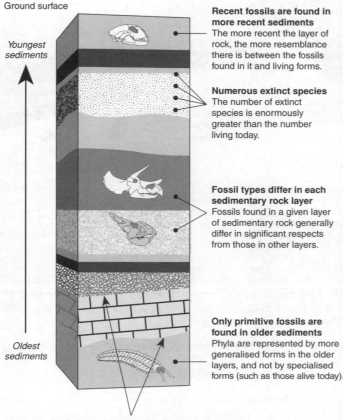

Ground surface

Youngest sediments

Recent fossils are found in more recent sediments
The more recent the layer of rock, the more resemblance there is between the fossils found in it and living forms.

Numerous extinct species
The number of extinct species is enormously greater than the number living today.

Fossil types differ in each sedimentary rock layer
Fossils found in a given layer of sedimentary rock generally differ in significant respects from those in other layers.

Oldest sediments

Only primitive fossils are found in older sediments
Phyla are represented by more generalised forms in the older layers, and not by specialised forms (such as those alive today).

New fossil types mark changes in environment
In the rocks marking the end of one geological period, it is common to find many new fossils that become dominant in the next. Each geological period had an environment very different from those before and after. Their boundaries coincided with drastic environmental changes and the appearance of new niches. These produced new selection pressures resulting in new adaptive features in the surviving species, as they responded to the changes.

The rate of evolution can vary

According to the fossil record, rates of evolutionary change seem to vary. There are bursts of species formation and long periods of relative stability within species (stasis). The occasional rapid evolution of new forms apparent in the fossil record, is probably a response to a changing environment. During periods of stable environmental conditions, evolutionary change may slow down.

The Fossil Record of Proboscidea

African and Indian elephants have descended from a diverse group of animals known as **proboscideans** (named for their long trunks). The first pig-sized, trunkless members of this group lived in Africa 40 million years ago. From Africa, their descendants invaded all continents except Antarctica and Australia. As the group evolved, they became larger; an effective evolutionary response to deter predators. Examples of extinct members of this group are illustrated below:

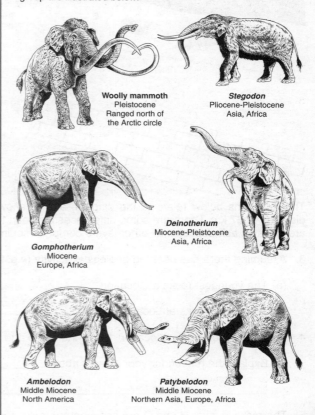

Woolly mammoth
Pleistocene
Ranged north of the Arctic circle

Stegodon
Pliocene-Pleistocene
Asia, Africa

Deinotherium
Miocene-Pleistocene
Asia, Africa

Gomphotherium
Miocene
Europe, Africa

Ambelodon
Middle Miocene
North America

Patybelodon
Middle Miocene
Northern Asia, Europe, Africa

- **Modern day species can be traced:** The evolution of many present-day species can be very well reconstructed. For instance, the evolutionary history of the modern elephants is exceedingly well documented for the last 40 million years. The modern horse also has a well understood fossil record spanning the last 50 million years.

- **Fossil species are similar to but differ from today's species:** Most fossil animals and plants belong to the same major taxonomic groups as organisms living today. However, they do differ from the living species in many features.

Evolution

1. Name an animal or plant taxon (e.g. family, genus, or species) that has:

   (a) A good fossil record of evolutionary development: _____

   (b) Appeared to have changed very little over the last 100 million years or so: _____

2. Discuss the importance of **fossils** as a record of evolutionary change over time: _____

_____

_____

Related activities: Fossil Formation
Web links: 29+ Evidences for Macroevolution

RA 2

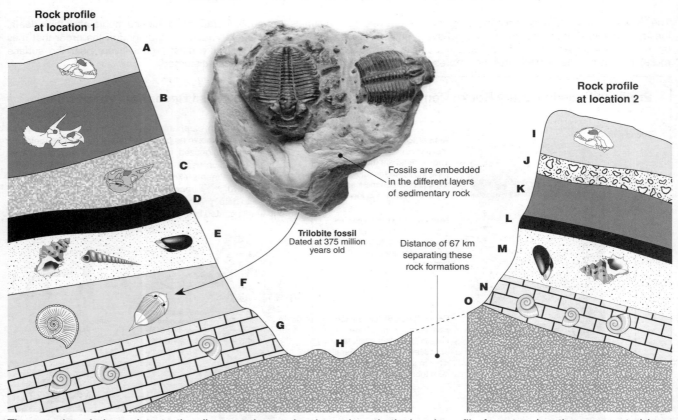

Rock profile at location 1

Rock profile at location 2

Fossils are embedded in the different layers of sedimentary rock

Trilobite fossil
Dated at 375 million years old

Distance of 67 km separating these rock formations

The questions below relate to the diagram above, showing a hypothetical rock profile from two locations separated by a distance of 67 km. There are some differences between the rock layers at the two locations. Apart from layers D and L which are volcanic ash deposits, all other layers comprise sedimentary rock.

3. Assuming there has been no geological activity (e.g. tilting or folding), state in which rock layer (A-O) you would find:

   (a) The youngest rocks at Location 1: _____   (c) The youngest rocks at Location 2: _____

   (b) The oldest rocks at Location 1: _____   (d) The oldest rocks at Location 2: _____

4. (a) State which layer at location 1 is of the same age as layer M at location 2: _____

   (b) Explain the reason for your answer above: _____

   _____

5. The rocks in layer H and O are sedimentary rocks. Explain why there are no visible fossils in layers:

   _____

   _____

6. (a) State which layers present at location 1 are missing at location 2: _____

   (b) State which layers present at location 2 are missing at location 1: _____

7. Describe three methods of dating rocks: _____

   _____

   _____

8. Using radiometric dating, the trilobite fossil was determined to be approximately 375 million years old. The volcanic rock layer (D) was dated at 270 million years old, while rock layer B was dated at 80 million years old. Give the approximate **age range** (i.e. greater than, less than or between given dates) of the rock layers listed below:

   (a) Layer A: _____   (d) Layer G: _____

   (b) Layer C: _____   (e) Layer L: _____

   (c) Layer E: _____   (f) Layer O: _____

Dating a Fossil Site

The diagram below shows a rock shelter typical of those found in the Dordogne Valley of Southwest France. Such shelters have yielded a rich source of Neanderthal and modern human remains. It illustrates the way human activity is revealed at archaeological excavations. Occupation sites included shallow caves or rocky overhangs of limestone. The floors of these caves accumulated the debris of natural rockfalls, together with the detritus of human occupation at various layers, called **occupation horizons**. A wide array of techniques can be used for dating, some of which show a high degree of reliability (see the table below). The use of several appropriate techniques to date material improves the reliability of the date determined.

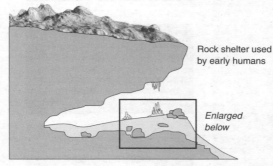

Rock shelter used by early humans

Enlarged below

Dating method	Dating range (years ago)	Datable materials
Radiocarbon (^{14}C)	1000 - 50 000+	Bone, shell, charcoal
Potassium-argon (K/Ar)	10 000 - 100 million	Volcanic rocks and minerals
Uranium series decay	less than 1 million	Marine carbonate, coral, shell
Thermoluminescence	less than 200 000	Ceramics (burnt clay)
Fission track	1000 - 100 million	Volcanic rock, glass, pottery
Electron spin resonance	2000 - 500 000	Bone, teeth, loess, burnt flint

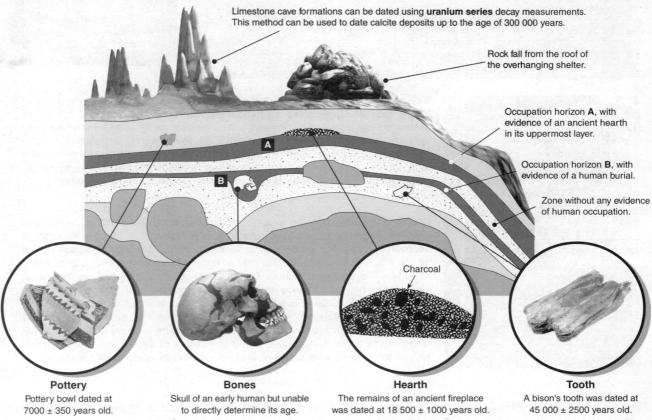

Limestone cave formations can be dated using **uranium series** decay measurements. This method can be used to date calcite deposits up to the age of 300 000 years.

Rock fall from the roof of the overhanging shelter.

Occupation horizon **A**, with evidence of an ancient hearth in its uppermost layer.

Occupation horizon **B**, with evidence of a human burial.

Zone without any evidence of human occupation.

Charcoal

Pottery
Pottery bowl dated at 7000 ± 350 years old.

Bones
Skull of an early human but unable to directly determine its age.

Hearth
The remains of an ancient fireplace was dated at 18 500 ± 1000 years old.

Tooth
A bison's tooth was dated at 45 000 ± 2500 years old.

Evolution

1. Discuss the significance of **occupation horizons**: _____

_____

_____

_____

2. Determine the approximate date range for the items below (Hint: take into account layers/artifacts with known dates):

   (a) The skull at point B: _____

   (b) Occupation horizon A: _____

3. Name the dating methods that could have been used to date each of the following, at the site above:

   (a) Pottery bowl: _____   (c) Hearth: _____

   (b) Skull: _____   (d) Tooth: _____

Related activities: Fossil Formation
Web links: Neanderthals: Dig and Deduce

RDA 2

Interpreting Fossil Sites

Human skull

Charcoal fragments (possible evidence of fire use and excellent for radiocarbon dating).

Bones from a large mammal with evidence of butchering (cut and scrape marks from stone tools). These provide information on the past ecology and environment of the hominins in question.

Excavation through rock strata (layers). The individual layers can be dated using both chronometric (absolute) and relative dating methods.

Stone tools

Photo: RA

istock

Searching for ancient human remains, including the evidence of culture, is the work of **palaeoanthropologists**. Organic materials, such as bones and teeth, are examined and analysed by physical anthropologists, while cultural materials, such as tools, weapons, shelters, and artworks, are examined by archaeologists. Both these disciplines, **palaeoanthropology** and **archaeology**, are closely associated with other scientific disciplines, including **geochemistry** (for **chronometric dates**), **geology** (for reconstructions of past physical landscapes), and **palaeontology** (for knowledge of the past species assemblages).

The reconstruction of a **dig site**, pictured above, illustrates some of the features that may be present at a site of hominin activity. Naturally, the type of information recovered from a site will depend on several factors, including the original nature of the site and its contents, the past and recent site environment, and earlier disturbance by people or animals. During its period of occupation, a site represents an interplay between additive and subtractive processes; building vs destruction, growth vs decay. Organic matter decays, and other features of the site, such as tools, can be disarranged, weathered, or broken down. The archaeologists goal is to maximise the recovery of information, and recent trends have been to excavate and process artifacts immediately, and sometimes to leave part of the site intact so that future work, perhaps involving better methodologies, is still possible.

4. Explain why palaeoanthropologists date and interpret all of the remains at a particular site of interest (e.g. animal bones, pollen, and vegetation, as well as hominin remains):

_____

_____

_____

_____

5. Discuss the importance of involving several scientific disciplines when interpreting a site of hominin activity:

_____

_____

_____

_____

_____

Darwin's Finches

The Galapagos Islands, 920 km off the west coast of Ecuador, played a major role in shaping Darwin's thoughts about natural selection and evolution. While exploring the islands in 1835, he was struck by the unique and peculiar species he found there. In particular, he was intrigued by the island's finches. The Galapagos group is home to 13 species of finches in four genera. This variety has arisen as a result of evolution from one common ancestral species. Initially, a number of small finches, probably grassquits, made their way from South America across the Pacific to the Galapagos Islands. In the new environment, which was relatively free of competitors, the colonisers underwent an adaptive radiation, producing a range of species each with its own unique feeding niche. Although similar in their plumage, nest building techniques, and calls, the different species of finches can easily be distinguished by the size and shape of their beaks. The beak shape of each species is adapted for a different purpose, such as crushing seeds, pecking wood, or probing flowers for nectar. Between them, the 13 species of this endemic group fill the roles of seven different families of South American mainland birds. Modern methods of DNA (genetic) analysis have confirmed Darwin's insight and have shown that all 13 species evolved from a flock of about 30 birds arriving a million years ago.

The Evolution of Darwin's Finches

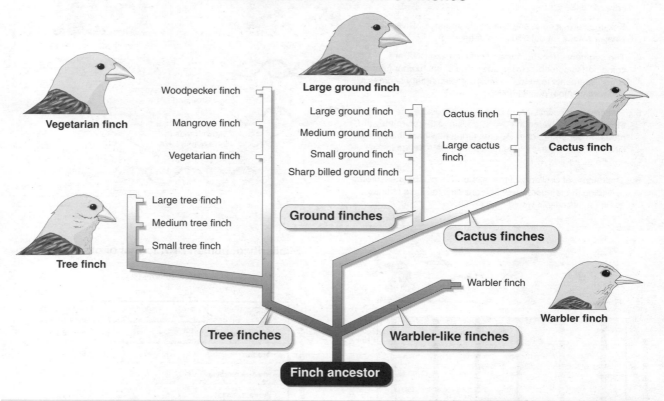

Woodpecker finch

Mangrove finch

Vegetarian finch

Vegetarian finch

Large ground finch

Medium ground finch

Small ground finch

Sharp billed ground finch

Large ground finch

Cactus finch

Large cactus finch

Cactus finch

Large tree finch

Medium tree finch

Small tree finch

Tree finch

Ground finches

Cactus finches

Warbler finch

Warbler finch

Tree finches

Warbler-like finches

Finch ancestor

Tree finches

As the name implies, tree finches are largely arboreal and feed mainly on insects. The bill is sharper than in ground finches and better suited to grasp insects. Paler than ground or cactus finches, they also have streaked breasts.

Cactus finches

Probably descended from ground finches. Beak is probing. Males are mostly black, females are streaked, like ground finches. Found in arid areas on prickly pear cactus where they eat insects on the cactus, or the cactus itself.

Ground finches

Four species with crushing-type bills used for seed eating. On Wolf Island, they are called vampire finches because they peck the skin of animals to draw blood, which they then drink. Such behaviour has evolved from eating parasitic insects off animals.

Warbler finches

Named for their resemblance to the unrelated warblers, the beak of the warbler finch is the thinnest of the Galapagos finches. It is the most widespread species, found throughout the archipelago. Warbler finches prey on flying and ground dwelling insects.

Evolution

1. Describe the main factors that have contributed to the adaptive radiation of Darwin's finches:

_____

_____

_____

Related activities: Adaptation and Fitness

Web links: Darwin's Finches

A 2

DNA Hybridisation

The more closely two species are related, the fewer differences there will be in the exact sequence of bases. This is because there has been less time for the point mutations that will bring about these changes to occur. Modern species can be compared to see how long ago they shared a **common ancestor.** This technique gives a measure of 'relatedness', and can be calibrated against known fossil dates to create a **molecular clock.** It is then possible to give approximate dates of common origin to species with no or poor fossil data. This method has been applied to primate DNA samples to help determine the approximate date of human divergence from the apes, which has been estimated to be between 10 and 5 million years ago.

DNA Hybridisation

1. Blood samples from each species are taken, from which the DNA is isolated.

2. The DNA from each species is made to unwind into single strands by applying heat (both human and chimpanzee DNA unwinds at 86°C).

3. Enzymes are used to snip the single strands of DNA into smaller pieces (about 500 base pairs long).

4. The segments from human and chimpanzee DNA are combined to see how closely they bind to each other (single strand segments tend to find their complementary segments and rewind into a double helix again).

5. The greater the similarity in DNA base sequence, the stronger the attraction between the two strands and therefore they are harder to separate again. By measuring how hard this hybrid DNA is to separate, a crude measure of DNA 'relatedness' can be achieved.

6. The degree of similarity of the hybrid DNA can be measured by finding the temperature that it unzips into single strands again (in this case it would be 83.6°C).

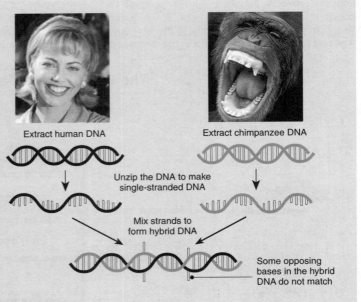

Extract human DNA · Extract chimpanzee DNA

Unzip the DNA to make single-stranded DNA

Mix strands to form hybrid DNA

Some opposing bases in the hybrid DNA do not match

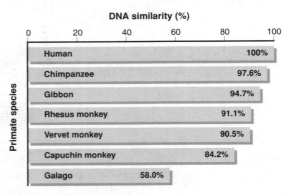

Flamingo · Ibis · Shoebill · Pelican · Stork · New World vulture

The relationships among the **New World vultures** and **storks** have been determined using DNA hybridisation. It has been possible to estimate how long ago various members of the group shared a common ancestor.

Similarity of human DNA to that of other primates

DNA similarity (%)

Primate species	DNA similarity
Human	100%
Chimpanzee	97.6%
Gibbon	94.7%
Rhesus monkey	91.1%
Vervet monkey	90.5%
Capuchin monkey	84.2%
Galago	58.0%

The genetic relationships among the **primates** has been investigated using DNA hybridisation. Human DNA was compared with that of the other primates. It largely confirmed what was suspected from anatomical evidence.

1. Explain how **DNA hybridisation** can give a measure of genetic relatedness between species:

_____

_____

_____

2. Study the graph showing the results of a DNA hybridisation between human DNA and that of other primates.

   (a) State which is the most closely related primate to humans: _____

   (b) State which is the most distantly related primate to humans: _____

3. State the DNA difference score for: (a) Shoebills and pelicans: _____   (b) Storks and flamingos: _____

4. On the basis of DNA hybridisation, state how long ago the ibises and New World vultures shared a common ancestor:

_____

Immunological Studies

Immunological studies provide a method of indirectly estimating the degree of similarity of proteins in different species. If differences exist in the proteins, then there must also be differences in the DNA that codes for them. The evolutionary relationships of a large number of different animal groups have been established on the basis of immunology. The results support the phylogenies developed from other areas: biogeography, comparative anatomy, and fossil evidence.

Method for Immunological Comparison

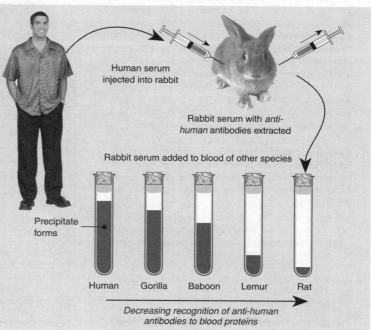

1. Blood serum (containing blood proteins but no cells) is collected from a human and is injected into a rabbit. This causes the formation of antibodies in the rabbit's blood. These identify human blood proteins, attach to them and render them harmless.

2. A sample of the rabbit's blood is taken and the rabbit's antibodies that recognise human blood proteins are extracted.

3. These anti-human antibodies are then added to blood samples from other species to see how well they recognise the proteins in the different blood. The more similar the blood sample is to original human blood, the greater the reaction (which takes the form of creating a precipitate, i.e. solids).

Human serum injected into rabbit

Rabbit serum with *anti-human* antibodies extracted

Rabbit serum added to blood of other species

Precipitate forms

Human   Gorilla   Baboon   Lemur   Rat

Decreasing recognition of anti-human antibodies to blood proteins

The five blood samples that were tested (on the right) show varying degrees of precipitate (solid) formation. Note that when the anti-human antibodies are added to human blood there is a high degree of affinity. There is poor recognition when added to rat blood.

Immunological Comparison of Tree Frogs

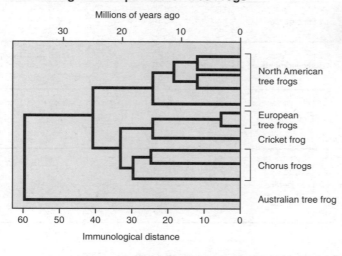

Millions of years ago

North American tree frogs

European tree frogs

Cricket frog

Chorus frogs

Australian tree frog

Immunological distance

The relationships among **tree frogs** have been established by immunological studies. The immunological distance is a measure of the number of amino acid substitutions between two groups. This, in turn, has been calibrated to provide a time scale showing when the various related groups diverged.

1. Briefly describe how **immunological studies** have contributed evidence that the process of evolution has taken place:

_____

_____

_____

_____

2. Study the graph above showing the immunological distance between tree frogs. State the immunological distance between the following frogs:

   (a) Cricket frog and the Australian tree frog: _____   (b) The various chorus frogs: _____

3. Describe how closely the Australian tree frog is related to the other frogs shown:

   _____

4. State when the North American tree frogs became separated from the European tree frogs: _____

Evolution

DA 2

Other Evidence for Evolution

Amino Acid Sequences

Each of our proteins has a specific number of amino acids arranged in a specific order. Any differences in the sequence reflect changes in the DNA sequence. The haemoglobin beta chain has been used as a standard molecule for comparing the precise sequence of amino acids in different species. Haemoglobin is the protein in our red blood cells that is responsible for carrying oxygen around our bodies. The haemoglobin in adults is made up of four polypeptide chains: 2 alpha chains and 2 beta chains. Each is coded for by a separate gene.

Example right: When the sequence of human haemoglobin, which is 146 amino acids long, was compared with that of 5 other primate species it was found that chimpanzees had an identical sequence while those that were already considered less closely related had a greater number of differences. This suggests a very close genetic relationship between humans, chimpanzees and gorillas, but less with the other primates.

Amino Acid Differences Between Humans and Other Primates

The *'position of changed amino acid'* is the point in the protein, composed of 146 amino acids, at which the **different** amino acids occurs

Primate	No. of amino acids different from humans	Position of changed amino acids
Chimpanzee	Identical	–
Gorilla	1	104
Gibbon	3	80 87 125
Rhesus monkey	8	9 13 33 50 76 87 104 125
Squirrel monkey	9	5 6 9 21 22 56 76 87 125

Comparative Embryology

By comparing the development of embryos from different species, Ernst von Bayer in 1828 noticed that animals are more similar during early stages of their embryological development than later as adults. This later led to Ernst Haeckel (1834-1919) to propose his famous principle: *ontogeny recapitulates phylogeny*. He claimed that the development of an individual (ontogeny) retraces the stages through which the individual species has passed during its evolution (phylogeny). This idea is now known to be an oversimplification and is misleading. Although early developmental sequences between all vertebrates are similar, there are important deviations from the general developmental plan in different species. Notice the gill slits that briefly appear in the human embryo (arrowed). The more closely related forms of the monkey and humans continue to appear similar until a later stage in development, compared to more distantly related species. From the study of foetal development it is possible to find clues as to how evolution generates the diversity of life forms through time, but 'ontogeny does not recapitulate phylogeny'.

Developmental stage	Amphibian	Bird	Monkey	Human
Fertilised egg				
Late cleavage				
Body segments				Gill slits
Limb buds				
Late foetal				

1. Study the table of data showing the differences in **amino acid sequences** for selected primates. Explain why chimpanzees and gorillas are considered most closely related to humans, while monkeys are less so:

_____

_____

_____

2. Briefly describe how **comparative embryology** has contributed evidence to support the concept of evolution:

_____

_____

3. Describe a commonly used biochemical method for precisely analysing the genes in organisms to determine their evolutionary relationships:

_____

_____

Homologous Structures

The evolutionary relationships between groups of organisms is determined mainly by structural similarities called **homologous structures** (homologies), which suggest that they all descended from a common ancestor with that feature. The bones of the forelimb of air-breathing vertebrates are composed of similar bones arranged in a comparable pattern. This is indicative of a common ancestry. The early land vertebrates were amphibians and possessed a limb structure called the **pentadactyl limb**: a limb with 5 fingers or toes (below left). All vertebrates that descended from these early amphibians, including reptiles, birds and mammals, have limbs that have evolved from this same basic pentadactyl pattern. They also illustrate the phenomenon known as **adaptive radiation**, since the basic limb plan has been adapted to meet the requirements of different niches.

Generalised Pentadactyl Limb

The forelimbs and hind limbs have the same arrangement of bones but they have different names. In many cases bones in different parts of the limb have been highly modified to give it a specialised locomotory function.

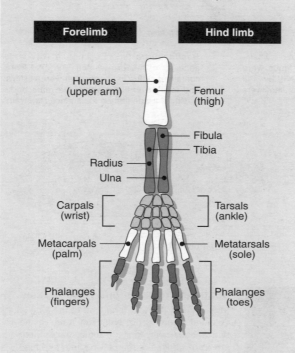

Specialisations of Pentadactyl Limbs

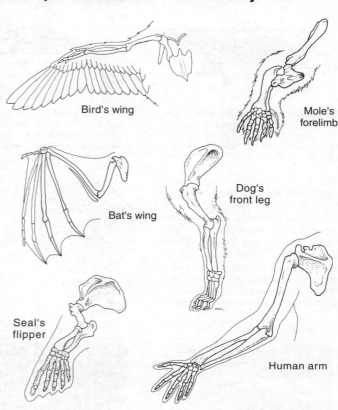

1. Briefly describe the purpose of the major anatomical change that has taken place in each of the limb examples above:

   (a) Bird wing: *Highly modified for flight. Forelimb is shaped for aerodynamic lift and feather attachment.*

   (b) Human arm: _____

   (c) Seal flipper: _____

   (d) Dog foot: _____

   (e) Mole forelimb: _____

   (f) Bat wing: _____

2. Describe how **homology** in the pentadactyl limb is evidence for adaptive radiation: _____
   _____
   _____
   _____

3. Homology in the behaviour of animals (for example, sharing similar courtship or nesting rituals) is sometimes used to indicate the degree of relatedness between groups. Suggest how behaviour could be used in this way:
   _____
   _____
   _____

Evolution

Vestigial Organs

Some classes of characters are more valuable than others as reliable indicators of common ancestry. Often, the less any part of an animal is used for specialised purposes, the more important it becomes for classification. This is because common ancestry is easier to detect if a particular feature is unaffected by specific adaptations arising later during the evolution of the species. Vestigial organs are an example of this because, if they have no clear function and they are no longer subject to natural selection, they will remain unchanged through a lineage. It is sometimes argued that some vestigial organs are not truly vestigial, i.e. they may perform some small function. While this may be true in some cases, the features can still be considered vestigial if their new role is a minor one, unrelated to their original function.

Ancestors of Modern Whales

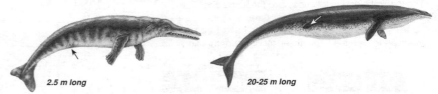

1.8 m long

2.5 m long

20-25 m long

Pakicetus (early Eocene) a carnivorous, four limbed, early Eocene whale ancestor, probably rather like a large otter. It was still partly terrestrial and not fully adapted for aquatic life.

Protocetus (mid Eocene). Much more whale-like than *Pakicetus*. The hind limbs were greatly reduced and although they still protruded from the body (arrowed), they were useless for swimming.

Basilosaurus (late Eocene). A very large ancestor of modern whales. The hind limbs contained all the leg bones, but were vestigial and located entirely within the main body, leaving a tissue flap on the surface (arrowed).

Vestigial organs are common in nature. The vestigial hind limbs of modern whales (right) provide anatomical evidence for their evolution from a carnivorous, four footed, terrestrial ancestor. The oldest known whale, *Pakicetus*, from the early Eocene (~54 mya) still had four limbs. By the late Eocene (~40 mya), whales were fully marine and had lost almost all traces of their former terrestrial life. For fossil evidence, see *Whale Origins* at: www.neoucom.edu/Depts/Anat/whaleorigins.htm

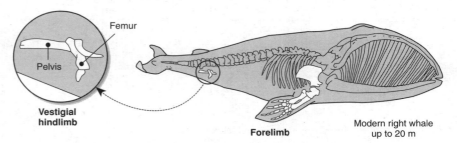

Femur

Pelvis

Vestigial hindlimb

Forelimb

Modern right whale up to 20 m

Vestigial organs in birds and reptiles

In all snakes (far left), one lobe of the lung is vestigial (there is not sufficient room in the narrow body cavity for it). In some snakes there are also vestiges of the pelvic girdle and hind limbs of their walking ancestors. Like all ratites, kiwis (left) are flightless. However, more than in other ratites, the wings of kiwis are reduced to tiny vestiges. Kiwis evolved in the absence of predators to a totally ground dwelling existence.

RM-DoC

1. In terms of natural selection explain how structures, that were once useful to an organism, could become vestigial:

_____

_____

_____

_____

2. Suggest why a vestigial structure, once it has been reduced to a certain size, may not disappear altogether:

_____

_____

3. Whale evolution shows the presence of **transitional forms** (fossils that are intermediate between modern forms and very early ancestors). Suggest how vestigial structures indicate the common ancestry of these forms:

_____

_____

_____

Antibiotic Resistance

Antibiotics are drugs that inhibit bacterial growth and are used to treat bacterial infections. Resistance to drugs results from an adaptive response that allows microbes to tolerate levels of antibiotic that would normally inhibit their growth. This resistance may arise spontaneously as the result of mutation, or by transfer of genetic material between microbes. Over the years, more and more bacteria have developed resistance to once-effective antibiotics. Methicillin resistant strains of the common bacterium *Staphylococcus aureus* (MRSA) have acquired genes that confer antibiotic resistance to all penicillins, including **methicillin** and other narrow-spectrum pencillin-type drugs. Such strains, called "superbugs", were discovered in the UK in 1961 and are now widespread, and the infections they cause are exceedingly difficult to treat.

The Evolution of Drug Resistance in Bacteria

Susceptible bacterium

Less susceptible bacterium

Mutations occur at a rate of one in every 10^8 replications.

Bacterium with greater resistance survives

Drug resistance genes can be transferred to non resistant strains.

Any population, including bacterial populations, includes variants with unusual traits, in this case reduced sensitivity to an antibiotic. These variants arise as a result of mutations in the bacterial chromosome. Such mutations are well documented.

When a person takes an antibiotic, only the most susceptible bacteria will die. The more resistant cells remain and continue dividing. Note that the antibiotic does not create the resistance; it provides the environment in which selection for resistance can take place.

If the amount of antibiotic delivered is too low, or the course of antibiotics is not completed, a population of resistant bacteria develops. Within this population too, there will be variation in susceptibility. Some will survive higher antibiotic levels.

A highly resistant population has evolved. The resistant cells can exchange genetic material with other bacteria, passing on the genes for resistance. The antibiotic initially used against this bacterial strain will now be ineffective.

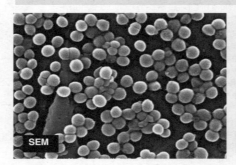

SEM

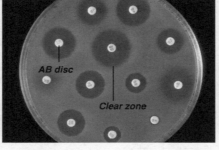

AB disc

Clear zone

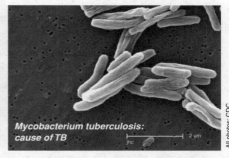

Mycobacterium tuberculosis: cause of TB

2 µm

All photos: CDC

Staphylococcus aureus is a common bacterium responsible various minor skin infections in humans. MRSA (above) is variant strain that has evolved resistance to penicillin and related antibiotics. MRSA is troublesome in hospital-associated infections where patients with open wounds, invasive devices (e.g. catheters), and weakened immune systems are at greater risk for infection than the general public.

The photo above shows an antibiogram plate culture of *Enterobacter sakazakii*, a rare cause of invasive infections in infants. An antibiogram measures the biological resistance of disease-causing organisms to antibiotic agents. The bacterial lawn (growth) on the agar plate is treated with antibiotic discs, and the sensitivity to various antibiotics is measured by the extent of the clearance zone in the bacterial lawn.

TB is a disease that has experienced spectacular ups and downs. Drugs were developed to treat it, but then people became complacent when they thought the disease was beaten. TB has since resurged because patients stop their medication too soon and infect others. Today, one in seven new TB cases is resistant to the two drugs most commonly used as treatments, and 5% of these patients die.

Evolution

1. (a) Explain how antibiotic resistance arises in a bacterial population: _____

_____

(b) Describe two ways in which antibiotic resistance can become widespread: _____

_____

_____

2. With reference to a specific example, discuss the implications to humans of widespread antibiotic resistance :

_____

_____

_____

_____

_____

Insecticide Resistance

Insecticides are pesticides used to control insects considered harmful to humans, their livelihood, or environment. Insecticides have been used for hundreds of years, but their use has proliferated since the advent of synthetic insecticides (e.g. DDT) in the 1940s. **Insecticide resistance** develops when the target species becomes adapted to the effects of the control agent and it no longer controls the population effectively. Resistance can arise through a combination of behavioural, anatomical, biochemical, and physiological mechanisms, but the underlying process is a form of **natural selection**, in which the most resistant organisms survive to pass on their genes to their offspring. To combat increasing resistance, higher doses of more potent pesticides are sometimes used. This drives the selection process, so that increasingly higher dose rates are required to combat rising resistance. The increased application may also kill useful insects and birds, reducing biodiversity and leading to bioaccumulation in food chains. This cycle of increasing resistance in response to increased doses is termed the **pesticide treadmill**. It is made worse by the development of multiple resistance in some insect pest species. Insecticides are used in medical, agricultural, and environmental applications, so the development of resistance has serious environmental and economic consequences.

The Development of Insecticide Resistance

The application of an insecticide can result in a selection pressure for resistance in pests. The insecticide acts as a selective agent, and only individuals with greater resistance survive the application to pass on their genes to the next generation. These genes (or combination of genes) may spread through all populations.

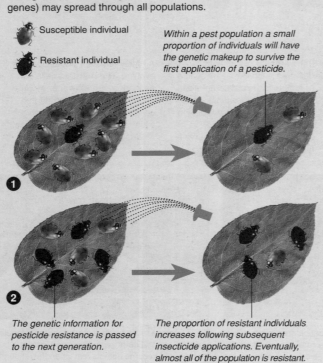

Susceptible individual

Resistant individual

Within a pest population a small proportion of individuals will have the genetic makeup to survive the first application of a pesticide.

❶

❷

The genetic information for pesticide resistance is passed to the next generation.

The proportion of resistant individuals increases following subsequent insecticide applications. Eventually, almost all of the population is resistant.

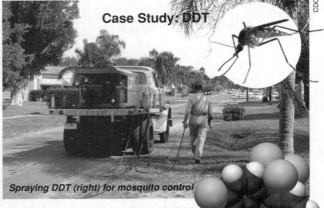

Case Study: DDT

Spraying DDT (right) for mosquito control

Mosquitoes are vectors for malaria in humans. In 1955, a global malaria eradication program was established to eliminate malaria by residual low level spraying of the insecticide dichloro-dphenyl-trichloroethane (DDT). Initially, this programme was highly effective, virtually eliminating malaria through many of the susceptible regions of the world. However, resistance soon developed in many mosquito populations as a consequence of widespread agricultural use of DDT and there were concerns about its health effects and persistence in the environment. The goal of malaria eradication using DDT was finally abandoned in 1969.

The agricultural use of DDT was banned in most developed countries in the 1970s-1980s. However, no other malaria control mechanism has proved as effective. In 2004, there was a worldwide ban on several persistent organic chemicals, and the use of DDT was restricted to vector control where it is used selectively as a spray on surfaces and in buildings. This use reduces the incidence of resistance in mosquito populations. Unfortunately, widespread agricultural use of DDT continues illegally in India where resistance persists.

1. Give two reasons why widespread pesticide resistance can develop very rapidly in insect populations:

   (a) _____

   (b) _____

2. Explain how repeated insecticide applications acts as a selective agent for evolutionary change in insect populations:

   _____

   _____

3. With reference to the use of DDT, discuss the implications of insecticide resistance to human populations:

   _____

   _____

   _____

   _____

   _____

Related activities: Resistance in Pathogens, Antibiotic Resistance

Ecological Principles

OCR: **Does not apply to AS course**
Applies to part of A2 Unit F215: Module 3

CIE: APPLICATIONS OF BIOLOGY
K: Ecology: organisation, energy flow, nitrogen cycle

Learning Objectives

☐ 1. Compile your own glossary from the **KEY WORDS** displayed in **bold type** in the learning objectives below.

Ecosystems *(page 328)*

☐ 2. Define the terms **ecosystem**, **community,** and **population** and describe examples. Describe the components of an ecosystem, categorising them as **biotic** or **abiotic factors**.

☐ 3. Describe an example a local ecosystem, including reference to the community composition and the abiotic factors that determine the ecosystem's characteristics. Use this example to illustrate examples of ecosystem, community, and population.

Habitat and Niche *(pages 329-330)*

☐ 4. Define the term **habitat** and describe examples. List the factors used to describe a habitat. Recognise that both biotic and abiotic factors affect species distribution in an environment.

☐ 5. Define the term **ecological niche** (niche), and identify the factors that are used to describe the niche. Recognise that organisms show physiological, structural, and behavioural **adaptations** for survival in a given niche.

☐ 6. Recognise the constraints that are normally placed on the actual niche occupied by an organism. Distinguish between the **fundamental** and the **realised niche**.

Energy and Trophic Levels *(pages 331-335)*

☐ 7. Construct simple food chains and a food web (containing at least 8-10 organisms), and use them to explain and demonstrate the terms **trophic level**, **producer** and **consumer**. Recognise that organisms are interconnected through their feeding relationships.

☐ 8. Describe how the energy flow in ecosystems is described using **trophic levels**. Explain how energy is transferred between different trophic levels in **food chains** and **food webs**. Describe the **efficiency** of this energy transfer and compare the amount of energy available to each trophic level.

☐ 9. Explain how the energy flow in an ecosystem can be described quantitatively using an **energy flow diagram**. Include reference to: **trophic levels** (scaled boxes to illustrate relative amounts of energy at each level), direction of energy flow, processes involved in energy transfer, and energy sources and sinks.

The Nitrogen Cycle *(pages 336)*

☐ 10. Describe the stages in the **nitrogen cycle**, identifying the form of nitrogen at the different stages, and using arrows to show the direction of nutrient flow and labels to identify the processes involved. Explain the role of microorganisms in the cycle, as illustrated by:
(a) **Nitrifying bacteria** (*Nitrosomonas, Nitrobacter*)
(b) **Nitrogen-fixing bacteria** (*Rhizobium, Azotobacter*)
(c) **Nitrogen-fixing cyanobacteria**
(d) **Denitrifying bacteria** (*Pseudomonas, Thiobacillus*).

See the 'Textbook Reference Grid' on page 7 for textbook page references relating to material in this topic.

■ Adds, J. *et al.*, 2004. **Exchange & Transport, Energy & Ecosystems** (NelsonThornes), pp. 2-26.

See page 6 for details of publishers of periodicals:

STUDENT'S REFERENCE

■ **The Other Side of Eden** Biol. Sci. Rev., 15(3) Feb. 2003, pp. 2-7. *The Eden Project: the collection of artificial ecosystems in Cornwall. Its aims, directions, and its role in the study of ecosystems.*

■ **The Ecological Niche** Biol. Sci. Rev., 12(4), March 2000, pp. 31-35. *An excellent account of the niche - an often misunderstood concept that is never-the-less central to ecological theory.*

■ **The Lake Ecosystem** Biol. Sci. Rev., 20(3) Feb. 2008, pp. 21-25. *An excellent account of the components and functioning of lake ecosystems. Food chains, food webs, and trophic levels are discussed in the context of the lake community.*

■ **Ecosystems** Biol. Sci. Rev., 9(4) March 1997, pp. 9-14. *Ecosystems: food chains & webs, nutrient cycles & energy flows, and ecological pyramids.*

■ **Microbes and Nutrient Cycling** Biol. Sci. Rev., 19(1) Sept. 2006, pp. 16-20. *The various critical roles of microorganisms in nutrient cycling.*

■ **The Nitrogen Cycle** Biol. Sci. Rev., 13(2) November 2000, pp. 25-27. *An excellent account of the the nitrogen cycle: conversions, role in ecosystems, and the influence of human activity.*

■ **One Rate to Rule Them All** New Scientist, 1 May 2004, pp. 38-41. *A universal law governing metabolic rates helps to explain energy flow through ecosystems now and in the future.*

■ **Hellbender** New Scientist, 3 Nov. 2007, p. 62. *Describes the niche and ecology of the hellbender salamander, and looks at how its habitat is threatened by pollution and anglers.*

See pages 8-9 for details of how to access **Bio Links** from our web site: **www.biozone.co.uk**. From Bio Links, access sites under the topics:

ECOLOGY: • EarthTrends: Information portal • Introduction to biogeography and ecology > **Ecosystems:** • What are ecosystems ... *and many other sites related to specific ecosystems of interest* > **Energy Flows and Nutrient Cycles:** • A marine food web • Human alteration of the global nitrogen cycle • Nitrogen: The essential element • The nitrogen cycle • Trophic pyramids and food webs

Presentation MEDIA to support this topic:

ECOLOGY
• **Ecological Niche**
• **Communities**

Components of an Ecosystem

The concept of the ecosystem was developed to describe the way groups of organisms are predictably found together in their physical environment. A community comprises all the organisms within an ecosystem. Both physical (abiotic) and biotic factors affect the organisms in a community, influencing their distribution and their survival, growth, and reproduction.

Physical Environment

Atmosphere
• Wind speed & direction
• Humidity
• Light intensity & quality
• Precipitation
• Air temperature

The Biosphere
The **biosphere**, which contains all the Earth's living organisms, amounts to a narrow belt around the Earth extending from the bottom of the oceans to the upper atmosphere. Broad scale life-zones or **biomes** are evident within the biosphere, characterised according to the predominant vegetation. Within these biomes, **ecosystems** form natural units comprising the non-living, physical environment (the soil, atmosphere, and water) and the **community** (all the organisms living in a particular area).

Community: Biotic Factors
Producers, consumers, detritivores, and decomposers interact in the community as competitors, parasites, pathogens, symbionts, predators, herbivores

Soil
• Nutrient availability
• Soil moisture & pH
• Composition
• Temperature

Water
• Dissolved nutrients
• pH and salinity
• Dissolved oxygen
• Temperature

1. Distinguish clearly between a community and an ecosystem: _____

_____

_____

_____

2. Distinguish between biotic and abiotic factors: _____

_____

_____

3. Use one or more of the following terms to describe each of the features of a rainforest listed below:
   Terms: *population, community, ecosystem, physical factor*.

   (a) All the green tree frogs present: _____   (c) All the organisms present: _____

   (b) The entire forest: _____   (d) The humidity: _____

Related activities: Habitat, Ecological Niche

Habitat

The environment in which a species population (or a individual organism) lives (including all the physical and biotic factors) is termed its **habitat**. Within a prescribed habitat, each species population has a range of tolerance to variations in its physical and chemical environment. Within the population, individuals will have slightly different tolerance ranges based on small differences in genetic make-up, age, and health. The wider an organism's tolerance range for a given abiotic factor (e.g. temperature or salinity), the more likely it is that the organism

will be able to survive variations in that factor. Species **dispersal** is also strongly influenced by **tolerance range**. The wider the tolerance range of a species, the more widely dispersed the organism is likely to be. As well as a tolerance range, organisms have a narrower **optimum range** within which they function best. This may vary from one stage of an organism's development to another or from one season to another. Every species has its own optimum range. Organisms will usually be most abundant where the abiotic factors are closest to the optimum range.

Habitat Occupation and Tolerance Range

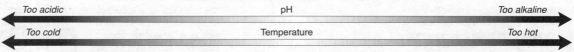

Examples of abiotic factors influencing niche size:

Too acidic — pH — Too alkaline

Too cold — Temperature — Too hot

The law of tolerances states that *"for each abiotic factor, a species population (or organism) has tolerance range within which it can survive. Toward the extremes of this range, that abiotic factor tends to limit the organism's ability to survive".*

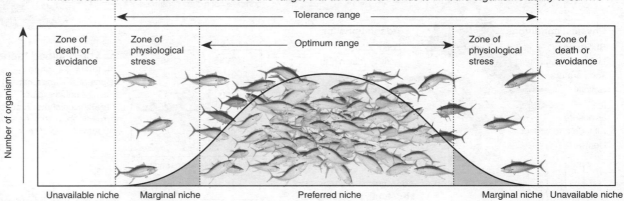

Tolerance range

Zone of death or avoidance | Zone of physiological stress | Optimum range | Zone of physiological stress | Zone of death or avoidance

Number of organisms

Unavailable niche | Marginal niche | Preferred niche | Marginal niche | Unavailable niche

The Scale of Available Habitats

A habitat may be vast and relatively homogeneous, as is the open ocean. Barracuda (above) occur around reefs and in the open ocean where they are aggressive predators.

For non-mobile organisms, such as the fungus above, a suitable habitat may be defined by the particular environment in a relatively tiny area, such as on this decaying log.

For microbial organisms, such the bacteria and protozoans of the ruminant gut, the habitat is defined by the chemical environment within the rumen (R) of the host animal, in this case, a cow.

1. Explain how an organism's habitat occupation relates to its tolerance range: _____

   _____

   _____

2. (a) Identify the range in the diagram above in which most of the species population is found. Explain why this is the case:

   _____

   _____

   (b) Describe the greatest constraints on an organism's growth and reproduction within this range: _____

   _____

3. Describe some probable stresses on an organism forced into a marginal niche: _____

   _____

   _____

Ecological Principles

Related activities: Ecological Niche

DA 2

Ecological Niche

The **ecological niche** describes the functional position of a species in its ecosystem; how it responds to the distribution of resources and how it, in turn, alters those resources for other species. The full range of environmental conditions (biological and physical) under which an organism can exist describes its **fundamental niche**. As a result of direct and indirect interactions with other organisms, species are usually forced to occupy a niche that is narrower than this and to which they are best adapted. This is termed the **realised niche**. From the concept of the niche arose the idea that two species with the same niche requirements could not coexist, because they would compete for the same resources, and one would exclude the other. This is known as **Gause's competitive exclusion principle**. If two species compete for some of the same resources (e.g. food items of a particular size), their resource use curves will overlap. Within the zone of overlap, competition will be intense.

The Ecological Niche

The physical conditions influence the habitat. The organism's tolerance to different factors in the abiotic environment will vary, presenting it with suitable conditions, or problems to be overcome.

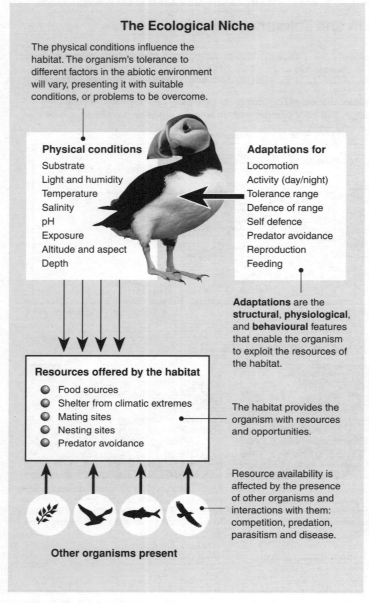

Physical conditions
Substrate
Light and humidity
Temperature
Salinity
pH
Exposure
Altitude and aspect
Depth

Adaptations for
Locomotion
Activity (day/night)
Tolerance range
Defence of range
Self defence
Predator avoidance
Reproduction
Feeding

Adaptations are the **structural**, **physiological**, and **behavioural** features that enable the organism to exploit the resources of the habitat.

Resources offered by the habitat
- Food sources
- Shelter from climatic extremes
- Mating sites
- Nesting sites
- Predator avoidance

The habitat provides the organism with resources and opportunities.

Resource availability is affected by the presence of other organisms and interactions with them: competition, predation, parasitism and disease.

Other organisms present

Niche Size

The ecological niche is dynamic. Niche breadth increases when resources are abundant or intraspecific competition is strong. During periods of limited resources or interspecific competition, niches contract.

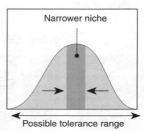
Realised niche of species
Possible tolerance range

The realised niche
The tolerance range represents the potential (**fundamental**) niche a species could exploit. The actual or **realised** niche of a species is narrower than this because of competition with other species.

Narrower niche
Possible tolerance range

Interspecific competition
If two (or more) species compete for some of the same resources, their resource use curves will overlap. Within the zone of overlap, resource competition will be intense and selection will favour specialisation to occupy a narrower niche (left).

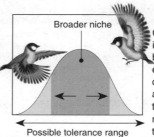
Broader niche
Possible tolerance range

Intraspecific competition
Competition is strongest between individuals of the same species, because their resource needs exactly overlap. When intraspecific competition is intense, individuals are forced to exploit resources in the extremes of their tolerance range. This leads to expansion of the realised niche.

1. (a) Explain in what way the realised niche could be regarded as flexible: _____
_____
_____

(b) Describe factors that might constrain the extent of the realised niche: _____
_____

2. Explain the contrasting effects of interspecific competition and intraspecific competition on niche breadth:
_____
_____
_____

Food Chains and Webs

Every ecosystem has a **trophic structure**: a hierarchy of feeding relationships which determines the pathways for energy flow and nutrient cycling. Species are assigned to trophic levels on the basis of their sources of nutrition, with the first trophic level (the **producers**), ultimately supporting all other (**consumer**) levels. Consumers are ranked according to the trophic level they occupy, although some consumers may feed at several different trophic levels. The sequence of organisms, each of which is a source of food for the next, is called a **food chain**. The different food chains in an ecosystem are interconnected to form a complex web of feeding interactions called a **food web**. In the example of a lake ecosystem below, your task is assemble the organisms into a food web in a way that illustrates their trophic status and their relative trophic position(s).

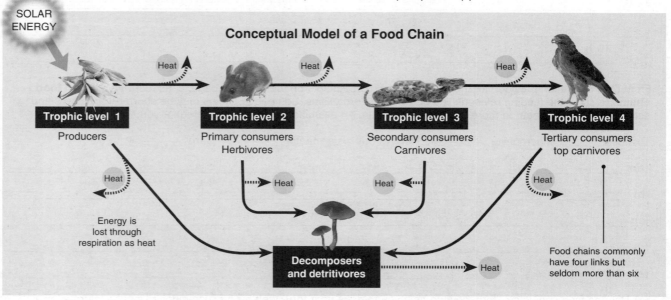

Conceptual Model of a Food Chain

SOLAR ENERGY

Heat

Trophic level 1
Producers

Energy is lost through respiration as heat

Trophic level 2
Primary consumers
Herbivores

Trophic level 3
Secondary consumers
Carnivores

Trophic level 4
Tertiary consumers
top carnivores

Decomposers and detritivores

Food chains commonly have four links but seldom more than six

Components of a Simple Lake Ecosystem

Autotrophic protoctists
e.g. Chlamydomonas
One of the genera that form the phytoplankton (or algae).

Macrophytes
A variety of species of macroscopic water plants adapted for being submerged, free-floating, or growing at the lake margin.

Protozan (*e.g. Paramecium*)
Ciliated protozoa such as *Paramecium* feed primarily on bacteria and microscopic algae such as *Chlamydomonas*.

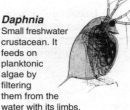

Daphnia
Small freshwater crustacean. It feeds on planktonic algae by filtering them from the water with its limbs.

Great pond snail (*Limnaea*)
Omnivorous pond snail, eating both plant and animal material, living or dead, although the main diet is aquatic macrophytes.

Diving beetle (*Dytiscus*)
Predators of aquatic insect larvae and adult insects blown into the lake. The will also eat organic detritus collected from the bottom mud.

Asplanchna
A large, carnivorous **rotifer** that feeds on protozoa and young zooplankton (e.g. *Daphnia*). Note that most rotifers are small herbivores.

Herbivorous water beetles
(*e.g. Hydrophilus*)
Feed on water plants, although the young beetle larvae are carnivorous, feeding primarily on small pond snails.

Leech (*Glossiphonia*)
Fluid feeding predator of smaller invertebrates, including rotifers, small pond snails, and worms.

Mosquito larva
The larvae of most mosquito species, e.g. *Culex*, feed on planktonic algae before passing through a pupal stage and undergoing metamorphosis into adult mosquitoes.

Hydra
A small carnivorous cnidarian that captures small prey items such as small *Daphnia* and insect arvae using its stinging cells on the tentacles.

Dragonfly larva
Large aquatic insect larvae that are feed on small invertebrates including *Hydra*, *Daphnia*, other insect larvae, and leeches.

Carp (*Cyprinus*)
A heavy bodied freshwater fish that feeds mainly on bottom living insect larvae and snails, but will also take some plant material (not algae).

Three-spined stickleback (*Gasterosteus*)
A common fish of freshwater ponds and lakes. It feeds mainly on small invertebrates such as *Daphnia* and insect larvae.

NYSDEC

Pike (*Esox lucius*)
A top ambush predator of all smaller fish and amphibians, although they are also opportunistic predators of rodents and small birds.

Detritus
Decaying organic matter from within the lake itself or it may be washed in from the ake margins.

Ecological Principles

Related activities: Energy Flow in an Ecosystem

A 2

1. (a) Describe what happens to the **amount** of energy available to each successive trophic level in a food chain:

_____

   (b) Explain why this is the case: _____

_____

2. Describe the trophic structure of ecosystems, including reference to **food chains** and **trophic** levels:

_____

_____

_____

3. From the information provided for the lake food web components on the previous page, construct **five** different **food chains** to show the feeding relationships between the organisms. Some food chains may be shorter than others and some species will appear in more than one food chain. An example has been completed for you.

   Example 1: Macrophyte ⟶ Herbivorous water beetle ⟶ Carp ⟶ Pike

   (a) _____

   (b) _____

   (c) _____

   (d) _____

   (e) _____

4. (a) Use the food chains created above to help you to draw up a **food web** for this community. Use the information supplied to draw arrows showing the flow of **energy** between species (only energy **from** the detritus is required).

   (b) Label each species to indicate its position in the food web, i.e. its trophic level (**T1, T2, T3, T4, T5**). Where a species occupies more than one trophic level, indicate this, e.g. **T2/3**:

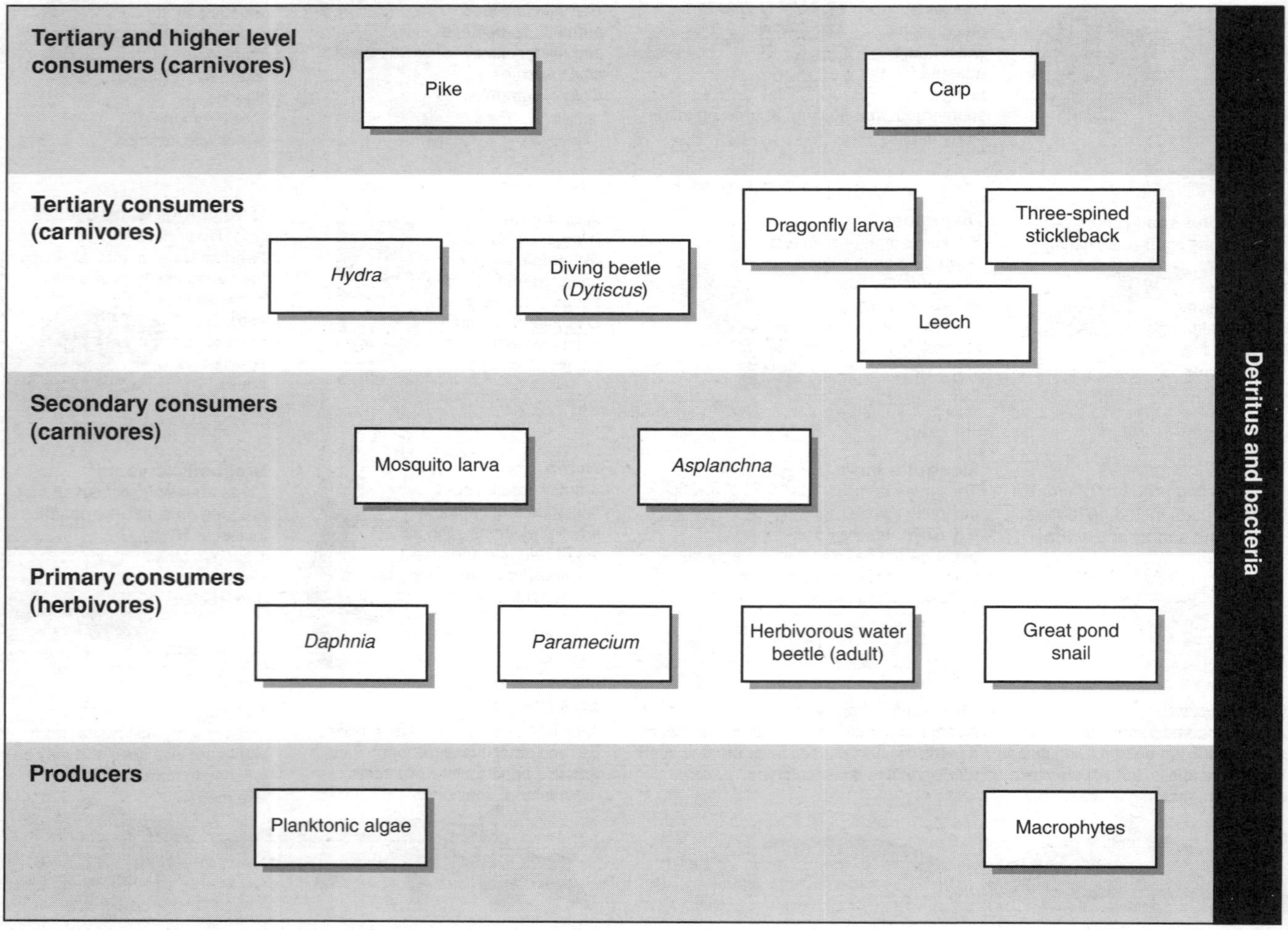

Tertiary and higher level consumers (carnivores)	Pike	Carp
Tertiary consumers (carnivores)	Hydra — Diving beetle (*Dytiscus*) — Leech	Dragonfly larva — Three-spined stickleback
Secondary consumers (carnivores)	Mosquito larva — *Asplanchna*	
Primary consumers (herbivores)	*Daphnia* — *Paramecium* — Herbivorous water beetle (adult) — Great pond snail	
Producers	Planktonic algae	Macrophytes

Detritus and bacteria

Energy Inputs and Outputs

Within ecosystems, organisms are assigned to **trophic** levels based on the way in which they obtain their energy. **Producers** or **autotrophs** manufacture their own food from simple inorganic substances. Most producers utilise sunlight as their energy source for this, but some use simple chemicals. The **consumers** or

heterotrophs (herbivores, carnivores, omnivores, decomposers, and detritivores), obtain their energy from other organisms. Energy flows through trophic levels rather inefficiently, with only 5-20% of usable energy being transferred to the subsequent level. Energy not used for metabolic processes is lost as heat.

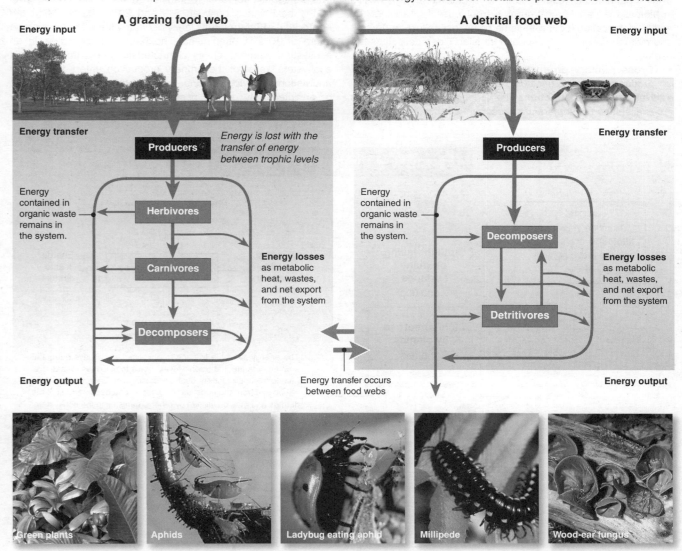

A grazing food web

Energy input

Energy transfer

Producers

Energy is lost with the transfer of energy between trophic levels

Energy contained in organic waste remains in the system.

Herbivores

Carnivores

Decomposers

Energy losses as metabolic heat, wastes, and net export from the system

Energy output

Energy transfer occurs between food webs

A detrital food web

Energy input

Energy transfer

Producers

Energy contained in organic waste remains in the system.

Decomposers

Detritivores

Energy losses as metabolic heat, wastes, and net export from the system

Energy output

Green plants | Aphids | Ladybug eating aphid | Millipede | Wood-ear fungus

Producers (green plants, algae, and some bacteria) make their own food from simple inorganic carbon sources (e.g. CO_2). Sunlight is the most common energy source for this process.

Consumers: Consumer organisms (animals, non-photosynthetic protists, and some bacteria) rely on other living organisms or organic particulate matter for both their energy and their source of carbon. **First order consumers**, such as aphids (left), feed directly on producers. **Second** (and higher) **order consumers**, such as ladybugs (centre) feed on other consumers. **Detritivores** consume (ingest and digest) detritus (decomposing organic material) from every trophic level. In doing so, they contribute to decomposition and the recycling of nutrients. Common detritivores includes millipedes (right), woodlice, and many terrestrial worms.

Decomposers (fungi and some bacteria) obtain their energy and carbon from the extracellular breakdown of (usually dead) organic matter (DOM). Decomposers play a central role in nutrient cycling.

1. Describe the differences between **producers** and **consumers** with respect to their role in energy transfers:

_____

_____

2. With respect to energy flow, describe a major difference between a detrital and a grazing food web: _____

_____

_____

3. Distinguish between detritivores and decomposers with respect to how their contributions to nutrient cycling:

_____

_____

Ecological Principles

Related activities: Energy Flow in an Ecosystem, Food Chains and Webs

RA 1

Energy Flow in an Ecosystem

The flow of energy through an ecosystem can be measured and analysed. It provides some idea as to the energy trapped and passed on at each trophic level. Each trophic level in a food chain or web contains a certain amount of biomass: the dry weight of all organic matter contained in its organisms. Energy stored in biomass is transferred from one trophic level to another (by eating, defaecation etc.), with some being lost as low-grade heat energy to the environment in each transfer. Three definitions are useful:

- **Gross primary production**: The total of organic material produced by plants (including that lost to respiration).
- **Net primary production**: The amount of biomass that is available to consumers at subsequent trophic levels.

- **Secondary production**: The amount of biomass at higher trophic levels (consumer production). Production figures are sometimes expressed as rates (productivity).

The percentage of energy transferred from one trophic level to the next varies between 5% and 20% and is called the **ecological efficiency** (efficiency of energy transfer). An average figure of 10% is often used. The path of energy flow in an ecosystem depends on its characteristics. In a tropical forest ecosystem, most of the primary production enters the detrital and decomposer food chains. However, in an ocean ecosystem or an intensively grazed pasture more than half the primary production may enter the grazing food chain.

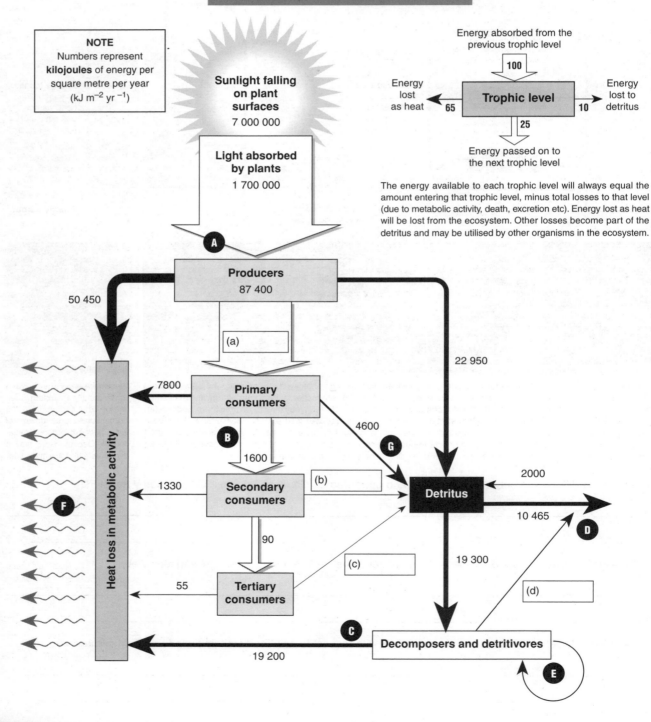

Energy Flow Through an Ecosystem

NOTE
Numbers represent **kilojoules** of energy per square metre per year
$(kJ\ m^{-2}\ yr^{-1})$

Sunlight falling on plant surfaces
7 000 000

Light absorbed by plants
1 700 000

Energy absorbed from the previous trophic level
100

Energy lost as heat 65 **Trophic level** 10 Energy lost to detritus

25

Energy passed on to the next trophic level

The energy available to each trophic level will always equal the amount entering that trophic level, minus total losses to that level (due to metabolic activity, death, excretion etc). Energy lost as heat will be lost from the ecosystem. Other losses become part of the detritus and may be utilised by other organisms in the ecosystem.

A

Producers
87 400

50 450

(a)

22 950

Heat loss in metabolic activity

7800 **Primary consumers**

B

1600

4600

G

(b)

1330 **Secondary consumers**

Detritus

2000

F

90

10 465

D

55 **Tertiary consumers**

(c)

19 300

(d)

C

Decomposers and detritivores

19 200

E

Related activities: Energy Inputs and Outputs

© Biozone International 2008
Photocopying Prohibited

1. Study the diagram on the previous page illustrating energy flow through a hypothetical ecosystem. Use the example at the top of the page as a guide to calculate the missing values (a)–(d) in the diagram. Note that the sum of the energy inputs always equals the sum of the energy outputs. Place your answers in the spaces provided on the diagram.

2. Describe the original source of energy that powers this ecosystem: _____

3. Identify the processes that are occurring at the points labelled **A – G** on the diagram on the previous page:

    A. _____   E. _____

    B. _____   F. _____

    C. _____   G. _____

    D. _____

4. (a) Calculate the percentage of light energy falling on the plants that is absorbed at point **A**:

    Light absorbed by plants ÷ sunlight falling on plant surfaces x 100 = _____

    (b) Describe what happens to the light energy that is not absorbed: _____

    _____

5. (a) Calculate the percentage of light energy absorbed that is actually converted (fixed) into producer energy:

    Producers ÷ light absorbed by plants x 100 = _____

    (b) State the **amount** of light energy absorbed that is **not** fixed: _____

    (c) Account for the difference between the amount of energy absorbed and the amount actually fixed by producers:

    _____

    _____

6. Of the total amount of energy **fixed** by producers in this ecosystem (at point **A**) calculate:

    (a) The total amount that ended up as metabolic waste heat (in kJ): _____

    (b) The percentage of the energy fixed that ended up as waste heat: _____

7. (a) State the groups for which detritus is an energy source: _____

    (b) Describe by what means detritus could be removed or added to an ecosystem: _____

    _____

8. In certain conditions, detritus will build up in an environment where few (or no) decomposers can exist.

    (a) Describe the consequences of this lack of decomposer activity to the energy flow: _____

    _____

    _____

    (b) Add an additional arrow to the diagram on the previous page to illustrate your answer.

    (c) Describe three examples of materials that have resulted from a lack of decomposer activity on detrital material:

    _____

    _____

    _____

9. The **ten percent law** states that the total energy content of a trophic level in an ecosystem is only about one-tenth (or 10%) that of the preceding level. For each of the trophic levels in the diagram on the preceding page, determine the amount of energy passed on to the next trophic level as a percentage:

    (a) Producer to primary consumer: _____

    (b) Primary consumer to secondary consumer: _____

    (c) Secondary consumer to tertiary consumer: _____

The Nitrogen Cycle

Nitrogen is a crucial element for all living things, forming an essential part of the structure of proteins and nucleic acids. The Earth's atmosphere is about 80% nitrogen gas (N_2), but molecular nitrogen is so stable that it is only rarely available directly to organisms and is often in short supply in biological systems. Bacteria play an important role in transferring nitrogen between the biotic and abiotic environments. Some bacteria are able to fix atmospheric nitrogen, while others convert ammonia to nitrate and thus make it available for incorporation into plant and animal tissues. Nitrogen-fixing bacteria are found living freely in the soil (Azotobacter) and living symbiotically with some

plants in root nodules (Rhizobium). Lightning discharges also cause the oxidation of nitrogen gas to nitrate which ends up in the soil. Denitrifying bacteria reverse this activity and return fixed nitrogen to the atmosphere. Humans intervene in the nitrogen cycle by producing, and applying to the land, large amounts of nitrogen fertiliser. Some applied fertiliser is from organic sources (e.g. green crops and manures) but much is inorganic, produced from atmospheric nitrogen using an energy-expensive industrial process. Overuse of nitrogen fertilisers may lead to pollution of water supplies, particularly where land clearance increases the amount of leaching and runoff into ground and surface waters.

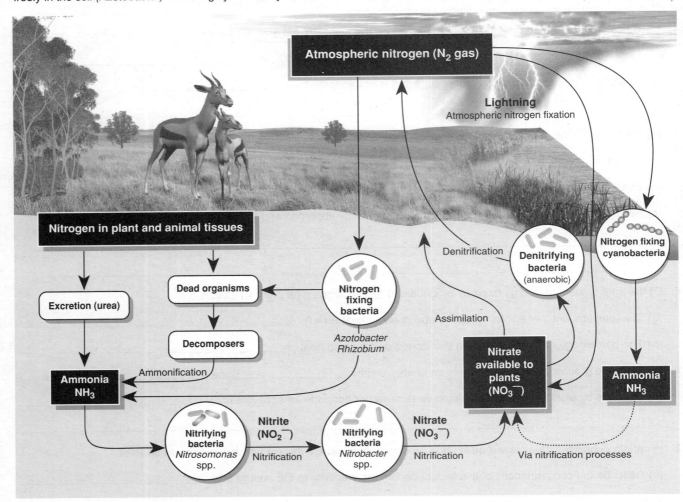

1. Describe five instances in the nitrogen cycle where **bacterial** action is important. Include the name of each of the processes and the changes to the form of nitrogen involved:

(a) _____

_____

(b) _____

_____

(c) _____

_____

(d) _____

_____

(e) _____

_____

Related activities: Amino Acids, Proteins
Web links: Nitrogen Cycle Animation

Index